MW01014605

More Praises from readers of

WWW. URIM AND THUMMIM .GOD

"I've read WWW. URIM AND THUMMIM .GOD twice, and readily recognize the scriptural references that come through 'Dr. Holland's' communication with God. What he discovers is the link of God to man - past, present and future. The material presented reflects established scientific theories and the absolute truths which can be discerned only through revelation from God to his chosen servants, the prophets. The Truth of Physics and the Truths of God are woven masterfully together as one truth. The heart of the book is Chapter 17, i.e. 'why do bad things happen to good people?' It is well worth the journey through chapters 1 -16 to reach this heart and enlightenment."
   - Diane K. Robinson, ER and Obstetrical Delivery Assistant

"If you had a chance to talk with God, what would you ask? Surprisingly, Mr. Swingler has addressed many of the questions I have pondered on my own. Furthermore, he's offered thought provoking, interest raising, and often comforting responses. The concept of conversing with God over the Internet, while amusing, seems at second glance almost logical in today's technological society. The book is an enjoyable, challenging read, and I recommend it to anyone with interests in archaeology, computers, philosophy, and mystery.... or to anyone who likes a story that will jumpstart their thinking cap. It's one of those books to hold onto for a second or third reading."
   - Mary Ranum, Working Mother - Psychiatric Nurse

"Mr. Swingler recorded a reading of his entire book when I told him I didn't have time to read such a long novel, but would be willing to listen on tape while I drive. I began to listen while washing dishes one morning, fully intending to stop, and then did some ironing so I could continue the story. I want to tell you, I got more cooking, cleaning, mending and ironing done than I have in years! I wanted to find out what happened next! I found it funny, exciting, interesting, thought-provoking and poignant - everything I look for in a book..... sort of a 'high class' Indiana Jones type historic novel with the academic hot topic of the day intertwined into it - the historic beginnings of philosophy, religion and spirituality. I loved it."
   - Barbara Langston, Bookkeeper

"I would like to commend Mr. Swingler for envisioning such a large project and for his desire to share healing truths in an accessible manner - for orchestrating the inclusion of such complex and powerful ideas into a fictional work. ......An intriguing idea, a great deal of thought-provoking material, a nice storyline. Chapter 17 (About Good and Evil) has wonderful truths, a good survey of history, and great imagery. Chapter 18 (About Women and Children) includes beautiful healing concepts, and comforting ideas."
   - Angela Colvin: Editor, Covenant Communications

WWW. URIM AND THUMMIM .GOD

Also by David H. Swingler

Dating the Past - The 1985 Calendar of the Ancient World

Writing In Antiquity - The 1986 Calendar of the Ancient World

*The Fingertip Guide to Ancient Art of the
        Mediterranean Region*

In Preparation for Publication:

The Urim and Thummim Study Companion

Urim and Thummim: The Second Journey

*The Rebirth of Venus, or,
The Twelve Fateful Myths:
        The Chronicle of Man's Inhumanity to Women*

Stupid Cupid: When Love's Arrows Fail

Candle In The Wind, a further tale of Marilyn Monroe

The Hollywood Film Therapy: Psychology from the Silver Screen

The Powers of Destiny: Foundational Human Traits Behind History

*A Fire at Twilight
- Collected Poems -*

Benjamin and Miriam of Judaea: A tale of Bible Days

The Touch

WWW.

URIM AND THUMMIM

.GOD

David H. Swingler

PUBLISHED BY HCAPRODUCTIONS
P.O. Box 2309   Oxnard, California 93034-2309

This novel is a work of fiction. The characters, incidents, dialogue
and story are the products of the author's imagination
or are used fictitiously.
Any resemblance to actual persons, or events, is purely coincidental.

Printed in New Delhi, India, at the Thomson Press India, Ltd.
FIRST EDITION
April 6, 2004

ISBN 0-931371-84-8

Preface quote of Stephen Hawking from A Brief History of Time
used by Permission.
Translations of the Dead Sea Scrolls, Nag Hammadi Library and other ancient texts and
codices read in Chapter 14, are used by permission.
Translations of ancient Aramaic Hebrew texts by Eugene Brannon,
Moishe Shamash and Yohanan Zevitt are used by permission.
Biblical quotations are from the King James Translation.
Special Hebrew-to-English denotations in Genesis and other passages made by the software
program produced by Kevin Taylor, are used by permission.

LIBRARY OF CONGRESS CATALOGUING-IN-PUBLICATION DATA:

Swingler, David H.

WWW. URIM AND THUMMIM .GOD / by David H. Swingler - 1st Edition
p.   cm.
ISBN 0-931371-84-8

1. Creation   2. Anthropic Principle   3. God – Proof, Cosmological
4. Archaeology   5. Civilization – History   6. Bible and Science
7. Biblical Cosmology   8. Mother – Goddesses – Palestine
9. Dead Sea scrolls – criticism, Interpretation, etc.   10. Astronomy, Ancient
11. Astronomy – Popular works 12. Women – History   13. Evolution – Religious
aspects – Christian 14. Biosphere 15. Environmental protection   16. Grand
Unification Theories 17. God – Miscellanea 18. Spiritual Life – Miscellanea

This is the full, unchanged manuscript

as it was completed

at the end of August, 1997

Nothing has been deleted or added.

For

Richard C. Swingler and Barbara McLean

*who made it possible for me to come into this world
and taught me to love nature, and all of its sciences*

and

Frank "Coach" Parker

*who gave me a chance,
taught me to believe in myself
and nudged me into The Path that can take us all Home.*

and

All The Ancestors

who had the courage to come first.

and

All The Parents Today

*who struggle to teach their children and themselves
how to treat each other better
so we may have peace and joy as our loving God wishes.*

and

All The Children Today

*who, no matter how old they are
can still learn
can still do better
and can still get it right.*

CONTENTS

CONTENTS

AS A BEGINNING

*"The initial state of the universe
must have been very carefully chosen indeed
if the hot big bang model was correct
right back to the beginning of time.
It would be very difficult to explain why
the universe should have begun
in just this way,
except as the act of a God
who intended to create
beings like us.*

*"If we do discover a complete theory,
it should in time be understandable
in broad principle by everyone,
not just a few scientists.
Then we shall all, philosophers, scientists,
and just ordinary people,
be able to take part in the discussions
of the question of why it is that we
and the universe exist.
If we find the answer to that, it would be
the ultimate triumph of human reason -*

*for then we would know
the mind of God."*

- Stephen Hawking -   A Brief History of Time

Foreword

Egypt, June 21, 1993
Elephantine Island, near Aswan cataract. Ancient Yeb.
The new university excavations

There was no shadow. No shadow at all.

Dr. Gene Brannon looked at his watch. Still a few minutes until noon, and already there was no shadow at all cast by the stake marking the corner of his excavation quadrant.

He squinted up at the sun, and back at the wooden stake sticking straight up out of the ground, carefully set in perfect perpendicular just for this mystical moment. There was no shadow. No shadow at all.

Over two thousand years ago the learned Egyptian Eratosthenes, appointed director of the great library of Alexandria, had come to this place near Abu Simbel, to the frontier outpost city of Syene just a little across the Nile, to see if reports he had read in a small papyrus book were true: that on this day of the year the obelisks of Syene cast no shadow at noon day. It said that sticks stuck vertical in the ground cast no shadow at noon day. Even the columns of the Temples, which always cast shadows from dawn till dusk on all other days of the year, on this day, at noon, cast no shadows. If one looked for the shadows, they were gone.

And, at noon in this place on this day every year, if one looked down into the deepest well, the reflection of the sun shone back up into one's eyes. The sun, at the bottom of the deepest well.

Eratosthenes had found that this was all true, and pondered deeply during the whole afternoon over what he had seen. For, far to the north in his beloved home, the great city of Alexandria, the obelisks kept their shadows at noon day all year, even on this day. Filled with the mystery of this profound phenomenon, he had pondered its significance for years, returning each year to Syene to be at this place on the solstice, to study this marvelous wonder.

He obsessed upon it until he learned its secret, its revelation.

The Earth is round. It is a sphere.

And, it could be measured, using the shadows of the obelisks.

Dr. Brannon's watch was reaching the exact moment of noon. Hour hand and minute hand were already aligned upon the Twelve, and the sweeping seconds hand had less than 30 seconds to travel before all three hands would align perfectly for an instant over the Twelve, when it would be exactly noon. He looked from the shadowless stick to the sun to the second hand of his watch, breathlessly waiting. Only seconds remained.

Ten, nine, eight, seven, six, five, four, three, two, one............

It was exactly noon.

Summer solstice, at Syene.

With fascination he looked from the sun to the stake.

But suddenly the silence was broken. One of his students called.

"Dr. Brannon, come over here! I think we've found something!"

From across the sweltering excavation site Dr. Brannon heard the call, and stood up to his full height in the stifling Nile heat. Sweat instantly trickled down his forehead into his eyes, stinging them into an even narrower squint against the brightness of the noonday sun. He could see the main dig awning, but nothing in its shadows.

Nearby him, Carl and Yvonne, the two student volunteers digging quadrants next to him, also stood up and shaded their eyes to peer past palms, trenches, rocky rubble and marker flags toward the excited cry they had heard. Dr. Brannon looked over at them. They too were almost blinded by the glare. Carl looked back and shrugged.

From the main dig awning, a girl's voice now echoed across the site, "Dr. Brannon! I think this is important!"

The two students looked back anxiously at Dr. Brannon, and then almost in unison threw down their hand trowels and brushes and ran through the palm trees and shattered blocks of hieroglyph-carved stones, toward the tarpaulin-canopied main dig near the bank of the Nile River, where the newly discovered floor and foundations of an ancient building were being carefully excavated. Dr. Brannon threw down his sketching pad and followed closely behind them.

Breathing heavily, they quickly reached the canopy where the three other student volunteers had spent all morning clearing dirt and sand away from an emerging section of huge floor stones discovered only three days before. Richard squatted grinning beside one carefully brushed and cleaned granite slab, and Sandra kneeled on one knee across from him, smiling broadly. Duane stood leaning on his shovel, a wide grin on his face as well.

"Look here," said Richard in unconcealed excitement, pointing down with his trowel at the long flat slab before him. He tapped the stone with the trowel handle. The sound was unmistakable. Professor Brannon, Carl and Yvonne looked up at each other in amazement and then back at the faces of their grinning colleagues.

"It's hollow underneath!" exclaimed Yvonne, her eyes wide with wonder and excitement.

"I know!" said Duane. "We never would have known, but a rock rolled out of Sandra's discard basket as she was carrying it out of the quadrant here, and it fell right on top, and viola! Hollow sound!"

"This may be a foundation dedicatory deposit," Dr. Brannon almost whispered.

"We've already taken photos establishing the floor as it is before we move the slab," Sandra said eagerly.

"Well, what are we all waiting for?" Dr. Brannon replied looking around the circle.

With Dr. Brannon quietly giving orders, quickly they positioned themselves at one end of the slab with shovels and a long pry bar. As carefully as possible they began the task of prying up and then lifting the slab at one end, raising it a centimeter at a time, until the underlip of the stone appeared and was clear. At that instant, Carl slipped his pry bar under it, pushed down with all his might, and swiftly stood up, putting his feet on the bar to secure the slab from slipping back down into its hole.

Dr. Brannon then motioned for Yvonne and Richard to slip their shovel blades under it, and lift. As soon as it was a few inches higher, Duane slid a heavy board under it from the side, spanning the hole to support the stone, and everyone sighed aloud in relief as it rested.

With another gesture of his hands, Dr. Brannon swiftly poised all of them except Duane at the raised end of the slab, and had Duane once again kneeling ready with a second board. On the count of three, everyone hefted the stone up higher, with all of their strength. The huge granite slab raised up enough for Duane to insert the second board well back toward its other end, and they quickly but gently lowered it back down again with a huff onto its two supports.

"There is something under it," puffed Sandra. "I saw inside. There is definitely something under it."

"I saw it too," said Carl between breaths.

"OK, now let's get in position on my side, slide it over the boards and open this thing," Dr. Brannon instructed, and in a moment they were all awaiting his signal, poised on their knees in a line to shove the stone off of its millenniae-old resting place.

"One, two three!" called out Dr. Brannon, and with a chorus of grunting, they shoved with all their might. Yet with less effort than they had expected, the huge granite slab slid away over the boards, and suddenly they all found their bodies stretched out over the gaping hole, their heads directly above it, their eyes peering down.

For a moment they hung in space this way, staring at the view below which beyond all doubt, no one had seen for over two thousand years.

One by one they pushed themselves up and leaned back from the slab, steadying themselves on their knees, to behold the contents of the large stone box now opened before them.

It was not much, by Egyptological standards. Just a large, curved fragment of an amphora jar, which looked like part of a giant egg shell, almost like a shield, under which they saw extending on either side a very large sword, filling the full length of the coffer.

But as they looked down, they suddenly realized that this sword was thicker, wider and longer than any sword they had ever seen.

"My gosh!" exclaimed Richard, "I thought these ancient Egyptians were all short people. Look at the size of that thing!"

"It's bigger than the old English broad swords, don't you think, Dr. Brannon?" suggested Yvonne.

Dr. Brannon sat transfixed as he stared down at the amphora shell and huge sword beneath it. His face filled with true awe, and the five students knew that they had found something indeed of rarity, even if it was only a sword and a broken piece of pottery.

"Yes, Yvonne, this is, I am sure, bigger than any English broad sword that was ever made. Sandra?"

"Yes, Dr. Brannon?"

"Find the camera and get ready to take the in-situ photos, please," he told her. "Carl, get the meter stick and lay it over here, so we can document this properly. No, not the small one, the big one. Put it right here. Everyone else, please step back so we can get these photos. Sandra, I think if you stand right about here you can get the box, the contents, the cover slab behind it, everything."

He traded places with her, and the four other students stood back to give her room. The flash of the camera was blinding even with the noonday Egyptian sun glaring in from all around.

Dr. Brannon looked up from the ancient flooring and sunken box with its modest treasures, turning his gaze out around the arid landscape of palms, stones, dust and river surrounding their small excavation camp. No one was around. No boats on the river. Only the palm trees motionless in the stifling heat of mid-day, and the slowly swirling waters of the Nile. No people come to watch and see what the Americans were digging up. Seldom did anyone come. The locals cared nothing for the things which were buried under the ground and jutting up out of the dirt from antiquity, except as these things brought tourists who paid money to see them, and to eat, and drink, and sleep in the hotels. Seldom was anything of spectacular art and beauty brought up from the ground, to excite a public interest among those already too familiar with the ever-visible glories of ancient Egypt's heritage. This big sword and broken amphora shell would not raise an eyebrow of anyone here. But the sword was the only intact object found yet in the weeks of digging on the small, narrow island of Elephantine, across from Syene, Aswan City, just down river from the cataracts in which Aswan Dam had been built.

As Sandra took photo after photo, flash after flash in the canopy shade under the bright, hot, dry desert sun, Dr. Brannon motioned to the others to take positions around the slab, so it could be moved, the boards removed, and the final unobstructed photos of the find 'in-situ' could be taken. Only then could they lay hands on the artifacts and carefully lift them up.

A second set of boards was positioned two feet from the hole, and in just seconds the group hefted the granite slab up, and over, and laid it down again on the awaiting boards. At the hole, Carl pulled the boards off the long sunken box, and Sandra got in position to photograph the artifacts without any obstacles in the view.

As she took the additional photos, Dr. Brannon turned and stepped away to the edge of the canopy shelter, peering across the Nile at the distant city buildings of Syene. Just beyond them, he knew, was the world's oldest, most ancient rock quarry, where in ancient dynastic times Egyptian slaves had quarried granite for the monumental statues of pharaohs, queens, gods and goddesses, stelae, building blocks and magnificent tall obelisks reaching to Ra, the sun. The quarry's last project, which would have been the tallest obelisk in all of Egypt, had broken in half before it was completely freed from the bed of stone where it lay. It was abandoned by its Egyptian stone-carvers, whose Pharaoh never returned to attempt another. The unfinished obelisk lay as it had been cut, broken in two great halves. It had become itself a monument for over two thousand years: the colossal symbol of a fading Egyptian power and glory, lost.

Sandra took the half a dozen more required pictures. Everyone gathered around the sunken box, kneeling in a circle. The moment had come.

"Who should do the honors?" asked Dr. Brannon, looking around the circle of faces.

"Sandra dropped the rock, so I guess she discovered it," said Richard.

"OK, Sandra, lift out the amphora panel," directed Dr. Brannon.

She lifted it up and held it tightly against her chest so she could see over it, and look down at the sword. As soon as she did, her gasp joined everyone else's.

"Oh, my God!" cried Yvonne.

"An inscribed metal plaque!" hissed Duane.

There, on top of the sword at about the mid-point, lay a small green copper plaque, slightly rectangular, very dark and heavily corroded but very visibly inscribed with writing.

As Dr. Brannon excitedly looked up from the sword and plaque to ask Sandra to put the huge, shell-like amphora fragment on the slab beside her so she could get the camera for more pictures, he suddenly saw the underside of the amphora fragment. He sucked in his breath and almost froze.

Sandra saw the abrupt reaction as his gaze fixed on the amphora fragment she held close to her chest. Without moving his eyes, he slowly raised his hand up towards her, eyes flooded with anxiety, and in this unexpected silence everyone looked up at his pointing fingers, and followed them over to Sandra. As they saw what he saw, eyes widened, mouths gaped open, and their faces filled with amazement.

Sandra, suddenly seeing everyone's eyes turn wide in shock as they saw the underside of the fragment she held with her bare hands so close to her chest, winced with the impending horror of what must be clinging to it.

"It's OK, Sandra, it's OK," quickly assured Dr. Brannon in soothing tone, "just don't drop it. Don't drop it."

"What is it?" begged Sandra, almost in tears.

"There's some writing, Sandra.......lots of writing on this side of the shard; many, many lines of writing........ and it's not Egyptian. We can see it from where we are, Sandra. It's not Egyptian. It's Hebrew!"

Her expression passed from tearful fear to joyous relief.

"Put it down, Sandra, very, very carefully. Hold it tightly, and don't drop it, please," Dr, Brannon's voice guided her quietly. "Duane, get a towel, quick, or a shirt or something to set it on so it doesn't bump directly on the stone," he ordered.

Sandra carefully laid the large fragment down on the burlap Duane found and set beside her as a cushion. Everyone gathered around it to behold the writing on this unimaginable find.

Dr. Brannon's heart was pounding and his hands trembled with excitement exploding within him. His eyes rapidly scanned the script, and though the students knew a precise translation would require time and patience, his expression of increasing joy revealed some sure knowledge of what this inscription contained.

He turned his gaze from the script and leaned to look down into the sunken stone box, now scrutinizing the copper plaque set atop the sword blade. Shaking his head in disbelief, as his body rose back up he closed his eyes, sucked in a deep breath and held it. Slowly then he let it out, opened his eyes and looked around at the others.

"The copper plaque is inscribed in Hebrew, too!" he announced.
"My friends, both of these are Hebrew inscriptions. Do any of you know what we have found?" he grinned as he raised his eyebrows and waved his hands around the circle.

"Well," ventured Duane, "this is the Island of Elephantine, anciently called Yeb. This is where the Israelites who escaped from the Babylonians in 586 B.C fled and made their settlement, and some kind of military garrison, I think, like mercenaries for the Egyptians. So is this their fortress or something?"

"No, Duane, this is infinitely more important than that," responded Dr. Brannon. "From the Elephantine papyri and ostraca that were found near here a hundred years ago, on the Island and in the excavations on either side of the Nile here, all published almost a century now, we know for certain that the Israelites who fled here and settled here built a Temple, about 565 B.C., a Temple to Yahweh! They spelled his name 'Yahu' in the papyri and ostraca, but it was definitely a Temple - the only Hebrew Temple ever built outside of Jerusalem, built on this island, but no one has ever located or identified its ruins!"

"Are you saying we've found a Jewish Temple of Yahweh?" blurted Yvonne.

"Yes! That is what I am saying! We have the proof of it right here before us!" exclaimed Dr. Brannon with a certainty that allowed for no doubt. "Even with the corrosion on the plaque, I can spot the Tetragramaton YHWH several times! And this huge big ostracon here that was face down on the sword," he reached out and turned it where it lay in order to better read the lines of writing, "this is some kind of a long dedicatory letter or statement, and it has all kinds of words I can pick out on it. Look here - 'Jerusalem' - and here, the Tetragramaton - 'YHWH' - and down here, at the end of line four, - 'Yehude' - Judah! Oh my gosh, I didn't see this before! 'Jeremiah!' Right here is the name 'Jeremiah!' If this is talking about the prophet Jeremiah, this is going to be monumental!"

"Why would it talk about the prophet Jeremiah?"

"Because: Jeremiah was taken hostage by the renegade Israelites who fled out of Judah and came down into Egypt! He was brought to Egypt as their captive! To the best of our knowledge, he died in Egypt!" explained Dr. Brannon.

He then eagerly returned his gaze to the large ostracon and continued to scan down the lines searching for words he could recognize easily in the text.

"'David!'" he suddenly exclaimed. "It mentions the name of David here!" he pointed, "and here is.......... oh my GOSH!" he exclaimed and halted, open mouthed.

He turned from the writing on the shard and got on both knees, staring down at the sword in the coffer. He reached in and gingerly lifted the green-colored plaque off of it, handing it to Carl, to set it carefully on the nearby raised slab. He then again leaned far down, this time slipping both hands underneath the sword which he gently grasped and with a grunt, lifted up and out of the coffer.

He held it up before his eyes, tilting it to better catch the light.

It was massive, almost five feet long, easily five inches wide, and in only seconds he found himself straining just to hold it up. It was heavy. He lowered it down, resting it in his hands on his thighs, and closed his eyes. All five students watched him in silence as he gently lifted its weight up and down on his legs. Finally he spoke.

"According to the inscription on the ostracon," he intoned every syllable deliberately, "this.......... is the sword of Goliath."

"Goliath!" echoed five astonished voices.

"...... which David dedicated to the Lord and in his old age kept in the sanctuary of Nob, just outside Jerusalem, to honor the priests of Nob. They were all executed by King Saul, for having given it to David the day the King angered and sought to kill him." he declared.

Amid many murmurs and awed exclamations, he smiled, opened his eyes and held it up high again for all to see. From all sides, their hands reached out and touched the huge sword held up in the air.

"The sword of Goliath!" said Carl, tracing his fingers along its edge.

"Do you know what this means?" said Richard incredulously.

"Yes," replied Dr. Brannon. "It means that you have to get in the boat and go straight across the river to the Department of Antiquities office and tell them we've made the discovery of the century!" he beamed.

"No, I mean...... yes, I know, but...... what I meant was...."

"I know what you meant, but part of our permit agreement is that we call in the authorities the instant an important find is made, and we've already perhaps gone a little further than we should have. But who would have guessed that a big pottery shard and a sword would be important? Jumpin' Jimminies I can't believe this!" he rolled his eyes shut again. Opening them, he still saw Richard, who had not yet moved.

"Shoo! Shoo...get out of here! You know where the boat is. Make a beeline and get back as quick as you can. We want to get this all squared away before nightfall."

Dr. Brannon then nodded to Duane and Yvonne to help him lift up the sword, and they placed it gently on the stone slab beside the ostracon and the plaque.

Sandra rewound the first roll of film in the camera, took it out, put it in the camera bag and put in another roll, which she proceeded to shoot entirely in varying angles of the three treasures. Dr. Brannon asked Yvonne to help Sandra position each of the three artifacts in turn for taking the best possible pictures of them.

While they photographed the huge sword and inscriptions, Dr. Brannon had Duane take measurements of the slab and interior of the sunken stone box. Carl brought paper and pencil and lightly made a rubbing of the Hebrew words on the plaque. Dr. Brannon himself began to hurriedly make a pencil copy of the Hebrew text written on the ostracon. By the time Sandra and Yvonne finished the photo session, he had only a few lines left to copy. As immediately as he finished the last word, he folded the sheet together with Carl's rubbing of the plaque, and put them both safely in his pocket.

Duane, squinting against the sun, spotted Richard on the docks across the river, talking to the Antiquities officials. As they headed for their boat, Richard got back in his, and the two boats started towards the site. Dr. Brannon walked to the shore to meet them.

The two officials nudged their boat into the muddy bank and quickly jumped out onto the shore. Richard was just behind them, in his smaller, slower craft. They walked with Dr. Brannon briskly up to the tarpaulin-roofed spot where the students awaited with proud smiles.

"So today is the big day," said Ahmed, the superior authority, an unusually wide smile on his face. Everyone nodded, and with a confusing medley of too many voices, they told of the find and pointed to the three relics laid out atop the long granite floor slab.

Ahmed and his assistant knelt down and examined the artifacts, turning the plaque and ostracon in the light to clearly see the writings upon them, and gingerly lifting the sword between them. It was heavy, more so than they at first were ready for.

"My goodness, this is a biggy," said Ahmed, still smiling. Laying the sword down again, he then ran his fingers across the wording on the inscriptions, and finally turned and looked up at Dr. Brannon.

"You are right," he said, "These are definitely not hieroglyphs, not Egyptian writing on these two pieces. Are you certain they are Hebrew, and not Phoenician or something like that?" he asked.

Dr. Brannon stepped forward affirming their Hebrew origin, and pointed to the several words he had already recognized: Jerusalem, David, Judah, Jeremiah, and Goliath. Ahmed laughed and shook his head in disbelief.

"You think the writing is saying that this is the sword of the giant Philistine, Goliath, who little David killed with the stone?"

"I'm virtually positive that the people who buried it here believed that it was," Dr. Brannon replied.

"And this plaque you say declares that this is the Temple to Yahu which no one has found yet.....until today, I guess," he laughed and raised his hand in sort of a salute to all the students and their director.

"This is excellent work, excellent work you have made here," he said, looking over the floor with its hole and the slab with its treasures.

"Tell me, did you take pictures of these things already?" he inquired.

"Yes, yes," assured Dr. Brannon, "absolutely. Everything is very well documented. Everything."

Ahmed signaled to his assistant to begin the job of wrapping up the antiquities and preparing them for the journey across the river to his office.

"Very good, very good," he said, and watched the assistant as he jogged back to the boat for packing materials.

"Listen," he continued, looking back to Dr. Brannon, "so you can have your photos of these things as soon as possible - I'm sure you will be going mad to be seeing them as we are having to take these things away before you have had even time to enjoy this triumph - I will take all of your film and have it developed for you myself, tonight, and bring them to you at your hotel in Aswan tomorrow morning."

Several of the students looked to Dr. Brannon in anxious protest, but he subtly waved them quiet and spoke.

"Thank you, really, for such a kind and generous offer, but we can take care of that ourselves," he said diplomatically.

"No really, I insist," replied Ahmed.

"No, thank you, truly, but...."

"No, Dr. Brannon, I am sorry, but you must understand, I insist. Officially, I must insist. We must have our own copies of any photographs you have taken, as you failed to call us before removing these very important artifacts from their resting place. We must guarantee that we have every documenting photograph in our files. So I'm afraid that when I say 'I insist,' I mean that I insist, Dr. Brannon."

Reluctantly, Dr. Brannon requested Sandra to roll up the film in the camera, and give it to Ahmed.

"And all other rolls of exposed film in the bag, please," he said now rather firmly, with his hand outstretched.

Sandra looked over at Dr. Brannon with pain in her face, but Dr. Brannon motioned for her to hand the bag to Ahmed.

By this time the assistant had returned and was beginning to wrap up the three relics. Dr. Brannon hurriedly rushed over to help him with the large amphora ostracon, which he so feared would be broken. They all watched as the plaque and then the sword disappeared under the wraps of several layers of newspaper and heavy tape. Ahmed fumbled through the camera bag and removed three exposed rolls of film, two from previous days, and the first roll from today which contained the photos of the undisturbed floor, the partially lifted slab and the objects exposed in situ.

"I think this is enough work for today," said Ahmed to them all. "I think you should all go back to the hotel now to celebrate your find," he smiled.

The mixed feelings about the demand of the film had made such visible tension among the students that it was obvious no one still felt like celebrating. However, Ahmed's outstretched arm somewhat forcefully ushered them to quickly pick up their personal belongings from around the site, and accompany him back to the riverbank and into the boat.

Ahmed stayed on the shore and waved to them in farewell as they shoved off and the boat backed out into the Nile waters.

"See you tomorrow," he smiled as he waved.

The group crossed the Nile in silence, and tied their boat to the dock. Still without speaking, they walked the few blocks to the hotel. Inside the lobby, they stood uneasily at the elevator doors, waiting for the elevator to come back down and lift them to the third floor.

"I don't like this," finally spoke Sandra.

"None of us like this," rejoined Richard, scuffing his heel on the floor.

"So what do we do?" asked Duane.

"Nothing," replied Dr. Brannon, glancing around the small circle at each face. "We go to our rooms, we sleep tonight and tomorrow we go back to the site and we continue working. That's why we're here."

The elevator came. Once upstairs, they separated to their rooms. No one felt like talking. No one felt like celebrating.

That night, none of the six excavators slept well.

Early the next morning, earlier than usual, they met in the lobby and then all went over to the docks except for Carl, who was left behind at the hotel to wait for Ahmed and the photos and negatives, as Ahmed had promised.

But as they approached the dock, Ahmed was sitting there on a piling, waiting. He stood up and walked to greet them.

"We must accompany you to the site this morning," he said with the artificial smile of a diplomat. They looked over at Ahmed's boat, and saw not only his assistant, but two new men they had never seen before, all waiting silently.

Thoroughly displeased, Dr. Brannon and his students got into their boat, and headed out across the Nile to the island.

Ahmed's boat passed them, and when the excavators arrived, he and the other three men were already standing on the shore.

Dr. Brannon and his students walked straight to the tarpaulin-roofed site of the find, and ducking their heads, stepped in under the shelter.

To their astonishment, the slab was back in its original place in the floor, and the boards were back against the dirt wall, just as they had been before the slab was raised.

"What's going on here?" asked Richard, his gaze darting from the floor stones to Ahmed, who was just entering under the tarpaulin. All four students and Dr. Brannon turned to face Ahmed and the three Egyptians who silently took their places a step behind him. He took out a cigarette, lit it, and blew the smoke away before speaking.

"What do you mean?" asked Ahmed with practiced calmness.

Dr. Brannon's usual ingratiating tone burst.

"What we mean is why has the foundation box slab been moved back and closed?"

"I do not understand," replied Ahmed, with a look of smug innocence and a slight smile. "What foundation box are you talking about? What slab?"

"This one!" Richard declared, walking over and stomping his foot on it. He looked up in wide-eyed surprise, and glanced around at the rest of his colleagues who also were suddenly even more alarmed.

The hollow sound was gone. It sounded solid. He went over and got a shovel and turned it upside down, tapping the tip of the handle on the slab which yesterday had yielded the find of a lifetime. It thudded solid, just as those around it which he tapped desperately in succession, thinking that perhaps he had somehow forgotten which slab it had been, and was confused. But all of them sounded solid.

"They're all solid!" Richard said to Dr. Brannon and the others, and to Ahmed, whom he now faced.

"Yes, they are all solid," agreed Ahmed, pulling a flat packet out of his inner coat pocket.

"This is what I see you already determined from your dig here, as your own photographs show, right here," he said, thumbing through the photographs until he came to the series of photos showing the clean, undisturbed floor - the photos which Sandra had taken just before they raised the slab.

"That is all I see here," said Ahmed, holding out the photos.

Dr. Brannon snatched the stack of developed photographs from Ahmed's hands and began to flip through them as fast as he could, and Yvonne, Sandra, Richard and Duane crowded around him to see. There were the photos from the several day's previous progress in the digs, and the establishing shots of the floor slabs in situ, but then nothing. Nothing else.

"Where are the photographs of the artifacts - the big amphora ostracon, the sword, the copper plaque? Where are they?" demanded Dr. Brannon as forcefully as he dared on a tiny island hundreds of miles up the Nile away from Consuls and protections of any kind.

"What artifacts are you talking about, Dr. Brannon?" asked Ahmed in quiet and distinct diction.

"The artifacts we found yesterday - the sword, the ostracon and plaque with Hebrew writing?"

"We saw nothing here yesterday," continued Ahmed, taking a deep drag on his cigarette and blowing it to his side, out into the breeze. Before anyone could again protest, he raised his hand and spoke more.

"When we came here yesterday, all we found was that you had uncovered this granite floor, we think some kind of a store house, perhaps a granary for the Temple of Khnum. The floor was just as it is now, and we saw no artifacts, no sword, no things with writing on them." He turned to his assistant, the very man who had wrapped up and carried to their boat all three treasures. "Did you see any artifacts here yesterday - a sword, some plaques or pottery pieces with writing on them?" he asked, looking back at Dr. Brannon.

"No, no, there was nothing here, just a bare floor," he affirmed.

"But we took pictures...." began Dr. Brannon, but Ahmed cut him off.

"And all of them we have developed for you, and you have them in your hand, all of them."

"Except for the photos of the artifacts - the big piece of amphora, the plaque, and the sword - we took lots of pictures!" "There were no pictures of any artifacts as you describe," Ahmed rejoined disdainfully.

"Furthermore, as of this moment, your permit is cancelled, and your visas are cancelled except for travel required to leave Egypt and go to your homes in America. You see, we have decided that this is an unimportant site, and thank you for revealing this to us by your test digs and excellent photographs. However, there is no further need to investigate this area, and should we find any purpose to do any further surveys in this vicinity, we have our own staffs who can do this for us. Thank you all very much, and that is all. You have fifteen minutes to pick up your gear and equipment and get it into the boats. My men will assist you in gathering all of your things, and you may please take advantage of our larger boat to get everything in one trip. You will not be allowed to come back. Do I make myself perfectly clear to you, Dr. Brannon?" he finalized.

"Yes, perfectly clear," replied Dr. Brannon with a look around to his students.

They packed and left the island of Elephantine, and were escorted to the hotel and then out to the tiny Aswan airport where they were given priority seats on the small commuter plane that would take them back to Cairo.

In Cairo they were met at the airport by a special envoy assigned the task of making sure they caught the first available flight back to New York.

On the way home, while 37,000 feet over the Atlantic, Dr. Brannon took the two pieces of folded paper out of his pocket, and slowly unfolded them, spreading them flat on his seatback tray.

His eyes ran over the lines of archaic Hebrew script on the rubbing, and on the copy of the ostraca inscription he had so hurriedly made. A strange impatience and indignant anger filled him, as he sat staring at the two critically monumental inscriptions. Then suddenly, without the aid of his books and dictionaries, he set himself to the task of translating them.

In the high, rarified atmosphere, with the passion of his anger and a need to feel any empowering he could enact, he became amazed even to himself in the fluidity with which the understanding and translation of the two inscriptions came.

When he had finished both translations - with an uncommonly sure sense of their absolute accuracy - he re-copied each one onto a fresh piece of paper, to read them at last without the distracting scribbles of trial wordings, cross-outs and refinements.

Immediately as he completed the clean copies, he called to his students and gathered them around his seat, and read to them the words which they had discovered buried under earth and stone for almost twenty-six centuries, under the granite floor slabs of the Hebrew Temple of Yahu on Elephantine Island in the upper Nile River in Egypt. They listened in somber silence.

"On the plaque was written this:

> *"Holiness to the Lord. The Lord is YHWH.*
> *I have surely built thee an house to dwell in*
> *a settled place for thee to abide in forever.*
> *Lord God of Israel, there is no God like thee*
> *in heaven above, or on earth beneath,*
> *who keepest covenant and mercy*
> *with thy servants that walk before thee*
> *with all their heart."*

"And," Dr. Brannon continued, putting the second sheet of paper on top, "on the large ostracon were written these words:

"I, Yehoniah, the faithful steward of Seraiah, High Priest to
Yahweh at Jerusalem, have fulfilled my oath as bound;
I have hidden up the lights and perfections of the Lord
in a resting place in the Wilderness of Judah;
as the Lord did show me his path and his way;
in the Strong Holds of David, in their place they rest.
This I have done as I was bound by oath to do.
My master was killed by the Chaldean, and I
was taken into Egypt with Jeremiah and the others,
by those who slew Gedaliah upon his throne in Mizpah
with the sword of Goliath that was taken from Nob.
Jerusalem is left desolate; The Temple is laid waste;
the children of the fathers still weep and shall weep
until the promise of the Lord is fulfilled in his time.
In the Lord they shall rest until his coming.
I seal this my word with the great sword of Goliath
we dedicate with David to the House of the Lord
The Lord is my rock and my fortress, and my deliverer;
My God, my strength in whom I will trust;
my buckler, and the horn of my salvation
and my high tower. Hear me, my God,
in the far land of my affliction:
I have fulfilled my oath as I was bound."

For a long moment no one spoke. Yvonne was softly crying, and Duane rubbed away the tear which had trickled down his cheek.

"Why can they do something like this to us?" asked Richard.

"Because I am just an insignificant professor, and you are just a few college students. They send us away with no artifacts, no photos, no proofs of any kind, and they know what will happen. Who will believe any of us, even if we try to say anything public?"

"But why did they do it? Are they going to take all the credit for the discovery now?" asked Sandra.

"No, I don't think so. I don't think they will ever tell anyone about it; it will never be published anywhere. I have been asking myself that same question, and the answer keeps coming back to me, 'why would the Egyptians want to create a holy Jewish shrine on their soil?'"

"What do you think they're going to do with the artifacts?" asked Yvonne.

"They may never be seen again," Dr. Brannon replied.

"Is it true that no one will believe us?" asked Carl. "We were there. We saw it all. Isn't there something we can do?"

"There is nothing we can do. There's nothing left at the site to show anyone but flat floor slabs. Now it's just another anonymous, unimportant fragment of a ruin up the Nile in Egypt. But there may be some one out there who will believe us."

"Who?" asked Sandra.

"I don't know," replied Dr. Brannon, staring out the window of the plane into space. "I don't know."

The students quietly went back to their seats, and Dr. Brannon sat in silence the rest of the long flight, winging over the earth at 37,000 feet as an ancient god might have done.

A tear trickled down his cheek, stinging in his eyes, as he saw himself, just yesterday, standing in the Egyptian sun by the Nile.

There was no shadow.

No shadow at all.

Chapter 1

7 PM: The Grant to Make Silent Stones Speak

I sat fidgeting at my end of the long table, armed with my few sheets of data, postit-marked books, official papers, and informal correspondences from museum archivists.

Not much of a presentation for a $200,000 Grant to go search for ancient artifacts in Israel.

Ten years of my life and the potential of unlocking thousands of silenced voices from our past rested in that small accumulation of papers. Though thoroughly prepared, in this moment of sudden-death approval or denial, I held none of the power, only the proposal. A proposal in which even few of my colleagues had faith.

At the other end of what seemed an unnecessarily gulfing distance, the seven-member body forming my erudite judgment panel was about to call our meeting to order. Whispered last minute consultations and reshufflings of the various stacks of reports, forms, computer print-outs and documents on the table created a hushed mixture of muffled voices and rustling papers in the otherwise quiet air of the chamber.

Finally, with subtle nods, everyone sat back, folded their hands upon the table, and turned their faces to my end of the room. All eyes rested upon me. Leonore Alexander, the chairperson, spoke.

"Mr. Holland, you have completed the formalities for a rather significant Grant from this Foundation, and this meeting, as you know, is the final inquiry into your request of funds for the archaeological and scientific project you propose. We have all reviewed your request, and find that we have numerous questions about what you are trying to do, and whether or not this organization should grant these funds for such a project. We assume that you are prepared to explain your theory and defend the approval of this Grant request?"

"I am," escaped my voice through smiling lips with as much positive body language as I could muster.

"Excellent. The questions will come from the Trustees, and we have agreed that each shall ask questions in turn, on a particular aspect of your proposal; after these topics are covered, questions will be open and informal. Allow me to introduce the Trustees who have been selected to form this Review Panel: I am of course Leonore Alexander, Chairperson of the Foundation. To my right are Mr. Edward Duncan, Dr. Sharron McPhetridge and Mr. Gregory Crandall; to my left are Dr. Julie Powell, Dr. Michael Spencer and Mr. Mark Lauterbach."

As their names were pronounced each smiled and nodded, with a few hand gestures around the table in way of welcome.

"This is the panel which regularly hears Archaeological Grant requests, with the exception of Mr. Lauterbach who is a special consultant from our Technology Research and Development Grants Division. He is here due to the unusual technology requests in your proposal."

Mr. Lauterbach smiled and nodded acknowledgement.

"We will begin with Mr. Crandall."

"Mr. Holland, I've read through all the papers you've given us here, and your project sounds quite fascinating: a trip to Israel, permits from the Department of Antiquities, a small archaeological site a hundred kilometers south of Jerusalem in the middle of a desert canyon near the Dead Sea, the search for undisturbed artifacts dating back almost three thousand years..... Honestly, most of us here are ready to take a few months off and join you!"

Restrained laughter and heads nodding in agreement.

"But then I get a little lost with your objective. This is a new topic for me. Even though I've read the statement here, would you please be so kind as to tell us, in your own words, what it is you hope to accomplish in an archaeological dig with all this electronic equipment as you list on your budget request?"

I cleared my throat and began what I knew was going to be a long uphill battle of persuasion. Reaching into my coat pocket I pulled out the little yellow and bronze-colored plastic toy rocket with its wires carefully wrapped around its body, a relic of my own past, and held it up before me.

"Mr. Crandall, and Trustees of the Foundation, when I was about ten years old, my father gave this to me. It only cost a few dollars, and yet each night as I would go to sleep it would bring the world to me. It has almost no moving parts. All that is in it is a small galena crystal, a tiny coil of copper wire, and something called a 'cat's whisker.' I'm going to pass it around the

18

room here so you can look at it while I explain."

Mr. Crandall stepped over and reached for the tiny toy rocket. Once in his hand, his eyes narrowed to almost a squint as he turned it around and scrutinized it from every angle. He had no idea what it was. As he sat down, he shrugged, and handed it to the next person, who also looked bewildered.

"What you have in your hands is a crystal-set radio. It requires no electricity. No batteries. It costs almost nothing to make, and in fact anyone can make one in their own home. To make it work, all you have to do is attach the alligator clip at the end of the one wire, - yes, that's it - to something that can act as a receiver: a chain-link or wire fence is best, like we had at my elementary school playground, or in the old house we lived in, I used to attach it to the little screw that held on the plastic plate of the electrical outlet by my bed so it was connected to the entire armored cable system of the house as an antenna, and then you put the earphone in your ear. In this model, the little ball on the tip of the rocket's nose pulls a little rod in and out -yes, like that - which runs the 'cat's whisker' wire across the coil of copper wire, giving you different channels."

By this time Leonore Alexander had it. Amazement filled her face. "And with just this you can listen to the radio?"

"Yes," I continued. "When I was a boy, 10, 11, 12 years old, I used to lay awake in bed hours after I was supposed to be asleep, listening to radio programs all over the country. The signals are in the air, and the galena crystal receives them and processes them within itself. This discovery in this little radio receiver and processor was the beginning of our crystallographic electronics and crystal computer technologies. It picks up what is there, and you listen to it! Only a wire coil, a crystal, and an earphone. I used to go to sleep listening to a classical station, just because that was the strongest signal I could pick up where I lived. Or, that I could pick up with that particular crystal. The crystal makes a lot of difference. Depending on the natural structure of the crystal, different parts of the radio wavelength spectrum come in more clearly."

"When was this radio capacity discovered?" asked Mr. Crandall.

"Almost at the same time as radio waves. My father said he had a crystal-set radio when he was a boy, back in the 1920's. He said everybody had them back in those days."

"So what is the relevant point here?" pressed Mr. Crandall.

"The relevant point is that crystals in their natural state receive and process radio waves. In computer applications, crystals essentially act as semi-conductors, superconductors, processors, and exhibit immense storage capacities. For a few dollars today you can buy a greeting card with a photo-electric cell, a crystal chip and a micro-speaker that plays music every time you open the card. There are no moving parts. This is all done through mineral technologies."

"I've seen them."

"A few decades ago a rather fanciful theory was toyed with, which suggested that natural crystals might be receiving - and recording - voice waves as well as radio waves. The suggestion was made that many stones to a lesser degree and especially crystals to a greater degree have been recording sounds and voices since the beginning of time. Theoretically, if we could find the clear crystal pendant which Cleopatra wore around her neck as she plotted with Mark Anthony to take over the Roman Empire, we could hear their voices, and listen to their conversation. If we could find the emerald jewel set into the handle of Alexander the Great's sword, we could listen to the deliberations with his generals and his commands given to his armies twenty-three centuries ago."

"And you believe this is possible?" asked Mr. Duncan.

"So far, it hasn't been possible. The trick has always been how we might access those stored voice imprints, decipher or decode them and re-assemble them into a real-time space continuum which could be played and listened to as any other recording. In a sense, like a tape recording, of voices and conversations thousands of years old. Or conversations made today."

Dr. Sharron McPhetridge spoke. "Am I understanding your proposal then, that the diamond in my ring, or the amethyst crystals in Dr. Powell's ear rings may be recording everything we say in this room, right now?"

"Possibly. We don't know if they are. But we don't know that they aren't. That's the hypothesis."

Mr. Crandall gazed around the room at the hesitant expressions on the other Trustees' faces. "This is a very new topic for all of us."

"This is a new topic for most people. We live in an amazing age. New technologies are being discovered faster than we can learn how to use them. Some recent advances in the computer sciences have come to my attention which, properly circuited and programmed, may be applied to this little known yet potentially rewarding hypothesis: decoding and playing back sounds recorded in certain types of stones and crystals, imprinted by human voice vibrations thousands of years ago."

Dr. Sharron McPhetridge now glanced around the table, and took over the questioning. It was her turn.

"So we have not misunderstood: you intend to listen to rocks?" she inquired. All eyes were upon me, awaiting my response, and not a single face belied the mixture of incredulity and curiosity which all seemed to share.

"Yes, I guess that's right. I intend to listen to rocks. Ancient rocks. The value is historical and linguistic: to finally hear actual pronunciations and accents of these ancient, dead languages of our human families' ancestry, in their common forms and contractions, slangs and vulgar usages. If we can achieve this, it will shed light on everything we think we already know."

"How much experience do you have in this science?" she asked.

"None at all - yet. But for that matter, nobody has any. I believe we are on a threshold which few have yet recognized."

Dr. Sharron McPhetridge looked urgently at Mark Lauterbach, yet he deferred to her, and sat back. She continued.

"Mr. Holland, the requisition list justifying your budget request includes on the one hand a complete compliment of archaeological materials for what appears to be a rather intense dig, while on the other hand you outline some very expensive and very specialized electronic and scientific equipment expenses, we assume for 'listening to rocks.' We also note that you plan to go alone on this project, which has confused us. Are you a computer scientist, or an archaeologist? What is your actual field of qualification here?"

"My field is classical archaeology. I specialize in the lives of the earliest Egyptians, Mesopotamians, the Greeks and the Roman Empire. Quite frankly, I'm more at home two and three thousand years ago than I am in the Twentieth-Century. Usually I'm either elbow-deep in a tray of pottery fragments or looking up some elusive discovery in an excavation report. I don't usually dabble in technologies or computer sciences. Yet the hypothesis that ten years ago some of us only talked about jokingly - a few of us wistfully - suddenly seems to perhaps be within our grasp. I want to put what equipment we can assemble together and put it to the test."

"But if you have no experience with this sophisticated assembly of computer equipment you are proposing we buy for you, how do you intend to make it work out in the middle of the Judaean desert?"

"What I am proposing to do is dig in an unexplored site, that has never been disturbed and most importantly, has been substantially covered by earth and rock for the last two thousand years, and to test certain types of stones and if I'm lucky, crystals of the kinds used in jewelry which often are found in excavations, all of which have been buried more than two thousand years, in hopes of electronically retrieving sounds, sounds which may have been recorded by voice imprint in these stones and crystals by living people in ancient times."

"And yet from what we have read in your proposal, you generously admit that there is no proof such stored sound patterns even exist."

"That's true," I replied.

"Then why go through all this?" she asked, not as a challenge, but with obvious desire to understand.

"Because there are strong arguments favoring the hypothesis."

Mr. Duncan cleared his throat and glanced at Dr. McPhetridge, who smiled with a slight nod and sat back. It was his turn.

"That is the part I wish to discuss," he smiled. "Please illuminate us with those arguments."

"Certainly. Sound is a form of energy. We don't really understand a lot about energy yet. Sound waves strike and penetrate things, and are absorbed by matter. This is a most basic common knowledge. Look around this room. We're talking, and our voices are broadcasting sound waves in every direction. Only the tiniest fraction of these sound waves, infinitely less than 1 percent, are collected and picked up by our ears, which funnel these sound waves into our inner ears, which process them in such a way our brains can decode and reassemble them into what we hear, to understand each other. But what about the vast majority of sound waves our voices are broadcasting in all directions, which don't enter anyone's ears? They travel through the air, and they hit everything else in this room: the walls, the ceiling, the floor, the tables, chairs, carpets, drapes, papers, books, pens, your suit and tie Mr. Crandall, Ms. Alexander's dress and glasses, Dr. McPhetridge's lovely hair and arms and hand, and very importantly the diamond in her ring; and, Dr. Powell's face and ears and her amethyst ear rings. All of the energy in all of these sound waves is hitting and penetrating all of these things in just the same magnitude as the fractional part we hear, which has funneled into our ears. Ask: what happens to the rest of all these sound waves as they hit all these other things in the room? They're absorbed. And, because they're absorbed, as soon as we stop talking, they're gone."

I stopped. In a micro-second, the last echoes of my voice were swallowed by the walls, the drapes, bodies and furniture, and the room went silent. Hauntingly silent.

The total silence of the chamber encircled around us, heavy and dense, suddenly a physical presence to be felt.

In this silence, a silence which the Trustees were consciously hearing for the first time in this way, they looked around the room at the walls, the drapes, the table and chairs, and at each other, in wonder. Before anyone could steal my thunder, I broke that silence.

"What you are not hearing is *absorbed sound*. Our voices broadcast the sound waves, which are a form of pure energy, and all of the waves are absorbed by the things in this room, including our own bodies. But once absorbed, what has happened to that sound? We are not sure. We assume that in soft and fibrous materials, such as the drapes and the tissues of our bodies, the patterns are disrupted and fragmented; received in pieces and stored in pieces. This idea may turn out to be a false assumption. We still have a lot to learn about the crystalline structure of molecules even in soft fibers, and of the chemicals in tissues and cells, but theoretically, for now, that's what we assume is happening: sound is lost in soft matter. On the other hand, though a large percentage of sound is reflected off of hard objects, some of the sound wave energy penetrates and is absorbed by the hard objects, and theoretically, that sound is intact, meaning it is not fragmented. The harder and more perfect the solid object, the greater potential it may have to receive and store uninterrupted and intact sound continuum.

"And you really believe this is possible?" asked Mr. Duncan.

"Well, we observe this reality: sound waves in - nothing out. *Voila*, the hypothesis: it is retained inside and may be retrievable."

Mr. Duncan turned to Dr. Powell, nodding. It was her turn now.

"What kinds of rocks do you intend to...... 'listen' to?" she asked.

"The harder ones. Basalt has a good crystalline structure. Granite is mostly quartz and feldspar. Serpentine. Carnelian. Jasper. Marble. Mica. Particularly any semiprecious or precious stones I may find which were part of jewelry."

"What would you hear in a piece of basalt, marble or granite?"

"The concept is simple. If a big stone was part of a wall in a house, it picked up conversations in that house: mother talking to her children, husband talking to wife, grandmother talking to daughter and granddaughter, children to children. If the stone was part of the exterior facing of the wall, it would have picked up conversations outside the house: man talking to worker, woman talking to child, chicken clucking, donkey braying, that sort of thing. A big marble column outside a public building would have theoretically picked up any conversations within range of it, even from across a street or forum: all the news from the town and distant lands, discussions between merchants and customers, speeches of senators, proclamations of princes and kings. On the other hand, a personal jewelry item made of crystal could contain conversations between a mother and child, discussions between good friends: excitement, tragedies, gossip, recipes, and idle conversation. Or, even the sounds of passion and poetry between lovers making love."

Dr. McPhetridge's hand subtly moved to cover her ring, and Dr. Powell suddenly found reason to reach up and adjust her earrings. I went on, pretending not to observe.

"Small jewelry stones, especially crystals are my main goal."

"What are the chances of your finding such small jewelry stones in a random archaeological excavation?"

"Pretty good. Most digs turn up a few, sometimes in the strangest ways. Stones and crystals turn up all over the archaeological world in digs. I even have a friend whose mother found a quartz crystal at Stonehenge in the 1930's. It was in the pushed up dirt from a gopher hole. But that's the 'pot luck' of my site and dig. I have no guarantee as to whether I will find any."

"Aren't most of the stones you find in archaeological digs only bits and broken pieces? If all the stones have been broken, what good will they be for playing back whole conversations?"

"We theorize that sound waves are holographic, much as light waves are. You've all seen holographic pictures for sale, of say, a flower or a dinosaur figure? It's a picture of a real object, and the light wave patterns are recorded on the glass or plastic in 3-D, holographically. The fascinating thing is that you can break the picture into pieces, and each piece becomes its own complete picture, only smaller. Even a tiny fragment will contain the entire picture. We theorize that sound waves imprint similar holographic pattern forms. So, a piece of the rock should be the same as having the entire rock, only we assume that the signal will be proportionately weaker, and harder to trace and retrieve."

Mark Lauterbach glanced with perplexity at the Chairperson, Leonore Alexander, with his hand slightly raised.

"May I please interject out of turn?" he requested. "I think this is the perfect place for my questions."

Leonore Alexander looked quickly into the eyes around the table, and all visibly agreed.

"Go on, Mr. Lauterbach."

He turned to me.

"Tell us a little bit about the equipment you want us to buy."

I took a deep breath, and pulled the requisition sheet out from within the pile. This was the hardest part. My gaze quickly scanned down the page.

"These are new circuit boards with experimental capabilities: a sound-impulse chip, a variety of complex retrieval program software packages, a kaleidoscopic de-scrambler chip with its own program interlinked to megafiles of cryptographic dictionaries; megasearch chips; sound re-assembly program software, and then a modified audio receiver and amplifier for detecting any syllabic speech patterns. Then there's special scientific multi-velocity, direct-to-tape digital sound recording equipment to record and interface playback with the megasearch observation systems. The translation de-coder mega-chips are made to decipher existing and unknown languages. It includes exhaustive dictionaries and grammars of ancient Hebrew, Canaanite, Eblaite, Aramaic, Phoenician, Moabite, Babylonian, Assyrian, Hittite, Egyptian, Greek, Latin, and other languages. I'm an artifacts specialist, not a linguist. The translator interfaces with a special scanner equipped to optically read papyrus, parchment, cuneiform clay tablets, pottery ostraca, and stone inscriptions. These systems interface with megastorage systems just off prototype assembly, for storage of whatever I retrieve, and to store the Translator Database and the Text Database."

"Text database?"

"Yes. It was thought that a complete file of all known ancient linguistic syntax examples might help the decoding program identify something as a syllabic pattern and lock onto it. This base includes virtually every known ancient inscription and published writings in all of the ancient languages I just mentioned, in both their original language syntax and in English translation, to interface with the search for any patterns which might even remotely parallel any known ancient dialogue."

"When you say virtually every known ancient inscription and writing, how comprehensive a file do you really mean?" he asked.

"Just that: the entire Corpus Scriptorum Graecorum and Latinorum; classical authors from Aristotle to Caesar to Philo Judaeus; the entire Hebrew Bible; the Dead Sea Scrolls - as much as we have been able to get of them; the Lachish Letters; the Elephantine Letters; all of the Hebrew and Aramaic Apocrypha and Pseudepigrapha; the Nag Hammadi Library; the Pyramid Texts; the Book of Breathings; Book of Opening the Mouth; Book of the Dead; the Moabite Stela, the Code of Hammurabi and about 180,000 cuneiform tablets ranging in language from Boghaz Keui Hittite texts through Sumerian, Assyrian, Akkadian, Eblaite, Ugaritic, Babylonian to late

Persian Aramaic cuneiform tablet texts; the Aramaic Targums and every other Aramaic and Hebrew text from the period we could find in a book, and on and on. The material includes everything from royal annals to worker's wage receipts to mythologies, accounts of the Great Flood, property titles, marriage agreements, adoption documents, personal letters, religious writings. There are hundreds of thousands of complete sentences. It's a pretty comprehensive file for the purpose."

"Why do you need such expensive recording equipment?"

"The recording equipment has to be very high-tech because I need to be able to record and play back at everything from hyper-speed down to sub-frequency speeds, with full computer enhancement. The plan is to hopefully discover a speed in which retrievable patterns might be identified. Once detected, the equipment then might render the stone-recorded wave patterns into a comprehensible syllabic image. The rest of the system is all for sorting it, and rendering it back into a time-continuum, and reassembling it into a phonetic sound playback."

"How will you power this out in the middle of the desert?"

"I'm going to use solar collector panels and rechargeable battery cells. They're on the list. I need about twenty units."

"Why not take a generator? It would be a lot cheaper."

"Yes, but the noise factor would be self-defeating. I need an environment which has no sound, or at least as little as possible."

"Mr. Holland, this is a lot of very expensive, very complicated equipment. While I can appreciate that you've been able to summarize for us what it is and what you intend to do with it all, you clearly admit that you are not a high-tech guru, and that you are not even a linguist: your professional experience is potteries, artifacts and excavations. Tell us: how does all this experimental equipment system work?"

"I don't know. It's highly technical. If you have to hear an explanation of that, you'll have to call in the hardware designers and software designers who've been inventing this system."

Everyone around the table shifted in their chairs. A few heads shook ever so subtly. The intensity level went up a multiple. Mr. Lauterbach waited until the rustling sounds quieted, and then asked,

"How will you use it if you don't understand how it works?"

"I just need to know how to operate it," I replied. "Basically, it's like turning on a light. We turn on a light without understanding how it works. There is a lot going on every time we turn on a light: electricity is being generated far away at a plant somewhere, carried through some pretty amazing cables and wires, maybe over hundreds of miles. It's being passed through transformers which upsize and downsize it, and regulate its hertz frequency. Finally it comes through the circuitry of the main box in a home or building. We see a switch, and a light fixture which is maybe incandescent, or maybe fluorescent. We turn on the switch, and get light. We don't have to understand anything about hydroelectric or nuclear generators, resistance in wires, what transformers are doing, or anything about the process which converts electrical energy into light. We just turn it on and use it. I'm just going to turn this system on and use it."

"This sounds more complicated than just turning on a light switch. How much training have you had with this system?"

"Two weeks, but that's mostly working with theoretical instructions and diagrams. The system isn't actually completed yet as we speak." More dubious expressions.

"When will it be completed?"

"The schedule is tighter than any of us wanted, but the finishing touches are being installed as we speak. The day after tomorrow I'm going to be given a dry run on all of it, and spend as much time as it takes going over the system set-up: wiring, patches, and custom fittings that interface with a variety of stone scans. Then it all gets packed and shipped to Tel Aviv. Two days after I get there, it will have cleared Israeli Customs, and I'll be ready to head out into the desert and use it. Designing it has been an incredible task, but once it's set up, I can use it."

"How can we be sure a person with no technical background can run a system so experimental it isn't even finished yet?"

"I have a three-year old daughter who can already operate a television and run a VCR. She doesn't understand anything about electricity, the cassette, or the magnetic tape in it, or how a VCR descrambles and reassembles sound and pictures recorded as patterns in magnetized iron particles in a tape, or how it turns them into the animation movie she wants to watch and hear on the TV screen. Yet she knows that if she pushes *this* button the TV turns on, and when she pushes *that* button the VCR lights come on. She knows that if she pushes that *other* button, the boring grown-ups tape we left in the machine last night will eject. And she knows how to hold the cassette she wants to watch, just the right way to put it in. That's amazing, you know: there are seven 'wrong' sides on a cassette and only one 'right' side that will work, and she knows how to do it now, every time. She knows then which button makes the movie come on the screen. She knows which button stops it, which button rewinds it, and which button ejects it when she wants to see a different movie. She's been doing this since before she was three, if you really want to know the truth. Her latest project is the remote, and she's on her way to figuring that out, too. Honorable Trustees, I'm just going to do as a little child does: put in the sample and push some buttons."

"Why don't you just take the technologist with you?"

"Because if another person is along, we're human: we'll talk. The whole idea is to test specimens unexposed to new voice imprints. We have no idea how sound imprints may be laid down within the crystalline structure, and therefore no idea how exposure to new energy patterns and sound waves may affect the orderly retrieval of ancient voice imprints potentially recorded in the stones."

Mr. Lauterbach shrugged, nodded with an expression of approval, and turned to Dr. Michael Spencer, who leaned forward and indicated his readiness to take over the questioning.

"That brings us into the next area of your proposal: the supportive data. You briefly state that there are 'metaphysical' evidences which further point to the possibility of stones acting as storage vessels for sound and actual voice communication."

"There are. The first is a statement in the New Testament, in the book of Luke, Chapter 19, verses 37 through 40. I heard this as a child in Sunday School. It's where Jesus tells the Pharisees that if his disciples and others did not testify that he is the Messiah - allow me to read this here - "I tell you that, if these should hold their peace, the stones would immediately cry out." Now, being the kind of kid I was, I stopped the class by asking "How could stones talk?" The teacher didn't have a very good answer, and just kept saying that if Jesus said it, it was true. I kept asking how, until she told me to be quiet. But I never forgot. So we could still ask: was Jesus lying?

"The second important reference is in Isaiah, Chapter 29: verse 4. He's speaking to a people who will be destroyed. Yet he says that after their destruction, they will speak from 'out of the ground.' Let me read here: "And thou shalt be brought down, and shalt speak out of the ground, and thy speech shall be low out of the dust, and thy voice shall be, as one that hath a familiar spirit, out of the ground, and thy speech shall whisper out of the dust." In the last hundred years we've seen this ancient prophecy coming true quite literally in the discovery and translation of all the inscriptions and papyri and clay cuneiform tablets we've found and keep finding. They come up from out of the ground, and they do speak to us out of the dust. Yet perhaps a more literal interpretation of this prophecy was also intended. Maybe we've reached the day we can make it happen.

"There's one more statement in the book of Habakkuk, Chapter 2, verse 11. Habakkuk refers to someone building a mansion with forced labor, violently driven, a terrible oppression, who thought his works of evil would be unobserved, secret. He says that though no one be left alive to witness it, still the evil shall be made known, "For the stone shall cry out of the wall, and the fastener out of the timber shall testify against it." This passage is particularly interesting technologically. Where stones and iron or brass fasteners touch, they form an electro-chemical interaction. The builder believed that the cries of the oppressed, beaten and driven mercilessly within the building's walls, would be contained in them and sealed, silenced. And so they would have been - absorbed into the stones in those very walls. Yet the prophet is interpreted as saying that the secret shall be discovered, because the stones with their fasteners shall cry out and testify." I concluded and closed the book.

"You think these verses refer to a capacity in stones to record sound?"

"I think they may. Habakkuk seemed to believe so. For centuries we've jokingly said, 'If these walls only had ears.......' Well, maybe they do."

"You mention in your proposal that there are Native American traditions which may support this theory as well," he went on.

"Possibly, yes. There is a Native American belief in 'Record Keepers,' stones which are set in the midst of a Council group to witness and hear all that is said, and keep it forever. A lot of people think this is a silly superstition. Yet a couple of centuries ago, which of us in this room would have believed that a quartz crystal can run clocks that don't need to be wound, and receive radio programs, and that crystals can run computers? Are Native Americans doing something silly by placing a special stone in the midst of important Councils to hear all the words and keep them?"

A unanimous medley of gestures disavowed any silliness at all.

"I'm glad you don't think so. Joshua did the same thing among the children of Israel, in Shechem. Read here, Joshua 24: 26 and 27: 'And Joshua wrote these words in the book of the law of God, and took a great stone, and set it up there under an oak, which was by the sanctuary of the Lord. And Joshua said unto all the people, Behold, this stone shall be a witness unto us; for it hath heard all the words of the Lord which he spake unto us: it shall be therefore a witness unto you, lest ye deny your God.' He states that the stone had heard the words, and was a witness. What do we know, really? The world is forever showing us that it is more than we can yet understand."

Mark Lauterbach glanced intently at Leonore Alexander, and with a wave of her hands in both directions and a nod, the questioning opened for everyone to speak at will.

Mark Lauterbach began.

"Mr. Holland, these are very interesting arguments you propose. However, we've consulted with a number of computer specialists, and they've all scoffed at this idea. They say it's impossible, that no sounds are being imprinted in stones, and there's nothing recorded in stones to extract."

"Perhaps. But the possibilities are worth at least a little bit of exploration and effort. Think of the reward if there is something there to access and retrieve."

"But," he persisted, "our sources in computer technologies tell us that there is no scientific proof indicating that sound or anything else is being stored in stones or crystals, naturally."

"Scientifically there may be proof. Please turn to page three of my proposal, and the paragraph about *Thermoluminescence*."

Dr. Sharron McPhetridge raised her hand and spoke.

"Yes, I wanted to ask about this. You mention here that further study into the exact nature of sub-atomic particle buildup observed in 'Thermoluminescent releases' may prove helpful as it may relate to this hypothesis. We're all a little vague on this - how do you pronounce it? Thermo-lum-in-es-cence? Could you explain this?"

"It's a phenomenon harnessed in dating ancient potteries, and detecting clever forgeries of expensive Greek vases. Quite simply, it was discovered that clay absorbs and stores natural 'radiation' at a somewhat constant rate. Importantly, during the firing process in a kiln, on the way up to 2,000 degrees Fahrenheit, all the 'radiation' is driven out. Thus a freshly fired pot or vase has a 'zero' superfluous sub-particle content. However, after firing, the clay once again begins to absorb and store sub-atomic particles, which we call by the generic term 'radiation.' What has been discovered is that a piece of ancient pottery re-fired in a kiln releases all of its absorbed sub-atomic particles as the temperature reaches 2,000 degrees, and goes again back to 'zero' superfluous particle count. By systematic sampling of potteries which could be accurately dated by external characteristics to the same time, such as six-century B.C. Greek Black-Figure amphora fragments, we learned that within a reasonable range, all of the fragments release about the same amount of radiation. Older pottery fragments tested release more accumulated radiation. Younger fragments release less. From thousands of tests, a scale for accurately dating potteries evolved. And, a method of detecting forgeries which are so good they challenge the eye of an experienced expert. Think in terms of a special Geiger counter built into a pottery kiln to measure the radiation driven out of the ancient pottery by the rising heat, and you understand the basic principle of 'thermo' - heat - 'luminescence' -radiating light."

"How does this relate to sound imprints in stones and crystals?" asked Mr. Duncan.

"If ancient potteries are absorbing and storing sub-atomic particles, we might reasonably conclude that all objects are equally exposed, and thus equally receiving them, perhaps equally storing them. They are probably being imprinted in stones and crystals."

"What is this radiation, though? Where does it come from?" asked Dr. Powell.

"That's a point. We don't know. It builds up at a measurable and predictable rate. It doesn't matter if the pottery is on the surface or buried: the rate of build-up is about constant. We say it comes 'from the cosmos.' We assume that this means the 'outer cosmos,' but what if we are wrong and this is ambient radiation being exchanged and released on the sub-atomic level which we're only now beginning to understand takes place in all matter all the time? Either way, more critically: we don't understand what relationship may be going on in certain stones and crystals as they are being simultaneously bombarded with this radiation which they absorb and store - and sound waves - a form of energy we observe they also absorb, and may store. How are the sub-atomic particles stored? Are they laid down in a pattern? Does that pattern structure fluctuate under the influence of sound wave frequencies? This concept is the basis of all sound recording mechanics. Does the one phenomenon perhaps cause a pattern effect on the other, which might be identified and thereby be made readable, and re-assembled into sound patterns? Or, are these sub-atomic particles which enter into all matter - clay, potteries, stones, crystals - energy residuals of earth sound waves themselves, which some materials, such as clay pottery, has been proven to store?"

Leonore Alexander glanced around the room with a smile.

"This is a very ambitious theory. I'm beginning to understand why you're fascinated with it," she said.

"I can't yet affirm any relationship, but it is at least certain that a statement to the effect that 'no scientific proof indicates that sound or anything else is being stored in stones or crystals, naturally,' is inaccurate. It excludes discoveries made and known in other applied fields. The idea has come to some minds that this radiation which we drive out of ancient things by heat perhaps should be examined in other ways, ways not yet imagined or explored. Right now we just fire up the kilns, heat up the ancient sherds, and observe and measure the particles we drive back into ambient space. Maybe we're missing something here. Maybe there are imprints from our past locked up in ways we haven't yet explored. And that's the final evidence for which we must allow: the evidence of negative evidence."

Gregory Crandall lifted his hand from the table, and Leonore Alexander nodded.

"What do you mean, 'negative evidence'?" he asked.

"The problem of assuming that 'no evidence yet found' means 'nothing is there to be found.' This is why we experiment. This is why we explore. If I believe that it should be possible to listen to the conversation between a mother and her daughter on the morning of her wedding 3,000 years ago in Mesopotamia because I've found the carnelian brooch her mother gave to her as a gift, as she combed her hair for the last time and explained what was in her heart to share as her daughter left the house, you and your high-tech sources will tell me that it is impossible - just because no one has ever found the way. Your side assumes the evidence of negative evidence, and assumes there is nothing to find. If I accept your evidence, I stop looking, and we will never find out. We will never know. We will never hear those voices. If you accept my evidence of negative evidence - that it may just be out there after all and we haven't yet found the right key - we keep looking, and we at least have a chance of finding something out there."

Mark Lauterbach interjected.

"The sources we've consulted are pretty 'up there,' and they say 'no way; not happening.'"

"I can only say in return that every scientific wonder of our age - and there are tens of thousands of them in the last three decades alone - each was absolutely impossible in the minds of all scientific intellects until the moment of its discovery and invention proved it to be possible. As long as it remained a 'non-existent,' until it was discovered, there was no belief. Today little children take for granted what geniuses would have denied possible a century ago - all that technology has done. There is so much we are just beginning to learn about the basic fundamentals of crystal pattern structure, on the molecular and atomic and even subatomic levels. Discoveries of the crystalline nature of the universe are cropping up more and more in unsuspected areas: proteins, enzymes, all kinds of organic compounds and tissues we think of as "soft" but which are "liquid crystals" in a sense: they are organic. Structurally, we know that crystals can even be living; but they fall into the criteria and form of tissues, and chemicals in our bodies, and in living nature. It's only at the most basic levels that we've begun to discover that a vast part of our existence is based on crystalline structure. How does this affect the universe as we know it? We don't yet understand; i.e. 'negative evidence.' There is so much we have as yet to understand in science, the untested applications to an ever-expanding panorama of possibilities aren't even imagined yet. Even in the field of archaeology, negative evidence has been a problem for a long time, a major deterrent to research and discovery."

Leonore Alexander cleared her throat, and paused for a moment to find a precise wording before she spoke.

"We like your proposal. We want to be convinced. Can you tell us an archaeological negative-evidence success story to help us?"

"Let me tell you three short stories," I smiled back. Now we were into the bread and butter of my life, my favorite things.

"First, the Hittites. Up until 1906, everybody just assumed that there were no Hittites. Everybody had heard of Hittites, but everyone knew that they were just a fiction made up by ancient Hebrews writing vanity literature. And why not believe so? Outside the Bible, nothing had ever been dug up with the word "Hittite" on it, not from the Hittites themselves or from any other ancient people. No clay tablet or papyrus or stone inscription referring to any dealing with this supposedly vast empire which, by Hebrew record only, supposedly reigned over half a millennium. There was only negative evidence. How could you hide an empire as vast and powerful as was described? So, the learned world declared 'There are no Hittites.'

"Until in 1906, during the routine excavation of a big tepe near Boghaz Keui, Turkey, Winkler uncovers a room full of cuneiform tablets, in a language no one had ever seen. Ten thousand tablets, at first. Then, as the dig expanded, thousands more were found. Almost immediately the oft-repeating word HATTI revealed that this was a great capital city of - the Hittites. Today we take Hittites for granted, just like the Greeks, Romans, Assyrians and Etruscans. But a hundred years ago today, if you talked seriously of Hittites, you were laughed at. Winkler never set out to prove Hittites, but nonetheless he did, and since then, the Hebrew writings have been documented and confirmed many times over by scores of other discoveries.

"My second story is Ebla. A hundred years ago today, no one spoke the name Ebla, because no one had ever heard of it. Perhaps you've heard of Ebla, the massive Canaanite excavation on the south Syrian coast of the Mediterranean? Well, even 30 years ago today, you wouldn't have heard of Ebla. Nobody had. It didn't exist.

"It was still hidden inside tell-Mardikh, about 30 miles south of Aleppo, in the middle of scruffy fields. Nobody had ever suspected that tell-Mardikh wasn't just a natural hill of earth until 1964, when a few pottery shards were noticed in the dirt near its base. So a dig was organized and began its first season in 1968, just to see what was in this hill. It turned out to be a major capital city, over 4,000 years old. The citadel city alone is 140 acres square. For the first few years nothing was known about it other than it was Canaanite. Then in 1974 a group of 42 cuneiform tablets was found. Before they could be translated, a cache of over a thousand more was found. Then a major archive of almost 15,000 tablets was found in a room that had collapsed in a fire and just been built over, all official records, covering a period of only some 60 years. Imagine: 15,000 tablets produced in just 60 years! Calculate how many hundreds of thousands of clay tablets we should have for a full history of just one ancient empire! Only about 20,000 tablets have been found at Ebla.

"As the translation began, 80% of the cuneiform texts were found to be written in Sumerian. But about 20% were written in a completely unknown language: Eblaite, closely related to Hebrew! About 5,000 are literary texts, and about 15,000 are economic and governmental. We've learned a lot from them: they confirm ancient city names such as Hazor, Lachish, Megiddo, Gaza, Joppa and Urusalima, which is the Eblaite spelling of Jerusalem in the third millennium B.C. And only about 15% of the tablets have been fully translated. We don't yet know what we will find in the details of the remaining 85%. And there are still 120 acres of the city left to excavate. It had a population of at least 250,000 people during its height from 2,400 B.C. to 2,000 B.C. All of these things were discovered only 30 years ago. Not only the name of this ancient empire had remained totally unknown, but a major city had gone undetected under ground until 1968. If you asked in 1967 the question 'Are there any ancient languages we have not found, or major ancient empires we have not discovered?' the negative evidence response would be, simple, 'No.'

"Yet Tell-Mardikh is the capitol city of a great, long-enduring empire we never knew existed: the Kingdom of Ebla. Its regional power extended over most of Turkey, Syria, north Mesopotamia and Palestine. The Eblaite empire and language went from non-existent negative evidence to a major historical ancient world power, overnight. It exists. It had always existed. It was always there, buried low in the dust. It fell into the laps of historians, and suddenly the whole picture of the ancient world as we had neatly organized it had to be altered. The ripple effect has been immense.

"The best part of this story, which shows how thin the line between our ignorance and our knowledge can be, is that with all of the 20,000 cuneiform tablets found at Ebla, even with the royal archive discovery, we still didn't know its name. And we wouldn't know its name, except for a single, solitary statue inscription found in the dig, which declared the kingdom's name: Ebla. That's when the irony hit home. Only then did we discover: we had actually known of Ebla for a long time, from a number of cuneiform Akkadian texts, which spoke of Ebla as a competitor of the Akkadian power. We had the proof of Ebla, but we ignored it. We just hadn't believed in it.

"And this brings me to my last story of negative evidence: I mentioned the Akkadians. Have you ever heard of the Akkadians?"

They looked around at each other affirmatively.

"Yes, we have, of course."

"Of course. Who hasn't? They were the main Mesopotamian power and empire between the fall of the Sumerians and the rise of the Assyrians in the Third millennium B.C. They were big, the biggest, for half a millennium. Look at any book today with an ancient historical demographics map for the third millennium B.C. and you see AKKADIANS printed across half of Mesopotamia, for a period of many centuries. But there's just one little problem."

"What's that?" asked Dr. Spencer.

"Akkad, more correctly - Agade - the capital city."

"What about it?" asked Dr. Powell.

"Well, it's lost. We can't find it. It's never been found. We have no evidence of it. By negative evidence, it never existed. At this point we might say that it must be a fiction of some ancient people writing vanity literature."

"You mean the center of the Akkadian Empire, the city of Agade itself, hasn't been found?" asked Mr. Duncan incredulously.

"Nope. All we can guess is: it's still out there somewhere under the sand."

"How is that possible?" asked Dr. McPhetridge. "Haven't great scholars been excavating in Mesopotamia for over a hundred years?"

"Yes, but it still hasn't been found, just as hundreds of other ancient cities large and small that we can read about in the texts, still haven't been found. We can't find lots of cities. Just as we can't find any artifactual evidence substantiating the lives and reigns of hundreds of neighboring kings, whose names we read about in the records of 3,000 years in cuneiform tablets and papyri. Not a single inscription or scarab or cylinder seal or seal stone from any of them. Only the mention of their names in a tablet or a papyrus. Nothing. By the rules of negative evidence, they're fictions. And they were kings. Imagine when we get to the common people: most never existed, if we go by negative evidence. We may find one mention of a name or even hundreds of mentions of a name, but it doesn't mean that we will ever find a personal artifact of that person's life and existence. Few people of ancient times are validated in more than one medium."

"What is 'more than one medium?'" asked Mr. Crandall.

"That means a hard evidence, other than just a mention in writing, some kind of artifact inscribed with their name as owner. You find a name mentioned in a tablet, and then you find a cylinder seal with that name carved on it, used by that person or an authorized steward, and now you can say with certainty that this person in fact lived. Or you find more than a seal stone: a public inscription or a funerary inscription, and if you can be certain that all of these artifacts speak of one and the same person, you've got a really well documented person. But that's rare. The number of people documented by more than just a name scribbled on a papyrus or wedged into clay on a tablet is very small when we calculate the numbers of people who obviously lived. Ultimately, when we talk about people's lives, the inscribed seal stones, legal tablets and papyri and funerary inscriptions are the only kinds of artifacts evidencing that any individual person ever lived. Most of the 'multi-documented' and therefore 'proven' lives are pharaohs, kings, archons, Caesars, queens, high-ranking officials, people who had the money and power to require official stamp seals, cylinder seals, public inscriptions in stone, and stone-carved funerary monuments."

Their faces still showed uncertainty. I went on.

"What that means for 99.9% of everyone who ever lived is: if during your life you never had a cylinder seal with your name inscribed on it, never had a personal scarab seal with your name on it, or a stamp seal with your name on it, or a funerary inscription, then there's nothing for us to even be looking for. This encompasses most common people....... and some major figures. Archaeology has a very erratic double standard when it comes to negative evidence and artifact proofs of this kind. Lots of figures and their deeds are historically accepted without evidence of any artifacts, while others are ranked as fictions by the same lack of artifact evidence. You'd be surprised how many of the famous names from history are known to us only from written sources, without one other shred of hard evidence. That also goes for many famous historical events.

"For example: do you believe Hannibal crossed over the Alps with a huge army and hundreds of elephants? We've never found a shred of hard evidence to show that he ever got near the Alps. Yet we read and accept that over 10,000 Carthagenian men died in the Alps, and their bodies lay scattered over the high passes along with their baggage carts, hundreds of elephants with their tack and fittings and all kinds of weapons, supplies, and personal gear all abandoned as they fell. Not a trace of it has ever been found. Yet we accept the story, without a single artifact from the site. Negative evidence says he never marched. I don't know that any serious scientific search effort has been made now that we have so much remarkable equipment at our disposal. Yet for now, there is no reason to go looking, unless you think there might be something to find. Personally, I'd like to look," I stated with an eager smile.

"I would too!" blurted out Mr. Duncan. "I'm ready to go. Anyone else want to come?"

Laughter from the others, several nodding their heads.

"Really, I mean it," he said enthusiastically. "After you complete this Israel project, maybe we should talk about a trip to the Alps. Aren't there metal detectors or sonar equipment these days that can find things under rockslides and through snow? My gosh, how many decades ago did the last expedition looking for Hannibal scour the Alps? We've got to have scanning equipment now that none of those people had back then."

"Yes," I continued, "we do, and that's the whole point. Negative evidence from old attempts in many areas needs to be re-evaluated with the new equipment and technologies now at our fingertips. We can search again and re-analyze. There are wonderful discoveries waiting to be found. What's still out there to be found and discovered may exceed everything we have already found, and thought was all there is. Think of it this way: if nature can hide the Hittites so well that every scholar for two hundred years can unabashedly slam his hand down on the table affirming that 'there weren't no Hittites' until along comes Winkler at Boghaz Keui; and if nature can hide a capitol city of 260,000 inhabitants which ruled a vast empire called Ebla and keep it unknown under just a few centimeters of dirt until 1978; and if nature still can hide Agade somewhere out there - the biggest and most famous capital city of one of the biggest ancient empires - then who are we to deny so casually the other little things that nature perhaps is hiding, that still escape our view, elude our detection, which defy our way of understanding? Just because we haven't found evidence of something, just because we've never heard of it, just because it doesn't fit into the scheme of things as we think they ought to have been, does that really mean it's not out there, waiting under a few centimeters of dust, or locked inside a stone, or a crystal, waiting to be found?"

Leonore Alexander lifted her hand and glanced around the table at everyone to halt the discussion, and she spoke.

"Mr. Holland, I think I speak for all of us, in telling you that at least I never knew we hadn't found any relics of Hannibal's massive disaster in the Alps, nor did I know these other stories of archaeology which show the thin veils that have shrouded discovery. You've made a very persuasive defense for exploring an unknown in spite of today's technological soothsayers."

All heads nodded in agreement.

"Could you please give us some idea as to the approach you are preparing to make in 'listening' to the stones you dig up?" she asked.

"We don't know how sound waves absorbed by stones and crystals may be stored within the structure," I told her. "Sound waves are energy, and so we assume that our search has to be on the molecular or possibly even at the atomic or sub-atomic level. The problem we've been trying to solve has required us to approach the question of sound recording and playback from not only the old fashioned methods, but to imagine and prepare to access sounds recorded in a manner heretofore unanticipated in the current scope of Quantum Mechanics."

Mr. Crandall smiled and interjected.

"I'm sorry, you're over my head. For a person who claims to not know much about high-tech stuff, you've completely lost me. Could you slant that down to a little lower level?"

"Sorry. Sometimes I forget we haven't all been burping the same baby. I'm getting more used to this than I thought. What we're talking about here is the mechanical or physical manner in which sound wave impulses and tonal frequencies are recorded, scanned for reading, and reassembled back into their original format as sound waves and tonal frequencies: voices, music, noises as we might hear in the normal background of a house or office or factory or street or seashore or meadow or forest. We all know these sounds, and we know the various mechanical methods used to record them and play them back. Let me show you. I brought samples."

I opened the flap of a large manila envelope and let the contents pour out with a clatter on the table in front of me: an old 45 RPM hit record of Sam Cook singing 'Chain Gang,' a cassette tape of Three Dog Night, a long piece of 35mm movie film from 'Ben-Hur' with the photo-optical sound strip at the side, a Macintosh computer floppy disc, and a laser CD of Enya. I began to explain.

"Here, we can pass these around. What most people don't realize is that we're still recording and retrieving sound patterns basically the same way Edison did over a hundred years ago. All these mechanical recording and playback systems use the same concept: they convert sound waves into 'bumpy' physical textures on a moving path. When the sensor goes over the path it 'reads' the texture, and converts it back into sound. Edison called his invention 'phonograph:' sound-writing. He discovered that sound funneled into a needle traveling along a metal or Bakelite tube, or a flat disc, vibrated faster or slower according to the higher or lower sound frequencies, and scratched a bumpy zig-zag 'path' into the surface of the metal or Bakelite. Higher tone bumps and zig-zags are closer together in the path; lower tone bumps and zig-zags are farther apart. Softer sounds cut shallow paths; louder sounds cut deeper paths. Once the path is made, every time the needle re-traces it we hear the sound. Play it faster or slower, and we hear distortion: voices that sound like little elves or giant freakish monsters. There are people who can look at the paths or 'grooves' on an LP of classical music and tell what symphony is recorded on the record, just by looking at the groove patterns.

"Magnetic tape and computer discs use the same idea. Recording heads magnetize the iron particles painted on the tape or embedded in the disc into patterns of magnetic 'bumps' it understands and reads. Film sound tracks and laser-optic CD's use light. See on the side of the movie film there, that clear plastic line going up and down with the jagged, toothy sides? That's sound recording, the actual 'sound track.' The jagged 'teeth' you see are basically the same little zig-zags and bumps made in phonograph record grooves. But here, instead of a needle, a light sensor 'reads' them and converts them back into sound. CD's use a laser beam first to 'burn' a micro-groove almost like a phonograph record, and then 'read' it through laser light reflecting off the bumpy texture in the micro-groove. It's still all the same technology, whether it's a needle, or a magnetic head, or a photo-optic cell, or a laser light, they're all reading off a bumpy, swervy track in metal or plastic. Its all the same basic mechanics which Edison discovered.

"My proposal follows the hypothesis that there must be other processes of sound storage and retrieval in the universe. We just haven't imagined them or discovered them yet. For lack of imagining, even though they must be there, we haven't looked for them and thus we don't know them yet.

"We all know that we can sit in a great hall and hear the musicians with their instruments play a Mozart symphony, and that this magnificent music vibrating in the air comes to our ears which receive those wonderful vibrations and convert them into a different kind of energy impulse which our brains store in such a way we can play it back in our minds as often as we want. The same way as a mother holds her baby girl in her arms and hears her tiny new voice gurgling and singing and making newborn baby noises, and then twenty years later, when that baby girl stands as a grown woman in white lace at her wedding, the mother still can hear those soft and musical baby sounds in her mind, her little baby girl. They're there.

"We don't know how these sound imprints are stored as our bodies absorb them, but they are. We know they are stored; we know we can play them back. Right now if I mention Ed Sullivan, you can all hear him in your minds. Or Elvis Presley. Or John F. Kennedy. Or the sound of a train chugging by. Or a kitten meowing. How do we play back these sounds in our minds? There is a different level, a different method of sound storage we experience within our own bodies, though we can't yet tap into it with a wire and play it out loud for others to hear. But it is there, and we can make it play for us, whenever we want to hear it: Mozart, or a baby daughter.

"Though we still have a lot to learn and understand, I believe that we now may have some new technologies which work in new ways which might access the voices from our human family in the past, absorbed into the crystalline structure of stones which were present when our ancestors lived and breathed and loved and struggled through their lives. I'm just asking for support in my attempt to try and hear them.

"I know there are those who swear no sound waves absorbed by stones or crystals are being stored, because there's no evidence. But they say this only from the viewpoint of what our applied technologies tell us: they neither detect anything nor read anything.

"Yet if you use the wrong technology and equipment to read and play back any one of these perfectly good and real recordings here on this table, you'll get the same result. If you run the strip of photo-optic movie sound-track through a magnetic tape recorder, what will you get? What will you conclude? Or if you try to play a CD in an old record-player with a needle, what will you hear? What will you completely believe?"

They all looked around at each other a bit bewildered.

"That there is no sound recorded on it," said Mark Lauterbach.

"Precisely. So, though we absolutely know sound is recorded on all of these media, if we try and play them with the wrong play-back equipment, they will not talk to us or sing; they will be totally silent to us, and keep their secrets. This is my hypothesis: to use new tools and new equipment and new systems in an attempt to unlock and hear the voices which may be waiting us from our past."

The sound of my last words echoed for an instant in the chamber, and then was absorbed into silence. The members of the panel turned to look at Leonore Alexander, and she quietly nodded.

"Mr. Holland, this was a very thought-provoking presentation. We would now like to take a short recess to discuss privately the findings of this panel's inquiry. If you could please wait outside in the reception area, the secretary will call you back as soon as we have reached our decision."

I went out into the waiting area of the lobby, and sat down to read a magazine. This could take some time. I looked up at the receptionist, who smiled the encouraging but uncertain smile of one who has watched many others sit and wait for such verdicts. As I thumbed through pages, more looking at pictures than reading, I recalled silent reflections of the long, wearisome efforts which now rested upon this moment.

Yet after what must have been less than thirty minutes, the receptionist stood up and motioned for me to return to the conference room. A decision had been reached.

As I entered the room and sat down again at my end of the table, I searched the faces of the seven members for signs of the verdict. It was as ambiguous solemnity; and, the several friendly smiles might merely be protocol manners

Leonore Alexander looked at me with a smile.

"Mr. Holland, you're quite a dreamer," she said.

"Thank you," I replied.

"You're welcome. Though some take that quality with caution, we see the dreamer as a seed. This Foundation has become what it is today because of the fruitful development of dreams. Your dream sounds worth pursuing, with at least the minimal budget you have proposed. Mr. Holland, you have your grant of $200,000. Good hunting in Israel, and when you come back, make us a report as exciting as this presentation has been today."

She stood up. It was over. I got it. I got the grant!

Everyone around the table was now standing and coming over to shake my hand.

The rush of getting the approval almost stunned me. I got up as the panel members came to me with smiles, handshakes and their congratulations. I could barely speak; as we shook hands they gave me their many encouragements. All I could do was keep saying "Thank you, thank you so much." Tears started to run down my cheeks. I brushed them off with the backs of my hands, and apologized, saying "Sorry, I didn't know I was going to get emotional like this."

Dr. Powell took my hand solidly for a moment, and looking into my eyes she told me "Passion drives dreams into realities. That's part of why we voted Yes. Half of the vote was for the project, which we like. The other half is for you: we believe in you, Mr. Holland."

With accolades still echoing in the air, I took my leave and walked out into the fresh night to my car.

Soon I was in my car driving the long way home. As I drove, visions of the expedition into the Wilderness of Judah filled my head. This was no longer a dream. All of the planning was not in vain. There was much to do now, in very little time. As so often occurs, approval had come at the eleventh hour of the eve of those plans, plans which had had to be made in blind faith of a positive nod.

The nod was mine. I would not have to spend the night making phone calls canceling all of the preparations and reservations. We were on.

It was an excited, thought-packed, interminable drive home. I arrived long after dark, home to my wife and young children. My beloved children, treasures of a second failed and third-final happy marriage, fast asleep. Pausing at first one bedroom door and then the other, the answer to the historian's eternal question was affirmed again wholly: if you could go back in time and change history, would you? Looking at the sleeping faces of my four angels, alive with the joy of being, no matter what heartbreak and misery had been endured and would have to be endured again for them to be, no, I would not change history, for they would not be. Love flowed from my soul hovering over them, and I embraced them in their dreams.

My wife was already awakened by my footsteps. It is funny how the faintest of sounds can become so loud in the still of the night, in the quiet of darkness, and awaken the most sleepy-headed.

"How did it go, Honey?" she murmured sleepily.

"I have the grant!" I whispered triumphantly. Quickly she sat up and turned on the lamp by the bed. After the first piercing light adjusted her eyes, she pulled away her hand and squinted at me.

"You got it?" she squealed with a hesitant smile breaking across her face.

"I got it!" I repeated in full assurance.

"Oh, Honey, I'm so happy for you!" she exclaimed. We embraced and rolled on the bed giggling in glee. "How much did you get?"

"The whole thing. We're on!"

She stopped and gaped at me in amazement.

"You got the whole amount?" she asked incredulously.

"The whole trip is on. All the equipment. No disappointments."

"When will you get the money?" she asked excitedly.

"They're gonna wire it tomorrow, and from there on, everything falls into place."

"That means you can leave as you planned?"

"As planned. They said they understood that airline reservations have to be made in advance and excavation permit schedules have to be worked out and set and they don't want me to miss a day on the permit," I looked into her eyes. "They even apologized for cutting it to the last minute."

She sat back and held me by the shoulders at arm's length, looked at me in joy and admiration; then she grabbed me back in a fierce hug, whispering,

"I miss you already."

While I rocked her, our arms holding us together as our souls communed in ties which vast distance would shortly pull, I couldn't help thinking how wonderful a thing it is to be with someone who shared missing; who upon your return, shared joy. Love undimmed.

We slowly let go of each other, and sat back more seriously.

"I've got a few things to do before coming to bed," I said. She smiled again, and squeezing my hand once, crawled back under the covers, closed her eyes and snuggled her head into her pillow.

"See you when you get here," she smiled with her eyes closed.

I turned out the light, left the bedroom and went into my study where I was now able to continue preparing for the trip.

Opening the manila folder with the precious excavation Permit from the Department of Antiquities of the State of Israel, I once again reviewed the time window which had been allowed me. The trip was for seven weeks, only 49 days. So much to accomplish in only 49 days. The actual Limited Permit itself authorized me to dig only six weeks. Actually, a bit less than six weeks. After arriving in Tel Aviv, going to Jerusalem, getting all of the final documents stamped and signed, picking up the equipment at airport cargo after it cleared Israeli Customs inspection, and buying the perishable supplies and foods for the trip, I was allowed exactly 40 days in the Judaean Wilderness to set up camp, make test trenches, dig what I could dig, find what I could find and hopefully have something to test, test it, be successful, get packed and get out.

I turned on my computer and modem, and began to ready things long poised for triggering in final preparation for the trip.

It was rather funny. Me, using a computer. The archaeologist, more at home in the ancient past than in my own century and time. But it was true. I could still remember the time I hadn't believed in computers, and certainly hadn't believed the predictions that 'some day everyone will have computers in their homes and be linked to stores, banks and offices, and be able to do their shopping from a screen. That was only fifteen years ago, in the early 80's. My old-fashioned mentality just couldn't imagine such a reality. I was like the forefathers who had called the automobile a passing fad, who couldn't see the advantage of one of those new-fangled things over a good electric typewriter. Always the archaeologist, living in the old ways, in wonder of the old ways. The Twentieth Century was, to me, still very much a foreign country.

If I thought this was funny, wait until I began using the equipment set-up about to be put in my lap for this expedition, I said to myself.

With that thought, I reached over and picked up the phone, another funny little invention of our times which allowed commoners such as I to communicate with anyone on the face of the planet at a moment's notice with just a few touches of the fingers. A definite improvement over papyrus and midnight courier on foot.

I pressed the numbers for my colleague-in-technology, Kevin Taylor, whose company had been designing the hardware and software systems for this venture. I did not have to wait long.

"Did you get the grant?" he blurted as he picked up the phone.

"Yes!" I gloated. "Boy, you weren't expecting any other callers tonight, were you?" I laughed.

"Not at this hour, not this night. So you did it, you old dust-brusher! Good work, my man!" he congratulated.

"Thank you very much," I replied. I knew he really meant it. This was a hard grant to get. "And guess what?" I edged.

"How soon do we get it?" he asked, knowing the key question.

"Wire transfer, tomorrow morning," I smugly informed.

"Wheeee-Hoooo!" he yelled, so loud I had to pull the phone away from my ear.

"Are you sure you're really one of those nerdy, scientist-type genius guys I can count on?" I joked back at him.

"Listen, David, this is a pet project of mine personally, and just the thought of getting it out for a spin and a test drive is pretty miraculous. Covering the expenses comes in a close second, a close second, my friend. So, you really got it. Hot damn! OK. I'm calm now. Let's do it. "

"We'll make it," I rejoined with him.

"Get your bags packed. I'll see you day-after-tomorrow, 10 AM at the airfreight warehouse. Get a good night's sleep."

"Will do. See you then. Good night," I said and put down the receiver.

I got up and went over to my file cabinet, opened the top drawer, and pulled out another manila file folder. I walked back to my desk, sat in the chair, laid it down on the desk top, and opened it.

My eyes began to once again read the words of the FAX letter it contained, which I had received two years ago: the FAX which had added fire upon fire to my virtual obsession with this whole quest.

"Dear Dr. Holland,

The following information I share with you in the strictest confidence, in the hopes that at least one person may believe. I have already related this information unofficially to my own staff colleagues and been scoffed and censured for 'academic unreliability.' I dare not push this any further for fear of losing my standing and position.

Last summer season, while conducting an excavation in a new and

41

previously unexplored area of Elephantine Island in the Nile River near Aswan in Egypt, one of my student-volunteers discovered a hollow floor slab which, upon removal, revealed a foundation dedicatory deposit. In the coffer were three objects: a huge double-edged sword not of Egyptian style; a large ink-inscribed ostracon shard with 23 lines of Hebrew writing - yes - Hebrew writing - and a smaller copper plaque, inscribed with 8 lines of Hebrew writing. The translation of the texts I give to you below, and say bluntly that: the ostracon is a votive dedication written by the hand of a man named Yehoniah, who calls himself the steward of the High Priest Seraiah in Jerusalem, in the days of Zedekiah, King of Judah. This ostracon declares the sword to be the sword of Goliath - no error, Goliath - which he claims was used to slay Gedaliah in Mizpah.

The copper plaque clearly dedicates the building to YHWH. There is no doubt in my mind that we discovered the foundations of the Temple built by the Jews at Yeb, known from the Elephantine Papyri.

We photographed the find, copiously. However, the local authorities confiscated artifacts and film, and we were asked to leave the site. The next day the slab had been returned to its original position; the coffer was filled in; the find of the artifacts was officially denied to our faces. My permit was cancelled. We were escorted back to Cairo, basically, deported.

Upon our return, I and the five students made all attempts to establish credibility in our find, but the reaction was harshly negative. My superiors contacted Egypt. The authorities denied all and laughed at the story as utter nonsense. They accused me of misconduct; I am now persona non-grata in Egypt, and on uncertain footing at the university.

In the last year, none of the five students have been able to get new visas to Egypt. A friend of one student obtained a visa, went to Egypt and took an Aswan tour; her photos of the dig site area show it has been completely filled in and covered, with no trace of it left. The place looks as it did before we began to dig.

The rubbing we made of the plaque and my copy of the Hebrew text of the ostracon were taken by the Board of Trustees as 'hoax' material and I presume they have been destroyed. All I have left are the translations I made on the plane coming home. They are as follows:

The brass Dedication Plaque says:

"Holiness to the Lord. The Lord is YHWH.
I have surely built thee an house to dwell in
a settled place for thee to abide in forever.
Lord God of Israel, there is no God like thee
in heaven above, or on earth beneath,
who keepest covenant and mercy
with thy servants that walk before thee
with all their heart."

and the big pottery shard ostracon says:

"I, Yehoniah, the faithful steward of Seraiah, High Priest to
Yahweh at Jerusalem, have fulfilled my oath as bound;
I have hidden up the lights and perfections of the Lord
in a resting place in the Wilderness of Judah;
as the Lord did show me his path and his way;
in the Strong Holds of David, in their place they rest.
This I have done as I was bound by oath to do.
My master was killed by the Chaldean, and I
was taken into Egypt with Jeremiah and the others,
by those who slew Gedaliah upon his throne in Mizpah
with the sword of Goliath that was taken from Nob.
Jerusalem is left desolate; The Temple is laid waste;
the children of the fathers still weep and shall weep
until the promise of the Lord is fulfilled in his time.
In the Lord they shall rest until his coming.
I seal this my word with the great sword of Goliath
we dedicate with David to the House of the Lord
The Lord is my rock and my fortress, and my deliverer;
My God, my strength in whom I will trust;
my buckler, and the horn of my salvation
and my high tower. Hear me, my God,
in the far land of my affliction:
I have fulfilled my oath as I was bound."

I have not had time to research what items, presumably from the Temple in Jerusalem, Yehoniah hid in the Wilderness of Judah; perhaps the Holy Candlesticks, the Eternal Lights. They may still be hidden and some day may be found. The Wilderness is a vast area, yet the En Gedi zone seems indicated.

That is all I can tell you.

I have all but suffered a nervous breakdown over this. Please do not communicate back on this matter, as I would prefer to imagine that you believe me rather than learn otherwise. Please do not call or write about this, as I cannot discuss it even privately. Two of the five students who were present and saw these things have been let go from the university as they would not give up their insistence of what is being called 'the Goliath hoax.' I cannot afford a single further disturbance to arise from it. Best of luck.

Yours Sincerely. Brannon."

Dr. Brannon had then been asked to leave the university.

He got an obscure job in an obscure small town at a junior college teaching general history.

Then his wife left him.

Then he blew his brains out.

I believed him. I had known him, and knew: he was not the sort of academic to desperately trump up a sensational story just for his own vanity; he didn't have to. Nor was he a jokester given to monumental pranks. Moreover, through the grapevine I had made contact with one of the five students who had been on his dig, and after listening to her account, there was no doubt that she believed every word she was telling me. She believed it. He believed it. I believed it. But no one else believed it. It was 'the Goliath hoax,' and the few who privately retold the story in hushed voices laughed as they said the name Brannon. Then they became quiet.

I had reflected often that Dr. Brannon was our century's Moses Shapira. More than a hundred years ago, Shapira had bought the first Dead Sea Scroll. A Bedouin had brought it to his antiquities shop in Jerusalem, asking for money, saying there were "many more." Shapira bought it and took his prize to London for authentication, where it was proclaimed the oldest manuscript of the Bible ever found. But in those cynical days of Graf and Welhausen, a jealous, ignorant and arrogant academia soon denounced it as a forgery. 'The Shapira Strips,' they had called them, and laughed. Discredited and ruined, Shapira took his life in a Rotterdam hotel. The pieces of the precious scroll, purchased from a Bedouin, found by the Dead Sea, were sold as novelties. The scroll, and its origins, was lost forever.

I was grateful that Brannon had sent me the translations before his death. They opened a window into a clearer view of a very tumultuous and obscured period of Biblical History. But most importantly, the long letter written by the man named Yehoniah revealed the secret of a Temple relic hidden in the desert. No Temple relics had ever been found, except for the inscribed ivory top of the staff of a priest, carved as a pomegranate, found in Jerusalem. Nebuchadnezzar had raped the Temple in his time; Titus had swept it clean in his: in Rome today his triumphant arch still brazenly exhibits in marble, carved almost two thousand years ago, the Table of the Shewbread, the Incensarium, the seven-branched gold Candelabrum and the Temple Shofar, trophies of his triumph over the Judaeans.

Yet as Dr. Brannon correctly interpreted, here was a message from ancient days saying that a precious object from the First Temple had been preserved, and lay hidden, waiting to be found.

The odd thing is that Dr. Brannon had not consciously realized his one simple error.

In hurriedly translating the Hebrew directly into English, he had failed to remember that a very few words from the Hebrew are never translated: they are always used as Hebrew words, for in Hebrew they mean something.

Such was the case with the words *lights* and *perfections* when used in conjunction with the emblems of the High Priest of the Temple. As I searched for references to the earliest Temple candelsticks, I found the original Hebrew words would have been *urim* for lights and *thummim* for perfections. They should not have been translated, I discovered, but left in Hebrew. Dr. Brannon had missed this exception.

I vaguely remembered these words, and did some further investigating. I did not have to go very far.

The *Urim* and *Thummim* were the sacred oracle stones of the Lord. The Holy crystal stones placed in the Ephod of Aaron by Moses, used to inquire of God. Passed down from High Priest to High Priest, even unto the days of Seraiah and the desolation of Nebuchadnezzar, they had vanished by the time the Jews returned from captivity in Babylon over a century later. Somewhere between the capture of Jerusalem and the Return, they were lost. Without them, Nehemiah had prohibited the most Holy ordinances of the Temple to the Levites, until one should stand with *Urim* and *Thummim*.

With them, a person could talk to God.

For over eight hundred years, High Priests, prophets and kings of Judah and Israel had spoken the most historic things over them, over these stones.

Little was known about them. Several fanciful theories, I found, but no sure knowledge of any kind. No one knew their shape, their exact size, no one even knew what kind of stone they were.

But by their name, I imagined it could be understood: they were 'perfect' in some way, so visibly 'perfect' in form that they bore this name. And perhaps, in the right hands, they shone forth in Holy Light, the light of God's presence shining in and through them.

Lights and Perfections.

The Urim and Thummim of God.

After I had searched the few, uninformative, speculative articles and papers written about them, having learned that we know nothing except that Moses suddenly had them for the High Priest and they became part of a special Ephod together with the breastpiece of Aaron, to speak to YHWH, I showed my wife this letter from Brannon and my few pages of scratched notes about these stones. Stones which could possibly contain the most important voices to be heard in all of our entire universe. Stones which might hold within them imprints of the very voice of God.

She had looked it all over quietly, slowly, deliberately, and looked up the references I had scribbled down from the Bible: Exodus 28:30; Leviticus 8:7-9; Numbers 27: 18-21 and in the book of Deuteronomy 6:4-9 .

Finally, placing her fingers upon the words *Urim and Thummim*, she looked up at me and said:

"These are what you want to find."

And somewhere out in the Wilderness of Judah, as I dug and sifted the dirt for semi-precious stones, and tried to unlock their secrets of sounds and shadowy voices, I hoped to also look for that which most people would say never existed.

But I would look, because I believed.

I closed the folder, and put it in my travel briefcase to go with me on the trip.

45

Back in the bedroom, I changed into my pajamas in the dark, and crawled wearily into bed. As I snuggled close to my wife and her warmth, she awoke enough to ask sleepily,

"Did you tell them what you're really looking for?"

"No," I mumbled. "There are some things best kept quiet. You can't tell people everything."

Chapter 2

Day Two: As A Child In The World

At the breakfast table my wife and I shared the news of my success with the children. As they heard that Daddy got the money and would be leaving tomorrow for almost two months, they instantly whooped and cheered. My daughter jumped up from her chair and ran around the table to give my arm and shoulders a hug. Her joyful, bright eyes spoke pure love and trust into mine, and we shared a precious moment.

"Mom *said* you would get it," my son grinned smugly.

"Oh she did," I smiled as I let go of my daughter and looked over at my son. "When did she say that?"

"Last night at dinner, while you were going to the meeting," he replied with a bigger smile. "We talked about it a lot. She said you could do it."

My wife's smiling gaze turned from him to me. It was that kind of support that gave me the courage to try against the odds. We were all overjoyed.

Breakfast was eaten in a carnival atmosphere. Why children always get so excited to see Daddy go away on a trip I will never fully understand, but I have always encouraged myself that it has mostly to do with the instant expectation of postcards to be received while he is away, and goodies, souvenirs, candy and hugs they know they will get when he comes home. The profound fulfillment a child experiences in receiving a postcard in the mail, addressed just to her or to him, with his or her name written on it, has always moved me with great pondering. The glee over anticipated toys and treats at homecoming never required meditation, though I have always felt somehow it is archetypal of something beyond my memory.

"Daddy," my daughter suddenly asked, "do we have to go to school while you're away on your vacation?"

I looked over at her with bemused surprise.

47

"Yes, you do, and I'm not going on a vacation. I'm going to be working! Who says I'm going on a vacation?" I laughed.

"Mommy says you'll be having lots of fun, like a vacation, while she still has lots and lots of work to do here every day," she said with big eyes looking up at me. I looked up at my wife with a smile.

"Well, that's true, but it will only seem like a vacation because Daddy's lucky. I like my work a lot, so it's fun. But it's still hard work."

"But why do we have to go to school? Why do we have to learn all these things, anyway? I don't even know what I'll use any of it for." she complained.

I looked around at my children's imploring eyes. Even being a teacher, this was a tough number to teach.

"For experiences," I said. "Each one counts. A lot of the things you learn you may think you'll never use, but you will. And the learning process you learned to learn them - *THAT* you will use every day, trust me."

"I heard Einstein flunked sixth grade math," blurted my son. "My teacher said he didn't learn any of the stuff he did in school."

"That's true," I nodded. "But Einstein was a special man. Do you know what made him so special?"

My children looked at each other and shrugged.

"What made Einstein special is that in his mind, he was always in school. He looked at the world, at the stars, the sun, the universe, and he always was asking questions. Nobody had answers for his questions. They were, well..... he said they were children's questions. But unlike everyone else, he didn't stop asking when he found out no one knew the answers. He just kept wondering, and asking. He said what made him different from other people is that he had never grown up. He always remained a child. He said that children ask the most simple questions. He was asking them still, the day he died."

"But if he didn't need to go to school, why do we?" she asked.

"Because most of us don't ask enough questions, and not all of us can think of the right questions, so we go to school, where they give the questions to us, so we can think about them. And by the way, Einstein went to school!" I tousled her hair.

"But she's right," echoed my older son dejectedly, "I don't think we're ever gonna use half the stuff they make us study."

I looked lovingly at my children. I wanted so much for them. This was where being a parent became a hard job: knowing from having traveled the road, knowing from experience the children lacked, knowing they wouldn't know until they journeyed more.

"The things you learn," I said, "you will always use, even if only by being able to recognize what you hear, and what you see. You'll understand what others talk about. You'll be more prepared for everything in life. You know, history is very repetitive. The life process is very repetitive. The more you know, the more things will come to make sense to you. Little things often are just like big things. Knowledge is treasure. It's like money in the bank. You can't just think of today. You have to think of tomorrow, and tomorrows in the future you can't even imagine. The more prepared you are, the more you'll recognize and understand what's going on around you, and the better you'll be able to grab it with both hands and get everything out of it there is to offer. So pay attention. Listen. Learn. Remember. No experience in this life is wasted. Take Daddy's word for it."

"So, I have to go to school while you're on vacation?"

"Yes, you have to go to school while I'm on vacation," I smiled.

We finished breakfast, and with much ado they scrambled and gathered their things and rushed off to school. I knelt down on the living room floor, and hugged and held and kissed each one of them, a moment of solid eye-contact with each one in turn, until the last one had been hugged and told "Be good. Just as you always are. I love you," and out the door they went.

"Kids," I sighed. "What can you do?"

"Ah-ah-ah," my wife smiled at me. "Remember what it says: 'Except ye become as little children........'"

I smiled at her. It was true. I knew the passage. I knew.

As I rushed to get my papers gathered into my briefcase, I thought about this dilemma. For it was a serious dilemma.

Could we become as a child? We hated being treated like kids!

Though we often wished we could go back to our childhood as adults, we resented being called children, and treated as children. What was wrong with this picture? As frustrated as we became as parents, we also still remembered what it was like to be a child. We hated it. We had been born wanting to be grown up, it seemed.

We wanted to be big, to have the privileges of grown ups. We wanted to do what grown ups do, and we played grown up. We did not want to be little children, and we often were angry over it all.

.As adults, most of us became angry the instant anybody even insinuated we were acting like a child. We hated being treated as a child. It was offensive to us. We felt talked down to, underestimated.

I had seen grown men and women become angry, even yell 'stop treating me like a child! I'm not a child!' I had seen men come to blows, because another had dared to call them a baby. Blows.

How would we ever become as little children when we so quickly heated up our blood pressure and got angry at the very thought of being called a child, much less of being treated as a child? All we had to do was touch that pride button, and pride set us off. I'm an adult! I'm too big for this kid stuff!

We needed to get over our pride, our irritation at being treated as children, if we were to become as little children. We had to.

I suddenly saw this as a terrible obstacle, this 'adult' thing.

How would we even recognize that we were too proud to be a child again, to inherit the Kingdom, and let it go, to go with the flow?

There probably was a test. But could we even once let go, and become, even for a moment, like a little child? Even for a short test?

Could we ever regain that sweet innocence? Could we let go?

Could we get through such a test, even if the reward was great?

It might be agonizing for some of us. But we needed to know.

As soon as I was ready, I gave my wife a hug and kiss, went out to the car, turned the key, and drove off to the university for my last day of lectures and presentations at the museum.

I thought as I drove. All day yesterday I had worked in anxiety, wondering whether today I would be sheepishly canceling my leave of absence, and all of the other myriad arrangements which had been carefully negotiated and organized for my departure.

Yet my hands grasped the steering wheel in full exhilaration this morning, knowing that the announcement would be positive and triumphant, even causing a bit of envy to a few doubting teasers. Though few at the university espoused my enthusiasm for the theory, any funded dig in an ancient site was occasion for excitement. Even the smallest pot shards were treasures to those who intoned what they were: travelers through time come to touch our fingertips, bringing messages of antiquity and the mysteries of life from across the great bridge.

Archaeology had always been just that to me: the bridge. It was not dirt, and dust, or rocks, or stones, or dry broken pieces of anonymous pottery found by the bushel basket, or foundations of long forgotten buildings or stubs of toppled walls, or fragments of bone, bits of wall plaster and charred pieces of wood. It was not even the things most people did think of as treasures: coins with faces of ancient kings and queens on them, gods and goddesses, long-destroyed buildings engraved with medallic art as they had stood when new; nor was it statues, or bronze figurines, or gold and jeweled treasures which lay waiting to be discovered and published with great flurry and fame. To me, all of these wonderful things brought me in touch with my true love of the past, the people.

I loved the people, and through these things I touched, the people came close to me, just beyond that touch. There is no greater wonder and awe-filling experience than to lift an ancient fragment from the dust, and know that the last hand which touched it before yours, had let go of it over two or three or four thousands years ago. How often had I felt that the shard which lay in my hand had been lovingly dropped there by the person who had left it for me, all of those years ago. I did not know any of their names, yet I saw their smiling faces, their joyous eyes, and without words, we communed with each other from our vastly separated times, suddenly joined.

In every bit and piece and fragment and shard is a part of a person, a person who lived, lived just as I do - breathing, eating, thinking, hoping, dreaming - and most bits and pieces actually hold more within them: moments and parts of many people's lives who had their part in the making and the daily use of that item. Archaeology was the bridge I had discovered which allowed me to enter their world, touch their time and place, and thereby touch them.

As I drove through the busy streets I looked around me at the people, and did as I often did - imagining we were all in another time, another place. I looked at their faces; their arms swinging to and fro as they walked, some intently, some casually, some excitedly, some dejectedly; so many forms of people walking along: shoulders, arms, heads, legs in stride; and in the cars: listening to music, to news, to talk show hosts telling jokes; talking to passengers, discussing business, family, last weekend, next weekend, telling a story, debating politics, driving to their myriad jobs to earn their bread by the sweat of each brow, just as every human being since the beginning.

I envisioned us all as Romans, and then as Egyptians, and then as Sumerians, and looked into the people's faces as I drove by. These were the faces I could have seen had I lived thousands of years ago.

We were still the same.

We, the people.

Nothing had changed.

This awakening and realization had become the foundation of my life's work and my most popular lecture: "Life in the Ancient World is No Different from Life Today." I would be giving that lecture this morning, to a bus-load of elementary school children on a field trip, who would come to see and touch real ancient artifacts and listen to a real archaeologist. At the museum we tried to encourage classes to come to the museum and lab. There was always a lot to see, and hopefully we left them with lots to think about afterwards.

I drove into the university parking lot and strode vigorously across campus to the museum building. The air was especially crisp and delicious; the sun particularly warm and energizing. What a difference a day makes, I thought. For I knew: the air and the sun were the same. It was I who had experienced a change. I was different. Yesterday's anxiety had mercilessly crowded my sight. Today's triumph and empowering anticipation cleared my vision, reshaped it, and opened my being to receive a fuller gift of the most simple, yet most wondrous constant that was always the same wondrous constant around me: the world in which I moved. Today I was truly in it. It was wondrous.

I reached the double glass doors and paused to get in step with the crush of students pushing to get into classes on time. The rhythm was everything. Once in sync, never a stepped-on toe, never a clipped ankle. Occasionally a hooked briefcase, but with the proper gentle lift and turn, the doorway ballet disentangled arms and briefcases just as quickly as we all merged, and the reverse process rhythmically spewed us on to fan out in all directions, each to his and her own destination within the halls.

Mine was the administration offices of the Department.

Being academics, the victory celebration was proper and brief, yet the heartfelt delight of all was shared in warm handshakes, words of congratulations and smiling faces. The several expected 'never-thought-you-would-make-its' and 'gee-if-I-had-known-it-would-be-this-easy-I-would-have-tried-for-a-grant-too' jokes made it all the sweeter to savor. The Director's "Well done" sent me on my way. It was, after all, just another day at the university.

I stopped quickly at the Requisitions office and told them of the full approval, which brought sighs of relief as they now could pay the invoices rather than send back the field equipment cautiously ordered in anticipation. I gave them the air carrier and flight number which the tech shipment would be on so everything could be delivered by tomorrow to be joined under one airwaybill. There would be enough to do without having two shipments to get through Israeli Customs.

In my office there was little left to do. All of the papers I would need had been gathered and waiting for weeks; a quick shove into the briefcase finished that. Nothing else was needed. The real material I required awaited me beneath the ancient soil of Israel.

It was now 9:15 A.M. In fifteen minutes the sixth-grade classes from the elementary school would be arriving, and it would be showtime for the next two hours.

I loved these occasions. And, as I had developed the approach that seemed to click, student field trip visits had become my special domain. Over all of the years of doing this, it always turned out to be a rewarding experience for me as well as the children.

My method was simple. I let the children help me find the child in myself. It had taken a while; it was unfamiliar at first. Holding on to the adult mystique I found was a tenacious instinct, hard to let go. But as I found my child, the children all became my friends. As we explored together, I saw again as a child. What I thought I already knew I saw again with a child's eyes; and with a child's wonder, I learned new things.

Then I let the adult I had learned to be help them see themselves - in everything they saw. That was the magical gift.

This way worked wonders. This was how it should be. At the annual meetings we professors had all seen and heard too often those boring lectures given by 'Dr. Dry,' the proverbial boring history professor whose monotone voice and dull lists of dates, old events and dirt clods left us literally 'in the dust.' The child in me had always known: this is not archaeology.

Archaeology is a time machine. Whenever the kids would come, I opened the door and let them take a ride in mine. Just as in the old Twilight Zone episode 'Kick the Can,' in the old folk's home, as I dared to play a game of Kick the Can once more I suddenly found the secret: we are all children inside. Archaeology was my 'Can.'

I got up, turned out the lights, and walked to the museum archive room to get my 'cans:' my box of ancient artifacts I shared.

Our game here would provide a key of understanding to all that is to come. By this brief panorama unfolding consciousness from our family in the Stone Age to the life of ancient Greece and Rome, they would grasp from where they come, where we are now, and what has been given to us. It is a journey and awakening that all need to make. Those who might pay attention to this scrutiny of our ancestors' lives would unlock great and empowering secrets of life.

At 9:30 sharp I arrived in my place at the museum doors, in time to watch the teachers get the children in order, in line, and quiet. The hall's acoustics magnified every echoing squeal and giggle. To the back of the throng, several boys became louder; quickly a push brought a shove with sharp voices rising. It was my turn to step in and help. I was used to this. Smiling, I approached them.

"Stop your fighting, children. Come on! This is an exciting experience. Let's not spoil it. There's room enough for everyone, and everyone can smile. Come on, let's see everybody smile!"

The boys made silly smiling faces at me, then at each other, and then broke out laughing. The group quieted, and we were ready.

"Good morning, everyone. Welcome to the University Museum."

"All right! Now, you're all going to be holding some real ancient artifacts and touching some real ancient things. Who would like to hold a real ancient Roman coin, a real one, from the time of Augustus Caesar two thousand years ago?"

All hands shot up again, with lots of jumping.

"Me! Me! I would! I want to!" came dozens of hopeful voices.

"Good. Well, you're all going to hold a real one, an ancient Roman coin two thousand years old, because we've got several of them, big ones and little ones, and we're going to pass them around."

Eager cries of "Oh boy! Goodie" on all sides.

"Now, as you've probably been told, I'm Dr. Holland, and I've noticed some of you looking at my shoes. Well, sorry to tell you, but I don't wear wooden shoes. Nope. No wooden shoes. Although I do have several pair at home. Yes, I really do. OK, Yes, you there."

From now on, questions would leap upon me from all sides.

"Are you really a archy-ologist?" asked a boy.

I held up my hands with fingers curled down as claws.

"See the dirt under my fingernails from digging in the ground?" Everyone strained and turned their heads to see. I turned my hands then to look at them myself.

"Oops, looks like I cleaned them this morning. Not to worry. Yes, I am a real, live archaeologist, and I have been to the pyramids in Egypt many, many times, and, yes, I went inside. Oh, it's huge inside. When you go inside the big pyramid in Egypt you get this unbelievable feeling because you're inside the biggest stone building ever made by human hands and you're inside it, like a little tiny ant. What did it feel like? It feels wonderful. Yes? Did I go inside the Sphinx? No, they don't let people go inside it anymore. What else have I done? I've been inside King Tut's Tomb, and been to the Acropolis in Athens, where the Greeks made those beautiful temples with the big marble columns, yes, that right, with the Doric capitals, very good. Who's your teacher? All right, good job! And, I've been to Rome, where the Romans were, that's in Italy, the country that's shaped like the boot...right, and I've been inside the Coliseum, and walked in the Forum right where all the Caesars walked; and, I've been to Pompeii.....yes, the city that was buried by the volcano. Yes, it's awesome. For once, the right application of the word. What's it like? Well, you get to walk through all the streets, with all the houses on either side that don't have any roofs any more, because the ashes and cinder stones from the volcano crushed them all, but they've been cleaned out so you can walk through them too, and you find yourself thinking: these are real Roman peoples' houses who really died here almost two thousand years ago in a volcano. And you just go block after block after block and walk into all these people's houses, and see the paintings on the walls they painted all those hundreds of years ago, and you walk out into the big open public square, the Forum, and you imagine what it would have been like if all the tourists you could see were wearing togas, and tunics, and soldiers with red capes and golden bronze helmets. After a while as you walk around you notice that everyone else who is there, even whole classrooms of children just like you, everybody's whispering. Yes. *Whispering.* It's the weirdest thing. It's like a ghost town, and so many people died there, that as people walk through the streets they just whisper. Ok, yes? Where else have I been? Oh, I've been to a lot of other ancient places, Timgad, that's a Roman ruin in North Africa; Stonehenge, that big circle of huge big stones in England; Macchu Picchu where the Incas lived high up in the Andes Mountains in Peru, places like that. Now, does that make me sound enough like an archaeologist for everyone?"

Lots of heads nodding approval, and a chorus saying "yes."

"Did you dig up anything in Pompeii?" asked a girl.

"No I didn't dig there. Why? Only the government digs there, and I've never been on one of their teams. Where have I dug? Well, I've been on a number of team digs in Egypt, on Crete, that's Greek stuff, and in Israel. Israel....where is Israel.... no, all the way at the far end of the Mediterranean Sea, just up from Egypt, down from....that's right, part of the Fertile Crescent. Wow, you kids really know your stuff. You've been preparing for this trip, haven't you? OK. What have I found when I was digging? Mostly little bits and pieces of broken things, like pottery shards, that's fragments of broken pottery jars and bowls and things. We find a lot of those when we dig; and lots of broken pieces of building materials like marble, and granite, and tuffa stone, that kind of thing; lots of little pieces of ancient glass bottles and jars, broken pieces of floor mosaics. What are floor mosaics? They're pictures made on floors with little square pieces of black and white stones just about the size of dice, yes, that's right, and the Romans used them to make black-and-white pictures on their floors, for centuries and centuries during Roman times, all over the whole Mediterranean area, so we find them all over the place. Yes, the floors were very pretty. Did I ever find some really good stuff? Sometimes some ancient coins that people had dropped and lost or buried to save them like in a bank, that kind of thing."

"Did you ever find a big statue?" asked a girl.

"No, I myself never did. That kind of thing doesn't really happen very often. Oh, don't look so disappointed. I'm not. I know many of my colleagues feel that their season was a waste if they didn't find an inscribed statue, but truthfully, we learn so much from all the little bits and pieces of pottery, glass, bricks, stones and little things we find, every dig is a treasure trove. Very often we find really special things, like rings, necklace pendants, bracelets, clay figurines, clay oil lamps, and all the other little objects people used and handled and touched in their lives. So every excavation is very, very important and very worthwhile. You know, a lot of people see movies like Indiana Jones, and they see huge excavations going on with wheelbarrows, and shovels, and tons of earth being moved with statues sticking up out of the ground and all, and they think that's what archaeology is. How many here have seen Indiana Jones? Some of you? OK, that's good; well, most archaeology is done digging little bits at a time, and then we carefully analyze what we find, even with microscopes looking in the dirt for fragments of skins and leather and wood particles, seeds, pollen and things that tell us about life in the times we're digging through. And every little thing we find, well, that's something left behind by someone in our family from ancient times, and it's precious."

More hands went up for questions, and more asked out loud. It was time to get into the center stage, however, and unfold the magic carpet into the time machine.

"I tell you what, it's time to go inside and discover what we came to see, and begin touching the things we can touch. Who wants to hold questions for a moment and go inside?" All hands up again.

"Alright. Come with me, and, *Welcome to the house of your family*."

I opened the doors, and with a wide sweep of my arms, invited the teachers to usher in their classes in the first great hall.

"Oooooooo," sounds rose in the quiet air as the children filed in.

The university collection was not impressive in the sense of big sculpture, nor architectural pieces, nor fabulous painted vases. Yet what we lacked in whole objects we made up for in beautiful color photography, which clearly showed what the fragments we displayed had been part of, and why they were wonderful, even as fragments. This was an exhibit of life, not things; of people and their ways of doing and living, not relics; of the homes and the lives of our ancestors, not art. Though the objects were things, and relics and art, they became more than that because we had chosen to present them as more than that.

The first hall was the beginning of our journey, which took us back to the hunter-gatherer times of our Cro-Magnon ancestors.

The small rolling cart with my time-machine box of artifacts stood by the cases of hunter-gatherer culture. Behind the glass, points and axes and tools were brought to daily-life relevance by pictures of tribal families, hearths, bison and wooly mammoths, cave paintings and petroglyphs. At the center was a huge circlerama of a Cro-Magnon tribal family, with mannequins of fathers, mothers, grandparents, children, babies, and a full re-creation of all the clothing, tools, foods and implements we know of from this time.

"Now the first thing I want all of you to do," I began, "is think of your own life every day as you wake up in the morning. Are you all there? All waking up? Oh, oh. Over there, yawning, you're not waking up yet. OK, that's better. Now, you wake up each day and think your life is really different than these people's lives back in the Stone Age, right?" I motioned back to the display cases which surrounded us, depicting Cro-Magnon life scenes. Heads nodding.

"Well, let's think in terms of your day. You wake up each morning still a little sleepy, and usually hungry, right? You need food during the day right? Oh - you want to eat now, do you? Sorry, we'll have to wait. And there's something else: hungry and waiting to eat. Think about this: every day as you wake up, you share the same, very same experience your ancestors we see here experienced as they woke up: still a little bit sleepy, the air is chilly, the floor is chilly. And when your tummy feels hungry, you are sharing the same experience your ancestors here experienced: you're hungry. Your ancestors got very hungry, too. Ah, these are not your ancestors? You don't think these were your ancestors? How many don't think you had Hunter-Gatherer ancestors? Oh, my! Wait till High School physiology and they'll straighten it all out for you. In the meantime, take my word for it: these are our ancestors, all of us. This is the beginnings of our family. And it's a really cool family. We have a really great family, in fact. I'm proud of them all. For right at the beginning of time, your family began to invent and make wonderful things. And, they woke up each day just as you do, felt things just like you do, and they often had to wait to eat just like you all have to wait now. That's right, no snack here today, sorry."

I stepped over to the box on the cart.

"Now let's get out some things we can touch."

I reached into my box and took out three Neolithic stone axe heads: one chip-shaped piece, and two which had begun just like it, but which had been further ground down and smoothed and polished until they were almost perfect. They were from Gaul, High Neolithic, and I loved them.

"What I have here are some stone axe heads just like the ones in the cases, and these are real, about 10,000 to 20,000 years old."

The really fun part began.

"Who would like to be the presenters here?" I asked. All hands up.

"OK. You, you and you. Here. You take this one; this one is for you to show, and here. This one's for you. Now, let's have you walk along in front of everyone so they can see and feel them. OK now, ladies and gentlemen, these are pre-historic stone axe heads, just like those you see in the exhibit cases, from Stone Age people, made by Cro-Magnon people towards the end of the Ice Age."

I looked at the name tags of the presenters and continued.

"Now, the one Gregory is passing around for all of you to see and feel is chip-formed. It was made by striking the edge of a stone with another stone, or a piece of bone or antler. With a little bit of experience, you can learn how to do this yourself, and you can make an axe head like this in less than an hour. Notice the name written on it in India ink. That's the site in France where it was found.

"The next two axe heads which Lisa and Michele are carrying around to you started out just the same as the one Gregory is carrying. After they were chipped, they were rubbed hard on another big stone and ground down until they became smooth, and then they were rubbed on smoother stones until they became polished as you see. Notice along the back end...that's right, the narrower, sort of square end....notice the little dips left from the chips we can still see, and along the side edges toward the back. Yes, those little dents. Those are the chips, just like the concave scoops we see in Gregory's axe head, and they were so deep that even after the grinding and polishing we can still see them a little."

I walked over to Michele and held her hand up with the smooth, polished axe head.

"If you want to, hold the axe head up to your cheek and rub your cheek on it. It's so smooth and cool feeling. It feels really good."

I leaned over and softly rubbed my cheek over the smooth stone surface. I went back to the case, and one by one, the children lifted up Lisa's and Michele's hands and rubbed their cheeks over the stones. Eyes widened and smiles widened with every experience.

"You see, our very ancient ancestors made truly beautiful and wonderful things, even out of just plain stone. Now, how many of you think these axe heads, which could have been used to cut small branches, or hunt, or fight in a battle - how many think these were made by men, and boys?"

Most hands went up.

"How many think they were made by women, and girls?"

A very few girls' hands hesitantly went up.

"Well, though we used to just automatically assume that 'Hmmmm, stone tools; men's things; made by men,' now we are beginning to realize that while the rough chipping may have been done by the men, just as it is in some cultures still today, it may have been done by women and girls. And, we are almost certain that the beautiful, smoothed and polished pieces we see here, were made by the women and girls who stayed at home while the men were out on their camping trips, hunting and showing off to each other. So, you four are right. These were made most probably by our grandmothers, not our grandfathers. Think of the hundreds of hours it took to rub and grind one of these down until it was perfectly formed and smooth like this. This is perfect beauty. As you touch them, think of the people who made them and used them. Try and imagine their faces. In your mind, thank them for making these beautiful things and leaving them for us to find so we could know them."

We then looked over the several dioramas of hunter-gatherer life and saw experience after experience they knew of in their own homes: a mother sewing clothing, cooking, nursing a baby, bringing home fruits and vegetables, seeds and grains, cleaning the living area, watching children play, caring for an elderly and sick family member. Yes, we knew these people.

"As you have all touched these stone tools, and felt them with your hands, some of you with your cheeks to feel how smooth and perfect they are, you have touched their lives to yours. That's pretty special. They have always been your family, even if you never imagined them before, but from now on you will always remember your family from hunter-gatherer times."

We walked from the case where a group of men were bravely hunting a wooly mammoth, using stone spears and axes, getting meat and hide and wool and bone and sinews and so many other things useful to sustaining life, and I came to a stop in front of the case highlighting life at the home hearth where the women, babies, children and the old took care of themselves and the household.

"In the last few decades we have been slowly recognizing the great debt of culture we owe to women. I want all of you girls to listen carefully here, and you boys, too, for if we don't understand and value our origins, and the origins of our finest ideas, we miss the greatest part of our family success. For most of recorded time, men have thought - incorrectly - that men had invented most of the elements of our culture, of civilization.

"Yet now we are coming to realize that it is women's contributions, yes - you girls - it was your great-great-great a-thousand-times-great grand-mothers who actually invented civilization while the men were off on their camping trips having fun, hunting, whooping it up competing and vying with each other over who was the bravest, who was the strongest, who had killed the biggest bison, or mammoth, or whatever, to prove who among them was going to be the boss, the leader, the chieftain. While they were off doing all that, where were the women?

"Back at home," said several children.

"With whom?"

"With the children," said many.

"And since it often took the men many days or even weeks to go off and find and hunt and kill a big animal, who had to take care of the children and the old?" I asked.

"The women did!" came the growing response.

"Do any of you have a baby brother or a baby sister? You? You? OK, you too? And many of you know them, or have another friend with a baby at home. What do babies do several times a day?"

"They poop!" giggled a boy toward the back. Everyone laughed.

"That's right, however, I was looking for another answer, something babies do several times a day that gives them something in their tummies to be able to poop?" I raised my eyebrows, asking.

"Eat," said a girl.

"That's right, they eat. In fact, mommies know that babies have to eat many times a day, just as bigger children do. Anyone here ever go a whole day without eating - no breakfast, no lunch, no dinner - no snacks - for the whole day?" A few hands up, uncertainly.

"I'm sorry you were hungry a whole day, but it's a good experience in some ways. I've gone hungry many times in my life, and I know what it is like to be hungry. However, if we go hungry too many days, what will happen to us?"

"We'll die," answered many children.

"That's right. And hunter-gatherer women, our grandmothers, stayed at home while the men were off on their camping trips showing off to each other and doing a real and needed job: getting meat for a whole tribe of their family back at home camp: their children, wives and parents who were old. The women had to provide food for everyone while the men were hunting, so what did they go and do?"

"They went gathering," said a beautiful girl with a smile.

"Yes, they went gathering. They had to discover what plants, herbs, roots, fruits and vegetables that were growing nearby were edible and could nourish their babies, and their children and their parents and the old, and of course - they got hungry too - for themselves, too. They had to have food several times a day. So they learned about growing things, and about birds and eggs and small animals and eventually some bigger animals like goats and sheep which could be tamed and would give milk for babies, and wool for warmth.

"So, women began to learn the science which today we call agriculture, which is the science of gathering seeds from plants which we can eat or with parts we can eat, curing and preparing the seeds, learning about the seasons and knowing when is the right time to plant the precious seeds so they will grow and bear fruit, planting the seeds in such a way that they are not too deep, not too shallow, in the right soil, in the sunlight, water enough to grow and mature, the right harvest time when the fruit or vegetable or grain was ripe, all the things we now take for granted, all which had to be learned and recognized to guarantee success, or there would be no food.

"And, agriculture includes the domestication of animals, which we now think women had a major hand in doing from the beginning. They were the ones at home who were always there to take the time to get to know, and

59

befriend the animals, and learn how to harvest eggs from birds, and milk and wool from sheep and goats, and later cows. The agriculture business is of course one of the biggest multi-billion dollar businesses all around the globe, and, it still feeds us today. That is the beginnings of our farming and domesticated animals - which lead to the fruit industry, cereal industry, bread industry, vegetable industry, spinach industry," many grimacing faces, "and the dairy industry with milk, butter, cheese and yogurt, and the poultry industry, and the meat industries: beef, chicken, sheep, goat, pig, and so on. The next time you eat just about anything, don't forget to say 'Thank you, Grandma!'" I waved to the figure of the woman kneeling at the hearth.

"From women's gathering plants, herbs, fruits and vegetables and seeds and grains and leaves and flowers, observing the animals of nature which ate them or did not eat them, experimenting with plants to learn which ones were not poisonous, another great and important discovery was made, which we have to credit to women, our great grandmothers: Medicine.

"The medical and pharmaceutical industries began in the hunter-gatherer period as women gathered herbs, and discovered that certain leaves and bark and herbs were medicines, alleviating pain, helping cures, which were aided by these medicines as they performed the medical acts of caring which we still today associate with mothers at home, and nurses in hospitals. Our Great Grandmothers quite naturally developed the medical knowledge of Obstetrics - that is having babies and taking care of women who are going to have babies, and it includes the medical science of midwifing, which is helping women at the moment the baby is being born. No matter what anyone says, women taking care of women in childbirth has to be one of the most logical ideas since breathing.

"And with each baby's first breath, our grandmother's developed another great field of medicine: Pediatrics - the care of infants and children. Women also were the ones who cared enough about the old to care for them, we now presume, all the way back into hunter-gatherer days. Thus the roots of Geriatric medicine - the understanding of old age and the care of the aged probably began with our grandmothers in the hunter-gatherer camp. In all, many multi-billion dollar industries discovered, and invented by women, our grandmothers. Thank you Grandma," I waved at the woman in the case.

"Now, how many of you like the idea of coming to school wearing clothes, instead of being naked?" Lots of chuckles, laughter and glances around the room.

"Clothing is pretty important to us isn't it? When the men brought the kill home: a bison, a mammoth, an elk, or any other big game animal, the work of the women again took over. The larger animals were butchered where they fell, and brought home in pieces, but a smaller animal could be brought home all in one piece. Either way, when the hunting party returned, the women would finish the butchering process and prepare all of the parts of the animal which were to be used in other ways: bones, claws, hooves, horns, tusks, sinews, hides, teeth, intestines, bladders, antlers, and so forth.

A lot of the kitchen-tool industry and tool-box inventions probably came out of women's early ingenuity, as well as the beginnings of the jewelry business, with pretty things such as teeth, claws, antler tips, feathers, pieces of horn. But one of the biggest and most needed parts of the animal was its skin, its hide, for clothing. Clothing was a primal concern for our grandmothers: that covering which keeps us from freezing in the winter, or dying of hypothermia, was a central need and central concern of the women who had to keep their babies warm, their children warm, and their elderly warm. Thus we find that the multi-billion dollar garment industry - leather working, tanning, garments made of wools, vegetable fibers such as flax for linen, and cotton, all were first imagined and invented or discovered by our grandmothers who were trying to solve the problem of keeping us warm when we were babies, and little children. So what do we say again?"

"Thank you Grandma!" we all said together this time.

"In short, we see that the life-sustaining skills and gifts which we call 'civilization:' agriculture, which is planting and harvesting food, and domesticating birds and animals for food; medicine for our health; knowledge of our bodies and our very birth for preserving and extending life; hand tools and kitchen tools for food preparation; jewelry and personal adornments; our garment industries with leathers, weaving, sewing, needles, threads, and warmth from the cold - not to mention looking cool- the credit for all of these comes from our roots in our family during some of our most primitive years: the hunter-gatherer years. This is a rich heritage from what we usually think of as merely crude and primitive times. They were neither crude nor primitive: we owe our earliest family a lot. So again, what do we say to Hunter-Gatherer Grandma?"

"Thank you Grandma!" they all shouted with smiles among themselves. To some it may have seemed silly, but they all got it.

"Now, you boys, don't think that the girls did everything to make civilization. Boys and men had a lot to do with both the survival of our families, and with providing for them. Meat and hides and animal parts were essential for life, and the men and boys faced great dangers getting them. The idea for chipping rocks and using them and other large objects as weapons and tools may have been ideas men came up with. Protecting the family against large beasts and unfriendly cousins was a regular job, at least we imagine so.

"Why did men do the hunting? As men never seem to get pregnant, and don't have babies, they were physically able to go out and scout for game meats all year round, which they did. Hunting for meat, which gave also hides and bones and other animals parts, kept men and boys busy a good part of the time. This was a very needed activity for the family. Have any of you ever heard the expression 'Bring home the bacon?'

"My Daddy says that to my Mommy sometimes when he gives her his paycheck," said a shy little girl.

"We still use the phrase 'bring home the bacon,' because at the root of this phrase is the old Hunter fulfillment - bringing home the meat. How many of you have Daddies who go out and 'bring home the bacon?"

Many hands go up.

"Daddies have been doing that for a long time, haven't they? Ever since hunter-gatherer times. And, there are all sorts of problems our families face today, and as fathers and mothers go out and face them, and solve these problems, we say they are 'slaying dragons,' fending off the powers which would harm our families. We know that our mothers anciently were often hunters and protectors too, as well as gatherers, and today many mothers are gatherers and hunters working outside our home each day. How many of you have mothers who go out as hunters and have a job outside the home they get paid for?"

Many, many hands go up.

"You see, Mommies and Daddies are still hunters today. Many of you have mommies who don't go out to work somewhere, and they work at home all day, doing the gatherer work we see here.

"My Daddy stays home and does the gatherer work," volunteered a proud boy.

"Many Daddies do these days. We have gatherers and hunters in our homes today, doing almost all the same things Grandma and Grandpa Hunter-Gatherer are doing here in our scene for us.

"How did this balance of family tasks and labors come to be? We note that the body size of boys and men made them bigger and we assume stronger, and their hunting and camping excursions probably would have made them strong, probably stronger than women, especially when women were pregnant and were sustaining a new life within their bodies. We observe that a sort of social agreement was framed at some early time, whereby the going out and hunting for large animals which gave meat, hides and other useful parts needed for survival was taken by the men. Just as the responsibility of fighting off attacking animals and unfriendly cousins who might try to take over a cave, or steal the meat, or take or hurt our families and children we assume was carried out by the men. In exchange for the risks to life and limb men encountered in these hunting and protecting responsibilities which men carried out while the women stayed home with the babies and gathered and cared for the children, elderly and the families, the women stayed at home and did their part: they had the babies and gathered and cared for the families. Both men and women had a lot of work. And that's what they did. It was a balanced existence. So we can also say: Thank you Grandpa!"

"Thank you Grandpa!" they now shouted and laughed.

"But, we now do see the life-sustaining gifts came from our grandmothers; and until just recently, we failed to understand that, and most unfairly, to remember that, give credit, and be grateful.

"The reason for this historical oversight is something which, to a large extent, we boys and men have to come to terms with, and this takes us to the next room of our journey through time: let's hand back the stone axes now, say good-bye to Grandma and Grandpa here, and to Uncle and Aunty and cousins and friends and move on in time to the 'Great Empires' room."

With the echoing of over a hundred voices and several hundred feet on the hard floor, we waved good-bye to our hunter-gatherer family scenes and walked through the doorway into the world of ancient Mesopotamia and Egypt: the Fertile Crescent and the first Great Western Empires.

Our collection was small.

From Mesopotamia we had only two clay cuneiform tablets, a cylinder seal and a stamp seal, several strings of early agate stone beads, three pieces of Hittite pottery and some bronzes from the Luristan period: a sword, an axe, two arrowheads and a bell from a horse's bridle.

From Egypt we had only a few ushabtis, scarabs, a few faience amulets, some beads, three minor bronze statuettes of Osiris, Isis and Harpocrates, and the base of a small granite statue which had a single line of hieroglyphs inscribed across it.

Yet to these real artifacts we had added an abundance of large color photographs of ruins and sites and more real artifacts; archaeological excavations in progress with vases and clay statuettes at the moment of their discovery; mannequins dressed in full costumes of Assyrians, Babylonians, Persians and Egyptians; queens and princes, scribes and family members, merchants and farmers; large colorful models of palaces and homes, of pyramids and barks, of chariots and a life-size sarcophagus with linen-wrapped mummy-mannequin inside, with reproductions of treasures from King Tut's tomb and other Egyptian cultural artifacts. The children's reaction was as always: Ooooohs and Aaaaaahs, and a sudden hush as they soaked it all in. I wheeled my cart into the center of the room and halted until it appeared the last child had followed us in.

"Is everybody in now? Very good. Well, as you can see, we have moved forward in our time traveling, and here we have another beginning: the birth of the 'Great Societies.'

"This room takes us to the time of the Sumerians and their successors in Mesopotamia and to the Egyptians along the Nile River, so let's take a few items out of the box here which we can touch that come from these times and places. I need three more presenters. Yipes! I'm being attacked. OK. You, and...back there, you, please, and.....OK, you there at the end. This is Yukiko, James and Robert.

"Now the first thing we have here is a string of hand-made agate beads, which I'm giving here to Yukiko, who will carry them around to each of you as we go through this room. This necklace is made from dark banded agate stones almost 5,000 years ago in north Mesopotamia by the Sumerians. Yes, that's right. You'll notice that there are several sizes of these long, sort of football-shaped stone beads, but what is most fascinating is that they are perfect, aren't they? Perfectly symmetrical, perfectly smooth, perfectly geometrical shapes that we would think had been machine made if we didn't know for sure that they were dug up out of the ground. Yes, they were. How do I know? Let me see here....yes, here's the tag and it says 'Yep! These beads were dug up out of the ground.' Can't argue against that, can we? OK, Yukiko, you can start this around. As this comes to you and you touch it, think of the person who worked with these stones grinding them into these beautiful beads; imagine the man or the woman who wore them, and look up and see their faces in your mind. Think of how long ago these were made and worn and feel that time in your fingers as you touch them.

"Now the second thing here, which I'm going to give to... Robert, is a Babylonian cylinder seal. It looks like a small piece of a stick, doesn't it? You will see that it has some figures of winged mythological beasts carved deeply into it, and some trees, and a man standing here. As you know, in Mesopotamia they wrote on clay, with little stylus sticks, in cuneiform...yes, that wedgy-looking stuff. After you wrote a letter, if you were important enough to have a seal, you rolled the seal on the soft clay and it left a seal impression. When you roll this seal along fresh clay, the carvings leave designs in the clay which we can see, that stand out and you can feel and touch. This is what you used to sign letters you might write, or have written for you by a scribe. Notice the hole drilled from one end to the other. It could be worn as a ring, or as a part of a necklace.

"How old is it?" asked a boy.

"This seal dates to about 1700 BC, that's about 3,700 years ago - about the same time as Hammurabi......they haven't studied about Hammurabi yet? OK, Your teachers will be telling you about Hammurabi soon, one of the most famous Ammorite Babylonian kings who had all the kingdom's laws carved in cuneiform writing on a big tall black *stele*, or pillar. When they do, remember this seal you are going to touch now, because it comes from his time and place. OK, Robert, you can start it around. When you all touch this, think of how many times it was rolled across a clay tablet to seal an important letter, or contract, or receipt of some kind, and imagine the hands which held the clay tablet and the seal.

"Lastly, James, you are going to carry around this Egyptian *ushabti*. These are figures which you would have buried with you, which with a special magic spell will come to life in the afterlife and do whatever you want them to do - take out the trash, feed the dog, clean your room, do your homework - who wants an *ushabti*?" almost all the hands went up.

"How many of you know a story about a young boy who is working for a sorcerer, who makes a spell and gets the broom to start carrying water for him?"

"Mickey Mouse! Fantasia! The Sorcerer's Apprentice!"

"Exactly. Well, that story is over two thousand years old, and was first written down by a Roman traveler visiting in Egypt. He heard the story of the *ushabti*, and wrote that wonderful little tale. Like so many things in life, we know how to get it started, but what is it we don't know how to do?"

"Make it stop!" rang out a chorus.

"That's right, so be careful. Now as this goes around and you get to touch it, notice that it has the face and folded arms of a pharaoh of Egypt. See? As you touch it, think of Egypt, and the cool waters of the Nile River; feel the sun warm on your back and shoulders; see the faces of the people who made this *ushabti* and sold it in the market place and bought it to put in the tomb of someone they loved, someone they wanted to have help with life's chores in the nether world. OK, James, take it around.

"All right. Here in this room we begin to see men's - that's you boys now - men's biggest contributions to our culture, which have manifest themselves more in the life-embellishing fields than in the life-sustaining fields our grandmothers had already given us, which as a matter of fact made this monumental step of progress possible. The more male-originating contributions are the developments of architecture and its brother engineering; trade and commerce; finance; navigation; art and literature and last but not least, government.

"Please remember that women have played their roles in all of these fields, just as men have played their roles in agriculture, medicine and the other fields originated and advanced first by women. It's fair to say that once our family has made a discovery, everyone has always wanted to get into the act, and to lesser and greater degrees, both men and women have made achievements in just about all areas you can think of.

"I want you to all remember at least this, if you don't remember much of anything else from today's visit through time: in spite of a lot of social imbalances over time, both men and women have acted much more as a balanced and balancing team throughout civilization than perhaps either one has ever fully realized."

"Now, look around at the exhibits here in this room and let's think about becoming city builders. How many of you woke up this morning in a city?"

Most hands go up instantly, quickly followed by the rest.

"Most of us live in cities today, don't we? Well, cities have been around for about 5,000 or so years, and some parts of the idea we're almost getting right now. How many of you like having a store nearby where you can buy food, and a store nearby where you can buy shoes, and one where you can buy....I don't know, what kinds of things do you like to buy?

"Video games!"

"Pizza!"

"Clothes!"

"Bikes!"

"Sports equipment!"

"For all of these stores to be here, you need a city. As our hunter-gatherer grandparents developed farming and herding, the ability to feed our families became more and more stable, thanks to Grandma Hunter-Gatherer. The need for good farm land where all those wonderful seeds could be planted and grazing land for all those great goats and sheep to feed on tugged our family away from the mountains and caves and hiding places out onto the exposure of the open valleys and plains. Villages with high fences around them were built, and soon bigger villages with stronger mud walls were built. Soon, keeping lands and keeping flocks became more important than going off on hunting and camping trips, and so we men started spending more and more time at home. Men still liked to go hunting, and falconing, and to prove our strength and skills, but these drives found a new fulfillment in having bigger lands, bigger flocks, bigger clothes, bigger jewelries made out of bright metals and sparkling stones, and bigger houses and palaces. Look around at some of the models we have here.

"As our families moved from hunter-gatherer living into settled village living, a new idea of ownership was born. Our hunter-gatherer family had already understood ownership of tools, weapons, personal adornments and jewelries, and perhaps items of clothing and caves and huts. But as we moved out onto the flatlands and became more permanent and self-sustaining, suddenly we owned land. We owned animals. We staked out our land, put boundary stones at the corners, and bought and sold it among ourselves. This new concept by itself may be responsible for the invention of writing, because we needed to have a way of recording our ownership of land. You will want to see the two cuneiform tablets we have over in that case there.

"Now, by this time we began to mark our animals, too, and bought and sold them among ourselves. With all of this buying and selling, and competing to own more land, and more animals, we find another sad chapter in our family's history.

"Unfortunately, we raided distant tribes and villages and took prisoners, whom we brought back and forced to work for us. We called them slaves, and we marked them, and bought and sold them among ourselves. Egypt is most famous for this, but the Mesopotamians also had slaves, and in fact most cultures in history have bought and sold our brothers and sisters as cattle at some point in their history. Do we have a history of slavery in our country, in America?"

"Yes," came the uncomfortable answer, with many nods.

"And most unfortunately, at some point, we men began to see our girls and women as things we owned as well, and so we traded, bought and sold them among ourselves. We're not sure just when or where, but the early respect of balanced contributions from both men and women was lost somewhere along the path, and men used brute strength to usurp the sovereignty of women as they used their power to take over ownership of our mother Earth.

"As man took over ownership of woman, the skills and knowledge she had were taken too. Knowledge about seeds and seasons and planting and harvesting, and domesticating animals and breeding them into larger and larger flocks and herds, all of which our grandmothers had discovered and developed with such great care and nurturing, we men stole from them as we stole their very freedom, all in the process of creating the great cities of our first great societies. Knowledge of herbs and medicine were eventually taken away, as were the very rights to have women helping women in childbirth. That was much later, but the process was set in motion here in the great new societies of the Sumerians and the Egyptians.

"However, women found new ways to exercise both value and power, and as cities and monuments and riches began to grow, women shared in them in a variety of ways.

"From this time forward, the great arts of architecture in building cities and palaces, monuments and tombs began to grow; and governments ruling great cities, and designing great cities, and fostering great statues, and arts and literatures.

"And wars. A lot of our human family's history is told through wars, often from war to war. Just as our hunter-gatherer grandfathers had to protect our families from aggressive attacking cousins, the growth of cities and regions of cities into empires was often brought to pass by wars, in which one group of cousins aggressively attacked another group of cousins to rule over them.

"You'll notice I say 'cousins' instead of 'the enemy.' I like to say cousins instead of 'enemies' because we really know: all of us on this planet are related; any attack on 'us' is by 'us,' an attack of our own family against itself. We forget this when we say 'other peoples' or 'enemies,' as if 'they' means 'somebody else.' On this planet, in this family, there is no 'them,' there is only 'us.' 'We' are all we've got. But this selfishness is ancient, and quite sadly, it goes on still today.

"In spite of what historically seems to have been almost constant wars, our early family still managed to make wonderful and beautiful cities and objects they enjoyed looking upon, things of beauty. This includes many, many things we still make and enjoy today. Look for types of things you still use in your life today that you buy in stores, and have in your own homes and community: clothes, jewelries, pretty ceramic vessels for cooking, flowers, and decorations; pretty buildings, monuments, and all of the other things you see here. Let's spend the next ten minutes or so going through the various exhibits here in this room and enjoying some of these beautiful things.

"And before you leave, see how many of the things we receive from these grandparents, such as city planning, streets, buildings, water systems, sewage systems, government, metal working, fine weaving, furniture such as tables and chairs, cabinets, writing, painting, sculpture, and all of these things which we have today because they came first, thought of these ideas, improved them, and gave them to us, and as you go out, say 'Thank you Ancient Family!'"

As the hundred-plus children from the four classes spread out around the room, I quickly wheeled my cart into the next hall, which was the end of our short tour. Here we had the Greek and Roman things, which brought us to the modern world. For most of what we have, use and are today in the western world is little altered from what we find in the Greek and Roman worlds of two thousand years ago. This collection was more abundant, for the vast quantities of material found in so many parts of the Mediterranean region were easily obtained for such an exhibit. The mannequins here wore Greek himatia, Roman togas and tunics, the full armor of a legionary soldier, and a mother with her children in their tunics. It was a good display.

My rest came to an end before I knew it, and the teachers with their children suddenly poured into the Hall of Greek and Roman Life.

"All righty! Here we arrive at the time in our journey where things are beginning to look more as we know them in our own time. As you look around the room and see the models, many of them will look just like buildings you know in our country, some of them even in our own city. Houses with white stucco walls and red tile roofs are pretty common, right? And we all know City Hall downtown? Well, I see most of us do, and it looks a lot like one of these Greek temples, doesn't it? Our football stadium looks a lot like the Coliseum, and our city streets look a lot like these Roman streets with sidewalks here in this photograph taken in Pompeii. This here is a picture of Trajan's Market in Rome, which was a first-rate shopping mall with over 300 stores and shops, in downtown Rome almost 2,000 years ago.

"In the many glass cases, you will see things which you have as modern types in your own homes: jugs; drinking vessels; clay oil lamps - think of lanterns or light bulbs; a sword - think carving knife for a turkey; arrow tips; a horse bit; a perfume bottle; belt buckle; eye make-up applicator; tweezers; needle; thimble; dice; coins; a nail; a finger ring; bracelet; earring; a plate; a bowl; a cooking pot; house key; a salt dish; a fish hook; a toy doll arm; and many other objects, all from 2,500 to 1,600 years old. You will see that most of these things you have in your own homes today. See how your items look pretty much the same as these ancient originals, or how they differ.

"Now, if everyone will form a big circle here in the middle of the room, I will hand you four ancient Roman coins for you all to handle and pass around the circle back to me. I'll pass two this way, and two this way so both sides have something to look at. Each side is getting a small silver denarius, which was about a day's pay in the time of Julius Caesar, and the big golden looking one is a bronze sestertius, which was one-quarter of a denarius. The emperors' faces on them are: Augustus Caesar; Claudius; Vespasian; and Antoninus Pius, and you should be able to make out parts of their names in Latin around the portraiture.

"While these are going around, after which we will let you go around as you please to enjoy the exhibits in this room, I'm going to hold up an item here, and see if anyone can guess what it is.

"Does everyone see it? This is Greek, made about 325 BC, about the lifetime of Alexander the Great, and it is a common household item. Most of you have had one in your lifetime already, and it is something you know. What do you think it is? It's made of pottery; it's rather round as you can see, and it has a cute little strap handle over the top, see? On this side there is a spout with a hole in it, and on this side, this thing sticking straight up like a tube? This has a strainer with little holes punched in the clay at the bottom of it. Who wants to guess?"

"A tea pot?" said a girl.

"No, but it does look a lot like one, doesn't it?"

"A water pitcher?" said a boy.

"No, a lot of people guess that too. Yes?"

"Is it for watering flowers?" asked a girl.

After several guesses, I finally asked what I always got to ask.

"Do you all give up?"

Everyone not handling a coin nodded yes.

"It's an ancient Greek baby bottle!" I told them, and held it up.

"A baby bottle?" several asked in amazement.

"Yes. Can you see it now? We get so used to thinking of things made of plastic and rubber, we forget that before rubber and plastic people still had lives to live. This spout strains out little bits of straw and grass from the milk as you pour it in, and on this spout you cupped and tied a little piece of leather which you stuck a hole in, and voila, baby gets a bottle of milk. Pretty clever, eh? And you thought we invented everything in the Twentieth Century."

About this time, the coins had worked around the circle and come back to me, so the children were released to look over the room. They spread out in all directions, amazement suddenly brightening face after face, filling eyes with awe and wonder as they saw things that were thousands of years old - which looked exactly like the things we still use today.

I stood for a few minutes and spoke to the teachers, answering the same questions which are always asked. After years of doing this, all of the questions began to repeat. I had come to know what the children would do, all of the variations, all of the moves, all of the questions. And the adults I found over the years were just as predictable, I knew all of their comments, all of their questions. The fun of it always delighted me, and I never tired of answering the same questions to each new person asking them. To them it was new. I delighted in the newness they were experiencing.

After about fifteen minutes of chit chat, it was time to gather the children all together, and sit them down for the final part of the journey: the Time Machine.

"OK kids, let's have everyone come over here to this carpeted area, and sit on the floor a few minutes to think about the experiences we've just had. We've come through a long period of time, and now I want to give each of you a chance to go back to the time of your choice, wherever you would like to go if you had your own time machine. Now, everyone relax, just get loose, relax, and feel comfortable and relaxed and good. Are you all relaxed and feeling good?

"OK. Close your eyes. Everyone. That's right. Eyes closed. Now pick a place you would like to go to, and pick a time. Any place, any time. Egypt of the pyramids and pharaohs and queens; Greece at the time of the Golden Age; ancient Assyria or Babylon with the Ishtar Gate; the time of Grandma Hunter-Gatherer; Rome at the height of the Empire. Think now, and see in your mind the place. See in your mind the architecture, the costumes and clothing. You know what it looks like. See the place and time you want to visit now in your mind. Now, dress yourself in the right clothes, just like you are in wardrobe at a movie studio getting dressed for a movie about your chosen time and place. That's right, put it all on; fix your hair just the same way the people where you are going do their hair. See how they do their hair. That way. Now put on the right kind of sandals or just go barefoot, which is always OK. You want to blend in when you get there. You don't want anyone to notice you, so you want to look just like they do. Lookin' good? Lookin' ancient? OK. Keep your eyes closed.

"Now, let's envision time traveling. If we had a time machine, it might be just like getting into a commercial airliner, and our journey back in time would be just about like a trip in a jet plane. Imagine yourself walking up to the time machine: it looks a lot like a big plane, but it doesn't need wings or wheels. Now, see yourself go in, dressed in your perfect costume, with just the right hair and jewelry and everything just right as if you just walked out of wardrobe for a big historical movie. Sit down, buckle in, and relax. You don't have to move. It moves for you, in time and space, just as an airplane moves for you in time and space. You don't even feel much movement.

"Just like on a trans-oceanic flight, you just sit, and eat some food, watch a movie or two, listen to some music, drink some juices and sodas, sleep a little, and then you are told the trip is over, please sit quietly and calmly until time rolls to a stop in the hour and day of your selected destination.

"When the seat-belt lights go out, you get out, and you find time travel is perhaps no more different than arriving in a foreign country. When you get out, it's just as a long plane trip: you never moved from your seat, but you are now in a completely different place, with different smells, sounds, clothing, foods, buildings, people, and ways. It's just like a trip in an airplane, except - you are not only in a different place: you're in a different time.

"Unless you were sure you were in a time machine, at first you might not even know it.

"But your watch no longer gives you the correct hour, and you want to get rid of it right away anyway, so no one will see it. The money in your pocket is not the currency accepted here, and so you keep that hidden so no one will be shocked to see it. You look around, and suddenly you realize: it has really happened. You have traveled through time, and you are in your chosen place, in your chosen time.

"And you are still you. The sky is blue, the clouds are the same as you have always known, the birds and plants all the same you have seen all your life. But these are the thousandth-generation grandparents of the birds and plants you have known.

"You walk down a street, and except for the fact that everyone is dressed up in costume from the same time and place as you, they look just like people you see very day. They have two eyes, two legs, fingers on their hands and lips around their mouths which are speaking to each other as they go about their business and pay you no attention. The language is totally different. You've never heard it before, and you don't understand a word.

"A donkey goes by, and it is as any donkey you have ever known, just as is the cow you then see, and the goat, and the chicken and the horse. They look just like any cow, or goat, or chicken.

"For all you know, this is just a movie set, for everything feels as familiar as any day and any place you know where you live now.   "But it is not.

"You are in the place you chose: Egypt at the time of Cleopatra or Rameses the Great; Rome at the time of Augustus Caesar or Constantine; Assyria at the time of Sargon; Greece at the time of Pericles or Aristotle; Israel at the time of the Temple.

"If you were really clever, and dressed as well as you could for the part in totally authentic costume and hair style, you will walk unnoticed all day through all of the streets and market-places of whatever ancient city you chose to visit, and no one will ever suspect you are not a native of their land. For most face types, even yours, whatever you look like, were found in most given lands then as well as now. You are dressed perfectly, everything about you is perfect. No one will suspect you - not until you open your mouth and began to speak!

"So, you decide: you will not speak!

"However, you will want money to spend during your visit to the past, right? Buy a little food when you're hungry - you can point. Buy a few souvenirs at the marketplace - again, you can point. So people think you're a mute. So what? Better than trying to explain you're from the future - in English!

"Since you want money, you will have to earn it. That is one of the other great universal experiences of all times and all places. We all get cold in cold weather, we all get hungry when we go a little time without food, and we all have to work to receive the things we want in life. Your life is no exception to this rule in your own time and place; it is no exception here in the past.

"Fortunately, the jobs of our ancient family members are jobs which duplicate much of our life today. You know the types of jobs and professions your parents have, and your friend's parents and some of your neighbors have? Other jobs you've seen back home while you're hanging out a shopping malls and around town? The jobs in whatever place and time you chose are actually very much related. In fact, you will find that most jobs have existed for almost five thousand years, with changes only in costume, language, and a few of the tools and methods of accomplishing the job.

"These are the same jobs people have worked at since the beginning. I will read them off, and with your eyes still closed, imagine yourself in each one of these jobs, in the time and place you have chosen, and when I have finished reading the list, think a moment and then choose a job for yourself, to earn some money and have fun on your ancient vacation.

"Here are just a few of the jobs which have been around in most times and places for the last 5,000 years. It's a long list, but listen: these are the jobs you still see in your neighborhood, and these jobs are still helping you and your family today. There were:

"Store owners and sales people selling cloth, jewelry, pots and pans, shoes, construction materials: such as bricks, lumber, stone, cement, iron; people making and selling and using transportation vehicles, selling spare parts for wagons and chariots; making and selling furniture, making and selling clothing of all kinds for men, women and children; growing, harvesting and selling foods such as fruits, vegetables, meat, fish, wine, milk, cheese, grains, honey, salt, and herbs, spices, perfumes, and medicines; making and selling other items such as wax, grease, and paint. Also making and selling useful items such as musical instruments of many kinds, tools for farming, gardening, building and fixing things, also weapons for self-defense and game hunting.

"Then there were sales of real estate, both commercial and residential, raising and marketing livestock, such as cattle, sheep, horses, mules, goats, and so forth; and of course there was banking: letters of credit, lending, leasing, and investment in commodities futures. There was business opportunity in import and export by both land and sea. Insurance sales and underwriters guaranteed cargos. Of course there were jobs in manufacturing all of these goods, as we've mentioned, and all the items you have seen today here in the exhibits of your time and place, as well as the production of the raw materials for making all of it, such as metals, woods, minerals, animals, all of which keep many people employed in your time and chosen place. The transportation industry in your chosen time and place includes truckers and handlers to move these products and foods all from country to city and from town to town, as well as warehouses to store much of it, with horses, mules, wagons and caravans.

"Of course there were professions for people such as actors, singers, writers, secretaries; there were bookshops, quick-copy and hand printing shops; there were artists, lawyers, judges, doctors, soldiers, consultants, locksmiths, bodyguards, gardeners, bakers, priests, firemen, teachers, architects, engineers, plumbers, carpenters, farmers, ditch-diggers, foremen, supervisors, accountants, auditors, shipbuilders and sailors, navigators, and pilots; map-makers, innkeepers, delivery couriers, cooks, waiters, domestic servants, barbers, hairstylists, tailors, manicurists, masseurs, boxers, jockeys, inventors, and repair people."

"All right, now, choose a job. Got one? Ready for tomorrow? OK.

"Now we are about to complete our journey. You have the right costume and clothing, and everything else; you have a job to earn your food and buy some things, now you need to get a good night's sleep and be ready for a full day tomorrow. So, walk through the streets, past the other people tired and weary from their day of work, on their way home to eat and rest and sleep, turn the corner into the little narrow lane past the small boy playing with a toy wooden horse next to the clucking chicken, and go into the open doorway of the house on the left, which is a small room with a comfortable straw bed in the corner for you. Close the wooden door behind you, and as you turn, see the small clay oil lamp which is lit for you on the rock stove, giving light to your small room.

"By the lamp with its small flickering flame of light, you see the clay jug of water, the fresh loaf of good brown bread, the figs and grapes, and the big piece of cheese for you to eat tonight.

"You pull over the low wooden stool you find in the other corner, sit down and begin to eat the food. The bread is aromatic and delicious; the figs and grapes sweet and succulent in your mouth. You drink a cup of the water, cool and earthy from the clay jug, and it flows into your mouth and down your throat more deliciously than any water you have ever tasted. You pick up the cheese and take a bite. It is different than cheeses you know, but it is delicious, and as you finish eating the bread and fruit and drink the water, you eat bite after bite gratefully, thankful in your heart to the unknown stranger who has left you this simple supper.

"With your hand cupped behind the small flame of the clay oil lamp, the flame rising up from the stubby twist of wick rising up out of the olive oil which fills it, you look around the room one last time, at the closed wooden door, at the mud-covered walls, the straw piled in the corner, welcoming you to come and rest, and the stones arranged for the cooking stove, and at your own hand, cast in the golden light of the small flame, and after taking a deep breath in and holding it just an instant, you blow out the small flame of the lamp, and in the total darkness, you take the two steps over to the straw, and laying down, close your eyes and almost instantly, you fall asleep."

I paused for a moment of silence. Every face was quiet, eyes closed, resting in their minds in the dark night of their chosen place and time.

"All right, children, without opening your eyes, it is time now to wake up. Sunlight is streaming through the high window of your little room, and outside you hear a man and a donkey walking by your door. Somewhere more distantly you hear a rooster crow. It is morning.

"Now begins your day. A day of life is an unending stream of decisions which you must make. Today you will be conscious of many of these decisions you usually fail to even think about, and you will suddenly understand that life is a series of opportunities given to you as decisions.

"As you awaken, you are faced already with your first decision. Do you wake up fully and get up out of bed? Or do you roll over and sleep some more? You roll over for a moment, and then arise.

"Now you are faced with your second decision: can you wait to go to the bathroom, or do you have to go now? Better to use the chamber pot here where you can find one. It is in the little room around the corner of your small room. When you come back, you are faced with your third and fourth decisions of the day: are you so hungry you must have something to eat now? And, shall I wear what I have? If you are hungry, look by the fireplace; you will see food has been left for you by the early morning servant girl. If you need a change of clothes, you will find them neatly folded beneath the straw where they served you as a pillow last night. Change quickly.

"Now you are faced with one of the day's most difficult series of decisions. As you go out into the street and begin to meet people, and interact with them, will you be grumpy, or kind? Will you be patient, or gruff? Will you have purpose in what you do, or be lazy and follow no goal? Will you go to your job you have chosen, which awaits you, where others are counting on your participation, or will you fail them and yourself and go sightseeing because the world is so filled with distractions you would like to see?

"Let us say that you have decided to go to work, for you have realized that this will be one of the greatest experiences you can have in your short visit in time: to see how your ancestors lived their daily lives and provided for themselves and their families so their generation could survive to bring forth the next generation, and the next, all the way up until your own generation came forth and you were born. For these are the ancestors who came before you, that you might come forth today.

"You walk through the smaller streets which feed into the larger streets, and follow those into the larger streets until you come suddenly into the great center of the great and wonderful place you have chosen to see. Before you stand the glorious things you have always imagined. They are not in ruins as you have always seen them in our time, but they are fresh and new and wonderful, and your wish is fulfilled: you have seen them.

"Filled with the rush of being where you are, yet you must go on to your job. You walk and follow larger streets into smaller streets, and then suddenly you are in front of the place you have chosen to work.

"Now you are faced with the second greatest series of decisions every human being faces each day: will you give your best, or will you do only as little as you have to do to get by? Will you be cooperative to make everyone's work day better and help the work go better, or will you inflict your own moods on others? Will you take joy in what you have done as you finish it, or find resentment in your need to labor?

"Perhaps not all of the people working with you are kind, or considerate, or friendly. Perhaps some of them blame you for a mistake you didn't make. Perhaps you have made a mistake, but no one has seen it yet. Each of these requires your decision as to how you will act, and what you will do.

"All around you are objects not yours, but belonging to others; all around you is property not yours, but belonging to others. Most of it you have no way of knowing who owns it. Again you are faced with the decisions: how will you treat these objects, this property, which is not yours. Will you take care of it and do everything you can to keep from damaging anything, defacing anything, or will you carelessly or intentionally just for sport ruin that which you see?

"I hope you are all making good choices, and having a good day.

"Now, the sun is high in the sky and passing its prime. Your stomach begins to growl, as does the other stomachs around you. You are hungry. The ancient stomachs around you are also hungry. Suddenly you find that regardless of the language spoken all around you, you speak the language of hunger. It is a universal language, spanning all time, all places, and all branches of our family.

"You are given your morning's pay because your employer knows you have no money, and with this small sum you gladly go out into the bustling marketplace where the wealth and wonders of your world surround you, available to buy.

"Here you are given the third great series of decisions. Will you buy the food that you need, or the treats you find so tempting? Will you buy food at all, or the fascinating trinket which has caught your eye? Will you spend all that you have, or buy only what you need for the moment, saving something for another hour? Will you decide to take without paying the item too costly for you to buy? Or will you choose to enjoy with your eyes that thing, and honestly leave it for another to buy, keeping your honor and freedom?

"We will say that as much as you want the precious object you have seen, you decide it is not worth the risk of suddenly ending your visit in shame, and that you have been able to quite well enjoy looking at what you cannot buy, and buying what you can and need for this moment. You go back to work.

"Your afternoon goes well, and by now, though you cannot speak, you find you can understand everything spoken around you. As you work, you hear conversations about homes and children and parents and neighbors and food and clothing and taxes and foreign kings. You hear anecdotes and everyone laughs. You hear the sadness of a friend who has died. You hear of weather, and weddings.

"When the sun is low, your day of work is ended. Your employer pays you in full, and you gratefully receive that which you have earned. On your way home, you pass by the marketplace and buy some food, and that wonderful little trinket which caught your eye earlier. Now you can buy it in honor.

"You walk through the streets again busy with people on their way home, weary from their day's work yet smiling in anticipation of seeing family and friends, and you find to your delight that someone who has noticed you are alone invites you to come home with them for supper. The warm smile captivates you; you smile back and follow. Walking through the streets, you feel a part of this people.

"At this new friend's home you meet the entire family: husband and wife, children, grandparents, and you see they love each other. You know they love each other. It is in their faces.

"As the evening progresses, you discover that their lives are filled with the same joys, the same fears, the same desirings, the same disappointments, the same hopes, the same dreams as you have come to know in your time and place and city. A daughter has married and now lives far away. Longingly her mother speaks the wish of just hearing her voice, just once more. In the marketplace stories are on everyone's lips of a wondrous new palace built by a far away mighty king, a thing of beauty and splendor; sighs of wistful wishes to be able to see its grandeur and majesty fill every heart, and eagerly you listen with them as Father describes it in every glorious detail, as he has heard from those who have seen it. Mother shows a beautiful tapestry she has just finished embroidering for the home, and everyone is proud. Sister tells of a friend who has been ill in bed for several weeks and has nothing to do all day. She is so bored. Brother then tells of a friend who has fallen from his horse, and has cried out in pain all day, holding his abdomen. The friend has become pale, and the physician's lowered eyes this evening foretold tragedy. All were saddened. In the moment of silence, you hear faintly from across the high stone walls music - flutes, harp, cymbals and a drum: a neighbor celebrates a feast with family and friends, and all those who live near enough suddenly go to their windows to hear the beautiful music. After a moment of hearing the faint music, the family conversation continues, and they talk about many things.

"Suddenly you realize that even if you could speak the language of these people, most of what you know from your time you could not talk about with them. They are obviously just as intelligent as you, but the things you might tell them - of jet travel, of movies and televisions and VCR's, of CD's and radio, of microphones and loudspeakers, of video games, computers and the Internet, of telephones and satellite communications, of freezers and ice cream, of cars and gasoline and electronics, of surgeries and medicines and antibiotics, of the workings of a living cell, of genetics and DNA - there are no words in their vocabularies for any of these things for you to use, no images in their minds to evoke as you try and explain.

"You would have to invent words for all of these things, and then explain the definitions of the words, and then describe things which they would never see and know only through the words you have managed to tell them. How would you do this? Though everything you have left at home in your time you know is real, would they believe you, as you made up words to tell them things you could not show them? They probably would not believe you, but smile and nod their heads, and forget what you told them, for they would be certain that you spoke folly, nothing to seriously regard. So you listen, and though you know vast knowledge, you keep silent.

"It becomes late, and after many yawns, you can see they all want to go to bed, and so do you. You must leave, and go home.

"With many gestures you smilingly communicate your thanks, and you walk beneath the stars down street after street to your house. Most of the houses are dark already, but a few still have lamps lit, and hushed voices echo out onto the street.

"You arrive home to your own house, and find the lamp is lit and awaiting you.

"The excitement and work of the day has wearied you, and you gratefully lay down on the straw bed. You lean over, and blow a puff of air toward the small flame of the clay oil lamp. It's tiny flame flickers once, twice, and then flutters out into darkness; the quiet, soft darkness of an ancient night.

"As you lay awake in your straw bed, thinking of the wondrous experience that has been yours in time, in this ancient place, you remember the world to which you are about to return. It is so much the same, the people, the houses, the buildings, the markets with foods and clothing and trinkets and treasures to buy, all made by the hands of the people who live around you in this time of the world, working each day to provide the joy of life to their families, their children, their homes. Yet you, even as a child, have more than they.

"You suddenly realize, that you have telephones and can call friends and family at any hour, no matter how far away; you can fly to far away places in jet planes, and speed along smooth highways in metal chariots; you have already in your youth seen all the lands of the earth, and the distant stars, and the workings of the human body, even seen life in a single cell from within a microscope, and all of this only from watching television, and seeing photographs in color magazines. You have heard music of all kinds, and can hear any music you choose at any time you wish, with no need of a crowded room filled with musicians to play just for you.

"Suddenly you realize, that in your time, to which you are returning, you can live better than any Pharaoh in his palace, better than any Emperor, Queen or King with all of their ancient wealth, for even if you have what you thought was little, in a simple small place, they had none of these marvelous things, and you have them all. Suddenly you see: you live better than Tutankhamen, Seti, or Rameses. Better than Solomon. Better than Alexander the Great. Better than Julius Caesar, Cleopatra, Augustus, Nero, or any of them.

"Then you realize that in this far distant ancient time and land you are visiting, the life of even the most simple person is counting: they are part of history. Because they live, certain things will happen. Every life here is leaving its mark, in things touched left behind, and in the passing on of learning. Every life counts.

"You realize that the DNA in your body most certainly carries within it the imprint of your ancestors of your own blood line within our human family. If you could look 'into yourself and see it, you would see the imprint of each and every family member back to the first generation. And tonight, your family of this generation in the past is somewhere near around you, also getting ready to sleep. You realize: if your relatives are not here in this city you have chosen to visit, you suddenly know and feel that they are somewhere, living, and not so far away, your own blood line grandparents, aunts, uncles and cousins, somewhere out in the night, under the same stars, somewhere in this world, this night. They are your family. Your heritage. You see them in your mind's eye, and what do you do? You thank them, just for living, just for struggling, and for being part of all that was and all that is."

"Finally you close your eyes, and you sleep. When you awaken, you will be back in your own time and place, and be ready to go back to school.

I paused a moment, a moment for their imaginations to travel.

"OK! That's it kids. Wake up. We're back home. Welcome to the Twentieth Century!" I called out.

As if from sleep, they opened their squinting eyes, stretching, rubbing their eyes, coming back into the light of day, back into their own time.

Most of them had sheepish smiles on their faces as they looked around them at the other students.

They had been there. They had seen.

As the children stood up and stretched, the teachers now had the task of sorting out more than a hundred children and getting them back into four classroom groups, a task only slightly less difficult than getting them to be quiet.

As the teachers hunted and gathered their students, and organized them into their distinct classroom societies and marched them out in fine legionary style, I couldn't help thinking what I always thought as I watched them walk out the museum doors.

You are the most recent recipients of the family's learning: you will pass it on.

You count. No life was unimportant in our reaching this time, this now, this today. No life was so small, so insignificant, that it did not color the picture its hue, and make a difference.

You count. You make a difference. Look around you and begin to imagine what your role can be: here is a world of ancient possibilities: jobs still alive, still serving the community, serving you, serving your family.

And you can, with training, become a torchbearer as you live your page of history. There is a place for you here. You count.

Remember your ancient fathers and your ancient mothers of ages past. You are children of a great heritage.

Never forget. Never forget who you are.

During the rest of my day, I had my own lunch when my stomach growled, and gave my last afternoon class lecture for the term. I drove home in time to see the sun go down over my city, my town, my street, my home.

This night was my last supper at home for many weeks, and as most things for the trip were in order, I spent the final hours of the evening and the night with my family, savoring each and every moment.

Late at night before going to bed, I went to my study and gathered several other papers which had come to mind during the day, and put them in my briefcase for the trip.

Among them was the letter from my Israeli colleague and friend, Yohanan in Jerusalem, inviting me, no, this time *insisting* that I visit him at the Palestine Archaeological Museum, where he urged that he had something very interesting to show me. Yohanan was an Assistant Intern working with the Dead Sea Scrolls. Though he did not openly say it, I sensed he was going to take me back where the thousands of scroll fragments were under study. No outsiders were admitted there, at least never in the past.

The invitation was unbelievable. I was going to be admitted into the highly secluded 'Keep' of the fragmentary treasures of the Dead Sea Scrolls, a place that was still off-limits to most scholars in the world even after four decades, the Scrollery Hall.

There, I would be the child in the museum, gazing in awe and wonder at all the treasures about me.

I clicked my briefcase closed, and wondered.

What could he want to show *me*?

Chapter 3

Day Three: Computers to Listen to Stones; the Departure

I awoke early and spent the first hours of the morning at the computer, putting in order the last preparations for my trip.

First I accessed the all-important bank account and verified that in the last twenty-four hours since the Grant had been credited, all the disbursements I had poised for wire-transfer had already been made. Time to cross-check payments and other details.

The airline interlink was showing correct flight and seat reservations, and the ticket now showed 'Paid,' so I printed out the coupons and securely tucked them into my briefcase. All systems go. Weather predictions in Tel Aviv said sunny skies as far as the eye could see. Excellent. Hotel reservations in Jerusalem confirmed the room was paid for and awaiting my arrival. Rental confirmation of the four-wheel drive to get me out into the desert showed contract pre-approved and funded. The IAATA link confirmed cargo reservations tonight for the special equipment which would be shipped immediately after my quickie-course training session with

Kevin: pre-paid space confirmed on the direct flight; customs broker alerted in Tel Aviv; pre-clearance with Israeli Customs already filed.

I went back to the bank access and now transferred most of the remaining amount into the new account opened for me the day before in Bank Leumi, for availability in Israel.

By nine o'clock I had eaten breakfast with my family, said good-bye to the kids and sent them off to school, kissed my wife good-bye at the door, and was in my car heading toward the airport where Kevin would spend most of the morning going over the final details of his new equipment before closing up the boxes and loading it on the plane. And all of this after having coordinated the most critical elements of this journey from my own home.

Surely, neither Alexander the Great nor Augustus Caesar could do what I had just been able to do, for all their power. The common man in this modern world could better command his destiny with the push of a fingertip, even to the far reaches of the globe, than conquerors and emperors had been able to do in ancient times with all their gold and armies.

Kevin was already awaiting me when I reached the cargo warehouse lobby.

"David! Ready to go?" he grinned.

"Stupid question," I said. He knew it. We had been pushing the envelope on this for six months and greater exhilaration was impossible.

"Well, you finally made it, didn't you! Can't say I'm surprised, but the money hitting our account yesterday was next to a miracle."

"I'm still riding the wave myself."

"Well, let's get to it."

By previous arrangement, we were given a large space in the outbound packing area, and Kevin took me back where the seven hardware components were arranged on a table, behind which their seven boxes lay open on seven wooden skids ready for packing as soon as we completed our crash-course on his system.

"Every part of this equipment is unique and experimental," he began. "It's all based on solid state physics and Quantum mechanics. This is the only software and hardware system designed to explore the theory of sound imprints recorded in stone and crystals, for your most welcomed project. A couple more days would have been nice, but schedules are schedules. We literally worked all night to finish this and get the last chips and boards installed. We've only had time to test out powering, to make sure it gets to every last component."

"So what are you able to give me?"

"More than we had expected. This project has sparked some real interest; we got suggestions from a number of sources. You have all newly designed circuit boards here with experimental chips and smart capabilities; in-line series and manual option-access circuitry for controlled expansion access to the boards not yet fully tested - but which you wanted delivered, and head office approved. They're the ones I told you we're working on, based in a new crystal application theory, using an analytical approach to crystalline structure we derived from new observations made in memory-core ferrite structures and reactive functions. We think they may be helpful here. In normal mode they'll be circumvented, but you can put them in-line and mix-and-match them with all the pattern I.D. systems, either in automatic kaleidoscope program, or direct selective override by manual options, any way you want to try.

"We've loaded in special new experimental software programs designed to search for interface possibilities with irregularities identified in structural patterns of the various rocks you listed which would have been present at known musical performances in ancient theater architecture, and the stones listed from palace court samples. And, one of the programs is the composite result of our computer analysis of Thermoluminescence emission patterns of pottery - recorded from a sampling of about fifty procedures, measured on a time-continuum of the smallest nano-second intervals the most advanced equipment can detect - as you requested."

"Has any of this tested out?" I asked.

"That's your job, my friend. We're just the theoretical designers here; you do the field experiments. Hegelstein Theory and all interrelated problems aside, we have no way of knowing if we're on the right track until potential-candidate samples that have never been exposed to random post-atomic fission particles in the air have been obtained and tested."

"So, are my pattern-recognition systems completed?"

"We think so. You've got translation de-coder mega-chips, with fully digitalized voice-audio-syllabaries made to sample the sound patterns of most major known ancient languages spoken in the area where you'll find your specimens. The people we had reading and recording these for you worked on faith, David, and they thank you for persisting until you got this Grant. You've got tens of thousands of vocal word imprints in access banks with full syntax format, in ancient Hebrew, Canaanite, Aramaic, Phoenician, Moabite, Neo-Babylonian, Neo-Assyrian, Hittite, Middle- and Late-Kingdom Egyptian, classical Greek, Latin, and a few others I forget just now, but they're all in there, David. It took a lot of people a lot of time to create this, but they recorded it and we designed the software to scan the syllable patterns for matches. It works about as fast as a good spell-checker with an unabridged dictionary. We tested it with a simple DAT recording, and it works A-OK."

"But will it identify syllabic patterns stored in unconventional manners within a structure?"

"That's the question we've tried to cover both by hardware approaches and software applications, as best as we could imagine. We've loaded in the software to work with the new chips designed to do that, and if recognizable patterns are detected with the scanning methods we've built into this, it should let you know."

"I guess that's all I can hope for," I sighed.

"Well, we gave you the additional bonus we talked about which R&D worked up for you: this unit is the special optical scanner, equipped to scan papyrus, parchment, clay cuneiform, pottery ostraca, even stone inscriptions to interface with your text-translator software. We've checked it out, too, and it's pretty accurate."

"You're saying that seventy scans of the same document all came up with the identical translation and wording?"

Kevin looked at me momentarily confused.

"We didn't try that many scans on the same document, but it probably would," he replied innocently. I didn't explain the joke.

"Last and probably most important, you've got the most powerful storage system in existence here, the prototype assembly, as promised. You can't believe how much we put into this baby. This is what may make this whole experiment work. Pound for pound, the size of the permanent reference data bases for random pattern search you have access to while interfacing the language chips with your mineral samples is huge beyond imagination. You've got I.D. search and retrieval here that makes Internet search programs look slow. We were able to install the textual database with everything you gave us on floppy disks: all your ancient inscriptions and writings, in both their original languages and their English translations, with digitalized voice-converter program which interfaces the sound patterns it creates with every search for sound patterns you make. It will signal you if it finds anything even remotely parallel."

I looked up at his triumphant beaming smile.

"Are you sure you don't want to come along on this trip?" I laughed, already on overwhelm with what was on the table before me. This was, I saw, a very complicated array of equipment.

"They shoot at people who look like me and you over there, don't they?" he chuckled back at me. "No thanks. I'm almost as hyped up about this as you are, but I think I'll stay here in the safe zone."

As he walked around behind the table and the units, I paused, staring from one electronic unit to the other. The self-assuring optimism I used to sell the Foundation Directors on my capability of pulling this off didn't feel so sure now.

"Come on," he encouraged, "I'm going to take you through a hook-up run with the cables, which we tagged and coded for you, and have you attach this rock sample on a dry-run to all five connector options. Look at this wire map we've made just for you. It's really pretty simple."

I walked around back where Kevin quickly showed me that the units were all labeled and numbered in order as they should be set up on my field table at the dig, and then one by one, we went through the three numbered boxes of cables, following the wiring schematic diagram and the tagged cables and ports for each. He was right. They had made it very easy for me.

There were five ways to expose samples to a variety of experimental impulse and scanning processes, each with its own hook up; and lastly, small specimens could be wired inside the sample chamber, and if I wanted to try a larger stone, there were special ten foot cables supplied. As long as I could get the sample next to the table, I could wire it.

"So there you have it," Kevin concluded. "Wire it up, find a likely ancient sample, hook it up, and it will do the rest."

I didn't answer. I just stared over the units and wires.

"You know," I said, "at the Foundation, they asked me how all of this works, at the hearing."

"What did you tell 'em?" asked Kevin.

"I told them the truth: that I didn't know how any of it works."

"You don't have to know how it works. You use it, and it works," he said raising his palms.

"I know: that's what I told them. I just use it, and it works. But now I'm asking: what have I got here? How does this set-up work?"

"Oh, boy. He wants to know how it works. Look, this is not good timing. We've got 45 minutes before all this has to be packed and loaded into a container to catch the flight. You're an archaeologist. You know about Egypt and Greece and Israel and artifacts. That's your briar patch: you go in and out without a scratch. This is my briar patch. Don't worry about it."

"Just the basics. Just explain the basics."

"OK, Real quick. Let's start with what you know. I know you've been studying a lot about sound and recording, and you understand the mechanics of record grooves, CD grooves and magnetic alignment on tape. Now: leave all that behind and think electronics. Let's see if there is anything I could explain you can understand."

"Go for it."

"First: do you know how electrical current flows in a copper wire? Anything about electron movement?"

"Not really."

"We call that a conductor. Do you understand how sound gets converted into electrical impulses and travels in a wire conductor?"

"No, I don't."

"Then you probably don't understand how more than one voice message goes over a copper telephone wire and through a fiber optic filament."

"No."

"Let's talk hardware. Do you know how transistors amplify, or control a strong current with a weak current, or how the negative electrons free flow and positive electrons move through holes?

"No."

"We call the materials used in transistors semiconductors, which means they don't conduct current as well as metal conductors. Are you still with me? How about basic transistors: junctions; current controls; channels; gates; NPN's; PNP's; FET's? Do you know how any of that stuff works?"

"No, I don't."

"Well all of that is simple radio electronics which has been around since before our parents were both born."

"I don't know much about electronics," I sighed.

"I know; but you do know what you do know, and that's why you're going out there and I'm staying at the lab. Do you know anything about conductive materials which give no resistance at all to the free flow of electrons?"

"No."

"We call those superconductors, and they create a continuous flow of current with no applied voltage; only they usually have to be cooled down to about absolute zero to work, so their potentials in computer sciences are still only theoretical.

"Don't know a thing about 'em."

"Do you know anything about how radio or TV is broadcast, anything about audio or video waves, how sound and images that are captured off vinyl records, CD's, magnetic tape, light-projected film, are then converted into electronic impulses, what those impulses are, or how the equipment works that sends them out into the air? Do you understand the fundamentals of how radio and video waves travel in space as compared to sound waves in air?"

"Not really."

"Do you know how audio signals and video images are re-formatted from radio waves and reassembled at the receiving end?"

"No."

"Do you know how a radio, or TV, or cellular phone sorts out multiple channels and signals all around it in the air?"

"No."

"Do you know how integrated circuits work in a micro chip, with hundreds of thousands of transistors, each with its own specific function?"

"No."

"Do you know how a spell-checker works as it interfaces a dictionary with something you've written?"

"No."

"Do you know how the Web Turbocrawler program works on the Internet, when you ask it to search worldwide for every document on the net that mentions, say, the Boston Tea Party?"

"No."

"Do you understand the simplest process that just makes letters appear on your computer screen when you tap a key on the keyboard? Do you know how the tap on the key gets to become a letter up on the monitor screen? Or how it is saved when you save it? Or how you can bring up the file when you give the command? How the touch of your finger on the screen tells the computer to select that function and how it then does as you've told it to do? Do you know what is really happening so that it does what you've come to expect it to do?"

"No, I don't."

"Then how am I gonna explain to you how all this here works?"

Kevin was smiling at me by this time, and I at him, for it was more than obvious I could not understand what this equipment would be doing, for I had no idea how the everyday appliances and computer equipment I already used did what they did.

"You've made your point," I conceded.

"Look, there's a ton of brain-hours put into this system," he emphasized, and with a sort of compassionate exasperation, said, "If you want to have a mental image of what all this is doing, think in terms of magnetic field sensors, and computerized CAT scanning, and computer reading reflective imaging, Nasa-type computer analysis and computer enhancement systems, and scientific equipment which works on the micro-level you think of in bio-engineering work, or DNA strand-analysis and gene searches, or atmospheric particle sorters like smoke detectors, and laboratory chemical identifiers and analyzers, the kinds of scientific equipment in a medical vaccine analysis laboratory, or a military cryptographic decoder, or a deep space listening program - you know, those kinds of things. Well, it's like all those, only different."

"Only different," I nodded my head. "Now I've got it."

"Different as in, 'applied to sound pattern recognition in unconventional formats.' What we've done is utilize every known technology we're aware of that can be applied to searching for patterns of any kind, and anomalies, of any kind, and we're hoping the combined power of this hardware and software will be able to recognize something which it can in some way reconstruct into what its data base says is sound patterns, syllable patterns and voice patterns. We're trying every imaginable system in every imaginable way, even in a few unimaginable ways."

"Right. I've got it: it's just like those things, only different," I smiled even more broadly.

"David, follow the instructions, and just use it. Maybe, if we're all really lucky, it may even work," he sat back a bit wearily. We both stared at the clean, new units.

"All this effort, and we're not even sure if it really works," I sighed and shook my head.

"Well, you wanted what we've got so far. This is it," he raised his hand toward the table

"And it doesn't work?"

"No. At least not on any samples we've tried. But that's the problem. Hypothetically, it should work. By all the calculations, it should work. But the Hegelstein Theory suggests subatomic activity artificially released in our century may have perhaps erased or at least impeded reassembly, 'the dropout glitch factor,' sort of like a hard-drive crash. We *assume* reassembly may be possible, but as we have yet to find and test an undamaged sample, which can only come from the past, we've had no chance to identify and model a real imprint, much less decipher and reassemble it into sound. So, how far are we from figuring out how to repair and download damaged 'natural storage drives' such as crystals which may be affected as Hegelstein suggested? Who knows?"

"I guess that's why my excursion has interested you so much."

"Exactly! No one else in the field is willing to even talk to us about this concept, much less go out into the sand dunes and try to find the perfect specimen for conducting research. The paradox of the Hegelstein Theory is that while we're not having any success yet, we don't know if we're not hearing anything because it's not there and never was there, or because we still haven't constructed the right programs, or haven't designed the right hardware, or if it's because as Hegelstein hypothesized: all of the samples we have used have been exposed to 50 years of subatomic particle infiltration which has displaced, disrupted or fragmented the stored patterns we hope to access!"

We sat for a moment in silence. The impact of this intense teaching and imprinting session had drained us. Finally Kevin spoke.

"So do you think you'll find them?" asked Kevin.

"Find them what?" I asked, totally immersed in technology and computers and electronics.

"Those things you're looking for, the Urim and Thummim. 'The oracle stones of the Lord,' you called them. Have you had any new clues or leads that might help you pinpoint where they could be buried?"

My brain changed gears, back to my world, my studies. Kevin was one of the few people I had trusted enough to share the remote possibility of finding my true goal, the Urim and Thummim. He knew I was searching not just for ancient Canaanite, Phoenician, Hebrew and Roman jewel stones, for earrings, pendants, ring stones and other crystalline artifacts which might contain voice imprints; that I hoped to find an artifact of value beyond imagining.

"Oh, the Urim and Thummim. No. I have no idea, Kevin. Finding them at this point makes the proverbial 'needle in a haystack' search seem easy. At least you see the haystack, and you know that if you just sift long enough and carefully enough, the needle's in that pile of hay somewhere. I have about a hundred square miles of haystacks to go looking in."

"That bad, eh?"

"The best clue I have is 'the Strong Holds of David.' But there's no such place written on the map; it's an entire area of canyons and cliffs and caves and hills around the oasis of En Gedi by the Dead Sea. I mean, it's easily over a hundred square miles. And that's only one small part of the Wilderness of Judah, a whole region of desert stretching South below Jerusalem. What I'm looking for could be put under your sandwich in your lunch box without making a lump. No, it doesn't look very promising," I shook my head.

"The Urim and Thummim," he said, staring at the floor by his feet as he cleaned imaginary dirt from under his fingernails.

"What are they like?" he looked up at me. "I mean, now that you're really going over there, I know you're going to find a lot of pristine ancient samples of semi-precious stones in your dig, but just knowing these things are hidden somewhere out there, it's pretty awesome. What do they look like?"

"Nobody knows. If you believe in this sort of thing, one day Moses has this special priestly breastpiece made of multi-colored cloth for Aaron, with a dozen different semi-precious stones sewn in its face, one for each of the Twelve Tribes. When it's finished, suddenly he's got these two stones that are supposed to be put in a special little pocket in it. It doesn't say they were 'made.' Moses *had* them. The whole thing is called the 'Oracle of Judgment' or just the 'Oracle.' The Urim and Thummim are 'to inquire of the Lord.' Josephus says that they were 'capable of shining out to give divine guidance.' It's eerie."

"Where did they come from, the stones?"

"We don't know. We don't know what kind of stone they were, how big or how small, if they had color, or if they were clear crystals. All the theories about them are based on fortune-telling stones of the Egyptians and Canaanites, and I don't think these were anything like that. Whatever they were - or are - Moses just suddenly had them."

"And Aaron and the priests and prophets could talk to God with them?"

"That's the idea, but it's a big controversy. Nobody knows, so everybody has a theory. Since most of the few mentions of their use just tell of 'yes - no' questions and answers, most of the theories conclude that they were used just to cast lots. But that doesn't hold up. The Bible uses the expression 'to cast lots' all the time, but always with other things. You know, when lots were cast, or drawn, like drawing straws, or marked bones or whatever?"

"Whatever," he nodded.

"Also, the few stories which talk about 'Urim and Thummim' are all very late: if you believe in the chronologies of the stories, we're talking hundreds of years after Moses and Aaron. The stories don't show very righteous or spiritually faithful people using them by that time, and all they wanted to know were personal questions like, 'if I go into this battle will I get killed?'"

"Well, that seems like a pretty reasonable question for a person to want to ask God, wouldn't you say?" Kevin smiled.

"Yes, but it only requires a 'yes - no' answer, so the theory has arisen that they were sort of 'heads or tails' type stones, used to decide issues as the flip of a coin."

"Is that what you think?" he asked, squinting deeply into my eyes.

"No. I think they were a whole lot more than that. Moses seems to have had them, ready to give to Aaron, after he spent forty days in the Wilderness where he received the word of God, and among other things, the Ten Commandments."

"If you believe in that sort of thing," added Kevin.

"Yes, if you believe in that sort of thing. Where did Moses get them when he suddenly had them for Aaron? I don't know. But I think they could be used for a lot more than the later custodians ever imagined. I think they could do a lot more than just answer the few 'yes or no' questions we have recorded. When Joshua was chosen to lead Israel, just after Moses, it says the High Priest Eleazar asked *counsel* of God for him with Urim. The story implies *extensive* instruction from God, of the kind Moses had been given. At any rate, what's most important to think about for our purposes in retrieving sound imprints, is that they were constantly worn by the High Priests for over six hundred years, from Aaron right on down the line. The High Priests were consulted on almost everything. So, they were exposed to voices all the time, the most historically important dialogues of their day. They would be a treasure trove of ancient dialogues, ancient events, of ancient lives."

Kevin sat for a long moment, and I could tell he was envisioning in his mind what I too, could imagine.

He suddenly looked at his watch and held it up for me to see. These boxes had a plane to catch. Hurriedly, I helped him disconnect cables and wires, and pack each unit in its individually numbered shipping box. The visual experience of putting each unit in its box would help me unpack and re-wire the whole system once I got it to the site in Israel. Every little thing.

I drove back home and without delay, quickly put the last things into my suitcases. As I was finishing, the children arrived from school. Rushing, I huffed the bags out to the car.

Back in my office I made one last scan of the Internet bulletin board and checked my email before leaving for the airport. Nothing important. A few Bon Voyages. Everyone knew I was going.

The hour of departure had come. I had to rush now.

My wife called the children to the front room to see me off and have all our good-byes, and for me to give the usual Daddy speech.

"Do all your homework and study hard. Be nice to each other. Help Mommy every time she asks for it and try to help even if she hasn't. Don't fight. Treat each other with respect. Don't forget to feed your pets, and clean their cages BEFORE they need it. I'm going to be gone for about seven weeks, so I'm really counting on all of you to take care of yourselves, take care of each other, take care of your Mom, take care of your animals, take care of the house, take care of the yard, and be good kids. When I come back I want to see all of you happy, the house neat and clean, Mommy smiling because you were good, and you smiling because you know you were always doing the right thing. You know the routine: I'm going to have some nice surprises when I come home, and I want everyone to be able to get their surprise."

I loaded my things into the car, and with the neighbor watching our children, my wife joined me, and we headed out.

My wife did as we always did, and dropped me off at the curb by the skycaps. We made our good-byes at home, and avoided the madhouse of parking and walking forever to the gate. As I got out the bags and set them on the sidewalk, she stood with a smile until I could give her the last kiss.

"Good luck," she said pouring her whole soul into my eyes. "God bless you, and I hope you find it."

"God bless you, too, and take care till I come home," I replied.

As she drove away, I showed the skycap my boarding coupon, checked my bags, got my claim stubs, and headed for the gate.

At a few minutes before 3PM I boarded, and with a quick stow of coat and briefcase over head, I buckled into my seat and sat back to finally rest. I loved the rest I got on airline flights. I never could understand all of my friends and people who said they couldn't rest on airplanes. The concept of such vast journeying accomplished so effortlessly always lulled me into a sort of euphoria that relaxed my every nerve and fiber, and for some reason, I just felt wonderful.

We chalked off only a few minutes late, and as the flight attendants went through the ritual of seat-belt and Emergency Exit instructions, I checked the aircraft configuration card in the seat pocket in front of me to spot the exits and rest rooms, and settled back for an enjoyable flight.

The plane taxied by terminals and cargo warehouses and out to the runway, and without delay we rolled into a turn that set us in takeoff position. The brakes jerked us to a brief stop, and with the sudden roar of the jet engines and rumble of the huge metal body we all sat in, I felt the slight ease forward as the brakes were partially released, and then the full thrust forward of our jet as the brakes were completely released and the aircraft lunged into its takeoff roll. Faster and faster until the white lines and black skid marks on the runway were speeding past in almost a blur, and then, the expected tilt back, rise and full rotation as we left the earth behind and were lifted up into the sky.

With an afternoon departure, the sun was still high, and the view across the land below was spectacular. No matter how often I flew, I never tired of beholding the wonder of the earth beneath me, spreading out as far as I could see, which grew and grew into an ever greater panorama as the jet climbed altitude. The earth, the sky, the clouds, the sun, it always filled me with awe.

This was the view which only the ancient gods had seen in olden times, and from my fiery chariot in the clouds, I flew above it all as the very gods themselves. Not an emperor, not a king, not a queen, for all their gold had ever seen what I was seeing at that moment. They could not even dream of it. Yet as we continued to climb in a widening circle upward, it was all mine for the taking in. No majesty could rival such a view as this, of the earth in all its splendor.

My thoughts momentarily turned to my wife, for she always marveled at this view as much as I did. This was one of the special things we shared, this love of the planet, of its enduring stability, of its fragile balance, of its awesome beauty.

The bulk of this planet would quickly come to separate us, for I would literally be on the other side of the earth in less than twenty-four hours. Yet even from that distance, I had always felt her, known her thoughts were in me as mine in her, and moved in the comfort of knowing that all was well at home.

Now, I was off on a great adventure, leaving her alone with so much responsibility and work. Yet she wanted me to do this, to follow this quest. She had always been supportive of me, and she was particularly supportive of this search for a key to unlock the past, the key to this idea of sound and voices locked away in the very stones of the earth.

And finally, today, I was on my way.

From the altitude the plane had reached, the sun out the window was very high. The flight East was a race head-on into the face of time, and I knew that with the change of solar-surface hours, the best thing to do was sleep. Long ago I had learned the secret of avoiding 'Jet Lag,' the very name of which begged for correction. For it was not the jet which lagged, nor anything else. It was time itself which was altered in its cycle as the body inwardly reckoned it from the direct exposure to energy from the sun, its true regulator. Yet to help my body re-adjust to a new schedule of night and day, all I had to do was eat little, drink as much as I could - but no sodas, no alcohol - and sleep as long as I could. Then, when I awakened, get up and get as much movement as possible. Light meals for two days, and the body made its adjustments quickly and almost painlessly.

I asked the flight attendant to not wake me for meals, and with my seat belt fastened and visible, I closed my eyes.

Very quickly sleep came from the last several days' exhaustion, and as I slept, I dreamed dreams, dreams of ancient places, people, and potteries and coins and bronzes, things buried in the earth which seemed to suddenly push up out of the soil all around me.

Sleep carried me through the night, and a truncated short day, all the way across the globe and over the Mediterranean, almost all the way to Tel Aviv.

It was an afternoon arrival, and the sun only a bit lower on the horizon behind us than it had been when I left home.

To me, it seemed as if I were still in the same day. It was as if I had only taken a short nap. Yet this was indeed already the next day, already advancing, even though it was still the same day for me.

How strange time is, I thought. When I fly home, I will fly with time, and by the clock I will actually arrive before I left. I will, by the clock, have several hours to re-live. Yet now, I fly against time, and I arrive after what should seem but a short nap of cramps and stiffness, yet I have lost a day.

Where did that lost day go?

It just ran past me, speedily as I slept, and now it is gone.

Or was it I who ran so speedily past it?

As I looked back, behind the plane through the window, seeing the sun still going down, I remembered the words,

"And it was morning, and it was evening, the Third Day...."

To me, this was still my third day.

I decided to count the lost day when I got it back on my return trip.

As the plane touched down at the airport, the sun was hours from its setting. I quickly got my bags and sent them ahead on the hotel shuttle to Jerusalem, with a good tip to assure they would already be in my confirmed, paid room when I got there later that night. Then I took a sherut cab to the spot along the beach I always went to, to start my journey into time and history in Israel. The cab stopped, I paid, and closing the door, I walked into the cool breeze with the warm light of the sun on my face.

I loved to walk along the beach from Tel Aviv to Jaffa. Jaffa was one of oldest cities in the world, silently laden with history heaped upon it. The ancient acropolis hilltop had a small excavation to visit, and around the hill were museum, shops, antiquity shops, and little cafes with good food, and an incomparable view of the sea.

The walk from Tel Aviv to Jaffa took only a little more than an hour, the same hour it took on foot thousands of years ago, when there was no option to drive a car and be there in ten minutes. I strolled from sand to rocks at the point, and enjoyed watching the waves pound upon the boulders at the base of Jaffa's acropolis.

Just before the sun went down, I wandered up the cliff side to the modern road, and from the ancient vantage point, looked out across land and sea as old as time itself, on which humankind had walked throughout our known and recorded history for almost five thousand years. I could not think of very many places where eyes could soak in such a panorama of time and history.

Images of ancient Canaanite and Phoenician ships heading into the golden-red sun burst into my mind, sails billowing in the stiff evening breeze, the musical chant of Mycenean Greek sailors carrying across the face of the waters; on the shore, the light of cooking fires in stone houses straggling up the hill filled my mind's eyes as much as being there could ever have filled my physical eyes. I paused, leaned on the rail, and looked out over the waves and land, all bathed in the sun's glorious last light.

Then, below me, close by, a sudden movement in the branches of a thin tree growing out of the jumbled rocks at the base of the hillside caught my eye.

A chameleon was slowly climbing along in the tree branches. Its oddly shaped green body and huge head with bulging eyes stood out starkly against the leaves in the golden light of the setting sun. I looked down. The stones out of which the tree grew were hewn and block-shaped, and I knew that they were part of the ancient walls which three thousand years ago had jutted up upon this hill and protected it from foes and fears of foes. I had arrived in the past.

This was, in its own way, time travel. For time was all around me, as much as anyone could ever feel it.

Here, I could see it, all around me and in my mind. Here, what could be seen in the light of my mind was no less real than the rocks and stones toppled around me below this hill.

Here, I could be in any of time's moments, for I knew these times and these people, all of them. This was the same sky and earth which stretched overhead and lay solid and firm beneath their feet, all of their feet. It was the same sky. Stretching out along the sandy beach were the same grains of sand, the same mounds of dirt, of earth, of dust which lay beneath my feet.

I walked down the road to the sherut stop, and got a cab to Jerusalem where I wearily but happily checked into my Hotel on the far end of King David St, near the ancient walled city.

My bags were in the room. All was in order, as it should be.

I undressed, and almost as quickly as I climbed in under the covers, I fell asleep, this time much too tired to dream.

Tomorrow would be a big day.

The beginning of a lot of big days.

Chapter 4

Day Four: In Two Jerusalems

I awoke in Jerusalem, the ancient city.

How I love to remember the feeling that consciousness gives, each and every time. For me, at least, I think no matter how long I might live in Jerusalem, I would feel the same feeling every morning I should awaken here. History occurred here. History lives here. History saturates everything that is here. History penetrates all who come here.

I was dressed and out of the Hotel door into the fresh air of morning before dawn. It was good to just stand in the darkness for a few moments, in front of the hotel on the sidewalk of King David Street, and breathe it in. Already, lonely cars were ambling along the dark street, and in the still quiet of the morning, the first faint noise of their arrival could be heard long before their bright headlights came over the slight hill on my right, and they puttered loudly on by. Once past me and farther down the hill, they turned as the road curves, and then again, until they were out of sight, and all was still once more, and quiet.

It was the quiet of a world holding its breath.

I stepped down into the silent street and crossed it diagonally under the lamplight, walking past the impressive, old King David Hotel to the new Hebrew Union College that had been built here since my first visits to the ancient city. My footsteps echoed softly in the silence. I looked up at the College, glowing in its bright night lighting, and I remembered in my mind what this place had looked like before the College was built, when this had been just a bare, scruffy hill overlooking the walled city of Jerusalem. But I could still get to my morning sunrise rock.

Just past the hotel frontage, I turned into the dirt path which followed along the parking lot fence and I walked the short distance between buildings until I came out behind them, and reached the place I always came to on my first awakening mornings in Jerusalem, where I sat and waited to greet the sun.

My rock was still there.

This was the rock I had come to on my very first trip here, on the hill which overlooks the city walls across the small valley below.

I sat upon the rock, the same rock I always sat on, next to a scraggly little acacia bush, and looked East out across the valley at the massive city walls containing the Old City, the part of Jerusalem that to everyone IS Jerusalem, now bathed in artificial light of man's making, eerie in the silent darkness of the morning. Far below, down in the valley, here and there on the narrow climbing road which comes up the hill along the feet of the huge stone city walls, cars rumbled their way in the dark, only the headlights visible. Even from this distance, the sound of their motors still traveled up to my hill and faintly broke the stillness.

I loved this rock, this hill and this view. It had been here a long time. This is a place where for at least four thousand years, maybe more, people had come to sit and await the sunrise, to see first morning's light gleam upon the city, upon Jerusalem. My eyes gazed upon the place where history lives.

Four thousand years ago Abraham had here paid his tithes to the High Priest Melchizedek. Abraham had walked where my eyes could see. On this hill three thousand years ago people sat to watch the workers set the foundations for the First Temple, right there, and watched its walls rise toward the sky in majesty. This is where people had sat twenty-six centuries ago and watched the Old City desperately struggle under siege of the Babylonian host, and fall. This is where people two thousand years ago had sat and watched the Passover crowds surround the city in jubilee and palms. Over the millenniae past, this ground had been trod by Canaanite, Phoenician, Habiru, Egyptian, Hittite, Israelite, Assyrian, Babylonian, Persian, Greek and Roman. Abraham, Melchizedek, David and Solomon, Isaiah and Jeremiah, Nebuchadnezzar and Alexander, Herod and Pilate, Jesus and Gameliel had all walked where my eyes could see.

Where my eyes could see, more history had occurred than I was able to study and learn in ten lifetimes. Yet in the short years of my lifetime, I had at least been privileged to see Jerusalem with my eyes, and walk with it under my feet, and touch it with my fingertips.

As I sat for a while looking around at the scattered pinpoints of light in the buildings within my view, morning came. The sky turned slowly from black to purple to dark blue, and then began to turn a rosy pink as the coming of dawn filled the horizon before me. The high clouds began to catch the bright glow of the approaching sun, and soon everything, the sky, the wadi below, the rocks, the bushes, the grasses, and the earth itself emerged out of the darkness and came to life bathed in hues of pink, orange, and purple shadows. Down below, all along the road, the lights illuminating the great stone walls suddenly went out in unison, and the formidable presence of the wall's mass was swallowed in the darkest of shadows, only their serpentine tops glowing in the reflected light of the pink clouds above. My mind was a whirlwind of images of many times and many moments in time, all of which took place here, before my eyes.

As the sun peeked its first peek over the silhouette of the Mount of Olives, not so distant beyond Jerusalem's mount, with bright rays bursting out across the dawn sky, suddenly a little sparrow swooped out of the heavens in front of me, and lit on one of the small branches of the stunted acacia bush at my side.

My eyes and my imaginings suddenly focused on the sparrow. It sat nervously on its little branch, twitting and ruffling its feathers, looking around on all sides, uncertain about my presence.

It looked just like the sparrows back home, half way around the world in my neighborhood in America. As it fluttered and twittered and jumped from small branch to small branch, suddenly the thought occurred to me: this sparrow is a descendent of the sparrows which lived here two thousand and three thousand and four thousand years ago. Its greatest grandparents had been here, and witnessed all that I could dream of witnessing.

I looked around me on the hill, at the acacias and grasses, now bathed in the full morning light of the sun rising ever higher over the Mount of Olives and Jerusalem there before me. Yes, these grasses here on this hill are also descendents of the same grass which bent in the breeze, under this same sun, sky and clouds two thousand years ago. Even as these rocks were here, and this soil was here, their ancestors were here, too. The DNA in each blade of grass, in each acacia bush, in this sparrow twittering almost within my reach, was here. The understanding distilled within me.

Through this place, and them, I touch the very past.

The morning continued to unfold, and as the sun rose higher and higher, the noise of the awakening city blared louder and louder in my ears, vibrating in my body. The narrow, shallow valley below now echoed with trucks, cars, jeeps, shouts in Arabic and Israeli, honking horns and roaring engines. I felt the echoed reverberations deep in my bones.

With the awakening of the city, though the sky above was the same sky of two thousand years ago, the intense reverberations of sound were entirely 20th century, and they eventually blotted out all ability to easily continue my fantasy of antiquity. This was not here two thousand years ago, this noise. The noise pollution was new.

I rose up and walked back to King David Street. Even though the distance down the hill to the old Walled City was not so far, I decided to ride. The traffic had already increased exponentially, both in the street and pedestrians on the sidewalk. So I waved down a sherut taxi headed along

King David Street toward the Old City walls, opened its door, and stepped a last step into the Twentieth Century.

"Jaffa Gate," I said, and sat back to enjoy the short ride.

My eyes were now filled on all sides with the bustling of life in this new day. Yet before I knew it, we were down the hill and crossing the busy thoroughfare in front of the Jaffa Gate.

"Here!" I said. The sherut driver spun the wheel and stopped abruptly in front of the towering white stones of Jaffa Gate, at the highest end of the walled city, and he held out his hand for fare plus a few shekels tip. Opening the door, one more step took me out into the noisy, dusty atmosphere of the crossroads of King David Street and Jaffa Gate, a truly ancient meeting place. I closed the cab door and the sherut quickly edged away into the slow-moving, impatient river of cars and busses and trucks, leaving me amid the chaos of horns honking and exhaust pipes echoing in a deafening roar off the stone walls and rock hill across the street. All around me, above the din of the traffic, from the surrounding crowded sidewalks, came shouts of Arabs and Israelis and tour guides and children's voices bouncing off the high stone walls, and completing the steady confusion of sound and noise filling my ears.

From here, in just a few minutes, with a winding walk through the bazaar, and a few minutes more into the new Jewish quarter across from the Temple mount, I would leave this modern world of noise behind and descend through time into the silent uncovered depths of the earth, down past brick and dirt and rocks bared back all the way down to the bedrock of Judah's desperate days of Nebuchadnezzar's besieging armies, to touch the stones which trembled as the city fell and the Temple itself was destroyed. This was my next destination, awaiting me at the bottom of a deep, square well dug within a house above the ancient precinct of the most ancient city walls. A unique private excavation.

Turning from the crush of cars inching along the road to face Jaffa Gate and its pulse of people flowing in and out, my gaze was drawn to my right, along the massive city walls which towered and rambled in curving majesty down the descending citadel of the ancient city almost as far as the eye could see. I knew every stone, from the uppermost restorations of Herod's towers down to the earliest unearthed foundations below street level, dating back almost 3,000 years to the days of Judahite kings. It was magnificent. As often as I beheld the walls, my blood quickened.

It had never mattered to me how many different kings or governors or sultans had built and torn down and rebuilt again these walls, nor over how many centuries, or how many different hands in diverse times had laid the stones which made them. They were a continuous existence, spanning ages which dwarfed me far more than their awesome size, always filling my being with their silence, their antiquity, and their presence in time.

My eyes followed the pressing flow of preoccupied people bustling up and down the hillside sidewalk, their passage squeezed between the street and the towering wall as a tiny column of ants beside a mountain, an endless trudging up and down the hill, all passing the spot where I stood. There were young Palestinians wearing red and black chequered *keffiahs* over their heads, old men in full robes and long flowing white *hattas*, Israelis with glasses and small yamikas on their heads, women old and young in dresses and jeans, children, soldiers, and foreign tourists of many nationalities, mixing together in an endless passing of faces and colors and purposes.

This place was the ancient crossroads, where the ancient loom of the ancient city gate wove its living tapestry of humanity into its ever-changing fabric of souls. I paused to watch the throngs of people as they pressed through this loom at the gate's mouth, pushing intently around each other as some went in, some came out, some pushing uphill and some downhill, merging and dodging and bumping and weaving together in a dance that had been going on like this within such city gates, unchanged, over four thousand years.

With full savoring of the ritual I was joining, I stepped forward, into the loom, and wove my way through to the gate. Its stained and patinated stones beckoned me make greeting, and with no thought of resisting, I purposefully wove my way through the people until I stood before the stones. Reaching out my hands, with palms and fingers eagerly outstretched, I pressed my skin to theirs. Touching the rugged stones thus, I walked several paces along the walls, reading each stone as a blind man would caress a poem in Braille, feeling their coolness in the shadows, their heat where the sun's rays lay full upon them, tracing their aged scars and wounds of time with fingers of love and appreciation for all they had endured.

Turning from the stones beneath the great arch of the gate and facing the merging crowds, I leaned back against the stones' ancient solidness, and for a moment I stood listening to the babbling sounds of myriad voices speaking together: English, Italian, Arabic, German, Israeli, French, and bits and pieces of who knows how many other languages. The vibrations of the babble echoing within the stone archway of the gate quivered through my body. Suddenly an Arab man near the street entry of the gate stood up on his toes and shouted with piercing decibel levels back into the throat of the inner bazaar to a friend. The man stood a few seconds, motionless as a boulder in the middle of a rushing stream, his eyes searching, until his friend caught up to him and they flowed out with the human tide.

Yet my path lay within the city. Before me King David Street plunged headlong out of view, down into the bowels of the city and the Suq el-Bazaar, an almost living artery clogged on either side with the burgeoning of myriad merchants' and shops' wares tumbled out on the cobblestones of the street and dangled from above, all but shutting out the sunlight which still managed to peek in over the second- and third-story roofs high above the narrow street.

As I made my way slowly through the throng, the delicious smell of the old city greeted my nose with its familiar bouquet: coffee beans roasting and brewing, sesame oil, incense, baklava and honey, perfumes, dates, figs, melons and freshly tanned leather.

Within a few short minutes, passing shops of shoes and scarves and foods and necklaces and souvenirs, I reached the middle of the Old City. I continued down the Bab el-Silsileh until its joining with the El-Wad Road coming down from the Damascus Gate to the North. Here is where bustling bazaar meets dimly lit warehouses and shops not for tourists but for the inhabitants and residents. I went up a few steps and zig-zagged right, through archways and short tunnels past sacks of rice, beans, lentils, corn, chick peas and onions, making my way to the gate-door where sunlight splashed into the darkness.

I always came this way, and came here to this place before going to my friend's house, hidden nearby deep in the maze of streets in the Jewish Quarter. I had to glimpse the Glory of Jerusalem.

Stepping out of the dark warehouses and out into the bright sun, squinting in the sudden bright light, I stopped a moment and stood gazing out across the wide open area and the path descending to the Temple Mount and Western Wall. People pushed by me from behind, on their way to the wall, and I moved aside to let them pass, so I could drink in this panoramic view. This was Mount Moriah.

From this high point across the Tyropoean Valley, the cream-colored stones of Herod's fortified acropolis glowed within the shadows of the morning sun, rising silently in its cool reflected light, the ancient Herodian wall of the Temple Mount. Beyond it, still silhouetted across the morning sky, the Mount of Olives stood as it had stood gazing upon this Mount since primordial time.

Atop the massive Herodian stone walls immediately before me, on the right, overlooking the New City below, stood the Aqsa Mosque on the Southwest corner of the Mount. Below it, descending farther right down the hill South I could see the dormant excavations of the City of David: foundations and steps and stones from three thousand years ago when David and Solomon built, and then Judahite Kings reigned over a divided kingdom, and defended city and Temple against Egyptians, Assyrians and finally Babylonians.

To the left, behind the closely packed houses built one atop the other, the golden Dome of the Rock towered glisteningly in the morning sun. Perhaps here Abraham almost sacrificed his son Isaac. Absolutely here, David began the First Temple which his son Solomon built so magnificently. Unquestionably here, Zerubbabel and his men built the Second Temple after the return from Babylon, which in the days of Yeshua ben Yosef of Nazareth was yet refurbished and enlarged in the grand building project of Herod, only to be burned and torn down by the Roman general Titus, son of the Emperor Vespasian in Rome.

The Herodian wall before me was built over the old city walls of Solomon, rebuilt after the captivity under Nehemiah's direction. These had been the city walls besieged by Egyptians, Assyrians and Nebuchadnezzar's armies. The view from where I stood was very likely the view of the attacking forces' camp twenty-six centuries ago, outside the city walls, waiting for starvation and weakness to ready Jerusalem the old for penetration and destruction.

History upon history upon history blew upon my cheeks with the morning breeze, the breeze which whispered over and down the ancient Mount of Olives looming in the distance beyond, blowing down and across the Valley of Kidron and then up and over the Eastern walls of this ancient place, blowing across and over this ancient Temple hill to whisper past me and go on over the densely built quarters of the city and beyond on their way to the ancient port of Joppa and the Mediterranean Sea; blowing past me in this moment I became part of all that has been here; blowing past me as I stood gazing and feeling the happenings ever haunting this Holy place.

Echoing up from the sheer face of the Wailing Wall directly before me I could now faintly hear voices, blending together, voices of men in prayer, voices of boys celebrating Bar Mitzvahs, voices of school children and their teachers learning the lessons of time and endurance, voices of women talking among themselves, as the men prayed, and the boys recited their lessons to receive a pronouncement of manhood, and the teachers told the stories of antiquity, and the children listened and whispered to each other.

Suddenly the shrill lingual cry of a dozen Yemenite women honoring a young Yemenite boy rose up and filled the air, their tongues warbling rapidly across their lips as they sang out in jubilee. Chills washed over me at the sound. I instantly remembered the film *Lawrence of Arabia*, where I had first heard this haunting cry of the desert women, a warbling shrill song of many women's voices piercing the dunes, here piercing the wide expanse of open space and echoing off the massive Herodian stone wall and up into the heavens.

Yet I could not tarry. My destination back in the Jewish Quarter beckoned to me. I turned, and weaving through men, women and children pressing to come into the Temple Precinct, I left this ancient place to enter another ancient place, a smaller but more private one.

In but a few short paces, passing under another archway back into the morning shadows, the residential Jewish Quarter began, and almost instantly the crowds were left behind. With every advancing step the incessant din of the marketplace faded more and more, until it was but a muffled echo behind me. Finally only the sound of my own footsteps echoed up from the dark grey paving stones as I walked down the tiny narrow streets alone.

One more turn and I entered the street of my friend, who for more than ten years had been slowly digging out the floors of his own home, deeper and deeper into the layers of historic rubble and fragments of relics to realize a lifelong dream of touching each day some piece from the past undeniably locked within the soil beneath our feet.

I had walked this narrow winding street many times before, over the last ten years. But today, as my feet echoed softly on the paving stones and walls around me, I could not keep back my pace.

In the letter two weeks ago my friend announced he had reached a major page of history 23 feet below his living room floor. Having laboriously excavated down through the upper levels of Palestinian occupation and ceramic tiles of Sultans and Moors; down through the layers rich with pieces of Byzantine jugs and several coins bearing the face of Christos; down through the earlier layers which he found strewn with bright red shards of late Roman terra sigilata plates and bowls, and the layer of ashes mixed with tiny jumbled black and white Roman floor mosaic *tesserae* in which he had found the copper coin from the third year of bar Koseba; deeper through the earlier layer with Herodian Roman pottery shards and the three denarii he found: one each of Nero, Tiberius and Augustus; below the layer with blackened burned beams of Maccabean builders in which he had found Judaean coins with Hebrew inscriptions of Hyrcanus and Yannai, below the layers with Hasmonean clay oil lamps and the silver coin of Alexander, he had finally reached the ground soil level of the First Temple times, the destruction soil of the Divided Kingdom, of Hezekiah's and Zedekiah's Jerusalem twenty-six centuries ago. To reach this, the heavy layer of toppled and jumbled Tobian stones and floor covered with charred remains of burnt Maccabean palace beams had been removed, and foundation fill dirt dug and removed to expose the 7th-century soil preserved below.

It was this original topsoil layer which my friend was now beginning to dig through in the damp, cool well beneath his home. In the southeast corner of this exposed ground was a circle of small stones and a fire pit, his letter had said, from the period when this area was outside the protective walls of the old Jerusalem city.

A Rabbi in his long black robes and fur-lined hat nodded as he quickly walked past me, as I reached my friend's house. His was only another door in the continuous white stucco wall. No one walking past it would ever suspect the shaft of discovery which plummeted just inside. With a touch on the bell, in only seconds, the door opened and my friend was pulling me excitedly inside.

"David, come in, come in, you arrive with a perfect timing."

I followed him left through the narrow hall which led to the tiny kitchen, where my gaze was drawn as it always was, to the right wall where the door to the living room once had been. In its place now stood the wooden platform with its strong metal rail, separating the fully modern kitchen from a free-fall into space, into his painstakingly dug abyss probing into the ancient past.

"Come, look," he motioned me to the rail. I looked down into the immense square well which used to be his family's living room. The large skylight he had built into the roof illuminated brightly almost all the way down the carefully dug, perfectly skimmed walls of the excavation, but my eyes could not see all the way to the bottom in the shadows as I always had before.

"You've really gotten deep," I murmured.

"Yes," he smiled excitedly, his eyes bright with delight. "And many important things have been found in every cubic meter," he pointed to the glass case on the opposite wall. It was cluttered with artifacts four and five deep, the smaller things stacked upon larger bits and pieces of many things.

"But sit down a moment and rest before we go down. I have something to show you."

I sat at the kitchen table between his case of ancient relics and the open well dropping down into the depths of antiquity itself, and marveled at the many new fragments and pieces which had been unearthed in recent months of diggings and sifting.

Moishe went to the case and took out a small treasure, part of a multi-colored glass alabastron, a woman's perfume bottle, which he had found in the destruction layer of the Maccabean palace. Though broken and only fragmentary, it was beautiful.

"Have you found any semi-precious stones, or anything made of crystal?" I asked.

"No," his brow rose with question. "Why?"

"Oh, nothing. Just a little project I'm working on, that's all. A recently excavated crystal brought up from 20 feet below might turn out to be very useful. I'll tell you about it later."

"Please do, and I'm sorry I've not found anything of the sort which could be of help to you." He smiled and shrugged. "We only can find what has been left, and here I must deal every day with the frustration of stopping exactly 12 feet and 7 inches east to west and 18 feet 9 inches north to south. That is the maximum extent which I can dig away, and not a spoonful more on any side. Look at these walls" he motioned to the precisely perfect walls, literally shaved in perfect vertical symmetry all the way down, "I do not cheat myself of a millimeter. But neither will my neighbors or the city allow me to cheat them. As the plumb line marks, there I must stop. The treasures of the Temple itself could be hidden two inches beyond the earth where I must stop, but still I must stop. The only freedom I have is downward. Still, 12 feet and 7 inches by 18 feet and 9 inches makes 234 square feet of space in which I may dig downward, a few centimeters at a time. But when I think of what lies buried under this city, perhaps just beyond this dirt in any direction, perhaps just beyond my fingertips, my little shaft of discovery with its tiny 234 square feet of area seems incredibly limiting."

"You've still done a remarkable thing here, Moishe. More than anyone ever dreamed you would do when you first started this. Look at all of the fragments and wonderful artifacts you have found." We gazed at the case filled with relics of history lived out on this very spot, undisturbed for centuries until he first touched them.

"Yet I think now I may have found something very important, David. I told you in my letter of the stones and the carbon and ashes which are a fire pit. This was exciting, but in the last two weeks I have found this topsoil is rich with many shards from Iron Age period: dateable shards of Israelite vessels, and two small fragments of very late Greek black-figure pottery, I think a kylix cup, but very small pieces. This is 5th-century Before Common Era, David, and 6th century, and 7th century shards I have been finding! I think a few of them may be Early Iron Age, maybe as far back as Solomon."

"Anyway, this morning, after breakfast, I went down to do some last digging in the soil I have finally bared here - you know how I like to do, at least a little every day - and this morning, as I know I have reached mostly God's own soil now and there is probably not much else to find buried any deeper, I took down a metal detector I borrowed from a friend, just for fun, just to see if maybe anything might be buried a little under the dirt, escaping my eyes. And in only the first few seconds, I got a bleep! I dug a little soil away, and it was a bronze arrow point! Then I found another, and another, and suddenly a little group of them, all in one tiny spot! I think they must have been dropped from a bag of points, not yet mounted on shafts, and lost in the dirt. I cannot yet say if they are, but I think they are Babylonian, from the siege army!"

He reached out his hand and poured the small greenish bronze arrow points into my hand. There were about 15 of them, still moist from the earth where he had dug them less than an hour before my coming.

"I only began in that one corner. Do you think you're rested enough to go down now and work a little? Shall we look for something more?" his eyes twinkled and his grin was impossible to mask.

"I'm right behind you, please," I said standing, waving him before me.

We quickly walked down the solid wooden stairway which over the years had extended ever deeper into the dig he was conducting inside his home. Down past layers embedded with Ottoman Turk stones and Mameluke ceramic tile fragments, past Byzantine pottery shards sticking out of the dirt sides I reached out and touched as we walked past them; down past Roman shards and pieces of white marble jutting out at toppled angles, cool to my fingers, down past layer upon layer of soil embedded with the stuff of ancient lives, ancient events, ancient private moments, ancient joys, ancient tragedies, ancient everyday life, all the way to the bottom. We walked out into the room.

Light from above reflected softly onto the dirt floor, and I stood where only my friend, and a few officials from the Department of Antiquities had stood in almost 2,600 years. My searching gaze quickly surveyed the entire floor area around me

"This is where I found the spilled arrow points. You can see, I'm down to God's earth now."

I looked around the floor. Yes, he was down to God's earth, but it was still dotted with a few fragments of ancient artifacts sticking up out of the dirt, telltale pottery shards. All I had to do was bend over and pick them up, feel them, smell them, and quickly be part of their being. The smell all around me was intoxicating. History, history filling my nostrils.

This was the bared topsoil of the hill outside the First Temple city walls, which he had carefully sifted down for two weeks until almost no shards appeared under his brush.

Moishe went to the far corner, to the stone circle with fire debris in it. We squatted down to see it as it should be seen.

"It is of larger stones than I first thought, before I dug down past their tops. The pit is not large, but large enough: see here, it is deep, and very, very used. Look at the heat-chipping all over the inside faces of these stones. This had to have fires in it many times, I think over a long period of time. All around this circle as I dug down inch by inch, and in the deepest ashes and carbon, I found many, many fragments of pottery, from at least 4th century Before Common Era back to early Divided Kingdom, I think 9th or 10th century BC."

"What do you think this was, outside the city walls like this?"

"I have been pondering about it, and finally the thought came to me that we are looking at a camp, a tent camp spot with a fire circle, one which was used every year. Every year at Passover time."

Instantly I saw in my mind what he was envisioning. Crowds of people coming to The Holy City to celebrate the Passover, with so many unable to lodge within the walls, making camp outside the city walls, with their tents, their families, their children, their animals. I saw the fire burning inside the circle of stones, burning cheerfully in the dark night, the darkness all around pushed back and away by the small light of the fire, illuminating the nearby tents, bathed in the flickering gold light of this fire, and of the other fires which were undoubtedly around this area, buried so close to us under the tons of historical built-up layers surrounding us in our tiny shaft dug down to this ancient topsoil. In the flickering light of this fire I saw the faces of women kneading balls of unleavened dough in their hands, smiling and talking to each other, glancing at the men and the children; the faces of the men seriously talking about things men talk of, and little children running around behind them, playing near the tents, firelight dancing on the faces of all and casting shadows on the tents all around as everyone anticipated the High Day. I heard the voices, and the crackling of the fire, the braying of a donkey, the cry of a small infant in the night. Yes, this was a yearly Passover camp.

"Of course. How many tents and camps and fires must have been on this hill across from the Temple? This is fairly flat land, and there were probably hundreds of tent camps here, every Passover," I mused.

"Hundreds, I have thought," he agreed. "From here they could go into the city down that way, through the Valley Gate, or if they were going to the Temple, they could go up that way, up to the North end and enter in at the Fish gate by the Tower of Hananel. As there was no water here, or at least I have never thought of there being water, I had always imagined most of the

Passover pilgrims camping on the other side of the Mount, in the Kidron Valley, by the east walls. Four gates were there in the ancient wall, and the Sheep Gate up at the North end on that side."

"I thought with the cemeteries and tombs on the Mount of Olives, that side wouldn't have been suitable for camps," I commented.

"You may be right. I had thought of that too, but it always seemed odd that there were more gates on the Kidron side. Perhaps most of them did camp on this side here, where we are, as you say. I'd like to think that - all around my home here. Anyway, with so many people coming to the city at Passover, the time must have come when this hill got very crowded with many people, many camps, and many fire circles," he said.

"People from all over Israel and Judah," I nodded.

"Yes. I have had several days to be thinking about this, and you know, the road from Jaffa and the coastal villages leads right up to here," he motioned North of us, "and who knows, maybe even at very early times those who came from the West arriving here by Jerusalem may have decided to pitch tents on this comfortable hill instead of walking one step more. The children could easily go and fetch water, right? Older people just want to stop and make camp," he smiled. "A yearly Passover camp explains the number of shards from such a wide time span. I am thrilled to know that here in my own home, I have this fire circle and these stones which I am sure is where my ancestors cooked their unleavened bread and ate their herbs and faithfully spent their days for the Passover."

He knelt with his hand steadied on one of the stones, his eyes distant, and I knew his mind was back with them.

"Well, let's go back to the place I left off," he said, standing.

He took me over to the corner, which was cleared to soft-packed topsoil, earth untrodden since the days of Malachi.

Moishe turned on the metal detector, and began to make wide sweeps back and forth above the earth, barely skimming its surface.

Another bleep. He centralized its location and we carefully scraped back the earth until a small dark pebble caught our eye. I plucked it from the dirt, and immediately recognized it, as did he.

"A Persian silver siglos!" He exclaimed. "The families returning from the Captivity brought money with them, Persian money!"

"Well, whether some one back from the Captivity lost it here amid a worker's camp which may have been here outside the city walls as they were rebuilding, or a caravan trader in from Persia lost it on this hill, it got dropped here not too long after the return."

Moishe stood and went over to the side of the floor, where the excavated dirt wall stopped his expansion, to a small pile of little wire stakes with bags tied to them, and brought back several.

"When I get too excited to draw each find onto my grid charts as I find them, I do this, and then I don't forget where everything was found," he explained. He dropped the coin into a little bag and pushed the wire stake just far enough into the ground for it to stay upright.

We then continued to make slow sweeps across the exposed ground, finding first another arrow point, and then two lead sling projectiles, one right after the other. One of them had cuneiform scratched onto it, and as his trembling fingers brushed away the moist soil and revealed them, Moishe burst out in glee.

"This says 'Yehude' in cuneiform! I have seen it before! They used to do this, write the name of their enemy on them before slinging them in battle. This is Babylonian, definitely!"

A few more sweeps turned up another coin, Greek, a bronze. Neither of us was sure of its origin, as it was badly corroded; we would have to go to the books later. It was probably 4th century Before Common Era, we were pretty sure of that.

Several other oddly shaped and unidentifiable scraps of copper were found, and then a finger ring, either of a child, or a very petite woman. Then another lead shot for slinging, uninscribed.

Behind us the floor was becoming a small forest of little wire stakes with bags dangling down.

We reached the far corner of the room finally, and the fire circle. Both of us had anxiously been pushing toward the fire circle, anticipating the probability of more chance losses by this night-time gathering spot. Small coins, jewelry items and other objects could be dropped and easily shuffled beneath sandals and bare feet in the poor light of the fire. We approached it with excitement.

But with growing disappointment for both of us he reached the stones without another bleep, and began to sweep the few meters first on the left side between stones and excavation walls rising up 23 feet into his home above, and then the right. No bleeps. Moishe then held the detector over the central ash pile itself, but no bleeps. We rounded the fire circle and he made what would be the last few sweeps over the remaining square meters which dwindled into the corner of his small private dig.

And then the detector yelped. It was not just a bleep. It was a loud and accented yelp which rose in tone over the center of whatever was buried there.

"Oh my goodness!" Moishe exclaimed. "He said that a big sound means a big thing made of metal!"

With three more triangulated sweeps over the floor, the center of this yelp was clearly pinpointed. Something big was here.

We looked at each other, and dropped to our knees to dig.

It took all of our will to patiently scrape and brush away the dirt from whatever was buried here. We were about four feet from the stones of the fire circle, near the corner of Moishe's dig. Deeper and deeper we dug, carefully, centimeters at a time, and still nothing.

Then as Moishe picked carefully at the lumps of hard packed earth, we heard the sound. It is an unmistakable sound, dull and hollow, made by any vessel which is buried and not filled with earth.

"I've hit something metal, David! It gives the feel and sound of something large!"

"Let's dig, Moishe, let's dig!" I grinned.

His eyes twinkled with glee.

Our hands started trembling so much with excitement, we were digging like schoolboys. We laughed at ourselves.

"It is probably nothing, only an iron strap from a kettle, or something simple like that," said Moishe without slowing his digging.

"We've all found so little metal in all of our digs, Moishe, but this sounds, well, I don't know, but it sounds intact, you know, solid, like whatever it is, it's still in pretty good shape," I said.

"I think so too, but I wanted to hear you say it," he grinned and continued scraping away dirt as I brushed.

Then the first part of it emerged. It was green, and instantly we knew it was copper or bronze, not iron.

Carefully but rapidly we dug around it. A spherical knob appeared as the dirt got lower and lower around it, exposing then the top of a cone or inverted horn-shaped stand it rested upon.

"What is it, David?"

"I don't know either. This is wonderful. Keep digging!"

Centimeter by centimeter the dirt around it got lower and lower as we continued to feverishly dig in micro-scoops. We cleared the dirt around it about six inches so we could keep going down, and it continued to flare out wider and wider until it was at least ten inches in diameter, at which point it quickly dropped down. It looked like the top of a Greek Orthodox church spire, with a ball on top about two inches in diameter. It was slightly oval, not entirely round.

We tapped it. It sounded hollow. We continued to dig.

Suddenly Moishe's digging went past a rim and was into dirt. He dug around on both sides and found that on both sides, it turned down, deeper into the dirt, all the way around. Suddenly we both knew what it was.

"A helmet!" we exclaimed together.

"But what kind?" I asked him. It did not look Babylonian, as I quickly scanned my memory, and it certainly was not Greek. It would have to be from before the time of Alexander the Great, as shortly thereafter this area was built over as a new Hellenistic city by the Tobiads.

Moishe gasped and then looked up at me. He almost whispered.

"David - please, God, may I be right - I think this is a helmet from the Temple Guard, I think of the First Temple.

The side and back rim was only slightly lower than the front, and in seconds it was sitting free in the dirt between us, held only by the grip of earth it had been pushed into over 26 centuries.

"Please stop for a moment," Moishe begged, reaching out his hands to push mine away from the hole. "For this discovery I must go up and get my camera and document it in situ. I must photograph this here, in the ground, as it is before we take it up."

I waited in silent exhilaration as he ran up the stairs for his camera. The sound of his impassioned feet pounding up the wooden frame stairs filled the quiet shaft loudly until he reached the top and disappeared into his home. As I knelt in the cool quiet of this deep excavation room, with only the sound of my own breathing to break the silence, I leaned over to examine the treasure we had just uncovered. It was wondrous. The few sculpted images of Israelites I knew from Egyptian and Assyrian walls and monuments flashed through my mind, and indeed I believed Moishe was right. The shape was that which Israel's enemies had depicted on the heads of Israelites, and whether a soldiers helmet or as Moishe thought, of the Temple Guard, it was unique, and wondrous.

Moishe came with feet pounding down the stairway, and very quickly took half a dozen photos from different angles, clearly establishing in the background that this was his home excavation, and its position near the fire circle. He put the camera over on top of the dwindled pile of cloth bags and wire stakes, and rushed back and knelt again opposite me.

"It sounds hollow," whispered Moishe. "I think it was intentionally buried here, by its position like this. It should come up in our hands now - I have dug away the dirt from all around it and exposed the rim. It should come free."

Our trembling hands took hold of it, and we agreed to gently tilt it to the side while lifting, to better break it free from the earth.

With a single gentle pry, the helmet jolted loose, dirt fell away and we lifted up the bronze helmet. It was quite solid, heavy, and sound, and we could already feel how well preserved it was as we lifted it out of its hole.

That is when the real find appeared.

To our astonishment, at the bottom of the hole where the helmet had rested, was revealed a small treasure trove, to us more valuable than any jewels or shekels of gold it could have contained. Our hearts were still pounding with the excitement of the helmet, yet what we saw now with our eyes made us suddenly forget this Temple treasure, and set it carefully down so we could gaze into the hole.

There, on the ground before us, sitting neatly in the center of the almost circular imprint of the helmet, were two pottery ostraca, face up, the writing on their faces clearly visible, and clearly in early Hebrew script!

"Oh, David!" sighed Moishe as he began to cry. "I have hoped against hope and dreamed against dreaming of finding something like this in my little hole in the ground. Look at this! Look at this! Look at what is waiting here for us. 'I will bless the Lord at all times: his praise shall continually be in my mouth. My soul shall make her boast in the Lord: the humble shall hear thereof, and be glad!'"

I recognized the Psalm he recited, and waited gratefully as he waved his hand for me to allow him to get the camera and take more photographs. I could see that they both were written in black carbon ink with brush, and they were perfectly preserved. Moishe returned with the camera. The blinding light of the flash shone on these small pieces of pottery with their tiny writings upon them, and reflected brilliantly up upon the walls all the way up into Moishe's house. I let Moishe have the honor of lifting them up out of their resting place of twenty-six centuries, to see them at close hand.

The first was written in elegant Hebrew; the second, which was larger and had been under the first, was a more hurried hand.

"David, I know you are not a linguist, and so I will read this to you," said Moishe, weeping openly.

"You can read the archaic Hebrew that fast?" I asked.

"Anyone who reads Hebrew and knows his portions could read this, for we all know it so well. I know it almost by heart."

Slowly with a clear firm voice he began to read.

"And it shall come to pass, when all these things are come upon thee, the blessings and the curse, which I have set before thee, and thou shall call them to mind among all the nations, whither the Lord thy God hath driven thee, and shalt return unto the Lord thy God, and shalt obey his voice according to all that I command thee this day, thou and thy children, with all thine heart, and with all thy soul; that then the Lord they God will turn thy captivity, and have compassion upon thee, and will return and gather thee from all the nations, whither the Lord thy God hath scattered thee."

His last words echoed in the deep shaft of the excavation, and rose up and out until we were left in silence.

"It is from Deuteronomy, the book of Words," he whispered. "It is the Book of the Law which Hilkiah the High Priest found in the days of King Josiah, which the Prophetess Huldah declared would shortly be fulfilled, that Jerusalem would be destroyed."

"What does the other one say? Can you read it, too?" I asked.

Moishe set down the ostracon, took a deep breath, and picked up the other one. After a short scrutiny, his eyes began to widen, and then more.

"It is a letter. The name of Zadok is definitely written here, and Jeremiah.....Jeremiah it speaks of! ..... also I think, no, no, I am certain: the name here at top and again at the bottom signing it, Seraiah ben Azariah. My God, David, this is from the High Priest of Jerusalem, Seraiah ben Azariah!"

We looked down at the ostracon in dumb silence.

"David, take the helmet and let's go upstairs. I want to sit down to translate this. This is a letter from Seraiah the High Priest!"

Once upstairs, Moishe quickly got some books off his library shelf and sat down at the table with paper and pen to translate the writing on the ostracon. I watched him as he alternately wrote, and hurriedly thumbed through pages, ran his fingers anxiously down columns of words until he found what he was looking for, and then wrote more. He worked with remarkable speed.

In less than fifteen minutes he was finished.

"It is not so hard, and I have studied the Lachish letters and other early ostraca so many times I am getting used to these letters and writings. It is a command to a man named Jehonadab ben Habaziniah, the Rechabite. Seraiah commands him, he says, *'as if we ate salt together'* to find the man named Essaiah ben Zadok, his nephew, and wait outside the city gate for a man named Yehoniah, his steward. I translated it into modern Hebrew because that is easiest, of course, and then I translated that into an English so I can read it to you. This is not the best English, David, but it is close. Let me read to you what I think it is saying.

"To Jehonadab ben Habaziniah the Rechabite, whom I trust, hearken to the deliverer (of this letter) from Seraiah High Priest. Covenant between us as if we (together) ate salt. Gather four men of might who drink no wine; find Essaiah ben Zadok my nephew. Await my steward Yehoniah by Valley Gate, whom Jeremiah sends with my instructions. The covenant of salt between us all. Behold, the wrath of God is fulfilled as prophesied in the days of my father's father. Do as I instruct and bury before the Holy City these words of the promise, that the Lord in his anger shall not forget his people. I am taken to hear the words of the Chaldean at Riblah and then to Euphrates. I am Seraiah ben Azariah."

"That is what I think it says," he said.

"What is the thing about eating salt?" I asked.

"I have noticed this in the Book of Numbers, which in Hebrew, we call Bemidbar - 'In the Wilderness'" replied Moishe. "When two eat salt together in a covenant, it becomes a permanent covenant between them which in loyalty neither one can break. What he is saying here is that this thing is vitally important, and as if they had eaten salt, he must do this thing he is asked, without fail."

"I wonder what Yehoniah's instructions were," I mumbled, touching the shard and gazing upon its writing.

"What orders he sent with the man called Yehoniah, we can't know. But the instruction to bury the ostracon with the Promise of the Lord before the Holy City, this was faithfully done, and for this reason we have found it here. This place where we are was out in the middle of an open hill in those days, with a full view of the walled city of Jerusalem, and from here you certainly would have been able to see the top of the Temple itself. These shards were buried here as this man was instructed to do."

"Who do you think wrote the first one?" I asked.

"From the look of the two ostraca, they both look like they are written by the same hand. I think we have before us two writings in the hand of Seraiah the High Priest himself. I am overcome by today's discoveries. How are you feeling?" he smiled.

"I'm a bit on 'stun' myself," I smiled.

"The 'words of the promise' we read of in the first ostracon," he pointed to it, "that is from Deuteronomy, which he is referring to indirectly as he mentions his father's father. We have a completed moment of history here on my kitchen table, on my own kitchen table, and in the whole world only you and I know about it yet. Imagine. Only you and I know about it yet."

"I can guess you will be busy this afternoon taking these to the Department of Antiquities," I told him. He sat deeper in his chair and looked down at the floor.

"You know, they have let me keep everything I have found so far, because nothing I have found has been either museum-worthy, or of national importance. But these," he looked at the helmet and two ostraca on the table, "these they are going to take from me, I know it. And that is right, for they belong to the people. But on the same day....... that is too soon. It's just too soon. And anyway," his voice suddenly changed to an irritated defensive, "I remember a teaching from the Midrash which says that when a man buys a field or a property, everything in it is his to own, even a buried treasure. This is Israel. Let the Rabbis argue that premise! But if I say nothing, no one will know that I have found them, and who will come here?"

"Are you saying you may not tell anybody, and for a while, keep them here?"

"If you don't tell anyone, and I don't tell anyone, I can enjoy them...... for a while. You know me, David. I didn't tear up the floor of my living room and dig this big hole in my house to become a famous archaeologist, or to get my name printed in journals or books. I did this because I love ancient things, I love them! All I wanted to do is touch my roots, the roots of my people I knew were buried under my floor. And I've found them! These things here, they've been buried here all this time! So, a few more months, a few more years even, what will it hurt? But there are other things, other things to worry about. You know, the Babylonians, they still have the Temple Mount, in a way. Those are Arab Mosques up there, my friend, not Jewish synagogues. Maybe these bits of clay and bronze here will cause a lot of trouble. We have orthodox Rabbis already wanting to take the Temple Mount by storm. Maybe because of these shards, they will decide it is time, now. We have Palestinian Arabs who will defend it to the death. Think of it! I do, and I'm afraid. I'm not ready for all that yet. I'm not ready."

"So what will you do?" I asked.

"The important thing is that they are safe. And they will still be here where they have been all this time, only I can live with them up here where I can see them, instead of down there. David, this is the last thing I will bring up from here. My dig is over. We have taken all that man has left here; all that is left below is God's earth. I want to enjoy these for a while. I'm an old man," he said touching the shards with the tips of his fingers. "I'm an old man. I will tell them.... soon."

He looked up me with questioning in his eyes, and asked,

"Am I doing wrong to feel this way, to do this thing, to keep these from being published, to want them here a while with me?"

I thought a moment very soberly, and candidly replied.

"If you Will them to the State of Israel when you die, they'll probably be published long before most of the other excavation finds unearthed on the planet this year are ever published, Moishe - no matter how long you live. Academics dig, and usually what they've dug up gets buried down in basements again. A lot of excavation notes go into boxes in store rooms. The world is used to waiting for a future day to learn the story of what was found. You have your reasons. The field excavators always seem to have theirs. Who's to say that your reasons aren't better and more justified? Either way, right or wrong, at least you can always say that you're following a long and very colorful tradition."

He nodded with a smile, and recited, "Until the kettle bottom is cleaned, shall it call the pot black?"

He saw my eyes resting upon the artifacts, and generously picked up one of the ostraca, and held it over to me.

I gently lifted the Seraiah letter ostracon into my trembling hands, quickly scanning over words which had not heard sound nor seen light for almost 2,600 years. There is only one word for such a treasure. Wondrous.

I held in my hand an inscribed ostracon affirming the life of Seraiah, last High Priest of the First Temple under Zedekiah, who was taken prisoner by Nebuchadnezzar and executed at Riblah near Damascus in 586 B.C.

Though I did not tell my friend, the name Yehoniah cried out to me from the unpublished Yeb ostracon Dr. Brannon had found at Elephantine, buried with the sword of Goliath. No one had believed poor Dr. Brannon's story, but Moishe's discovery now almost certainly confirmed the truth of the Yeb report: here was the same Yehoniah; the words of Seraiah clearly called him 'my steward,' which according to Brannon's report, had been the title that Yehoniah had given himself, 'steward of Seraiah the High Priest of Jerusalem.' Yet in honoring Moishe, I could tell no one. No one would know yet of Yehoniah, his life, his oath, his mission, his secret, his journey, his service to YHWH in Egypt, his Temple dedication, his death.

Yet with this confirmation, I at least now had two additional names to search for in the scantily published inscription translations for another clue. Perhaps something would come up yet.

"May I have the piece of paper with the English translation?" I asked him, with all the begging I could put into my eyes.

He looked down at the paper and hesitated a moment. Then he reached over, carefully tore off the part scribbled in English, and held it in his hand. With his other hand he picked up the salt shaker from the table, and shook some out onto the table top. Putting down the shaker, he wet his finger in his mouth and then pressed it on the salt. He held up his finger for me to see the white crystals of salt all stuck to it.

"Eat salt with me, my friend, and covenant that you will keep this thing to yourself until I tell you otherwise," he grinned.

I put my finger in my mouth, and pressed my wet finger tip down into the salt on the table, and held it up for him to see.

"Salt covenant," I smiled.

"Salt covenant," he smiled back. And we put our fingers in our mouths and ate salt crystals in the ancient manner of bonding trust. He handed the paper to me, and I folded it and put it in my pocket.

"I must go now. I have a lot to still do in preparation for my dig in the desert," I said.

"What is it that you will be doing in this dig?" he asked.

"I'm going to listen to rocks," I said as matter-of-factly as I could.

"Listen to rocks?" he furrowed his brow. Then he raised his eyebrows in a knowing smile, and waved his hand in a circle in the air.

"From a man who listens to rocks, who would believe you about this, anyway?" he chuckled and motioned to the helmet and ostraca on the table. "I'm safer than I thought."

"Very funny. I'll see you in five weeks, Moishe. Shalom," I said, and he walked me to the door, and I was out again walking in the streets of Old City Jerusalem.

As I walked back over the cobblestones and pavings I now could envision all of the tons of buried artifacts and historical debris which certainly lay packed in the soil between my feet and bedrock below. Countless treasures, of who knows what astonishing value.

I walked up through the crowds of the El Wad Road almost all the way to the Damascus Gate, where the Suq Khan Ez-Zeit splits off back down into the city, and stopped at a small cafe for lunch. The crush of people thronging through this amazing thoroughfare filled the air with a constant din, and filled my eyes with its color and vibrance. I kept thinking about the incredible find I had witnessed this morning, of which I could tell no one. The unbelievable irony that my Yehoniah was mentioned in this letter filled my mind with questions to which I nor anyone else had any answers. I wondered how a person who has just had such a powerful experience could set it aside and go on with a normal day, but life does go on and I had an afternoon appointment I could not in good faith break. So I rested and calmed myself and meditated on the surging crowd before me.

At about two o'clock I got up and walked back down the El Wad and onto a less crowded side street to reach the shop of my old Bedouin Arab friend, Haj Abdul El Badawi. His family had been small dealers of antiquities for four generations, but none of his sons were interested in continuing the trade. Perhaps for the best, for the times were rapidly changing, and there was little and less future to be seen every year. When Abdul died, his business would die with him.

I turned the last corner and saw his eldest son, Hassan, standing by the door looking my way. It was just like him, to wait for me. I always felt I had a body guard with me when I went anywhere with Hassan. His face lit up and he raised his hand in greeting.

"David, my brother, you are here. Welcome!" He put his arms around me and gave me a bear hug, as always.

"Father will be so happy to see you," he smiled. He ushered me into the shop, and Abdul, and his grown sons Taufik, Muhhamed and several other of his younger children all stood and greeted me.

Abdul had three wives, and twenty-seven children. He and his family had "adopted" me many years ago, and had tried very hard to get me to take a Bedouin wife, too. I remembered this comedy of real life now as we hugged and greeted each other. The whole family had so urgently tried to persuade me, with such simple sincerity, I was profoundly touched while at the same time, terribly amused.

"But I am already married," I had insisted.

"This is no problem. Our women are used to having another wife to share; she will treat your wife as a sister and love her," they said.

"But in America, we can only have one wife. I could not take her home," I told them.

"This is no problem! She can stay here. When you come here, your wife is waiting for you. Very happy man, indeed!" they smiled.

"But I am only here two or three times a year, maybe four times at the most, and only for a few weeks," I pleaded.

"This is no problem! Bedouin woman is very patient, and waits well," they assured me hopefully.

"But I do not speak Arabic, and how will we talk?" I had reminded them.

"Oh, this is no problem. She will learn English with you, and see how much time she will have to study while you are away," they comforted me. Thinking I might have better luck putting them off with a 'type' requirement, I laughingly told them,

"Well, if I were to pick a wife, I would want her to be about as tall as I am, which is very tall, and she should be very thin," I said.

"We have!" they eagerly responded with wider eyes, seeing that now I was telling preferences. I realized I had made a tactical error: they thought I was interested. How could I wriggle out of this without offending anyone?

"And," I furthered quickly, "she would have to have light sandy-colored hair and blue eyes," I ended, smugly thinking I had won the day. Wrong. Joyfully they rejoined,

"We have! We have this type of woman for you! Shall we take you to the village now?" they cried triumphantly.

I finally had been forced to explain to them that it was just impossible, and with all of the thanks in my heart, I had to decline, for it was against my religion.

"Oh, then this you must abide, and we understand."

As I was finishing the rounds of hugs and hellos and pulling sweets out of my jacket pockets for the little children, Taufik, the talkative son in his later twenties waited for me with outstretched arms. He looked into my eyes, and he knew, for it had become a joke among us, I was remembering this story.

"My brother, are you thinking about a Bedouin wife?" he smiled.

"Yes, I am remembering the story," I confessed, and we all laughed.

We sat down and as I do not drink coffee, Hassan sent off one of the younger children to get me a large pitcher of fresh squeezed orange juice, with which the shops of the bazaar abound. I was semi-famous as the man who always drank orange juice.

"Tell me of our family, Father," I asked. "How is everyone?"

I had to always call Abdul 'Father,' ever since I was 'adopted' into the family. When this honor had first been given to me, and I was told that from now on I could call Abdul 'Father,' I had never imagined how serious a thing it was. Then one time during a visit I had slipped, and called him Abdul as we and several of his older sons were walking down a street. Immediately all of the sons stopped in their tracks and very lovingly reminded me, "No, he is Father, you do not have to call him Abdul any more," and I had immediately apologized, and as soon as I said 'Father,' and 'Brother' to all present, all had visibly relaxed and returned to happy ease, and we continued our walk.

'Father' told me about his children, and wives, and grandchildren, and about business, and in turn many questions were asked about my family, and my children, who were still too young to have children of their own. For indeed, Hassan, my eldest brother, was several years older than I. Pictures were pulled out of wallets and shown around, and we drank orange juice and coffee and everyone had a wonderful time.

'Father' finally showed me some common but very fine quality ancient potteries and clay oil lamps of the kind I usually liked to buy, which he had been saving for me, as usual bought from the desert Bedouin who were his kin, and we quickly concluded an agreement and Hassan put the things I wanted in a box to await my return from the desert wilderness.

"So this time you will spend five weeks in the desert in a tent?" asked Taufik. "I told you that some day you would become Bedouin!"

"What you are going to do there?" asked 'Father.'

"You will laugh at me if I tell you," I teased them.

"No, no, we will not laugh," he said, and then he chuckled and looked around the room, and added, "well, maybe we will not laugh. What you will be doing that may make us laugh?" he smiled.

"I'm going to spend five weeks digging and......listening to rocks"

Everyone laughed.

"Why you are listening to Rocks?" asked 'Father.'

As I briefly told them of the new computers, and that I hoped to hear sounds recorded in crystalline-structured stones and crystals, they listened more and more seriously. They knew of computers, and televisions, VCR's, and of video games, and cassette tape and CD music, and they respected that I knew many things they did not know. They asked me if it was really possible with computer equipment to hear voices recorded in stones, and I had to honestly tell them.

"We don't know. But I have some pretty fancy new equipment, and I'm going to try," I said. Hassan glanced at his watch and tapped it with his finger for Father to see.

"Would you like to take a walk up to the Aqsa Mosque with us, up on the Haram el-Sharif?" asked Hassan. That is the Arabic name of Mount Moriah, the Temple Mount. It was the first time I was being invited to go to prayer with them. I was very honored.

"Yes, I would like that very much," I replied.

The Al Aqsa Mosque was the third most holy shrine of Islam, after Medina and of course, the Black Stone in the Kaaba of the Great Mosque at Mecca. The Kaaba, traditionally believed built by Abraham and Ishmael, was the small cube-shaped building under the open sky which the Great Mosque of Mecca had been built to protect.

It is the Black Stone, actually, which all Muslims face when they pray, whether at the Al Aqsa Mosque in Jerusalem or anywhere else in the world. This had always been of strange fascination to me, for, the Holy Black Stone in the Kaaba was a huge meteorite. That a billion and a half people on our planet bowed down on the ground five times a day to face a meteorite fallen from they sky as they prayed to God was, to me, more than remarkable. Why a meteorite?

The enormous nickel-iron stone - traditionally believed given to Abraham by the angel Gabriel - was an object from space, from beyond our earth, which had survived the fiery holocaust of entry to land among us. It was seen as a gift from God, brought by an angel. This meteorite represented God, in a very real way, as the most sacred object in Islam; we were going up to the Haram el-Sharif to face it, and pray to God. I saw this as a profoundly relevant act, yet intellectually, I was without any understanding why.

From the shop we walked down the streets and eventually came out on the same gate landing I had stood on this morning. By this hour now the sun was full upon the Herodian wall, and it gleamed in the sunlight. As I knew my 'brothers' were not very fond of the Israelis, I was careful not to return my gaze to the Wall and the myriad worshippers and tourists down at its base. Instead, I carefully stayed to the left of them, so I could keep my head turned right as I spoke to them, and thus we had a pleasant walk down into the Tyropoean valley and up the steps to the entry onto the el-Sharif.

At the top of the steps, just outside the Herodian wall there were a number of young Israeli soldiers with their automatic weapons, as is common in so many places all over Israel. However, security is especially

116

thick at the Haram el-Sharif. As we walked by these guards, they eyed me with expressions of disgust. Hassan subtly kept his eyes constantly roving around all sides, and instinctively moved over between me and the weapons. Though I had never asked him directly, I think his love for me is such that if some one ever were to point a gun at me, he would stand and take the bullet before allowing me to be hurt.

I had grown accustomed to distrusting and unfriendly looks from others when with my Bedouin 'family.' Because of my beard and glasses, I looked like a Jew, though I am not. When we were passing among Israelis, I could only imagine they thought me a Jew, and wondered why I would be fraternizing with Arabs, for which, by their expressions, they despised me. When we went out of Jerusalem and into West Bank and other Palestinian villages and towns, among purely Arab crowds, they too looked at me with disgust, and even though I was with Palestinian escorts, I often saw angry expressions on the faces, and heard loud shouts. The first few times this happened, I asked my 'brothers' what the people were saying. With some embarrassment they honestly told me that these people thought I was a Jew come to spy on them, and, Hassan would tell me, 'they were saying unkind things.' After a few such experiences, I stopped asking, but I always felt a tangible sense of tension wherever I was with my Bedouin 'family.'

As we went through the tunnel and came out onto the vast flat plateau of the Haram el-Sharif, I asked Hassan and Taufik as we walked,

"When was the Aqsa Mosque built?"

Taufik answered. "Aqsa Mosque is here for three thousand years," he said as a school teacher might explain to a small boy.

I could not help myself: I suddenly stopped cold in my footsteps where I was, and all the others had to halt and walk back several steps to where I had stopped. I was dumbfounded by what Taufik had just said.

"Wait a moment," I said with a smile, "I'm a bit confused here. Perhaps I have mixed up my dates, so please help me if I am wrong, but didn't Mohammud begin his mission as Prophet of Allah and Islam about 620 A.D, with the flight to Medina, and all that?"

"Yes," replied Taufik. Hassan and Muhammed nodded their heads in simple agreement. Yes, that was right.

"Then I am confused," I continued. "If Mohammud began his mission and started the religion of Islam about 620, 630 A.D," I said, "then that would be about fourteen hundred years ago, correct?"

"Yes, Mohammud was about fourteen hundred years ago," confirmed Taufik. The three of them stood around me with such caring and helpful faces, I almost felt embarrassed to ask.

"Then how could this Mosque be three thousand years old?" I logically asked.

"Oh, Mohammud, he only rebuild the Mosque, and make it more beautiful than it was before," explained Hassan. Taufik nodded.

"There was a Mosque here before Mohammud?" I inquired.

"Oh, yes," continued Taufik. "First Mosque was built by Solomon," he said. The three smiled and nodded, for surely this cleared up the confusion, and they took my arm and Hassan gallantly waved his hand forward as an usher, and I walked with them to the Aqsa Mosque.

As I took off my shoes to go in, I was stunned by the impact of what had just been told to me. Not only would the Arabs fight to defend these Mosques, this and the Dome of the Rock, being two of the most Holy shrines of Islam, but they matter-of-factly understood that their Mosque was three thousand years old, built originally to Allah by Solomon.

I suddenly saw the makings of the terrible conflict converging, which would some day be fought over this ground, over the same Holy building which one side believed was built by Solomon for their God Allah, and the other side believed was built by Solomon for their God Yahweh. There was no possibility of reconciliation.

After prayer we went out of the city in Hassan's sherut cab to 'Father's' house in the outlying country. As Bedouin had lived for millenniae in tents and only had begun to live in houses for a few generations, 'Father' typically allowed his sheep to live in the ground floor of his two-story cement-block house, and he and the wife of this house and their children, and Hassan's family lived upstairs.

When we arrived at the house, 'Father' introduced me again to his wife of this house. I rarely saw her, and I put out my hand to shake hers. As she extended her hand, she quickly draped a kitchen cloth over it, completely covering her hand from her wrist out over the fingers. Unhesitatingly I continued to reach out my hand to hers just the same, but to my surprise, the instant I would have grasped her hand through the cloth, she pulled it back and left me shaking hands with the kitchen cloth. She giggled with embarrassment, and said something to her husband, Abdul. He and Hassan both laughed and smiled back at me.

"My first wife is very religious," said 'Father.' "She goes to Mosque and prays many times a day. After a woman is married, she should not touch any other man but her husband. She says she is very sorry but she does not want to do something for which she will have to go and pray, because she is very busy cooking dinner."

All four of us laughed, and with warm welcome to me, she then disappeared back into the kitchen. We went to the family room to talk. I listened one by one as many younger family members told of what they had been doing since my last visit. I felt very honored.

That night, as had become tradition, we ate lamb and rice for dinner, with home-made Bedouin bread. Only the men were allowed to sit at this dinner, and a few favorite younger sons. We sat cross-legged on the floor, with the huge platter of boiled and fried rice in the middle, and the large platter of roast lamb passed around the circle. No utensils are used, and I had long since learned to grab a handful of rice, squeeze it into a fat cylinder with my fingers, and opening them into a sort of cupping position, tuck my thumb down at the bottom of the cylinder of rice and pop it into my mouth. My ability to do this always brought smiles and "ahs" of approval.

Though I always took a healthy portion of roast lamb, which I love, seldom was I able to eat what I had taken until quite late in the meal, and tonight was no exception. This is because, as the guest of honor, all of the others around the circle would reach over and give me a large piece of their own shredded lamb as soon as any of them noticed that I was ready to eat another bite. The simple genuinity of this gesture has always touched me, and the love it expressed without words made every bite taste better than almost any food I could ever eat.

As we ate and talked and laughed, I could not help but think of the reality that this is how all tent-dwellers, Habiru and Judaeans had eaten in ancient times, and in the dimly lit upper room where we sat I filled my soul with the image of all of us gathered together to eat and celebrate our reunion, in the same manner our ancestors must have done in the time of Isaiah, and Solomon, and David King over all Israel. I certainly felt like a king that night.

After dinner, and more orange juice, we sat and talked of many things. It was as in olden times, sitting around together at night, telling stories to one another. This was the Bedouin way. One of the younger sons asked me a question about problems between the Palestinians and the Jews, and quickly all of the others chided him and told him that we did not talk politics with our brother David from America. I do not understand Arabic, but the instruction they were giving was clear to me, as it had happened a few times before as younger brothers grew up and joined the group for the first time.

Muhammed, who had been my translator on the first night this had happened years ago in the small West Bank village where their other two mothers lived, asked me to tell the story.

I remembered it well. It was a subtly different memory for me than for them. I had not been in my home, as they were. I was a stranger, deep into Arab territory on the West Bank, in a village which had not seen a person of my looks for three years - and that person, I was told, an archaeologist, had been found killed, presumably by persons who thought him to be a Jewish spy, not an archaeologist. Being alone in this village, I had become more than anxious when the conversation of the Village Elder, for whom Muhammed had been translating, began to ask me politically volatile questions. But my family liked this story, and as it pleased them, I turned to the young man and began again to tell of the night I was asked political questions.

"The whole village was gathered after dinner, and almost immediately I was asked by the Elder, quite abruptly, "Why is the United States helping Israel to destroy us?"

"I honestly told him 'I don't know about these things.'

"I was told of a number of very horrible things which, they said, the Israelis had done to Arab villages and Arab children. Some of them were

119

truly horrible, and I had to say, 'If these things are true, I grieve with you for these tragedies.'

"When again I was asked why the United States and the Americans were helping the Israelis who were hurting them so much, I had to tell him the truth, that I did not know if Americans were directly involved in these conflicts."

"I was told that all of the problems were caused by the presence of the Americans, and if it were not for the Americans, there would be no trouble in Palestine."

"I told the Elder of the village that I was not a very political person, and I did not know much about politics, but I knew about history, and that I was very intrigued by his thought that 'if it were not for the Americans, there would be no trouble in Palestine.'"

"I spoke of history, the history of this land here. I am an archaeologist, and the artifacts in the dirt tell their tales. The artifacts show that this land has been possessed by many, many peoples, over a long, long time, and has been much troubled. It has changed hands repeatedly throughout history, and there have been wars here, fighting over this land, and trouble, for almost all of the last five thousand years of time."

"I told him how archaeology has seen that this land was a bridge between two mighty ancient worlds: Mesopotamia and Egypt; between the riches of the Middle East and the Mediterranean nations of the West. It was a crossroads, traveled over since earliest Sumerian times. It was fought over in Old Assyrian times; and again in Old Babylonian times. Then it was overrun and taken from the Sumerians and Old Assyrians and Ammorite Babylonians by the Hittites; and taken from the Hittites by the Egyptians. Times of trouble increased. The Neo-Assyrians took it from the Egyptians, but as soon as they fell the Egyptians took it back. But then quickly it was taken by the Neo-Babylonians, who kept it only a while and then lost it to the Persians. But the Persians were troubled by Alexander of the Greeks, and after his death, it changed hands again and again through infighting among the successors of Alexander: the house of the Ptolemies in Egypt and House of Antiochus in Syria. Their troublings in this land were so frequent that a man had to ask his neighbor when he awoke in the morning 'in whose kingdom do we awaken today?' But then the Judaeans began to wax strong, and they took it for themselves again, but among the Hasmoneans and Herodians the land changed hands many times within their houses. One of the Herods finally gave the land to the Romans in exchange for his brother's throne. Even the Romans kept the land only a few hundred years.

"Finally this land was taken from the Romans by the Arabs under Mohammud, but they kept it only a few hundred years. A thousand years ago it was taken by the Seljuk Turks for a short time, and then by the European Christian Crusaders, but after less than a hundred years it changed hands again and was taken by Saladin. Arabs again had this land until less than a hundred years later the Egyptian Mamelukes took it and kept it for three hundred years. Then the Ottoman Turks took it, with great wars, and kept it until only a few generations ago. It was the British who took over control of Palestine in 1920 as a British Territory, and it was the United Nations who declared for a Free State of Israel in Palestine.

"I then told him: 'The United States is only 200 years old in all of the history of fighting over this land, and tugging it back and forth between many hands. Yet you say that if the Americans were not involved, there would be no trouble here.'

"I said: 'Tell me, how did your ancestors start wars here then, before there was a United States?'

"When Muhammed translated this last question, the Elder of the village turned and spoke excitedly to the whole group, with much waving of his hands and nodding of heads, and then abruptly he turned, and said 'Very good answer. Let's talk about something else.'"

"Since that time, I have been relieved of answering political questions."

My younger 'brother' nodded with smiles and they laughed as a few words in Arabic were exchanged.

We spoke of other things, antiquities and family, ruins in the desert and grandchildren learning to take their first steps, and had a delightful evening. When Hassan could see that I was getting tired, he told the family it was time for me to go to my hotel, and he drove me there.

As we drove through the unlit roads and then suburban streets, alternately blinded by oncoming headlights and then by the thick darkness of night, following the narrow path of his own headlights which briefly cast their light on pavement, sidewalks, empty fields, old buildings, haphazardly parked cars, telephone poles and pedestrians plodding their ways home in the dark, I thought of the evening. Having Arab friends here in Israel had never been without tension; with each passing year the tension in the land grew, and it became more difficult. With every newspaper article I would read back home about a new bombing, a new outburst of shooting, a new demonstration and riot, a new curtain restricting and limiting Arab workers and families and their travel between regions and cities and parts of cities, I thought of my 'family' here, my friends, and worried for them. When I came here, I could see nothing different, and life seemed to be going on unchanged. But I knew this was not true.

Though I was now relieved from answering political questions, and these things were not talked about among us, I knew they were a part of life more and more in this land, among these people.

Hassan looked over at me, quietly nodding along in the night, looking out the windows, peering out into the night and seeing all I could see even in the darkness, seeing as much as I could see before I would once again go back to my country and have only these memories of all I was able to see in my brief visit. I looked over at him, and we smiled at each other, the warm smile of brothers who live far apart and know how to communicate without words, who know that thoughts across even great distances are not sent in vain. Smiling, he turned back his gaze to the road, and we continued driving on into the city, the city of Jerusalem.

My morning with Moishe seemed already so far away, and yet the writing on the ostraca, living again in mighty power as his voice gave the ancient words life after twenty-six centuries buried in the dark earth - buried ever deeper and deeper as time heaped its progress and debris upon them - sounded in my mind, quietly expanding in an ever-widening echo, just as the sound waves of Moishe's voice had set them rising into the air, each syllable a vibration broadcast up and out in all directions across the land.

I had told Hassan's younger brother the story, and recounted the ancient passing of peoples and nations and armies over this land, but I had not spoken of the prophecies. I had not spoken of the things uttered which once uttered must surely come to pass, of which not one jot nor tittle could be left undone.

I had not told him that the day was fast approaching when the children of Yahweh would come to take back the place of Yahweh, to build a new House to Yahweh, which the children of the same God, only called by them Allah, would fight against in terrible fighting to keep the House of Allah from being torn down, to keep the new House of Yahweh from being built in its stead. Two sides both rallied to the same House, both believing in its roots under the same hand of Solomon, and in its holiness to their God. A frightening picture.

Yet the ostracon speaking low from out of the earth had already whispered low from out of the ground, and the children who had heard its voice were already gathering, and the day was growing late.

Tomorrow I would stand in the Rockefeller museum across from the Lion Gate of the ancient city, overlooking the Kidron Valley, and because I knew someone, I would enjoy the rare privilege of looking over the thousands of small fragments of the Dead Sea Scrolls. I would talk with my Israeli friends, and talk of scrolls, and talk of words written on scrolls.

As I loved Moishe and my many Israeli colleagues, so too I loved my Arab friends and my Bedouin brothers and sisters, mothers and father, my adoptive family. The blood and pains and tears were a vision I could not bear to even glimpse for more than a few seconds, and so I shut it out, and peered into the night passing by us along the dark streets of Jerusalem.

We reached the hotel, and Hassan got out to come around and bid me farewell. As he hugged me, his face became serious.

"My Brother, things are not as they were before here. These times are becoming very bad. You know this. Where you go, out by yourself, these places are not safe for you, looking as you do."

He took his car keys from his pocket, and opened the trunk of his sherut. Atop the boxes of jumbled accumulations lay the red and white chequered *Keffiah* he always wore, with its intricately hand-woven fringe border made patiently by his wife. He reached down and took it up, and pressed it firmly into my hands, against my chest.

"Wear this as you travel. I do not fear for you from the Israelis; they always think you are one of them. It is my people I fear will do you harm. You look too much like a wandering Jew," he smiled. "Anyone who sees this" he ran his fingers along the hand-made fringe, "knows you cannot buy this, for only from an Arab friend can you have it. Wear this, and go with God."

With many wishes for a successful and safe expedition into the desert, we hugged and I watched as he drove away into the night. I stood and watched the car's red tail lights get smaller and smaller until his car went out of view down the hill toward Jaffa Gate, and disappeared. The echo of the car's motor finally faded away, and I turned and walked across the lawns to my hotel.

Inside the hotel the night porter gave me my key. I took the elevator up to my room, and gratefully lay down on the bed a moment before getting ready for sleep. This had been a most unimaginable day. A day that could only happen in Jerusalem.

After a quick shower, I turned out the lights and climbed under my covers.

Bed felt wonderful.

My eyes closed felt wonderful.

I was exhausted by this long day.

As I lay in my bed falling into sleep, I thought of Seraiah, Yehoniah, and the last hours of Jerusalem before the Chaldean's destruction order to burn the Temple and inner city, and wondered about the instructions Seraiah's letter alluded to for the three men. I had never dreamed of such a fortuitous discovery crossing my path.

I was so close. I had actually touched a letter from Seraiah. I had confirmation of the man named Yehoniah; he was indeed steward to the High Priest. I knew part of his instructions: he was told to take the Urim and Thummim and hide them in the wilderness of Judah, and did so in the area of the Strong-Holds of David.

And, I knew two more names than I had known before the morning had dawned.

Chapter 5

Day Five: The Dead Sea Scrolls

I awoke early again, and in the cool, semi-darkness of morning, I left the hotel, walked down King David Street to Jaffa Gate. The streets were deserted; the gate empty and mine alone. Without another soul in sight, I walked into the quiet and deserted streets of the inner, old city, down past streets of tightly closed and locked shops, through the central bazaar and then up the far street to the Lion Gate at the North East end of the walled city of Jerusalem. I passed only two persons during the entire walk. What an amazingly different experience for anyone who has only known the crowding masses and deafening noise of the inner city during a busy day.

The Lion Gate itself, however, was almost never crowded, no matter what time of day. It is perhaps the least used of all the great stone gates of Jerusalem, for it opens next to the Kidron Valley which is still open land, and inside its arches are only residences and schools, not shops and colorful goods. The Jaffa Gate on the West side and the Damascus Gate in the center of the North Wall handled the greater portion of the city's foot traffic. But the Lion Gate enjoyed two significant distinctions, even if it could not boast of traffic.

First, from the Lion Gate one looks out over the entire Kidron Valley, the ancient majesty of the Mount of Olives, and sees over its rim almost all the way to the rooftops of nearby Bethany, one of Yeshua's favorite resting stops. Historically, to celebrate his last Pascha, he came down the far road on the Mount of Olives, crossed the stream which runs the length of the Kidron Valley, and came up the hill passing right through this very spot,

124

which in those days was outside the ancient city walls.

Today, on the hill almost directly across from it, across the main North road which enters the city from the Kidron, is the Rockefeller Museum: the largest and best single collection of ancient Habiru, Canaanite, Phoenician, Israelite, Judahite, Jewish and Romano-Jewish artifacts in the world. And, the official headquarters of the Department of Antiquities of the State of Israel, as well as the main repository of the priceless Dead Sea Scroll fragments.

This was my destination for the morning.

My morning walk through the inner city, unimpeded by the normal throngs in the empty streets, had brought me to the high city Lion Gate very early, too early. The Museum and Department of Antiquities would not be open for several hours.

I therefore walked as I had planned to do, down the panoramic road into the Kidron Valley which makes its way over to the early morning vegetable market where I could watch the venders and buyers negotiate today's prices on cabbages, lettuce, cucumbers, melons and a host of other farm produce. The atmosphere of a public food market such as this - unchanged and ancient as the very foods over which they haggled - was of perpetual fascination to me. As I walked past stalls and trucks and dollies loaded with boxes, I saw in such open markets of the common people the living heart of any place I could visit. Though I may never go inside many peoples' homes, everything I saw would in just a few hours be on its way in thousands of homes, one piece of green at a time, and somehow my eyes felt privileged to see this intimate view of local hearth and home life. Here I saw the tastes of the common people in what they wanted and needed every day; the fruit of the soil, the harvest of the laborers who endured the noonday sun and coaxed from the earth, water and sun the life-giving energy of the land. I love market places.

From this one, in the basin of the Kidron Valley, one could look in any direction and see the vistas of history all around. From North to South all along the East view was the Mount of Olives; from here the view of the East Wall of the city and the sealed Golden Gate rose up magnificently in the bright light of sunrise. In this Valley a thousand stories had been acted out, over the last four thousand years. I soaked in the wonders around me, both ancient and modern.

After a while, I decided it was time to walk back up the hill and wait in the gardens outside the Museum.

In front of the Museum is a semi-circle of beautiful, elevated gardens, very inviting as a prelude to the archaeological journey one would find waiting inside. A triple row of olive trees grows around this hemicycle, a formidable stand of trees. Having nothing better to do, I strolled through the grove of young olive trees. It was wonderfully peaceful.

As I reached one point along the garden, I suddenly heard a dull scratching sound somewhere nearby. I stopped and looked around. Set into

125

the ground every few dozen meters I noticed there were sunken 50-gallon drums for trash. From inside the one nearest to me I again heard the same dull, scratching sound. I walked over to investigate.

There, at the bottom of the metal drum was a hedgehog, trapped in a sunken trash barrel between old olive trees, trying to climb up and out. Delightful little creatures, they were always scurrying curiously around, sniffing into everything. Armed with thousands of spines to point at the slightest danger, they presented the ambiguous personality of seeming to fear nothing while inwardly they feared all. They carried much more protection, it seemed, than needed. This one had not yet seen me, and so it tried one more time to claw its way up to the top, which was quite far above its reach.

I took a step closer, and kneeled down to watch. The instant I knelt down and got close, the hedgehog saw me. In a flash it rolled back and curled itself into a ball, its stiff, sharp-pointed spines sticking out in all directions. The little animal had become a spiny sphere, motionless at the bottom of the barrel. Little did it understand that I could help, and wanted to help it. All it saw was my immensity, and in blind fear, it instinctively hid from my face.

I stood up, and looked around the garden among the trees until I found two fallen branches, which I carried back to the sunken drum. The hedgehog still lay motionlessly curled up at the bottom. Using the two branches as giant chopsticks with an oversize meatball, I made several unsuccessful attempts to lift it out to freedom. Finally on the fourth try, I managed to roll it up and over the drum's rim and it rolled onto the grass. I sat and watched, expecting it to uncurl and run away, but it remained in a ball, motionless where it lay.

The hedgehog stayed curled up for at least ten minutes before finding the courage to relax and open its eyes to see if it was safe. First, its nose hesitantly protruded out of the ball, then it uncurled and rolled onto its feet. For a moment it just stood there, cautiously looking around and sniffing the air, until it felt certain no danger lurked nearby. I sat motionlessly and watched as it sniffed its way along the grass between the olive trees, and waddled its way over the hill down into the Kidron valley.

After an enjoyable hour of meditation in the quiet olive garden, the Museum finally opened. As the only visitor waiting outside the door, I went in to a museum I could claim as all my own.

The collections in the Rockefeller Museum are arranged chronologically, from earliest times to latest times, and each group of cases allowed focus upon a space in time which archaeologists had divided as different and separate from the next. Some of these time periods span milleniae, while others encompass but a few hundred years. The divisions were sometimes based on cultural or technological changes within the people and their crafts, while others were sometimes based on political swings of rule. Roughly they followed the development of stone tools, the discovery of copper and bronze, and the proliferation of copper and bronze usage in its earliest, later and last centuries as a primary metal before the discovery and proliferation of an easy method of working iron. Thus were the cases labeled in large signs written in three languages: English, Arabic and Hebrew.

Yet these periods seemed also to find comfortable dimension within Biblical time periods: Neolithic, Chalcolithic and Early Bronze Age comfortably filled the primal, pre-Abrahamic years; the Middle Bronze Age began about the time of Abraham's birth and filled the Patriarchal period; about the time of the extra-Canaanite sojourn into Egypt we found the Late Bronze Age dawning, which coincidentally ended and was supplanted by the new Iron Age I just about the same time Joshua was thought to have supplanted the populations of Canaan with the families of Father Israel, and filling the period of the Judges. Then, at just the same time as the Monarchy arose with Saul, David and Solomon about 1,000 BC, the sign coincidentally noted the beginning of Iron Age II. This Age in Israel ended in exactly the year 586 BC, by notice of the large red-painted letters up on the wall, which thus signaled both the end of the Iron Age and the beginning of the Persian and Hellenistic Periods on the date of the destruction of the First Temple. After this, of course, came the Roman Period, and then a stream of times known exclusively by their majority ruling powers.

These were the terms in which we perceived time in this small corner of our ancestral world.

I rather rushed this visit, speed-viewing the Neolithic-Chalcolithic cases with their hunter-gatherer points and potteries, and then each wondrous exhibit in turn: the Bronze and Iron Ages up through the apex of Rome in this ancient land, and beyond.

Due to the collections' condensed presentation in only two small halls, each filled with half of this series of chronological cases, it created an especially fascinating historical capsule to be swallowed quite well in a minimal amount of time.

In each case could be seen immensely famous objects which were the archetypal photo illustrations of every book published on these subjects. Here I stood before the unique, 3,800 year old 'Toby mug' crafted in Tel el-Yehudiyeh style ware, its haunting face and eyes peering directly into mine. Here they all were, the real things. Here, one's eyes got to drink them in, the actual objects made by gifted ancestral hands, just sitting there on a shelf among all the other objects, nothing to even set them apart from the more common daily items surrounding them.

Of course, not every famous artifact was here. The paleo-Hebrew inscribed Kuntillet 'Ajrud *pithoi* jars, the Taanach cult stand and Khirbet el-Kom tomb paleo-Hebrew inscription, all from the tenth- to eighth-centuries

127

BC, were not here. These inscriptions and the crude painted drawings spoke of and depicted 'Yahweh and his asherah.'

Yahweh's wife.

From these and other inferences in excavated synagogues it had been learned that ancient Israelites had unquestioningly known of or believed that Yahweh had a wife, whom they worshipped with him, and whose blessings they invoked upon themselves and their loved ones. Unlike YHWH, her name had either never been revealed, or it was not preserved in the writings, and so she was spoken of only as his 'asherah' - his wife. This was an ancient teaching among Israel now openly admitted by biblical scholars, for which there was significant biblical evidence in the Bible texts, as well as the Talmud, but it was also a subject that few wanted to acknowledge or talk about, so it was just ignored. However, the Khirbet el-Kom tomb inscription, found so close to Hebron, put the belief right in the heart of Patriarchal land. I had seen abundant photos of these much-debated treasures, yet I yearned to behold the actual artifacts.

God's wife.

What a concept.

Strolling by the glass cases, I paused many times for the briefest of moments before objects famous as well as anonymous, all loved in my heart for what they were and what they represented to me from the hands of our fathers and mothers, and I drank deeply.

After my customary tour through this wonderful time capsule, I went into the back corridor and found the door marked "Employees Only" and knocked.

My friend Yohanan, a younger Israeli archaeologist, was expecting me. He cautiously opened the door a crack, and seeing it was I, let me come in. Suddenly I was behind the scenes where few visitors ever get to go.

As we walked through the inner corridor past offices and laboratories crowded with ancient vases and architectural pieces being reassembled from fragments and restored, we enjoyed our reunion. Yohanan had been doing well, and his family was healthy and safe. We quickly arrived at the Department of Archaeology office where I needed to settle the final formalities of my Limited Permit.

My Limited Permit was open for a general category of sites in the Judaean wilderness, most of which few people could imagine why I would want to go investigate. They were not very 'promising' sites for those who had to 'publish or perish,' nor even to the casual antiquity-lover who might be contented with the smallest of finds.

Most notably, they were all in horribly hot, dry, naturally hostile territory, far from many excavator's hopes of wonderful things to be found under comfortable skies within range of at least some modern conveniences. Yet I had ulterior visions, visions I could not share even with my good friend Yohanan.

I was shown several dozens of mapped, tested, but un-excavated sites. I scanned the map carefully, and chose a site which was along the trail of the Wadi Barachah, which begins south east of Jerusalem and curves deeper and deeper south and west towards the Dead Sea, until it finally emerges just north of En Gedi, the general region of 'the Strong Holds of David.' A good central camp.

"Are you sure that's where you want to dig, Dr. Holland?" the official asked me. She smiled as I nodded, and my choice was quickly entered in the book and on my permit forms. It was done.

Yohanan then escorted me back to the place I had pined to see but until now had never entered: the most important scholarly rooms, the large halls where the Dead Sea Scroll fragments are studied on tables under glass and kept in wide, shallow drawers.

We walked down a hall, down some steps, and then, with a turn in through a door, under amber lights, we were there.

Before us, everywhere I looked, were the Dead Sea Scrolls. Not the complete ones, the few which everyone always sees in the pictures. Those were across town, in the Shrine of The Book. These were the tens of thousands of scroll fragments, including the vast findings of the cave known as Q4, laid in flat drawers between silk. They were like so many partially assembled, chaotic puzzles made of corn flakes and potato chips, each with a few shriveled, fading Hebrew letters on them, placed in groups of similar materials, calligraphy, appearance and, where possible, into fragmentary reconstructions of texts and books, almost 600 of them.

As I walked down the aisle, I marveled at the miracle that any of them survived to be studied at all. Nineteen centuries in the elements had taken much, leaving only these tatters beneath my gaze. Then the Bedouin had ransacked the caves, further shattering fragile, dry parchments thought to be of no value because they were just fragments. Finally the French made arrangements with them and the Jordanian Government, on whose political soil Qumran sat, to pay five dollars and change per square centimeter of scrolls recovered, and the caves were then systematically dug and sifted, yielding their precious troves of crumbling scroll pieces, all brought here.

Though now the fragments rested serenely in drawers and flat glass cases all around me, as I continued to slowly walk down the aisle, I remembered the reality which had troubled these small shreds of sacred scrolls. Even here they had not found peace. Originally hidden in the Dead Sea caves to escape an ancient war, in 1967 they had been frantically swept from their cases and bundled off to the damp basement of a bank in Jordan to escape another war, the Six-Day War which recaptured Jerusalem. Humidity, light and rough physical handling took more toll. For many fragments, the photo plates painstakingly made by Najib Albina in the early 50's became the only means of study and translation. But even those photo plates had been damaged by moisture. Aside from the dozens which had become clouded and illegible, no one knew exactly how many damaged negatives had been actually thrown away.

I stopped and bent over to see an especially intact group of larger pieces, well rejoined and nearly complete. To me, it was beautiful. The ancient handwriting was clear and dark, unusual for the condition of most. The case next to it was empty.

As I stood again, my glance suddenly scanned the room, and I noticed that many of the glass cases were empty. Then I recalled: only the scrolls under immediate study were out from their drawers in the dim lights. Exposure further faded many writings.

"How is the work going?" I asked Yohanan. He was patiently following along behind me, aware of the initial impact a person experiences, the momentary obliviousness to all else but the scrolls.

"Oh, we're moving along just fine," he smiled. "There are two volumes almost ready to go to press, and many more reaching the end of preparation. It's still slow, but it's happening."

His words concealed great meaning. After the first decade of bulk arranging of the fragments into what appeared to be composite groupings of texts and books - about 500 in all - by the late 1950's the fragments had greedily been parceled into the hands of eight scholars who were supposed to 'within reasonable time,' transliterate the ancient Hebrew into modern Hebrew, and then translate that into their own languages - French, Italian, German and English - and publish them for the world. But this had not happened.

Handwritten transcriptions were hastily copied, preserving visible, legible phrases, words and letters, but not calligraphies or more critically, datable writing styles. The transcriptions became the basis of continuing work, and the scrolls themselves were studied less and less - perhaps a blessing in disguise. Yet the work itself was done less and less. There was little money, and life always seemed to be in the way. Only one member of the original team, John Allegro of England, published his complete assignment of fragments, yet his rushed work was so filled with errors that it required more pages to correct than had been used in its original publication.

"How is Dr. Tov?" I asked politely, still too absorbed in the presence around me to think of conversation.

"He's fine. He's in England just now, in Oxford."

What a reversal. And what a difference.

It was most remarkable, but none of the original custodial scholars of the scrolls were Jews. In a misguided original premise, someone had thought that Jews might tamper with the contents, and perhaps destroy words or phrases which might speak of Messiah, or worse yet, of Yeshua, the one called Christ. Yet the almost all Christian panel - one agnostic had been intentionally included, John Allegro - jealously hoarded their allotments of fragment groups, and for long years 'outside' scholars, no matter how high, nor how qualified, were excluded from even seeing the scrolls, much less the transcriptions or photographs of the fragments. As time passed, a little, but very little was published, then less, then nothing.

For twenty years, these scraps of ancient scrolls had lain virtually ignored, lost in attending to the pressing matters of scholar's lives and careers, and the politics of jealousy and pride.

But these men became old, and then one by one, they began to die. A new group of scholars slowly began to inherit the jealously sequestered fragments, photos and transcripts, and the precious concordance created in the 1950's of every word in context of the non-biblical fragments - still unpublished, though it was perhaps the single most useful tool ever created for studying ancient Hebrew and Aramaic. The work resumed, but access to the scrolls remained carefully secluded; exclusion kept even the best scholars outside the circle of first-hand knowledge.

During thirty years only 100 of more than 800 fragmentary scrolls were published. By 1990 fully four hundred still awaited the light which a war against Rome and nineteen centuries had denied them.

Yet despite theories of conspiracy to silence the scrolls, there had never been one. The simple human factors of apathy, lack of funding, taking on too much to do, procrastination, individual pride and jealousy had been enough to all but bury the scrolls again.

Finally new custodians had been appointed, among them Jews, and then a new Chief Editor, Emmanuel Tov, an Israeli, assisted by the American, Eugene Ulrich, and Emile Puech of France.

Then, mysteriously, what survived of the Najib Albina negatives - nearly 2,000 photo plates of most of the fragments - suddenly appeared in published form in America. The doors opened.

Now the day had come that many Israelis were working with the scrolls, and publication through the Oxford Press was steadily progressing.

And even a lowly archaeologist as I was now strolling among the cabinets and cases, breathing in the aroma of the scrolls.

I stopped and again gazed around the room, taking it all in. The great treasure trove surrounding me, for all its immensity, represented perhaps only 15 to 20 per cent of each scroll before deterioration, all that was left of the original 500-plus scrolls hidden in the caves. Much more of each was missing than preserved, and thus with the thrill of seeing each fragment came the gut-wrenching anguish of imagining what had been, and had survived until perhaps painfully recent time, but was now lost forever.

As I walked past tray after tray of glass-covered scroll fragments, I was filled with the awe of the task. It was like trying to read what was left of books printed on rolls of paper towels after someone had haphazardly splattered water on them, viciously torn at the soft pulp, and ripped away huge jagged portions of them down to the bare cardboard core, leaving only small disjointed chunks of layered pages which somewhere in time had fallen apart as so many flakes of a mouse-eaten French pastry.

Though great progress had been made with some fragments using 'roll positioning,' a new method of scrutinizing damaged edges for repetitive patterns that identified pieces of the same chunk of the roll, making it

131

possible to 'unroll and position' them accurately where they had been in the page, for a majority of the pieces the process remained much the same as a long-term chess game being played by masters. Every so often someone would return to a 'game board' and make a new move, adding a new fragment which they had identified as belonging to the growing text being slowly formed, one tiny piece at a time.

My friend showed me newly translated portions of scrolls, none of them yet published, and several entire new texts. I knew this was a great privilege: the translations were being worked out all over the globe by scholars dealing with photographs of the texts as reconstructed, and the secrecy with which the finished work was guarded before publication was still total. The fact that I was not a linguist nor in scroll research gave my friend the discretionary freedom to show me what other eyes would not see, perhaps for years. I read over them ecstatically.

They were as he said: nothing earth-shattering, but many a tantalizing turn. And, to the student who loved these things, every little morsel seemed to nourish some starving void. Here was a feast.

"So, have you basked in the glow long enough?" Yohanan smiled as we reached the far end of the hall.

"Yes, I think my feet are actually touching the floor again."

"Then come here," he beckoned me. "I want to show you the thing I alluded to in my letter."

"Yes, I wondered about that," I cajoled. "You seemed excited. What is it?"

"I made a new discovery four weeks ago," he kept walking.

"And what is that?" I inquired.

"Three new fragment joins, made on a rather rare item, a wrist tephillah, or phylactery." He took me over to a cabinet and opened a drawer. Many intact phylacteries, unrolled next to their small opened leather cases, lay beside the assembly tray of his fragmentary find.

I knew that about thirty tephillin had been found among the Dead Sea discoveries, published in several journals, but I had never seen any of them. Here they were, in front of me laying side by side in the drawer. And there, on the right side, looking for all the world like a contrived arrangement of minute bits of potato chips, was a long rectangle of little pieces with tiny black letters on them, the fragmentary wrist tephillah. Wrist tephillin differed from phylacteries worn on the Rabbi's foreheads in that all of the passages written upon them were inscribed on a single, long piece of rawhide leather, instead of several smaller pieces rolled separately.

"How do they compare to phylacteries used today?" I asked.

"Remarkably. Though they have most of the same passages from Exodus and Deuteronomy, there are a number of additional and quite different verses, quite long. They form some distinct groups."

To most people, the placement of three small pieces of decomposing leather into a puzzle would not seem cause for excitement. Yet at this late

132

stage of reconstruction, new joins were painstaking, and rare. He seemed especially elated. I didn't quite understand why.

"So what did you discover?" I asked, smiling at my friend.

"The whole thing," he said in humble awe as he gazed upon it.

I was amazed. This was not just three joins. It was his project.

"I identified the first pieces two years ago, mixed in the 'minutia' trays - the un-sorted, un-assigned, loose fragments, so small that no one really pays them much attention. I thought, 'no one will know,' and it was something I could do myself. Little by little, it's been growing. I'm not really supposed to be making joins."

"No one knows you've been doing this?" I asked incredulously.

"No. But they're just flakes. It's not such a big deal. There's a certain amount of confusion still in the assigned fragment lots - you know, the original divisions and sub-division lots? And the inventory of what's assigned, what's published, what's not assigned and what's not published is sort of incomplete. These were only flakes. Anyway, I just wanted to do something fun. I don't want to get into trouble."

"How did you recognize they were all from one text?" I asked.

"By the small size of the letters. I suspected they might be part of a tephillah. So, I started systematically scrutinizing every little fragment, and after a while, I could spot them pretty readily. They're very thin parchment, like little pieces of a potato chip. As I found more and more of them, it became possible to begin reassembly. I thought I had found as much of it as there was, and then a few weeks ago I had nothing to do for a few hours, so I decided to go rummaging again, and voila! Three more pieces. It was a rather complete tephillah already, but now it's even more complete. See, these three pieces........ here, here, and here!"

"That's wonderful!" I patted him on the back. It was wonderful. Few people could possibly imagine or appreciate how tediously difficult these random discoveries of joins could be.

"What's really thrilling is that this tephillah is one of the oldest texts found among the Dead Sea writings," he continued, gazing at it in the drawer, visibly proud.

"How old?" I asked.

"I was thinking Third, maybe Fourth century BC," he smiled. "I'm not the best paleographer, but I calculated that dating. The letters are sort of square, but then, they're a bit shriveled, and they still have a very distinctive archaic look to them. However, I would have continued to date the tephillah to about 350 BC, if I hadn't made these last joins. As I placed these last three fragments, I noticed something I hadn't seen before, on one of the other fragments."

"Oh really?" I leaned forward for a better look. "What?"

He didn't answer. After a longer-than-normal pause, I looked up from the drawer at him. He was grinning from ear to ear.

"What?" I prodded.

133

"This is the really exciting discovery!" he said with a bigger grin, as he reached for an envelope resting on the top of the cabinet.

"I accidentally touched and flipped one of my previously placed fragments - this one right here - and in the lighting of the angle as it landed, leaning against this other fragment, I thought I saw a ghost of a single letter, written on the back side. It was almost invisible, and with the poor condition of all these fragments, I wasn't sure if maybe it wasn't just a stain or a faint wrinkle. But I wanted to be sure, so, I very carefully took the whole thing over to photo lab, and made an infra red enlargement of the whole back side of this as I had assembled it. I did it by putting the whole thing on glass, getting the pieces as close together and aligned as possible, and then mounting the infra red lights and camera underneath."

"So what did you find?" I asked in exasperation.

"This," he said triumphantly pulling an 8"x10" photograph out of the envelope.

The infra red photography had revealed an entire, additional body of writing on the back side of the tiny scroll.

"A palimpsest!" I blurted out.

"Yes! A palimpsest." he affirmed.

"And guess what?" he grinned even more.

"What?" I begged.

"It's signed!" he beamed, and pointed down at the bottom.

This writing was unlike a normal tephillah or Torah scroll, which always had horizontal lines creased into the leather on which the scribes wrote in almost perfect script. As my eyes were gathering, this writing was uneven, without ruled lines.

"A letter?" I asked hesitantly.

"Yes, from Seraiah ben Azariah, the last High Priest of the First Temple!" he declared proudly.

I was stunned.

Could it be possible?

I took the photograph unbelievingly.

Things like this just didn't happen.

Only yesterday I had helped Moishe uncover the two pottery ostraca written by Seraiah, and here today was now another document by his hand.

If I could have let out a whoop, I would have, but this was the scholarly hall of the Dead Sea Scrolls, and one spoke in hushes and whispers here.

"Are you sure?" I asked incredulously.

"The writing is so faded," he told me, "that except for the one letter I barely could see in the cross lighting, you can't see anything on any of the other fragments. It's totally gone to the naked eye. Look how scratchy the writing is. This was done with a make-shift pen and make-shift ink. No wonder it faded out. I had never suspected there might be a secondary-use palimpsest on it because of what it is: a tephillah. But here it is."

"So what does it say?" I asked, unable to to tell him of what I already knew about Seraiah.

"That's the really amazing part," he grinned some more. "There are a lot of *lacunae* as you can see here: missing parts - a lot of individual letters gone, some groups of letters, in some cases an entire word - but it's essentially complete."

He motioned over his treasure for me to appreciate its completeness.

"Because of the prescribed tephillin passages from the Books of Moses on the front side - which are easily placed together with precise spatial relationship from the Torah - it's been possible to make a very accurate configuration of what's here, so I'm pretty sure of exactly what's missing.

"What does it say?" I was almost begging now.

He reached into the manila envelope again and pulled out a typed page. With a deliciously smug smile he handed it to me.

"I think Seraiah wrote this just before he was executed at Riblah," he said as I took the page in my hands.

I read in growing exhilaration the words before me, which even though fragmentary, told me more than I had ever hoped to learn.

"To my (*)t(***)rd Yeh(**)iah
deli(**)r the sticks y(**) ha(*)e hid(***)
and instruct Es(**)iah ben Zado(* **** ***)
and J(**)ona(*)ab b(**) (**)bazi(***)h who
sh(***) await you (*)y the Va(****) Gate
to take (****) eve(*) unto (*)r Ham(**)lach
where (***)y may be pr(***)rved,
and (***) Y(**)onia(*) on y(***) oa(**)
take (*** ****) stones of (*** ******)
(****) the Wild(****)ss (**) Haz(**)on-tam(**)
where the (**** ***) guide you, that (**)
(***) may rest until (***) return.
"Prepare (** ***) way (** ***) Lord,
make straight (** ***) desert
(*) highway (**) our God."
By (** ***) hand, Seraiah ben A(*)ar(***)"

"I'm having trouble filling in the holes," I told him. "Have you made a reconstruction of the *lacunae* yet?" I asked hopefully.

"Well, you know how restorations go. Five different scholars will give you five different reconstructions, and then if you ever find a complete text, it's different. But the reconstruction of the lacunae I've suggested in this next sheet," he now pulled out a second typed sheet from the envelope, "seems to fit rather straightforwardly."

He held out the sheet for me to see.

"I don't think there will be much argument at all. Anyway, the last part of it is a quotation from Isaiah, and it reads almost verbatim with what we have in the Qumran Great Isaiah scroll 1QIsa."

I took the second sheet, with his reconstructed, almost complete reading, and carefully drank in the words:

"To my steward Yehoniah,
deliver the sticks you have hidden
and instruct Essaiah ben Zadok *** ***
and Jehonadab ben Habaziniah, who
shall await you by the Valley Gate
to take them even unto Ir Hammelach
where they may be there preserved,
and you, Yehoniah, upon your oath,
take the **** stones of the ******
into the Wilderness of Hazazon-tamar
where the Lord may guide you, that there
they may rest until my return.
Prepare ye the way of the Lord,
make straight in the desert
a highway to our God
By my own hand, Seraiah ben Azariah"

"What does it mean?" I inquired.

"Well, on the back side of this tephillah, or phylactery, the High Priest Seraiah has written a letter to a man called Yehoniah, his house steward, a Levite, ordering him to deliver the Temple scrolls to an Essaiah ben Zadok who is to take them to Ir Hammelach for safe keeping, and some other instruction which is unintelligible to me, something of stone which is to be hidden, but I don't know what or where. The scrolls, however, are to be guarded and protected by Jehonadab ben Habaziniah, a Rechabite, who is to find them shelter in the Lord away from the enemy, at Ir Hammelach."

"Where is Ir Hammelach?" I asked.

"That's the City of Salt," he grinned.

The name electrified me.

"In the Covenant of Salt," I whispered in amazement.

"What?" he asked.

"Oh, the name 'City of Salt' made me think of the 'Covenant of Salt,' you know, the thing mentioned in the book 'In the Wilderness,' Numbers, about eating salt? It had to do with making and keeping an oath, an unbreakable covenant. Where is the City of Salt?"

He grinned more broadly.

"It's the real name of Khirbet Qumran!" he replied.

"You're kidding?" I was astonished. "But I thought the oldest scrolls found there only date back to the early 3rd century BC!"

"That's mostly true, but you know how these scroll datings are argued: usually as late as possible, in spite of the prestige of an earlier date.

Remember Zeitlin? He was still arguing an 11th-century A.D. date for these scrolls long after archaeological and paleographic evidence proved they were pre-Herodian. And the linguists didn't even blush when major books of extra-biblical pseudepigrapha and apocrypha they had always denounced as 'definitely Medieval' works were proven to be part of biblical, Temple-era Judaism, because copies were found within these scrolls. The cave copies proved the books to be a thousand years older than the linguists had assured us. The originals are still older. How old? We don't know. Until the proofs are found, everything is said to be later. Even with the proofs, scholars are still stubborn. You should see what happened with the C14 testing."

"I thought Carbon 14 testing validated everything," I said.

"That's how it was told publicly. They tested almost nothing, and the results were hushed, glossed over and empirically ignored, because they came out older."

"How much older?" I asked.

"Two Masada scroll fragments - both dated by handwriting theories to no earlier than 30 B.C. - were tested by Carbon 14 method: one passed close to muster; the other showed to be as early as 193 B.C.! Much earlier! Yet in spite of a C14 date of 193 B.C. they still call it '30 B.C.' Why do Carbon 14, then? And did you know, that out of the over 800 scrolls found in the eleven caves in the general Qumran area, only eight scrolls were Carbon 14 tested? Only eight scrolls! That's only one percent of all of this, and they stopped testing! One of the eight scrolls they took to Zurich was a copy of the *Testament of Kohath*, and it yielded a median C14 dating of about 370 B.C.! You know how C14 works - a mid point in a bracket of a couple hundred years - the scroll could actually be a century older, 450 B.C., easily. However, C14 is ignored and *Kohath* is still affirmed as about a 150 B.C. scroll. Even though C14 testing showed almost all of the eight scrolls to be probably much older than paleographers say by handwriting theories, the later dates still remain on them. Don't ask me why. However, there have always been a few academics who argue for the earlier dates based on parallel evidence. Carbon 14, paleography and linguistics are inexact sciences at best."

"So how old are these scrolls, then?" I inquired.

"Though not one scroll is an original except the Copper Scrolls - all of the parchment and papyri are scribal copies - most of them are Hasmonean copies, maybe 250 BC earliest. There are some scholars, though, even before the C14 dating of the *Kohath* scroll to 370 B.C., who want to date a number of the scrolls here to as early as 450 B.C., even though they are not originals, based also on paleography and linguistic evidences. Actually, there are several, universally uncontested older scrolls, small fragments, which have been positively identified as being very, very old. There are a number of really old things in all of this. But this tephillah here is by far the oldest scroll now. It dates to about the same time as the other 'oldest document' of all the scroll finds: the Wadi Murabba'at papyrus found in

1952."

"What's that?" I asked.

"It was found in one of the caves which Simon Bar-Kosiba's men used as a hide-out during the Second Jewish War in Roman times, and it's still one of the unexplained anomalies, because it's so old. The papyrus has four names on it with some numbers, nothing more, and it's securely dated by paleography to the early 6th century BC, the time of Jeremiah, just before the Captivity, like this tephillah. Interestingly enough, it also has a very faint palimpsest underneath the list of names, much earlier, dated to the time of Isaiah, mid to early eighth-century BC, so its re-use in Jeremiah's time is over a pretty old document. But that's mostly illegible."

"So what does this discovery of Seraiah's tephillah in Qumran mean?" I asked, looking back at the translation of the letter, and then down at the ancient fragments in the drawer only inches away.

"This palimpsest written on the back of this tephillah may suggest the beginnings of the Essenes, and of the 'Covenanters' at just the time that Gaster, Rabinowitz and Walker originally proposed, at the destruction of First Temple. More importantly, it indicates the hiding of the scrolls from the Temple in Jerusalem at Qumran, as a sacred commission created by the crisis of the Babylonian conquest and the Deportation," he beamed.

"So are you saying that the Qumran community was started in the sixth century BC?" I asked.

"No, the buildings were in ruins and uninhabited from 586 BC to Hasmonean times, early second-century BC," he said. "And we're pretty sure now that the first Hasmonean use was non-religious."

"But if the First Temple scrolls were hidden there....."

"They would have been safe with or without sentinels," he affirmed. "They could have been hidden and retrieved later."

"You think they were retrieved?"

"Without a doubt. And an important secret was handed down: in time of crisis, there was a place for securing the writings of Judah. It had worked before; it could work again," he said.

"I always thought the Qumran group that left these scrolls were Essenes, a sect of priests and scholars, devoted to the purity of the Temple and the Law, and that Qumran was basically a Yeshiva, sort of a scriptorium and a kibbutz," I confessed.

"In 1947 when Dr. Sukenik saw the first three intact scrolls, including the 'Rules of the Community' scroll, he instantly thought of the Essenes, a fraternity of pious separatist Jews, and suggested the scrolls were probably Essene, because of the mention of the tribe of Essenes down by the Dead Sea in Pliny's old Roman history. However, two big problems: Pliny distinctly locates the tribe much farther south, right by En Gedi, midway down the coast. He describes En Gedi distinctly, qualifying its agricultural fertility for that region. Only a couple of centuries later, Dio Chrysotom places them even further south - *'near Sodom,'* he said - which has always traditionally been located all the way down at the south end of the Dead Sea. As you know, Qumran is at the top, the north end. Let's face it: all the ancient topographs are pretty accurate, right down to naming little villages so small we don't even know about them any more. How can we suddenly claim gross geographic vagueness and blundering just because it pleases the paradigm? The other big problem is that as Pliny tells of this amazing, isolated sect that has no women or children and has 'only palm trees for companions,' he carefully emphasizes to his readers that they are just above what had *'formerly'* been En Gedi, and that the town is now an abandoned ash-heap - *just like Jerusalem is now a pile of ashes,* he says. This was a post-war setting. In other words, Pliny recorded someone's observations of a tribe of Essenes near the *ruins of En Gedi*, after the fall of Masada, when Jerusalem had been burned and destroyed by the Romans. Pliny's Essenes were twenty kilometers down the coast and have to have settled near the ashes of En Gedi after 74 A.D."

"I don't get it. What's the problem with that?"

"Pliny's history describes Judaea as it was in 77 A.D., four years after the Roman War, nine years after Qumran was in ruins. There was no Ir Hammelach any more."

"Ah-haaa!" I acknowledged. "I see the point. But didn't Essenes live at Qumran before the war? Didn't the excavations prove that?"

"When the Khirbet Qumran ruin was first partially excavated, in 1952, the 'Essene' theory for both the scrolls and the ruins was already enshrined. It had already become the *a priori* story - scrolls were found in the desert, so they had to be Essene; there are ruins nearby, so they have to be where the Essenes who made the scrolls lived. Tautologies bloom that way: once you fix the *a priori*, any and all evidence is massaged, tortured, made to fit with a shoehorn, or silenced. Even though the Qumran ruins had twice before been charted, once as a Judahite fortress and once later as a Roman fortress, when the French scholar in charge of the dig came, Father de Vaux - a celibate, medieval-style monk who wore the old brown robes with white rope sash and everything, bent on proving that celibate monks like himself had made these scrolls and lived there - he quickly styled Qumran a monastic religious center, because the scrolls had been found in the nearby caves. There were no excavated evidences of a monastic sectarian habitation there. But the die was cast. All the early theories thereafter championed the Essenes as the 'Qumran Sect:' the monks and scribes of a 'Qumran Monastery.' Father de Vaux wanted to see monks like himself in the discoveries, and he and Father Milik and almost all the others obliged him in every story they published. Even the *Zadokite Damascus Document* has been made to fit the *a priori* paradigm: though it speaks clearly of its writers going to Damascus - a perfectly good ancient city and quite credible destination - the theory has flatly pronounced that 'Damascus means *Qumran.*' It's an obsession, and it goes on."

"So what do the final excavation reports say?" I inquired.

"De Vaux never finished or published the final excavation reports, but a review of the original data evidences the villa was an early Judahite military outpost, and then a Hasmonean fortress, not a monastery: strategic view of the entire north end of the Dead Sea and both coasts; heavily reinforced walls; three-story military defensive tower. Most importantly, excavations revealed heavy siege by the Romans, apparently over an extended attack. The Romans finally got in and took the place by literally digging tunnels under the walls. In other words, the Romans didn't just walk in and take it - it was tenaciously defended, with prolonged fighting by its occupants. The Essenes are well known by all ancient sources to have been more than just pacifists: they shunned all weapons, forbid all weapons, and even forbid any crafts which could 'lead to mischief' - weapon making; yet Qumran has a forge, a big one. Real Essenes would neither have had the weapons to make such a stand, nor the religious persuasion to do so. Thus we have to ask, who was there, that held out and fought the Romans so hard and so long?"

"Who was it then?" I asked.

"Certainly Jews, certainly nationalistic Jews who believed in Israel, the Torah, the scrolls and in the Temple. Certainly there were religious Jews in the garrison who observed the Law, as evidenced by the presence of a *mikveh*, a ritual washing and purifying pool. But why not expect that in a Jewish, Temple-era fortress? These soldiers were protecting the country; they had a right to ritual purity, too. And certainly, they were Jews with wives and children, as the cemetery next to the ruins abundantly attests. But it seems clear that it was not a Yeshiva, not a 'monastery' of monks as de Vaux dreamed it to be."

"But what about the clay jars found there, just like the ones the scrolls were buried in? And the inkwells in the 'scriptorium?'"

"The jars are real, and there's every evidence that a few storage jars from the fortress community were given to help the frantic priests, or Essenes, or who ever it was who put the few Q1 scrolls into the few jars hidden in that one cave. But my gosh, remember: it was only one cave in eleven caves, and only a few scrolls were in jars among almost ninety scrolls in that cave. None of the others were in jars. Think: over 800 scrolls found in eleven caves spread over the wide 'north end desert' coming from Jerusalem, and most of them only wrapped in linen, if protected at all. There were only a few jars, in only one cave. The biggest cache of scrolls, Cave 4, which had almost 600 texts in it, had no jars at all; the scrolls were actually buried directly under dirt. If you want to talk about jars, remember: a big pottery kiln was found in the garrison ruins. Whoever was there could have made all the pottery jars they wanted. The war was a long time coming to Qumran, at least two years. Remember, the rebellion erupted in 66. Jerusalem was a long time in falling; the end took weeks of mop-up before the Romans headed down toward Masada to route the Zealots there. So, the advance of the Romans was no last-minute surprise. If this was the planned community act of a united *Yahad* living at Qumran, why didn't they quickly make a lot of jars, enough to properly protect *all* of the scrolls? As for the 'scriptorium,' it's now recognized as a 'triclinium,' a Hellenistic dining room for officers and visiting superiors from Jerusalem, much nicer than the mess hall for the garrisoned troops and their families. You study Roman history; you know how it was: the upper class loved to read and write as they reclined and relaxed in the triclinium. Very military. A few handy inkwells for responding to frequent communiques from Jerusalem, for writing out regular reports, letters, and the like, just as you would expect in the triclinium of a camp with officers commanding a few hundred souls. But while they found inkwells, there wasn't a scrap of papyrus or any other writing stock, or scroll fragments, as were found at Masada. It was a triclinium."

"So where did all of the scrolls get copied?"

"They didn't, at least not at Qumran. Just look at the scrolls in these cases. With over 850 scrolls identified now, over 90% are by a unique hand. From Cave 4 alone there are over 500 different handwritings in only about 580 scrolls: virtually every one is by a different hand. The twenty-one copies of Isaiah found in Cave 4? All by different hands. Thirty-six copies of Psalms - all by different hands. None of the scrolls are original first writings, either; they're all copies of earlier originals. These aren't multiple duplicate copies made over and over again by the same scribes. Each is an individual copy, each by a different scribe. It makes no sense unless it's a gathering. And yet all of the evidence has been manipulated to fit the paradigm of the first imagination, and what doesn't fit by manipulation, is ignored.

"One of the biggest issues that's arising is the virtually total absence of 'community and personal' documents among all of this religious literature. Jews were just like everybody else in that regard: they wrote personal letters, and had private documents. Knowing as we do that the Essenes, once officially admitted to the Yahad, gave all of their property to the organization, there should have been volumes of receipts, deeds, titles of ownership, leases, legal documents regarding family matters and relationships, witnessed testaments of legal proceedings, that sort of thing - the sort of writings which are the bulk of such community papers. That was the finding in the Jewish settlement in Yeb in Egypt, the Wadi Murabba'at papyri from the Bar Kochba war against Rome, the vast Cairo Genizeh find, and dozens of non-Jewish community discoveries. If a religious community living a few hundred yards away from the caves had grabbed all of its important papers and stashed them, where are all of the personal papers and community records of finances, titles to income properties, letters to other groups of Essenes, purchases of foods, materials, and all that should have expectedly been stashed with the precious scrolls?

"Then you have to balance the fact that almost all Essenes were celibate men, yet none of these scrolls speak of celibacy, and in fact many of these sectarian scrolls declare the purpose of purity as being the guarantee to the

141

holy of righteous 'seeds' - abundant children. Not very Essenic. And then there's the cemetery: so many, many graves of women and children. The evidences just keep stacking up."

"So there were no Essene scrolls really found at all?" I asked.

"To the contrary. There are many that are probably Essene. But you see, the Essenes lived all over Judaea; many of them even lived in Jerusalem. The famous 'Essene Gate' in the walls of Jerusalem was just recently found, just wide enough for one person at a time to squeeze through - it was for Essenes to leave the city to use their toilets, just as we read in one of the scrolls of 'Rules.' In other words, those Rules were for Essenes to follow in all of the places they lived, including all of the Essenes living in Jerusalem."

"A special gate was built in the walls of Jerusalem just for the Essenes to go outside the city to use toilets?"

"The Essenes were a very important group of Jews at the time: we've learned a lot about them through this find. They called themselves 'Saints;' they believed strongly in Israel as God's true people; they were very Messianic and believed completely in the imminent coming of the Messiah, as did many other Jews at the time, but they were readying for his coming; they believed in a purified Temple with an undefiled priesthood; they gave all that they had to the 'community,' which meant the entire Essene following all over Judaea, sort of a 'united order;' they did indeed love the scrolls and were noted for studying the scrolls and for having libraries. But then again, even private Jews had libraries, as did Synagogues, and the Temple; they believed in angels and demons and the ultimate war between good and evil; they believed in a celestial Temple to be built in the last days; they believed that Piety was necessary above all things and that if one had to go out into the desert to establish it, even by a lake of salt water, that was OK. Yet Josephus was clear about the fact that Essenes lived in most cities in Judaea, with many in Jerusalem. They were well known, the 'Third Sect' of Judaism.

"The group of surviving Essenes Pliny wrote of after the war with Rome were living in isolation down by the ruins of En Gedi, by the great Salt Sea. Yet as more of the sectarian scrolls found in the eleven caves are published, even these from Cave 4, we see the doctrines and laws in these scrolls are not just Essene, but Sadducean, Pharisean, Zealot, and some we can't place at all. The religious laws conflict with each other, from one scroll text to the next. Judaism was very sectarian, it seems. And yet, many of the hymns, songs and poetry, as well as other literature, are entirely non-sectarian: they're just good, beautiful Jewish writing from the time. These were not the unified, copied duplicates of a single sect, but the gathered writings of an entire generation, from all the varying Judaisms of Israel, hidden under siege of war.

"Obviously, scrolls survived, either in Judaea, or with Jews in the diaspora outside Judaea, because the Council of Jamnia had scrolls to edit and canonize as a Bible only a few decades after the loss of Temple. But these scrolls, here, these were left out, and eventually lost, or, perhaps the rabbis at Jamnia only had what they had, and they didn't have all this, because it was in the caves at Qumran. It's been so much easier for orthodox Judaism and orthodox Christianity to pretend that all this belonged to some radical splinter group, because then they don't have to deal with it in coming to terms with the real roots of their current beliefs, many of which have drifted substantially in dogmatic ways; but these scrolls reflect what Judaism was, and what immediate pre-Christian Jews believed. That's what's so exciting! The Essenes are still the Essenes, and everything about them is true, and remains important and beautiful as we come to understand the thinking of a very special group, yet the truth about the scrolls as a whole, a gathering of Judaism, reveals even more profound truths than the myth. It's wonderful."

"A lot of books are going to have to be re-written," I whistled.

"They will be. People have to let go of myths. The pieces of the puzzle are all real, there's no doubt about that. But the story putting it all together has been contrived and manipulated to preserve a paradigm. We have the artifacts and remains of a ruin alright: it was inhabited; and nearby in the cliff's caves, we have found hundreds of scrolls. However, the paradigm and story that was structured to link them all together is a wishful making of those who wanted to believe in it. A group of Essene monks may have come with scrolls to hide like so many others, perhaps even been given shelter in the fortress at the end, but this wasn't the 'mother camp' of the Essenes. The caves were a known hiding place, and as we have found, many books were brought and hidden up. We just need to see the true paradigm. Reality will prevail."

"How long do you think it will be before the truth prevails?"

"Well, an entire generation of Israel had to die off in the Wilderness before their children could go to the Promised Land. It was the same problem. Those who were raised on the myths of Egypt refused to let go of the old false beliefs. I think the next generation will make it to this promised land. It's a bright horizon. And, there are still a lot of unanswered questions to work out in the puzzle. The Copper Scrolls alone provide decades of site hunting and research. De Vaux said the Copper Scrolls with their detailed descriptions of myriad caches of treasures and scrolls scattered all around Jerusalem in caves and tombs was a fiction, of fantasy treasures. It's not. It's very real. Everyone knows that now. It's likely that Origen's mid second-century A.D. discovery of Hebrew scrolls in a jar in a cave near Jericho is the very jar of scrolls which the Copper Scrolls says was hidden there. They speak of other caches of scrolls, too. Another one near Jericho we can be pretty sure was already found in the eighth century, recorded by the Nestorian Patriarch Timotheus I, in another, larger cave, near Jericho, just as the Copper Scrolls say. Traditional Qumranology says that 'near Jericho' means Qumran, denying any other place could have been a cache; but that's seven miles south of Jericho in days of foot travel, not close at all. Again, ancient topographs have a habit of being painfully accurate - that's what makes them so useful to archaeology. The tide has turned on the Copper Scrolls; the tide will turn on the Qumran ruins and these scrolls, too."

"So," I shrugged, looking around the room with a new consciousness, "the scrolls weren't all copied by scribes at Qumran."

"It appears they weren't," he shook his head.

"Then where did they come from?" I asked.

"Probably from all over Jerusalem, and from synagogues all around Judaea. Rome was ransacking the country in war, destroying every symbol of Judaism they could lay their hands on. The scrolls must have been hurriedly taken to the caves around Ir Hammelach again, the City of Salt of Herod's day. Isn't it significant that the Jews as a whole were anxious to preserve their writings, and hiding scrolls for later recovery is a very 'Jewish thing?' Dr. Golb has been proposing that for decades; he's probably right. There were and still may be other hiding places, too. Maybe the question we should be asking is what designated Ir Hammelach as one of the primary places to hide scrolls from the enemy?"

"So does this palimpsest of Seraiah help?" I asked.

"Perhaps. When I found the name Essaiah ben Zadok and Jehonadab ben Habaziniah, I immediately thought of the papyrus list of names from Wadi Murabba'at. It was always thought to be the oldest document from the entire body of material out of all the caves, definitely First Temple time. This tephillah text itself is probably late seventh-century writing; it's now the oldest from Qumran. But the letter on the back has to have been written in 586 BC, probably in August, probably right at the destruction of First Temple."

"What did you find, on the Wadi Murabba'at list?" I asked.

"Neither of these names appear in the Murabba'at papyrus."

"May I see it, the list of names?" I requested.

He took me over to the book shelf in the corner, pulled out a large volume, and thumbed through the pages. It was in French.

"Here it is," he pointed as he located it.

I looked down at the photo of the small grayish brown papyrus. Four lines of Hebrew were visible on it, and nothing else.

"What are the names?" I asked him.

"Let me see," he said, and read the papyrus for me.

"We have a Nimtar ben Hausi; and an 'Abi ben Sabi; an 'Il'ada ben Karshon and Sama'yahu ben Yau'azar," he said and gently laid the book on the table. "Each one with a number. Nobody we know."

"These names don't match up with any other documents or writings?" I asked.

"No, I've checked exhaustively. But you have to appreciate that very little has come down to us from First Temple days, much less the siege decades of Nebuchadnezzar. These are apparently just common people, part

144

of the otherwise nameless masses. When I found the tephillah palimpsest a few weeks ago, I thought it might bring this piece of the puzzle into focus."

"Does it?" I asked.

"I think it still may be relevant," he replied.

I thought a long moment, knowing I could not divulge what I knew from Moishe's ostracon.

"Really!" I mused and stood back philosophically. But I could see Yohanan was not finished. "What do you think?" I asked him.

"The tephillah palimpsest clearly gives an order to hide the Temple scrolls. Was it ever carried out? I don't know. I know of ancient traditions and stories mysteriously alluding to vast treasures of gold and silver - the Temple treasury - hidden from the Babylonians. Why not the scrolls? Why not believe that this list of names is a detail of men whom this Essaiah ben Zadok and Jehonadab ben Habaziniah took with them as body-guards for the scrolls from the Temple, hiking cross-country to the City of Salt, to Qumran? There probably would have been a lot of scrolls to carry."

"How many scrolls would there have been?" I asked.

"Easily thirty, maybe more. We can assume that after Josiah's public reading of the Book of the Law which somehow escaped the desecrations of Manasseh and Amon and was found hidden in the Temple in 621 BC, that he would have searched and scoured the land for copies of other scrolls that had survived, and gathered and copied all of the relevant national writings he could have found, to restore copies to the Temple library. We know that even in those days many private people owned 'popular copies' of the scrolls and kept them in their homes. There were a lot of literate people in Israel in the seventh century, many priests, many scribes, many wealthy men who feared God, or whose fathers had feared God, who kept family genealogies and other records. In the frenzy of Josiah's reforms, wouldn't he have sought other 'old books?' People may have even brought their scrolls to Josiah and loaned them to the King to be copied, and received royal favor. It's happened in other places. Pergamum. Alexandria. Josiah started a scavenge hunt, I'm sure."

"I don't remember any mention in the histories of Josiah finding other scrolls," I confessed.

"Just because there's no mention of it in the histories, should we rule out something so logical that it must have happened? In the second century B.C. after the Jewish revolt against Antiochus, Macabbees says that a search was made for books, and every writing that could be gathered was brought to the Temple, where a library was again formed. We know that shortly after the rebuilding of the Second Temple, a library suddenly materialized. Think: by the time Seraiah was High Priest, who knows how many scrolls, or what size of a 'library' might have been assembled in the First Temple?"

"What scrolls would they have had?" I asked him.

"Lots. In 600 BC there were dozens of early texts and literary scrolls long in existence: histories of Adam and the Patriarchs; histories of Moses;

the Book of the Covenant; histories of the Judges and the Kings; the writings of the prophets: Amos, Hosea, Isaiah and Michah; maybe other prophets which are lost - Nathan, Gad the Seer, Ahijah the Shilonite, Iddo the Seer and others. Look at all the new names and writings we've learned of in these Dead Sea discoveries. It's obvious we've lost so much. There were certainly original written histories of Saul, David and Solomon."

"Some people think Saul and David and Solomon are myths."

"Just a few years ago at Tel Dan they found a basalt stone inscription in paleo-Aramaic, from the 9th century BC, which boldly speaks of 'The House of David' and 'King of Israel' in the same breath. The discoveries keep coming. We know that there were genealogies, and other historical records, accounts of the Kings of Judah and the Kings of Israel. Hezekiah's historicity is validated by the Siloam tunnel inscription. Think of it: if he had that carved in the rock in the midst of a desperate war, why wouldn't he and the other kings have commanded full records kept on scrolls, which was easy by comparison? They must have. All the ancient kingdoms kept records, since writing began. Inscriptions in stone and clay tablets survive, and papyrus and leather survive in dry places. But let's face it - most of the records of the ancient world have been lost. The only reason we have the Sumerian, Hittite, Assyrian, Babylonian, Persian and other Mesopotamian records is because they wrote on clay, which survived the elements. The climate in Egypt preserved a few precious papyri, but they wrote a lot on stone. The Israelites wrote everything on leather, and it just rotted away. What you see in this room survived because it was hidden away in caves intentionally, for protection, and most of it hasn't survived. All we have are these fragments. So we haven't found any of the old, original texts. Is that reason to conclude that there were no early writings?"

"But weren't a lot of the stories memorized and told by word of mouth, you know, the 'Oral Tradition?'" I asked.

"Yes, absolutely. But think: the Proto-Sinatic alphabet was already in use by 1500 BC, and the archaic Hebrew alphabet and written language was fully developed and flowering by 1,000 BC. My gosh, the Gezer Calendar was a schoolboy's lesson text! We're talking about an alphabetic system and highly literate people in early times. History shows that when people can write, they do. Kings record their deeds; priests write liturgies and prayers; prophets write visions; storytellers tell stories. There had to be lots of writings. Israelites had wealth. Money pays for scribes to copy books and records. People had copies, for prestige, for teaching their sons, for family piety. If Josiah was so impressed with one book, the Temple certainly would have gathered and copied scrolls from all around the land. It makes no sense to think otherwise."

"Yes" I agreed, "and as you reconstruct this text, the order to take and hide them is here on this tephillah. But you don't know if it was carried out. Is there any way to securely tie these two documents together, the palimpsest and the list here?"

146

"I don't know that there is, but I don't know that it's necessary. A lot of people fled the land in the days of Nebuchadnezzar. The list gives numbers after each name: 14, 10, 5 and 6. After each number is a little mark, which looks like the archaic Hebrew letter 's.' The translator suggests the 's' may represent *'seah,'* measures of grain, but he's uncertain; he actually adds a question mark in parentheses, see here? What if it was 's' for *'sefarim:'* scrolls?

"Fourteen thin *sefarim.*

"Ten medium sized *sefarim.*

"Five big *sefarim.*

"Six big *sefarim.*

Each man was loaded with what he could carry. The Wadi Murabba'at caves are very high up, very hard to reach. Why would a grain list be there? It took a lot of climbing to leave this list in the cave. If left by people fleeing Nebuchadnezzar, what were they carrying? They were fleeing with something."

"Perhaps with scrolls," I smiled.

"They could have become the followers of Essaiah ben Zadok," he grinned back at me. "The first 'Covenanters.'"

"Sure," I said, savoring the moment, "And after Cyrus allowed the Jews to return, and the Second Temple was finished, their descendents might have taken the scrolls back to Jerusalem."

"Where," his voice softened and he spoke more passionately, "they would have been expecting to become the core of the new Temple Priesthood, because of their holdings of the precious scrolls. But there was no unity at Jerusalem, infighting was rampant, and they would have wisely held back disclosure. In the meantime, these descendents of Essaiah, the People of Essa, Zadokites not of the direct lineage but of the brother, the Covenanters who kept the scrolls, copied and compiled them, and continued to keep in contact with those who worked with the rebuilding of the Temple precinct. Two more generations arise during which time they would have kept close ties with the Temple priests, still secretly caring for the scrolls, copying aging ones, editing and compiling and writing. But still no political respect from priests, Nehemiah or the locals."

"What finally ended the standoff?"

"I think they secretly sent a copy of the Book of the Law to a relative in Babylonia, to Ezra, as proof of their claims, with a plea for authoritative support."

"Which he got from the King," I remembered.

"Yes! Ezra, Seraiah's direct descendent, suddenly gets himself elected as the new Teacher of the Second Temple by Artaxerxes, because he comes forth with a Book of the Law. The Chaldeans allowed no scrolls to be taken to Babylon: that was the whole beginning of the Oral Tradition of the Mishna and Talmud. But did the Book of the Law survive there orally? It would seem not. It's pretty clear the Law had to be re-learned by the people after its reading at the dedication of the Temple walls with Nehemiah in 444. It was entirely unknown. But Ezra comes to Jerusalem with the Book of the Law, the gold and silver treasures from the Temple, and a letter from Artaxerxes proclaiming him the supreme Priestly authority in all the land."

"With authority to judge, and to punish, whether it be unto death, or to banishment, or to confiscation of goods, or to imprisonment," I interjected.

"Exactly!" he agreed. "Where did Ezra suddenly come into possession of a Book of the Law in Babylon? Not too long after the arrival in Jerusalem, we read that Ezra has put Nehemiah in charge of a new library of all the sacred books 'which were gathered.' Where did copies of all the other books come from later in a burned-out Jerusalem? Perhaps we now know! After the popular reception of the one book, the Covenanters might have revealed to Ezra their entire holdings, hoping to be given authority. He may have simply taken the scrolls from them as his entitled family property, which they were, and when they protested, excluded them from the Temple altogether. This would explain the sect's long-standing hatred of the Temple priesthood and their jealous separation from the Temple, and from Jerusalem. But they didn't give up all of the scrolls to Ezra."

"What do you mean?" I asked.

"They kept one book for themselves," he replied, "which they felt Jerusalem didn't deserve."

"Which book was that?" I asked.

"The Sixth Book of the Torah, what we call the Temple Scroll," he said. "The copy Yadin obtained, which is over at the Shrine of The Book, probably found in cave Q11, was made not much before 50 A.D. But there are fragments of two earlier copies of it here in our holdings, right in this room, found in other caves, dating to about 125 BC. It's a visionary scroll, but it's rooted in the earliest writings, and it was virtually unknown even in Herod's day. They kept it."

"Is this your own theory?" I asked.

"Yes, but you know how these things are. There are already so many theories, it's hard to get anyone to consider anything. And you know the new non-consensus policy: we're supposed to be at a standstill on new theories until the last scroll is published. Anything to protect the old paradigm a little longer! The other intern here to whom I've shown the tephillah palimpsest told me not to disclose it, period. That's easy: nobody even knows this tephillah is here. The 'flakes' it was among were either on one of Albina's photo negatives that got water damaged or that was thrown away, or he never photographed these minutia at all. He didn't photograph everything. Anyway, they're not in the photos. I checked."

"But why conceal a discovery like this?" I asked incredulously.

"This whole Qumran thing is so volatile. The other intern's right. 'They'll just say it's empty speculation,' he told me, 'because there is no proof the First Temple scrolls were in fact removed and successfully hidden.' It's just a theory. No one wants to hear of an 'earlier' hypothesis for the scrolls because it derails all the constructions of the textual theorists. But what are all the theories and arguments today? It's scholar against scholar, and none of them has any definitive proof, so what should any of us believe? Was the Qumran ruin a monastery of monks? Were the scrolls the sectarian writings of the Pharisees? The Saducees? The Zealots? Or the Essenes? Was there a 'Qumran Sect' at all? Or was it a private villa? A resort for the wealthy? Or a Fortress? Were the Kittim Greeks or Romans? Were the scrolls written in Hasmonean times? Was the Wicked Priest a Hasmonean? Or were they written in Christian times? And was the Wicked Priest Jesus, and the Teacher of Righteousness, John the Baptist? These are all academic theories, with scholars vying among each other for theory supremacy! What indisputable archaeological data is any of it based on? It's almost all elaborate interpretation! And what about the *unconsidered* evidence still waiting to be found in the dirt? This tephillah was there! It says there were First Temple scrolls, and they were ordered hidden! And I can't tell anybody," he sighed and looked over at me. "Except you."

I couldn't think of a single thing to say. I just shrugged towards him with an expression of exasperation, and shook my head.

"You see what's happening out there," he pointed. "There's worry about the reaction of the Palestinians, and the ultra-orthodox Rabbis who grab onto this kind of nationalistic stuff. In a sense, the older intern is right. We've already found the final generation's copies of the scrolls this palimpsest talks about. Why stir the pot? There are a lot of problems here, politically. Look at what's been happening. One archaeological discovery has already been the direct cause of bloodshed on the Temple Mount. You saw what happened when they opened the Tunnel. People got killed! Things are a mess over here. It's really been getting in the way of the work lately."

"Why do you think Seraiah used the term 'sticks' instead of 'books' or 'scrolls?'" I asked, changing the subject back to the palimpsest. I needed to learn everything I could from it.

"A number of places in the Torah use the word 'stick' for a written scroll or book. My guess here is that even though he didn't expect any of the enemy soldiers to be able to read Hebrew, he used as many unfamiliar expressions as he could, sort of a code, to safeguard the message. Nebuchadnezzar's plan was to demoralize his enemies by destroying all of their emblems of country and nationality, to strip them of any identification around which they might rally. Obviously, sacred books would be high on the list of things to destroy, along with the Temple, and the priests. The former: he destroyed; the latter: he executed. Seraiah probably died very shortly after writing this."

"What about the passage quoted from Isaiah?" I asked.

"Oh, they did things like that in those days. He probably just wanted to make the instructions seem more authoritative. A good stirring quote like that would have given courage in a time of chaos," he replied.

I could not tell him of Moishe's great discovery made only yesterday less than a mile away, nor of the Yeb Temple dedication text from Brannon's discovery. Nor did I dare tell him of my knowledge that the 'stones' were unquestionably the High Priest's Urim and Thummim. Yet I knew I needed to study every word of this letter.

"May I have a copy of the translation?" I pleaded calmly, trying to appear casual yet anxious enough to persuade, while hiding the bursting excitement I felt jumping up and down inside me.

"I will give you a copy of this text, with your promise that you will not publish it," Yohanan smiled. He knew I wouldn't. Yet it was a real problem, academics stealing glory from each other, in every field from Greek vase painters to scrolls, even to publishing borrowed papers under their own names without changing a word. It had happened before. In the scroll world things were more subtle, such as borrowing theories and tactfully shifting credit. All of these were only slightly less odious than the newest 'scroll disease,' of translators innocently slighted of mention in secondary, popular publications suddenly slamming the editors with huge lawsuits without warning, to the financial ruin of all but the lawyers. Money sorely needed for real work. But Yohanan knew that I was neither so hungry, nor so false a friend. And, I wasn't a linguist. I followed him to another room where he made a photocopy, which I slipped into my briefcase. I gratefully clicked it closed.

With this, we wished each other well, and I left.

It was later in the afternoon than I had thought.

As I reached the busy street in front of the museum, and stopped to look up at the massive stones walls of Old Jerusalem before me, my head was reeling with the impact of this discovery. I decided to forego a taxi and walk beside the high city walls to the hotel, to think about all this. It was only a little more than a mile.

I began to walk, my mind back in the past, trying to re-live the moment of Yehoniah receiving this cryptic message from Seraiah. He must have gotten it through Jeremiah, as the ostracon Moishe found yesterday had stated would be done. But Jeremiah had also been taken in chains all the way to Ramah before being released under guard to go live at Mizpah. When had he found Yehoniah? Where?

Suddenly I was knocked over backwards by a pounding shock and deafening percussion blast. Smoke filled the street; screaming people cried out everywhere; shattered bits of debris were flying through the air and falling all around me. I was near the Damascus Gate. A bomb had exploded somewhere in the street just up ahead.

Before I could even think of getting back on my feet, as the rain of grit, metal fragments and debris was still falling, gunfire erupted. People ran by me shouting and pushing, some to get away, some running toward the blast area to help those who were crying out in agony. The street was suddenly turned to chaos: shouting, screaming, crying, car engines racing, horns honking, tires squealing, guns firing, bullets whizzing overhead and ricocheting off the stone walls, sirens in the distance.

I pulled myself to my feet, and was almost knocked over by frenzied people running from the escalating riot.

The scene I beheld was terrible. Blood splattered shop walls; shattered windows littered the sidewalks; pieces of meat lay in the street beside fallen bodies and abandoned cars. Israeli soldiers were already positioned and firing at Palestinians who were firing rifles at them. Dozens of other Palestinians were throwing rocks from behind the protection of cars and trucks, and the rocks rained down around the Damascus Gate entrance. Shooting was coming from everywhere, and people were falling. Bullets flew zinging around my head, peppering the walls nearby.

As my senses recomposed, I realized this was not a place to stay. I bolted across the pavement to the nearest side street entrance and ran into it just as tear gas grenades were exploding down by the Gate. I ran half a block and saw another narrow street which would get me past the war zone and back to my hotel. I ran toward it.

But just as I turned into it I slammed headlong into a rush of young Palestinians, and I was knocked down. Yelling angrily, they began to beat me, and I momentarily thought 'this is the end of my trip.' But at the nearby blast of gunfire they instantly dispersed and ran on, leaving me sprawled on the pavement, alone.

I rolled myself onto my knees, grabbed my briefcase and fled through the streets as fast as my legs would carry me. Block after block I ran past running people, some running to, some rushing from the bombing site, until I got farther away and the shooting and yelling began to fade behind me in the distance. The streets were quickly emptying, and soon I saw almost no one as I ran on and on.

For a moment I stopped and gathered my bearings. The gun shots were far in the distance. I had reached a part of town that was virtually deserted. After determining the right direction, I walked the rest of the way to the hotel, shaken, but alive.

From the hotel, sounds of gunfire could still be heard echoing distantly in the streets.

I washed my wounds, my face and hands, and lay down on the bed, in shock of what I had just witnessed and escaped.

As the whirling in my mind slowed down, I was filled with the overpowering realization of how little things had changed since the days of Yehoniah. I saw it so clearly, *things are not so different. The war still rages.*

After I was rested, and my pulse had gone down to normal, I got up and went to the table where I opened my briefcase and took out the precious papers it contained. How lucky I was it had not been taken by the mob in the street.

I lay the translation of the new palimpsest Yohanan had just given me beside the Brannon papers with Yehoniah's Yeb Temple dedication, and beside them I set the Moishe ostracon translation I had just gotten yesterday.

As the echoing gunfire continued, I stared at the three pages with their transcripts of writings. With all three documents laid out before me on the table, I began to try to piece together what could be reassembled of the story.

For two years I had had only the Yeb ostracon, the Yehoniah dedication, which had been unverifiable. This was now validated absolutely by the Moishe Seraiah ostracon and the Dead Sea tephillah palimpsest I had seen this morning. *I, Yehoniah* had been vindicated.

From the Yeb dedication came two significant clues.

First, *I have hidden up the lights and perfections of the Lord in a resting place in the Wilderness of Judah.* It alleged the Urim and Thummim had been hidden in the Wilderness of Judah, a vast desert South of Jerusalem, extending east to the Dead Sea, a very big place.

Second, *in the Strong Holds of David.* It specified the Strong Holds of David, an area well known from history: the rocky, cave-riddled wilderness surrounding the oasis of En Gedi by the Dead Sea. This specific area, though infinitely smaller than the entire Wilderness of Judah, still covered anywhere from 25 to 50 square miles, depending on how wide a circle you drew around En Gedi. All of it was barren and rocky: a maze of canyons, hills and cliffs dotted with myriad caves.

These clues had led me to choose the specific area of this excavation, even though I had no proof of authenticity.

This morning, based on only these clues, I had made my final site selection near En Gedi.

So, I was now sure: I would be in the right general area.

I could now see that for my work, the main value of the ostraca Moishe discovered in his 'basement' was the knowledge that Yehoniah had been a real person, *until my steward Yehoniah finds you,* and that his Yeb Temple dedication had to be absolutely authentic. Brannon had not perpetrated a hoax; he had been cruelly destroyed, and a great find with him.

However, the two names I had learned, *Jehonadab ben Habaziniah,* the Rechabite and *Essaiah ben Zadok* were not proving to be of any use in solving this mystery, except as they certainly assured me of the direct tie between all three documents.

Historically, just knowing of the existence of the ostraca and of their role in a desperate mission at the fall of Jerusalem 26 centuries ago was exhilarating. But Seraiah's letter only told them *Await by Valley Gate* for instructions; and from the reading of the letter written on the back of his tephillah, it was clear that these two men were given another mission, separate from Yehoniah. The tephillah-letter's specific instruction about 'the sticks:' *take them even unto the City of Salt where they may be there preserved* left no doubt as to an early use of that site as a hiding place for sacred books. Yet this pointed only to Qumran and scrolls, a lead already exhaustively searched and richly rewarded three and four decades ago after the accidental find of the first cave of scrolls which yielded its ancient scribal treasures. The Moishe ostracon was a dead end on the Urim and Thummim.

The Seraiah tephillah palimpsest might, however, possibly provide some new clues to help narrow the Urim and Thummim enigma.

Placing it before me, I scrutinized it line by line.

The several uncompleted lacunae were easy for me to fill in with the other two documents I possessed. After ben Zadok the missing words had to be *'my nephew,'* which Seraiah had carefully noted in the Moishe ostracon. The lines referring to the scrolls were already proven by the Qumran finds.

Then came the words *you, Yehoniah, upon your oath.*

These last lines of the palimpsest were the part which made cryptic allusion to the Urim and Thummim.

I felt rather secure in completing the two lacunae here with 'sacred' or 'holy' stones... of the 'ephod.' Surely this is what was missing. The Yeb letter openly named the *'lights and perfections of the Lord.'* In this hastily written letter Seraiah had cloaked his instruction using words he perhaps hoped were too obscure for Babylonians who might intercept the letter and know some Hebrew. Thus here to Yehoniah, desperately calling upon the oath which Yehoniah so fervently spoke of as 'fulfilled' in his Temple dedication in Egypt, Seraiah had to be alluding to the sacred stones, the holy objects of the ephod, the Urim and Thummim.

Yet here in the palimpsest Seraiah instructs Yehoniah to *take the (Holy) stones of the (ephod) into the Wilderness of Hazazon-tama*r.

Where was that?

I pulled out my atlas-dictionary of Ancient Israel and looked up Hazazon-tamar.

'Hazazon of the palm trees,' it was translated. The name referred to the camp location of a large Edomite army that had marched against Jehosaphat in the 9th century BC, and that it was.... near by or perhaps synonymous with En Gedi. *Perhaps*, it said!

This was so frustrating! Though I knew it was a miracle that we knew anything about these ancient places spoken of in writings thousands of years old, still we knew so little. About these deserts we knew next to nothing. I had names, names used even in the Bible, but they had been vagueries in their time and were even greater vagueries now: the Wilderness of Judah; Hazazon-tamar; the area of En Gedi; the 'Strong Holds of David.' How could I have so many names to guide me and still know nothing of an exact place?

Yet the article said more. *Hazazon-tamar* was also associated with the ancient 'Ascent of Ziz,' a steep canyon pass connecting the Dead Sea plains near En Gedi to the inland hill valleys of Jeruel near the town of Tekoa, joining south of Bethlehem on the road to Hebron. I looked at my map. No marking of a place called The Ascent of Ziz. The book said the place may have been called the 'Ascent of Haziz,' but this too was uncertain. This, however, would place Hazazon-tamar away from En Gedi proper, somewhere within the hills and canyons. This made more sense. The Strong Holds of David would have been within the hills, not out on the flat plain at En Gedi.

The article also said that in the midst of the Ascent had been an ancient Amorite oasis settlement. The location was noted as 'uncertain,' but 'perhaps to the NW of En Gedi.' Could Seraiah's *Hazazon* be this place Haziz? The ancient Ascent of Ziz?

But then came the phrase *where the Lord may guide you* which was similar to the idea of the phrase in the Yeb dedication: *as the Lord did show me his path and his way.* After all was said and done, once he got into the general area, Yehoniah had ultimately been instructed to act on his own. Both these phrases alluded to reliance upon divine inspiration for the choice of the hiding place.

How would I find a place selected by intuition?

Lastly, here was the quotation from Isaiah. I took a sheet of paper and wrote it out: *Prepare ye the way of the Lord, make straight in the desert a highway to our God.*

I could not help but feel that Yohanan's casual dismissal of this passage as merely an authoritative encouragement was mistaken. I had seen the ostracon Seraiah had written in which he charged Jehonadab with burying the ostracon before the city walls of a fallen Jerusalem, a message to God himself to not forget his people. This was not a man who wasted words, or quotations. As the ostracon he had written quoting Deuteronomy had been for a precise purpose, I could not help but feel that this final quotation was also some sort of coded instruction to Yehoniah in carrying out his mission.

With the three ancient letters on the table in front of me, I sat and tried to piece together this final message.

The Wilderness of Judah, and especially the Strong Holds of David, was a labyrinth of wadi canyons, caves and natural ridges and citadels. The Wilderness of Hazazon-tamar, as opposed to just denoting En Gedi which was on the plain by the Dead Sea, was the area behind the oasis, in the hills and wadis and cliffs: in the wilderness. All of the references were to this stark, barren land brutally cut into jagged cliffs and canyons by nature over the eons, the wilderness.

Again I repeated the words, this time reading them out loud: *Prepare ye the way of the Lord, make straight in the desert a highway to our God.*

They said nothing to me.

How would I find such a hiding place?

I felt just as lost as before. There were hundreds of miles of wadis twisting throughout this area, and all looked virtually alike.

I glanced at my watch. It was late. Suddenly I was sleepy, very sleepy.

154

I could do no more.

There was one last thing I did before going to bed: I again studied the topographical map of the area by the Dead Sea. I poured over the elevations and cuts through the land and pondered hard. I followed ridges and wadis with my fingers, from Jerusalem south into the Wilderness, first following one way and then another, thinking, trying to imagine: *How would I have done this if I were him? Which path would I have taken?*

But I saw too much on the map. There were so many paths to En Gedi, so many square miles of hiding places, so many which on the small paper map seemed logical, and possible; within any one of them had to be hundreds of spots which could have been chosen.

Eyes drooping, sleep overpowering me, I saw the map could not speak to me.

Exhausted, I went to bed, to sleep, thinking of Yehoniah.

Suddenly I awoke. I was wet with sweat, my pillow and bed sheets soaked. For a moment I was confused, where was I?...... then I remembered. I was in Jerusalem, in my hotel. My heart was pounding. In the dark I could hear.... my breathing was labored. Why was I soaked with sweat? I felt uneasy, anxious, a mixture of anxiety and exhaustion, as if I had been running, as if I had been frightened, but I did not know why.

I turned on the light and looked around the room.

Everything was the same. Nothing was out of place.

I could remember nothing I had been dreaming, if at all I had been dreaming. The anxious feeling was beginning to dissipate.

Then I remembered today's violence in the street, by the Damascus Gate. It was terrible.

I got up and went to the window. Pulling back the drape a bit I saw the street below, empty in the lamplight, no cars, no people. With a heave I opened the window. Standing as still as I could, I listened to the night air. No shots. No sirens. No shouting. The night was still and hushed. It was over.

I walked back to the writing table and sat down, rubbing my eyes. The clock by the bed revealed the hour. 2:35 AM.

On the table, the papers lay as I had left them. My eyes strayed to the last lines of the palimpsest translation Yohanan had given me, written by the hand of Seraiah. These had been his last written words. When he wrote this, he had no idea he would be executed so shortly. None of them had. He expected to be paraded before the king, bear insults and perhaps a few lashes, and be marched on to Babylon as all the others had been before. But it had not been so.

As I stared at the words, daydreaming, imagining the pitiful prisoners in chains, dusty, thirsty, weary as they were brought before their captor, the words on the page began to separate into phrases I had not perceived earlier.

I wrote them separately on another piece of paper, just as they had been written by Seraiah, in three lines:

Prepare ye the way of the Lord,
make straight in the desert
a highway to our God

Suddenly they began to speak to me.

Prepare ye the way of the Lord. Yehoniah was being told to prepare a way, a path, a place for the Lord..... no, the Urim and Thummim of the Lord. The Urim and Thummim were used to inquire of the Lord; they were a link to God. They represented God. Prepare a way for them, prepare a place for them, Seraiah was saying.

Make straight in the desert .... The place he should choose should be as a landmark, a place which somehow was 'straight.'

A highway to our God it ended. A highway. High. A way which is high. Straight and high.

The Urim and Thummim must be hidden in the desert in a place somehow fitting a description of 'straight and high.'

In the Strong Holds of David, a wadi with straight cliffs?

I pulled over the map and searched it. They might be hidden on a high cliff. Somewhere near must be a feature which Yehoniah would have interpreted as 'straight.' The place must be near En Gedi: a place high in the rocks, perhaps on a vertical cliff, straight up, or with a view straight down a wadi from the summit, or along a straight run of a wadi..........

Too many possibilities!

As the Babylonians would have still been roaming the area, killing and destroying, the place must be away from beaten trails. Isolated. Hidden. Unreachable. Accessible only to God.

I looked again at the topographical map:

I still saw too many places which were straight and high, for the entire region was covered with such geological formations. Yet as I strained at the map, my eyes wandered back toward Jerusalem a bit, over the region north west of En Gedi. I gazed at the small area on the map, pondering, pondering.

History recorded that En Gedi was devastated about the same time as Jerusalem, so the Babylonians had already sacked and razed it by the time Yehoniah would have gotten there. He would have avoided the place. Finding En Gedi destroyed, perhaps he began to turn back north even before hiding the stones. In the ostracon Brannon found in Egypt he said that he had been in Mizpah with Jeremiah when Gedaliah was slain. He must have gone back north again as soon as he had fulfilled his oath and hidden them. The area north west of En Gedi was almost certain. It had to be the place.

Looking closely on the map in that area I could see a long, straight segment of wadi, with sheer cliffs whose high end led North. Several miles back down its valley, still far from the Dead Sea was a crook with a widening and a small mesa flat, on which was clearly marked the black dot of a small ruin recorded by the State of Israel. The site key said Bronze and Iron Age houses at a now dry spring. Unexplored, it said. I tapped my finger on the spot. It felt good.

This would be the place I would dig. This would be the center of my walking search for the possible resting place of the Urim and Thummim. The Department of Antiquities would give me this spot.

I circled the area in pencil.

Tomorrow, I would go and change the Permit to this new site.

Satisfied and optimistic, I went back to bed, and fell asleep.

Chapter 6

Day Six: Into the desert

I slept late this morning, a thing that almost never happened on excavation trips. The excitement of new mornings almost always awoke me. But not this morning. It was late: 8:30 AM already. Yet I felt well rested; in fact, very good, a favorable beginning for a promising expedition. Obviously, my body's powerful circadian cycles had already adjusted to their uprooting and replanting under the sun's earlier rhythms in Israel's part of the world. This unavoidable proof of the sun's influence on our tangible physical lives, our bodies, set in motion by the earth's daily rotation and our body's rhythmic exposure to light and darkness, and perhaps something more in the energy of the sun and its light, so dramatically revealed in our desynchronized groping exhaustion in daylight hours and restless waking in the silent dark which we affectionately call "jet lag," never ceased to fascinate me. This time, I thought, I had adjusted rather nicely.

In short order I was dressed. Today was my last day in Jerusalem; I would soon be heading out into the Judaean desert and beginning almost six weeks of isolated excavations, in great hope. Without delay I gathered my things and got packed for travel.

My bags soon were ready by the door, and I pulled out my agenda book and ran my finger down the checked list of jobs remaining to be completed or resolved before leaving Jerusalem.

There was very little left to do.

And, as always in this wonderful time of technology and invention, the last details of preparation for leaving on the dig could be easily finalized by phone from my hotel room. A few calls shortly verified that everything was to be ready and waiting for me at the airport; my rental vehicle was fueled and waiting at the rental company lot, and my groceries and supplies were boxed and waiting at the emporium as ordered and prepaid. The push began.

But it was still too early for the most important job of the morning: the Rockefeller Museum and the Department of Antiquities: the site change. This bit of business would have to be done in person, perhaps with groveling. I did not know. But change the site I must, no matter how much cajoling might be required. I settled into a chair with my charts and maps and studied the topography of my chosen area with renewed scrutiny.

In the light of Jerusalem's morning streaming through the window, the new choice, the new site which had captured my eye in the middle of the still night, looked ever more promising. Definitely, before I could do anything else, the excavation site recorded on my permit only yesterday had to be changed, changed to this place, the one which had loomed so large last night, the one which looked more and more right today.

At 9:30 AM I checked out of the hotel and stood by the curb in the warm Israeli morning air, ready to begin this adventure.

A sherut stopped and the driver quickly put my bags in the trunk. His smile drooped when he learned I was not going to Ben Gurion Airport in Tel Aviv, but he seemed happy enough when I told him our first stop would be the Rockefeller Museum, and he would get waiting fare before going across town.

As he drove a few dozen yards ahead and then pulled into a driveway to make the U-turn back towards the walled Old City and the museum, my eyes drank in all that was around me on this busy street, taking in every detail. It would be many weeks before I would once again see these streets, or any streets, or people rushing along on sidewalks, talking to one another, calling out to each other, or driving in their cars, or shaking tablecloths from balcony windows of apartments, or children laughing with each other as they walked to school, or women treading to market with the bags to fill with food for their family to eat this day, or old men sitting and watching the traffic go by, watching, seeing, drinking in the day before they too embarked on their journey, the great journey that would soon take one and then another of them from this life and its daily scenes.

I felt akin to the old men as they sat, hunting for even the most mundane moments of life passing by here on these everyday streets, reaching out with their eyes to gather it all in just one more time, precious treasures not to be missed, not one little part of it, not one laughing child, not one crouching cat by a doorway, not one woman's greeting to her neighbor, not one dusty car rumbling by. They had come to understand: all of it, even the most simple dry leaf blowing along the dust of the dirty sidewalk, was too precious to miss.

My six-week journey into the Judaean Desert was a more temporary absence from all this than theirs would be, yet seeing the old men sitting in the morning sunlight, some with deeply wrinkled faces, some with toothless smiles as they talked to each other on the low wall by the street where they sat, so old, reminded me of the frailty of our bodies, the shortness of our sojourn here on this earth amidst this hustle and bustle of life, and of the eventual leaving it all which awaited every one of us at some time in our every future.

The traffic opened for a moment and the sherut driver seized the opportunity to quickly pull out across the street and turn back toward the walled city. We sped down the hill and out into the plaza before the huge, majestic walls, and I filled my eyes with them as we turned left and drove up and around the corner of the walled city and then along their ancient presence to the far end of the road where it drops down into the Kidron Valley. He stopped in mid-traffic by the Lion Gate for his left-turn against morning traffic entering the city from the East, and we waited several minutes before he could edge forward and then cut through into the Museum driveway.

I told him that I might be ten or fifteen minutes, and he turned off the motor. Quickly I got out and went into the museum, making my way back to the Department of Antiquities office.

The woman behind the desk was surprised to see me again. She was even more surprised when I requested to change the site I had chosen only yesterday. Her surprise grew yet more as she found the new site in her official site register book, the site I showed her on the map which I now wanted. It was one of the most remote sites, one which no one had ever wanted because it was so isolated and dry, in such an unbearably hot and dangerous area.

She looked at me a bit strangely, but granted the site change without any hesitation. I was immensely relieved.

"Why do you want this site?" she asked inquisitively as she began the process of changing the permit. "Americans always want big, impressive sites where they think they will find something to make them famous. According to the registry book nothing is there at all but some crude Late Bronze and Iron Age foundations." She looked up at me and smiled. "Do you know something we don't know?"

"More isolated is better for what I'm doing," I smiled back. I didn't want to get into any conversation, just get the change and get out. We would know if I knew something they didn't know when I returned in six weeks.

She methodically crossed out the previous site identification and proceeded to write in the name of the new site.

"This is......" she spoke slowly as she wrote ".....the Wadi Hasasa," and she showed me the new site name and identification written on the Permit. "That is where you are now permitted to dig."

Her words stunned me.

"What is this place called?" I asked her, craning my neck to look down at the Permit, scarcely believing my ears and eyes.

"The Wadi Hasasa, just inland north west of A'in Jidi by the Dead Sea. That's the place you have circled here, on your map," she showed me my circle.

I couldn't believe it. Seraiah's words echoed in my mind.

"Thank you ever so much," I said with a rush of adrenaline surging into my blood, trying to keep cool and appear casual. "Thank you....Thank you very much!" I said as I gathered my documents and put them back into the briefcase.

I walked back out through the corridors repeating to myself: *Wadi Hasasa...... Hazazon-tamar.* There could be no mistake. This was the name Seraiah had written to Yehoniah. It might be the site of *H'aziz....... the Ascent of Ziz.* Whether the original ancient location remained preserved at the modern Arabic name place might not be so, but there was no doubt that it must be close even if not exact: Seraiah's instruction to Yehoniah had quite possibly been fulfilled within this small area of the Judaean wasteland.

This was Hazazon-tamar, Seraiah's expressed hiding place of the Urim and Thummim of God.

Electrified with excitement, I walked out of the museum into the sunlight. For a moment I just stood gazing at the towering stone walls of the city across the street, re-gathering my thoughts. I had several things still to do. Where was I going now? What did I have to do now? The vehicle. The four-wheel drive. The car rental office.

The sherut driver turned on the motor as I opened the rear door and got in; after hearing the address of the car rental office, he nodded and headed out into traffic toward the center of the new, modern city of Jerusalem. My whole body tingled as we bounced our way through Jerusalem. Everything was falling into place. As we drove through the streets I watched more of the life of this city around me, all the way to our destination.

Before I knew it the driver was parking by the agency door. As he got my bags out of the trunk I readied his money for the fare, and gave him a good tip. His eye lit up and a warm smile thanked me most sincerely. I watched him get back into his car and pull out into traffic, leaving me on the sidewalk beside the rental office door.

I was here. My trip was beginning. I picked up my bags and headed through the door.

As I walked in, I saw several people were ahead of me in line. I would have to wait. The woman behind the counter acknowledged me and pointed to the seats. Yes, I would definitely have to sit down and wait. But the excitement had calmed a bit by now, and I knew: there really was no rush. There was no hourly time schedule now. I was entering into 'remote excavation time.' From this point forward, time was to be measured in a different pace then everywhere else on the planet, for I would become a time unto only myself. There would be no clocks, no appointments, no other

161

person to regulate time with or for. Only the sky and the air, the sun and the stars, the rocks, dust and dirt, the desert, the day, the night. And, when I felt them, hunger and weariness. Time would be a thing carried only within me, mine to use as I saw fit, when I wished, as the work at hand seemed fit, and I knew: I would little observe it as more than a blur.

For, alone, in the vast expanse of the desert, there would be little to regard of time but my need to fill the intermittent hunger arising in my body and to rest my body's exhaustion as it came. What else was there to direct me in any measuring of time? I would sleep when I willed, work when I willed, eat when I willed. Time, always calculated in anxious minutes and urgent hours at home and at the university, regimented and delineated by so many artificially organized routines, was suddenly suspended from its daily rounds. A new time of no more than waking and sleeping and working, of day and of night, weeks without anything to distinguish one day from another, or one time from another, was about to begin.

I took a deep breath, exhaled, and glanced around the room at my surroundings. .

There were several chairs, a sofa, a coffee table with magazines in many languages, and over against the wall, a large salt-water aquarium with colorful coral reef fishes next to more chairs. I walked over to the aquarium and knelt to see them better. They were beautiful. I chose a chair with a good view of the fish, sat down and continued watching them swim while I waited. Some were from the nearby Red Sea, while others were airlift imports from the myriad coral atolls and reefs of the South Pacific.

A grandfatherly man, waiting in the chair beside me, sat with his hands clasped in his lap, also gazing at the fish.

"Beautiful, aren't they?" he remarked, and nodded toward the aquarium.

"Yes," I replied.

"My grandson wants me to get some for him, but I don't know anything about keeping fish," he said, gazing at them swimming slowly in the clear water.

"Oh, it's not so hard," I said with a friendly smile.

"You know about them?" he asked with raised eyebrows.

I had kept aquaria from the time I was 10 years old until I was in my early thirties, about twenty years. For ten years I had kept a 200 gallon tank stocked to the brim with many of these fish we saw here, and more.

"Yeah, a little," I replied.

"You keep these fishes, salt water fishes? That's what he wants, you know, like these: salt water fishes."

"Yes, I kept salt water fishes," I nodded.

"So how do you do it...... set it up, I mean?" he asked.

"It's not so hard. All of the required things you need, to set up the tank, you can buy in aquarium shops: sea salt crystals and all the needed minerals and trace elements, kits to monitor salinity levels, prepared foods, all kinds of fish to introduce into the aquarium you prepare, water heaters to keep the temperature within the tolerances they can survive, thermometers so you can monitor what's happening, coral and sand and gravels, water filters, PH kits and adjusters, books telling you how to do it all, everything. It's not as if you have to invent it all, and imagine how it should be until you have it all perfect."

"Still sounds very complicated," he nodded.

"Most of the hard work's setting it all up. Caring for it's pretty easy. Basically, you're just creating a little ocean. The world's oceans all take care of themselves. Once you get a tank properly set up and seasoned, it almost takes care of itself, too. If you had a big enough tank, it would keep itself," I told him.

"Seasoned?" he raised his eyebrows again, smiling. "A fish tank needs to be seasoned? I thought you only seasoned them when you cook them."

"It's not the fish - it's the habitat you're creating for them. You can't just fill it with water and throw them in. They'd die. The by-products of their own life processes, you know - wastes and exhalations - would accumulate and kill them. You've got to set up a system that will purify itself and provide them everything their bodies need to be healthy while it neutralizes the body-process by-products from their breathing and eating and swimming, just being alive, you know. Otherwise, it would just build up until nothing could live in it. The tank has to be seasoned and conditioned. It just takes a little preparation time."

"How long a time?" he asked.

"For a little tank like this one here, just a couple of weeks."

"What takes a couple of weeks?" he inquired further.

"Its a biological process that prepares the environment, you know - the water and the sand - building up enough organic matter in the environment and filling it with balanced populations of the micro organisms you need to handle the biological life processes of the bigger organisms, you know, the fish you want to keep."

"The tank needs micro organisms? Why?"

"Well, you're starting with a barren environment - just the sterile glass that the aquarium's made of. And when you first put in the sand and gravel, and the rocks and coral to create the habitat, and then the water with the sea salts, it's all 'dead' too. Everything's sterile. Sterile water, sterile sand, sterile rocks. There are no micro organisms or any dissolved organic matter for micro organisms to feed on, and they're what create the bio cycles that bio-degrade all the wastes to keep the water fresh and clean. If you put fish in right away, while the environment's still barren, they'll all die. Even with everything you do, the first fish you put in a new salt water aquarium always die."

"So how do you get these micro organisms into the water," he shrugged.

"You put in some fish," I replied.

"But you just said they would die," he protested.

"That's right. So, you start the whole system by putting in fish you don't intend to keep, fish you don't plan to keep as the final population you're setting it all up for," I told him.

"Then what happens?" he asked.

"Well, the fish immediately begin to put organic matter into the water. Then you feed them, which puts more organic matter into the water. But that's what you want: the environment has to have lots of organic matter to get seasoned and perfectly balanced. While this processes is beginning, the micro organisms naturally on the fish float off into the water, and they multiply. But as the system isn't balanced yet, they create what we call a 'bloom' until there are so many of them that they kill almost all of themselves, and the fish," I told him simply. His puzzled expression was humorous. Everyone always got puzzled at first. It sounded crazy, I knew, but it was the only way to establish a healthy total environment in which the fish you wanted to keep could stay alive.

"This is some way to set up a place to live," he shrugged.

"It's not anything you're doing or not doing that makes the big die-off, it's just the natural cycles which have to be established by building up the various smaller life forms and organic matter needed to make a life-sustaining environment. You need colonies of several different micro-organisms which process the wastes of the fish you eventually want to keep. There have to be billions and billions of them to balance everything, even in a little aquarium like this."

"But you put in things just to have them die?" he asked shaking his head.

"Well, you have to prepare the environment to support the fish you want to keep, or they will die." He was looking at the beautiful reef fishes, healthy and swimming among the coral and rocks.

"Explain," he requested.

"Very simply, fish give off waste: ammonia through their gills, and solid waste, all which decomposes and turns into ammonia. Ammonia is very poisonous, and salt water fishes are hyper-sensitive to it. It kills them even in very small quantities. When the ammonia levels reach the critical level, the fish all die. You leave them in the tank, to decompose into more ammonia and organic compounds. They become part of the organic matter you need in the water. Now, there are several families of specialized bacteria that bio-degrade waste. The first eats the ammonia and multiplies fantastically. It turns the ammonia into another chemical which is the food of the next bacteria family which feasts in a chain of decomposition. This makes a bloom of the next toxic chemical, and allows the next family of bacteria to grow, and so on until the waste is completely bio-degraded. Each bacteria in turn blooms into proliferation as its food supply blooms. In the end, when the seasoning time is completed, the organic matter is distributed evenly and harmlessly in the water, and all of the toxic waste is gone. The environment is prepared, and you can introduce the fish you really wanted to put in it from the beginning."

"Say that all one more time. I want to understand this," he asked attentively.

"As the first fish all eat and breathe, and uneaten food and waste begin to spread into the environment, there are so few living micro-organisms available to process it all that the ammonia level builds up with a sudden spike through the ceiling - not literally, but on the chemical scale - and whatever fish you put in it first all die, poof. But in doing this you've set in motion the process, and the tank begins to season. Each successive population which establishes itself in the aquarium adds to its final ability to keep alive the fish you really want to put in it. The first group of bacteria eat the ammonia and multiply into a huge bloom, which makes a chemical nitrate bloom, which is their waste from feeding on the ammonia. The nitrate spike is also poisonous and would kill the fish. But then the nitro-somer and the nitro-bacter bacteria come to the rescue. The first eats the nitrates and gives off nitrite which makes another poisonous spike, but the second one eats the nitrites and gives off pure nitrogen as waste, which is harmless even in huge quantities. In fact, nitrogen is the main plant nutrient in fertilizer. It's part of what makes the algae and seaweed and grass and everything else green on the planet to grow. Anyway, an aquarium is far from being a completely self-sufficient system like the ocean, but if you do it right, it can come close. You still have to feed the fish of course, because you'll never have your own complete food chain in an aquarium, only a little algae. And by the way, algae in a salt water aquarium is good - you want it: some of the fish will graze on it, and it's a water purifier. It removes a lot of toxic wastes from the water as food, just like the plants in the ocean. When you harvest algae from your aquarium, you actually remove some of the toxic wastes bonded in the plant's growth."

"Sounds pretty ingenious," he smiled.

"It's just a step by step process. You go from barren and sterile environment to ready and prepared living place able to receive the special fish you planned to keep from the beginning."

"What do the fish eat?"

"The natural food chain won't survive in a small aquarium, so you have to give them prepared foods. In the oceans, truly seasoned and prepared oceans and seas, the whole food chain thing is amazing. For the big fish to exist you go from thousands of single and multi-celled life forms up to swarms of little plankton shrimps, and invertebrates and polyps and fish larvae and sea weed, even the big fish themselves that eat and get eaten are part of it all. It's mind boggling how much food, how many varieties of food there are in the oceans, and how each one completes part of the essential balance in the system. But you won't have any of the natural food chain in your aquarium - it couldn't survive in such a little system."

"So, a food chain I won't have in my aquarium, but what do I feed them?"

"Store-bought food. Commercial aquarium supplies are getting pretty good at harvesting and preparing healthy mixes of foods these days. Food preparations are made from sea weed, fish, shrimp, squid, plankton, things like that. And you need to remember to add mineral trace elements periodically to the water as they get bonded in the organic build-up and precipitate out of the water into the sand. Trace elements are very important," I added.

"How do you get those?" he asked.

"They sell them in aquarium shops, like vitamin drops. When a fish dies in the ocean, all of the trace elements and organic compounds in its body are returned to the water. But in an aquarium, we have to remove dead fish, because the environment is so small that one dead fish could pollute and poison the whole environment and kill everything in it. In nature the whole ocean system of organic matter and minerals is self-perpetuating. Over a long period of time the water has become fully prepared to support life, loaded with trace elements, organic matter, all kinds of life forms which continually replenish the system as their bodies bio-degrade and return to the water. So the food chain itself replaces a lot of the needed trace elements and organic compounds in a constant cyclical manner. And, the water is in contact with the minerals on the ocean floor and shores and gets replenished with more minerals washed in from rivers and rain run-off. Since your aquarium will only be glass and a little bit of coral and maybe a few rocks, you have to supply the things it can't get to stay healthy."

"So, what fish do I put in to begin with?" he asked.

"Whatever you want," I said, "as long as you understand that they will die. Most people who live near the ocean start with something free out of a tide pool or from a fisherman. You could do that pretty easily here," I motioned toward the Mediterranean sea.

"What did you start with, when you started your aquarium?"

"I started my first big tank with a huge octopus I got from a fisherman at a pier. No, really! It was fascinating! The arm span was about six feet. It was big. It liked shrimp, and ate really well. I began to feed it by hand, and with its tentacles it would feel at my hands and keep touching until it found the shrimp, and then take it right out of my fingers and eat it. It could tell the difference, and it wasn't interested in my fingers at all. Just the food. Amazingly intelligent. The first and only time I tried to give it some cheap bait shrimp, which cost so much less than fresh shrimp, it took it and tasted it, but spit it out. Too far gone, I guessed. I tried offering it another one, hoping it might be fresher, but it felt it around with its tentacles, and - I couldn't believe it! - pushed, literally pushed my fingers and the spoiled shrimp away with its tentacles! It could tell it was a bad shrimp just by feeling it! I had never had any idea they could push! I thought all they could do was pull. Anyway, it was amazing. I loved it. It lived almost ten days. I spent a lot of time with it every day. By the time the ammonia bloom reached lethal levels and it died, we had become pretty good friends. I felt terrible. It's pretty easy to get attached to animals, even ones you know you need just to make the whole system work. It's hard when they die. I loved my octopus so much I was really tempted to get another one when the tank was completely seasoned, but I knew that I couldn't. If I did, it was so big compared to the fish I wanted to put in there, I could never have the fish I really wanted because it would eat them all, and I really wanted the colorful reef fish. So, as you're setting up your tank for your grandson, I suggest you pick something your grandson won't get so attached to. It's hard seeing wonderful things die. Anyway, once the tank goes through this cycle and you've established the colonies of micro-organisms, which live on the sand and gravel and all over the coral, you can put in the fish you wanted all along, the fish you planned the whole environment for. If there are no disease organisms introduced with them, usually you don't have any more problems for a long time, and things run pretty smoothly."

"Disease organisms?" he asked wearily.

"Mostly protozoans. They attack the fishes' gills. They're part of the micro food chain in the ocean. In nature, out in the open sea, the water currents wash them away before they multiply into harmful levels for the fish, out into the deep waters. They never become numerous enough around the fish to cause trouble. But in a little aquarium, they multiply unchecked and then suffocate the fish. That's the difference between a small tank and a global ocean. However, they're very easily eradicated with just a little copper sulfate. It kills all of the protozoans and doesn't hurt the fish. Once they're gone, as long as you don't accidentally re-introduce any on fresh food or new fish, you can go years without any more problems. It's really quite a remarkable chemistry going on in a tank like this. It's what's going on in all the oceans all over the planet."

"This is going on in all the oceans?" he asked.

"Yes. And the oceans are big enough that once they became seasoned, they perpetually regulate and balance themselves because they're as big as they are. But in an aquarium, without the big size of nature, you have to watch things very closely. Nature is already set up to take care of all of its own problems. In an aquarium, you have to become Nature's hand. One thing I tell you - as your grandson learns a little bit about salt water aquaria, he'll come to really appreciate how perfectly balanced the chemistry of nature is."

"So, you need to be a chemist to have one of these?" he shook his head. "I don't think my grandson will make it."

"No, it's really very easy," I encouraged. "You don't really have to know much about it. You just set it up, put in the fish, feed them, and the bacteria which are on the fish and in the air all around us all over the planet, pitch in and do what they were made to do. Follow the steps, and when the balance has settled everything down, you're ready to introduce your intended species. A child can do it. How old is your grandson?"

"Twelve."

"No problem. A twelve year-old can set up a micro ocean environment with no problem, once he understands it. To set up a big one for a whole planet, that would take a bit more work."

Just then, the last customer at the counter left with her keys and it was my turn. The woman behind the counter beckoned to me.

"Nice meeting you," I said to the man, and we shook hands.

"You really like fish, don't you?" he smiled.

"Yes, I do."

"By the way," he asked, "are you a teacher?"

"I am," I confessed and smiled.

"I never would have known," he replied and smiled back. "Thank you for a very good lesson on aquariums."

My paperwork at the counter took only seconds. All this time it had been ready and waiting. Keys in hand, I tossed my bags in the back and pulled out into the traffic of Jerusalem, the New City. From numerous previous trips this was not unfamiliar territory for me, and without pause I drove to the market and picked up the fresh and canned foods I had ordered to supplement the dried desert supplies shipped with the excavation equipment from the university.

I next drove West through the low Israeli mountains to the Mediterranean, to Tel Aviv. Rocky hills and evergreen pines were entirely reminiscent of places I knew back home. For all the Earth's diversity, I was ever amazed at how familiar distant places often appeared.

As I drove out of the hills onto the coastal plain with Tel Aviv in view ahead, the panorama of the Mediterranean Sea filled my eyes. And it filled my mind with more thoughts of fish, salts, minerals and food chains. Out there, below that crystal-like surface, was a system so functionally elaborate and perfect for sustaining life that it literally kept this entire planet alive.

The day the oceans died and stagnated as a polluted mass, the planet would die.

Few people ever even thought of how the ocean and its myriad microscopic and larger life forms served to purify the waters of the planet. Yet because of the water-purifying character of the oceanic food chain, from smallest denizen to mightiest predator, the system kept a delicate balance perfectly, processing and purifying everything that was put into it, making life on land possible all over the globe through the cycles of atmospheric water circulation irrigating the continents far and wide, the islands, and the seas.

Yet this view I beheld, the blue Mediterranean stretching out away from the shore to the horizon, had not always been here. In times long past the Mediterranean Sea had dried up - cut off from the world's oceans at the Straits of Gibraltar by the movement of continents being rearranged from that first great primordial land mass that rose in the primordial sea.

All of this water, this great sea before me had evaporated down into a dense salt lake, so dense that the Dead Sea would seem virtually fresh. But then even that water had evaporated, leaving only the salt, a massive caked layer hundreds of feet thick at the bottom of the deepest valleys thousands of feet below the level of the mother oceans outside.

The Mediterranean Sea had dried up, completely. It had become a great valley from one end to the other.

There had been no French Riviera, nor any coasts at all, only sloping land going far down below sea level to incredibly salty, dead lakes here and there.. Italy had no coasts, nor Greece; there were no islands, no coast along Turkey, Syria, Lebanon, or here along Israel. Egypt to the south had no coast, and the Nile River, no longer meeting a sea at sea level, had over time cut down through the soft Delta and dug a deep channel that eventually extended far north into the land. There had been no North African coast, just as there had been no South European coast. One could have walked down the sloping land from Italy across the valley and up the slopes to the plateau of Carthage, on dry land. All of this great sea of water had evaporated, and the world's greatest below-sea-level valley had grown forests deep below where ships sailed today.

As I drove down the hill looking at the scintillating blue expanse of sea, I tried to imagine beyond Tel Aviv a dry shoreline and dry dirt flat, and beyond that, descending, a great and dry barren valley, within whose distant center were white hills and valleys, all glowing white, yet not with snow.

The image was eerie, and created a silence within my mind, as a time holding its breath.

Then my imagining was startled by the opening of the floodgates at the far end, far away at Gibraltar, the first waterfall of the mother ocean gushing in, far away at The Pillars of Hercules. When the earth groaned and moved back and the oceans again breached the Straits, torrents of sea water and fish came cascading down into the deep salt valleys, perhaps one of the most spectacular sights ever to have been seen.

The sea crashed in, and in, and in for a hundred years, so they say, until this valley was filled, and once again joined with the oceans. Life had entered again with the cascade of waters, and eventually, in time, everything became properly balanced again and it filled with all kinds of life.

Though it had died, yet it now lived again.

But even now, due to its tiny Gibraltarian umbilical, there was still little current exchange between it and the mother oceans beyond. I shook my head as I drove, gazing out upon the waters, unable to imagine the volume of evaporation taking place before me.

This great sea lost more water each day from evaporation than it received from all of the rivers draining into it - the great Nile, the powerful Danube through the Black Sea, the mighty Po, the coursing Tiber, the swift Ebro, the stately Rhone. The total number of gallons per minute had to be staggering. Such a vast flow, and yet it was far from enough to offset what was invisibly rising up into the air before my very eyes. And so the mother

Atlantic was literally feeding this imprisoned sea every day, a dependent child, ever hungry.

I marveled in trying to imagine the total mass of water surface evaporation going into the air over all the oceans on the planet every day, which only here gave some idea of its magnitude because of its near isolation from the mother.

As I neared the outskirts of Tel Aviv I steered away from the roads leading into downtown, following the signs to the airport. Finding the Customs warehouse was rather easy in a small facility such as this, and shortly I was receiving my shipment. It was already cleared by the broker, and all the documents were in order. My friend at the Rockefeller Museum had called as promised. In just a few minutes, everything was packed in the four-wheel and I was ready to go into the Wilderness of Judah.

The drive took me back to Jerusalem, along the ancient Jaffa road route, probably the same route used over thousands of years to go from the port city of Joppa to the interior. The entire West end of the Mediterranean had been the crossroads of antiquity, and this key coastal center was one of many connecting places of people and goods traveling between land and sea. Cargo and travelers from ships met caravans and groups going in all directions: South by land to Egypt, Ethiopia and Nubia; North by land to Mesopotamia and then East and beyond. I gazed around the countryside as I drove, imagining people dressed in a variety of ancient clothes treading the dusty road, caravans of camels, rich and poor mingling together on the single artery of travel for all, the lowly and the high. It had all been here. These hills had seen it.

I decided to go through Jerusalem one last time before heading South into the desert. The countryside highway became city outskirt highway and then suburb highway until finally traffic began to slow me down. Yet it was worth it. This is a city I love.

When I was only a few blocks from the center of the New City, suddenly, just a little behind me, another bomb blast shattered the street and sky and air, obliterating a car and wrecking half the block around it. I was stunned. The blast actually lifted me up in my seat, and shook the entire car.

It was a nightmare *deja vue*. People were scattering everywhere; gunfire suddenly rattled from several directions; screaming filled the street. What was going on in this city? It was just as yesterday all over, except this time I was in a car. The incident was behind me. I could flee.

Without waiting for the cars in front of me to move, I glanced around and without further thought, maneuvered the four wheel onto the sidewalk, already deserted, and drove into the adjacent alley, only to emerge onto the next street with a gunmen opening fire on me. As I spun the steering wheel left and punched the gas, bullets clanged into the metal body of the four-wheeler and whizzed by on all sides. Blue-white smoke billowed from the wheels and I saw my chance; I floored the pedal for more smoke and sped away from the gunfire in a cloud. Another quick turn put me out of range.

170

Merging into traffic I kept driving block after block until shortly I was driving through streets peaceful and normal as if nothing were happening at all. So quickly I had passed into an untouched part of the city. I shook my head in amazement.

What would be an international news incident by tomorrow was unnoticed and still unknown here only a few minutes away from where it was erupting.

I marveled that in a country and city where these incidents were actually rare, two had occurred within days and both had come close to killing me. The shock of this second experience reached saturation. Suddenly the desire to get out into the sheltering isolation of the Judaean Wilderness possessed me, and I turned my vehicle out of town.

As David of old, I left the city of Jerusalem in flight.

Out of the Jerusalem and on the road South to Hebron, I began to see military vehicles, more and more military vehicles heading toward Jerusalem. At the Israeli checkpoints spaced along the highway an air of tension prevailed. By radio, I thought, they must know. The young Israeli soldiers huddled in the sandbag machine-gun nests were wide eyed and very alert. I continued my way South toward Hebron and the wadis that lead to the Dead Sea.

Looking at the hills and plains around me as I drove, I remembered that this was the general direction Yehoniah would have taken twenty-six centuries ago. I had, in the last few days, imagined his fleeing the city of Jerusalem, smoke-filled and fire gutted, with the instructions given by Seraiah burning within his mind. My guess was that he had made his way East out of the city, crossed overland, and then began his descent South into the outskirts of the Wilderness of Judaea en route to his appointed destination within the Strong Holds of David. Somewhere along this very road I probably had passed over his footsteps, if I was not actually following them from time to time.

The sun overhead was high in the sky, and already heat waves dazzled the road as I drove. Mirages of phantom water puddles scintillated far in the distance, only to shrivel and evaporate into the dry grey pavement before they were reached.

How many ancient travelers, water supplies dwindling, had seen similar shimmering pools of water ahead in the desert sands, only to see them shrink and disappear as they approached, always replaced by yet another and then another always farther and farther away. I was able to rehearse to myself the scientific explanation of what I was seeing, casually lecturing my intellect with the scientific principles of optical physics, of heated and cooler air densities and their relative light refractions and phantom reflections appearing as water, ideas expressed in exact, descriptive word-thoughts in my mind, thoughts which my generation had come to know and understand with words invented for absolute clarity.

I thought of the ancients, walking these deserts, knowing nothing of air densities, of light waves with refractive behaviors, having neither ideas nor words to imagine the cause of this thing which they saw so clearly but which they could never reach, and I wondered what thoughts had filled their minds about what was happening before their eyes, teasing them, tantalizing them, taunting them. What powers had they imagined that seemed to delight in playfully leading them on in vain, whetting yet never quenching their thirst? But even they in their generation had learned to know that these visions were not of water to be obtained. Just the thought of their knowing that mirages were not water, only tricks played upon their senses, was in itself a fragment of respectable knowledge.

My car sped onward over the hot Judaean road toward Hebron.

Though with every passing mile I was further and further from any danger, still I remained nervous until I reached the Valley of Berachah, now called the Wadi el-Arrub, and turned East onto the dirt road heading into the barren Judaean Desert hills. This was the direct canyon path leading from Jerusalem to En Gedi and the Dead Sea, used since most ancient times. More than likely Yehoniah had followed this way on his mission to bury the Urim and Thummim. It was the way to my dig site.

Once I felt I was safely away from the highway, I finally stopped the car to rest, shake off the shock of the bomb incident, and check for damage.

There were several bullet holes in the car. And I noticed a chunk of plastic side paneling toward the rear torn off by the bomb explosion itself. I had not even been aware that the car had been hit. It was a miracle that no windows had been broken.

I opened the back hatch door and lifted it up. I had counted five bullet holes in the body. Where had the bullets gone? I searched through the boxes of food, suitcases and large water containers, and discovered that aside from some holes in a few shirts and pants, and a few leaking cans of soup, several water containers were bullet-holed. Fortunately the water had drained harmlessly down onto the back deck floor and out of the vehicle. My greatest fear was the computer equipment and solar cells. However, a full examination of each individual box revealed that no bullets had passed through them, and no water had penetrated them. In my usual packing habit to keep as much visibility as possible, I had not stacked them but laid them side by side on the deck floor. The bullets had all come through at higher levels, sparing the precious electronics. Though my water reserves were reduced, unlike the ancients, I still had the ability to drive to water and with little difficulty, refill them.

Relieved by the findings of the hasty inventory, I drove farther East on the dusty dirt road, deep into the Judaean Desert, entering into its labyrinth of wadis.

From this time forward, I did not see another living soul.

This was a forsaken desert wasteland, a place of heat, scrub plants, deep rain-carved wadi canyons with dry, choking dust, and occasional bones of sheep, goats and donkeys reminding all who entered here of what their

172

final fate could be.

This was the refuge of robbers and prophets, rebels and patriots. Here thieves and murderers had evaded capture and justice. In this labyrinthine maze of cliffs, caves and dry washes, David and his loyal men had evaded King Saul's armies, moving and hiding among the treacherous rocks and winding blind canyons. Here Judaean Zealots had hidden from Roman legions and defied its might during two devastating wars. The last, under the command of Simon bar Kochba, had made headquarters in many of these winding canyons, perhaps this one here. As these dry stones testified, his war had ended with the complete banishment of all Jews from Judaea. It was hard to relate to the immensity of history which these unbearable cliffs and canyons had witnessed.

Much like the Grand Canyon, or Bryce, or Zion's Park in America, these water-cut ancient wadis towered up above me as I drove deeper and deeper into the Wilderness.

Whenever there was a fork, I chose the road leading north east, for this was the direction to the Wadi Hasasa. At times the road doubled back up another canyon, and then up to the plateau and ridges above. At these times I was momentarily on top of the world in this wasteland.

This top surface region was barely above sea level, a thing I was reminded of as I drove upon it and could finally view across several of these rocky ridges. Shortly the road went winding its way downward again, continuing its serpentine path through the canyons, parched tributary streams and rivers of sand which plunged into the below-sea-level regions of the Dead Sea.

My work, and my next six weeks would all be spent hundreds of feet below sea level. The Dead Sea itself was over 1,200 feet below sea level. The air was thicker; the heat more stifling than most places on Earth. Here, at the bottom of the Rift Valley, more of the Earth's atmosphere was piled up above me than I would ever experience anywhere in my life. The waters which through the ages had cut these deep canyons ran downward in channels below the level of all of the waters of the face of the Earth, seeking their final resting place in the thick, salty water of the Dead Sea.

Riding along the bottom of the canyon road I gazed upward at the top ridges on either side of the wadi. Descending from top to bottom, alternating rows of stone cliff facings and soft fallen soils created a sort of staggered stairway. Cascading down upon tier after tier of ledges were steep sliding slopes of loose talus, miniature alluvials, each falling off onto the level below it until at the wadi base a fanning veil of earth plummeted down to rest at the bottom of the canyon. I knew that from here, when sudden heavy rains would come, the tons of this dry earth would be quickly turned to mud and slush, sluicing its way down the wadis in violent flash floods, making rivers in the desert. Though everywhere I looked there was only dryness and rivers of sand, deep canyon wadis such as these could only be cut by water, and great rushing torrents of it over much time had made all that was here to see. The testament of great waters was everywhere.

Few people outside of the deserts knew that some of these dry river beds ran with water for many months during the year. Old tales and legends and stories spoke of 'rivers of water' in the desert, rivers of water which ancient Habiru and desert Bedouin distinguished from rivers of sand they knew well and traveled upon, for they were dry. Rivers of sand, rivers of water. It was a land of strange citadels, foreboding silence and stark majesty.

My mind's imagining saw images of warriors in brass helmets and red tunics, hermits in long robes, bearded holy men and stalwart women daring the devices of harsh nature to live in this land. My eyes looked over the panorama and envisioned the movement of peoples over many centuries, the history of this barren yet oft-sought place of desolation. How many secrets were buried here? How many ancient tales were whispered in the soft breezes whirling up from the Dead Sea through these dizzy crags and teetering precipices? How many voices that had echoed within these high stone walls had here been silenced?

After about an hour's drive I left the main dirt road and took a north eastern fork onto a smaller dirt road, deeper into the Wilderness of Judah. I then turned onto a smaller and then a smaller dirt road, until finally my road became only the dirt path of sheep and goats.

This road I had taken suddenly took a sharp incline upward and followed along a steep sandy wadi all the way to the top of the ridge. At the top I stopped and I got out of the vehicle to survey the landscape around me. I was basically between two deep wadi, not-so-miniature Grand Canyons, which I could see both converged about a mile ahead, abruptly terminating the narrow finger of ridge upon which I was parked. Somehow I had made a wrong choice among the labyrinth of dirt roads; from here I could go no further. Worse, there was no descent except the way I had come. I could not turn around.

I got back into the vehicle, put it in reverse, and slowly backed down the hill almost a mile, where I then took the other fork down the larger wadi instead of up.

I was glad for the four wheel drive.

After another hour of rather tortured driving, with the sun dipping lower in the sky, I emerged from the great wadi at the edge of the Dead Sea. Searching the map for my location, I was uncertain; I turned south, to the right, towards En Gedi. Nothing looked familiar on the map. My guess was that I had strayed too far north.

After so many hours in the confining wadis, driving along the views of the Dead Sea and its austere perimeter of high stone cliffs was breathtakingly spectacular. Geographically, this was a remarkable place. Qumran was a day's walk to the north; En Gedi perhaps a twenty-minute drive to the south. And all that the eye could see was below sea level, except for the tops of the cliffs.

I drove past several small Kibbutzim and waved back at the smiling people who looked up from their farming to wave at me. I imagined Judahites and Israelites of antiquity farming the same land, not much differently than the way these small family plots were being tilled and planted. I drove on.

Continuing slowly south I felt that I must be close to the wadi mouth which would lead me to the Hasasa and my site. Stopping again to confer with the map, I now began to recognize cliffs and outcroppings with map markings. Yet I was still uncertain: one wadi looks about the same as the next. Some small, some vast and high, all stretching back into the arid cliff regions of the Judaean Wilderness.

Squinting against the glare from the cliffs on the opposite side of the Dead Sea, I peered down the narrow coastal strip in the distance. Was that the oasis settlement of En Gedi in the distance?

It was.

Another look at the map identified my exact location, and fortuitously, almost directly to my right I could look up the wadi which would finally lead me to the wadi Hasasa and the remains of my ancient ruin.

Leaving the narrow green swath of plant growth beside the toxic mineral salt waters of the Dead Sea, I turned my back on the Rift Valley and headed into the high-walled wadi before me.

It was like entering into the mouth of a dry Grand Canyon. Though I knew the walls were not nearly so high, they were still certainly 1,500 feet if not 2,000 feet high, solid stone rising up beyond view above me on either side as my tiny vehicle entered into their shadows, following my small dirt path timidly along the side of the dry river bed between their bases.

With fewer difficulties than I would have expected, I followed the winding road and finally arrived at the mouth of the Wadi Hasasa. Though I should have reached it from the other side in my northern descent through the Wilderness, the scenic longer tour had been useful to my learning as well as beautiful. Useful in that I now knew these wadis had to be respected: they could be very deceptive, and getting lost within this wilderness interior was much easier than I had imagined. Beautiful in the awesome majesty of sheer stone carved by running water, standing stark against the Judaean sky just as they had stood two thousand and three thousand and four thousand years ago when historical figures of biblical fame had walked here.

Though the Wadi Hasasa bed continued to climb higher and higher into the rocks, a glance out the window and up revealed the tops of the high canyon walls above me were no more within reach than at the canyon mouth. I drove and drove and finally after another half-hour's drive, I came to the site.

It was easy to spot. The wadi suddenly widened and the walls angled back, opening the canyon into a rather large, flat mesa of unexpected size and advantage. The course of the water, when it ran in this wadi, had cut a semicircle around the south wall footing, about ten feet below the current road. To the right, on slightly higher ground, a plateau area commanded a view of both the wadi descent going down toward the main canyon and the Dead Sea, and the wadi ascent up into the Wilderness beyond which lay the fertile valleys between Jerusalem and Hebron. I squinted up at the tops of the canyon walls at both ends of the clearing. In wartime, a sentinel placed at these strategic high lookouts could give early advance warning of any arriving travelers or armies. In peacetime, this was an ideal retreat site for a villa, and would be still today except for its lack of water.

I parked the four-wheeler and got out. It felt good to stretch my legs. Knowing the dig site was on the raised ground, I climbed up the fifteen-foot embankment and walked onto the plateau. Gazing around me, the view of what would be my home for the next six weeks was quickly summed up. The Wadi Hasasa site was indeed a remote and desolate dig. Crowded by bleak canyon walls jaggedly climbing to the sky on all four sides, crookedly cutting their path through the ancient limestone, I would at least have shadows in the morning and evening to keep the temperatures cooler.

The excavation area was easy to spot, too. I saw it across the mesa, not centered but more to the north-west end, up against the north canyon wall footing. I walked over to it, scanning the ground as I walked, looking for evidences of habitations. In untraveled, virtually untouched places such as this wadi hidden up in the canyons, surface debris often remained for thousands of years. I had walked off-road sites along the upper Nile under the searing sun of Egypt and found Pre-dynastic pottery shards laying right on the surface, just where they had been dropped five thousand years ago. Breezes alternately covered and uncovered such ground surfaces with shallow sand, but when blown clean, untouched history lay at your feet. This dry, hard ground was blown clean, and its treasures it did not withhold. Almost immediately, beside the small stones and pebbles which had lain naturally since before the time of man, I began to see signs of ancient lives left as they lay. Yes, there were pottery shards here and there. Bronze Age. Iron Age. Roman. A good sign. A very good sign.

Before I knew it, my strides had reached the villa site itself. There wasn't much, as the woman at the Department of Antiquities had said: just a group of ancient walls from a group of varied buildings jutting hap-hazardly up out of the dirt, and at the base of the wadi itself, a small stone-lined oasis spring, long fallen into serious disrepair, and very, very dry.

But this site was mine, for six weeks.

I now noticed over at two different places that test-trenches had been dug by the team which had officially catalogued the site. I walked over to the closest one and bent down to examine the dirt piled up by its side, and peer down at the exposed soil inside the trench walls. Even in the poor light of the shadows I saw bits and pieces of pottery, brick fragments, edges of rough hewn stone and pieces of charcoal from a fire. There were many, many pottery shards sticking out of this trench's walls. I stood up. This had been a heavily lived-in habitation, in spite of its location. Or, perhaps, I thought, because of its location. I gazed around to get a better feel of the original buildings and room layouts. Yes, this had once been a sizable villa of some distinction, judging by the overall size.

Not as insignificant as the catalogue implied, I thought.

I next walked over to the remains of the springhead at the base of the north wadi wall. Artesian springs were part of what had carved these limestone canyons and made the numerous caves hidden within them. They fascinated me - water, surging up pure and sweet from a hole in the dry ground. Where slow-flowing water running through sand hits solid rock and can go no further, it rises to the surface, making springs as this one had once been, long, long ago. Perhaps David and his men had drunk from this spring during his days of hunted exile.

The spring had obviously not known water for a very long time. The shaft of the spring was fallen in on itself, leaving just a dry funnel of gravel sinking into the dry ground. The stonework had suffered much over the centuries, and little actually remained of it. Yet my eyes saw enough to know it had once been a fairly large springhead, probably perennial, capable of sustaining many lives.

I looked up from this dry hole and all around me.

This was it. This was my chosen site.

As I was quickly losing the daylight, my immediate need was to carefully set up camp before nightfall. I went back down the embankment to where the four wheel was parked, and began to unload gear. My packing back at the airport in Tel Aviv had been thoughtfully planned: the first boxes before me as I raised the rear hatch were the two tents. I carried them one at a time back up the embankment and set them down to study this problem carefully.

Remembering that Howard Carter had unwittingly set his tent directly over the entry way of King Tut's Tomb, delaying his discovery for years, I picked a spot on the east side of the anciently habited plateau which seemed unlikely to be over any thing of man.

The two tents went up with ease, one for the equipment as lab and office, the other one to sleep and eat in. With several more trips back down to the vehicle I set up the tables inside the office tent, and after carrying up the precious equipment, I unpacked the seven computer units in order. Following the numbered cables and the wiring map Kevin had made, I quickly wired them up, ready to start the next morning. I thanked Kevin for the simplicity of his plan.

Next I brought up the things for the living quarters. I set up my cot, the breakfast table, and arranged the food boxes on the right side of my tent. The water containers, reduced from five to two by bullet holes, gave me an uneasy feeling. However, the three with holes in them still held some water, which I determined to save. Putting the three partials by the two full ones, I saw the job as completed.

I stepped outside to view my fully established camp. It was complete. And all of this was accomplished while I still had daylight reflecting off the tops of the highest wadi wall.

After a short walk up the wadi and back, in the darkening shadows of twilight, I sat down in my camp chair and looked up at the rugged cliff walls towering above me. Stars were already beginning to appear in the night sky. I did not want to bother lighting the lantern tonight. It was enough to be here, to be set up, and to sit as the night enveloped the earth and me in it.

I began thinking about the Hazazon-tamar of Seraiah's hastily scribbled message. This was the wadi Hasasa. But no one today was exactly sure where Hazazon-tamar had been. Hazazon of the date palms, it meant. There were no date palms here. Not now, at any rate. This particular wadi was not the bleakest part of the Wilderness of Judah, but it was stark. At En Gedi there had obviously been date palms in most ancient times, and they still grew at the oasis. Many date palms.

Yet the ancient dry spring at this site, over by the north-west end of the villa, carefully lined with hewn stone, was indication of perhaps abundant water. There could have been date palms here, many of them. This could have been a thriving little oasis. It inferred the possibility of crops. Certainly crops could have been grown on this ample plateau within the wadi, which may have had water running in it after some winters. The whole area around this part of the Wilderness was filled with springs and anciently had been home to wild goats, thus there had been an abundance of limited foods for hunting and gathering, at least for a small group as might have inhabited a villa such as this.

The Song of Solomon mentioned vineyards at Hazazon-tamar. Vineyards could have grown here, I thought, but again, En Gedi and its immediate surroundings were much more suitable for lush gardens where grapes might have grown. Out on the narrow coastal plain, the modern Jewish kibbutzim I had passed grow early vegetables, I knew, but the intense heat of the Dead Sea Valley was too great during the summers, too dry and hot. Yet with water from the ancient spring, would this piece of desert be brought to flower?

What would I find here? Would I find any exploitable gemstones to listen to? Would I find any exploitable construction stones containing imprints of ancient voices? Would the high-tech equipment I had lugged all the way out here into this forsaken wadi work if I indeed did find stones of a type that could be interfaced with this incredible system of technology?

More importantly, would I find the Urim and Thummim which Yehoniah affirmed in the Yeb dedication he had hidden somewhere near this place in which I sat tonight? Were they waiting for me somewhere near, hidden away in the dark of centuries, near me right now? Had Yehoniah fulfilled his oath in this place?

With many questions to answer, and only six weeks to search for answers, I decided to go to bed and sleep.

By now the night was fully black, and the walls of the wadi towering on both sides made this a dark place indeed. Only directly above me was there light, light from the myriad twinkling stars.

Whether these wadi walls were the same walls of rock and sand and gravel which Yehoniah had visited and walked upon and seen all those centuries ago, I could not be sure tonight.

I did not yet know if anywhere around me was something I could feel we shared in common, he and me.

Yet as I looked up at the sparkling stream of night sky wedged between the high canyon walls, one thing I did know for certain.

These were the same stars Yehoniah had known.

Over time and space, we shared the stars.

Chapter 7

In The Wilderness: Weeks of digging

My eyes slowly fluttered, squinting at the light.

It was light, but not bright, eye-piercing light. It was shadowy light. My eyes struggled and finally squeezed into a narrow squint.

Green. All I could see was green, hazy green.

The air all around me was still and silent.

Very still.

Very silent.

It was morning.

As my foggy brain registered that I was awakening, the quietness and stillness of the air distilled upon my consciousness. I listened. There was no sound. It was as if the earth held its breath. Nothing. The silence was eerie. There were none of the usual sounds I heard around my tent in camp. No crunching footsteps on the gravel and dirt outside as someone walked by. No birds chirping. No clanking pots and pans at a close campfire or cook stove as someone prepared breakfast. No distant chopping wood echoing off a forested mountainside. No muffled distant voices, or children's laughter, or adults telling stories over coffee. No far away barking dog. No car motor starting up and revving, driving away to river or lake to go fishing. No noises of other campers awakening and beginning their day. Nothing.

Only silence. Total, absolute silence.

I could not remember ever being so completely aware of silence. I lay on my cot, looking up at the green ceiling of the tent. Slowly I became conscious of my own breathing, and the close echo of my breathing off the tent sides. I held my breath.

I could hear my heart beating.

I was alone.

My eyes were accustomed now to the light, and I opened them a bit more. The ceiling of the tent came into sharper focus above me, and I slowly traced the seams up one corner and then down the other. I traced the dim half-shadows cast on the sleek fabric by the aluminum tube frames outside.

Green is nice, I thought. I was glad we had chosen green. I would not see much green for many weeks, except for this tent.

Sitting up on the cot, I rubbed my eyes. I wiggled my toes and stretched a good stretch. Standing, I unzipped the door flap, and tossed it back over the side of the tent to peer out at my wadi.

Cool fresh morning air instantly rolled in around me.

I gazed up and around at the unbelievably high towering canyon walls, and sucked in a deep lungfull of that cool, fresh, clean desert air. It was as no other air I had ever savored. Exquisite. Rich. I stood for a moment just savoring the air.

It was the first morning.

The first morning in the field was always a mystical experience for me, and the air was always its magician. By it I suddenly found myself reconnected to all the natural elements of the Earth. It flowed into my body through my nostrils and lungs, and I feasted.

Was this the smell of the air on the primordial morning? I tried to imagine what the air must have been like centuries ago, before the Industrial Revolution, before the internal combustion engine. It must have been intoxicatingly good. Air that nourished like a food. Air with the taste of life.

Though I usually didn't notice the taste of chemicals and pollutants back home, I tasted their absence here. I could always taste their absence in nature, far from their hazy clouds clinging to the cities. Yet from jet travel, I knew that the whole planet was now covered with a pall of pollution. Looking down to the Earth's distant horizon, it was clearly visible from the jetstream heights, reddish brown within our planet's thin layer of atmosphere. Even into this deep remote canyon by the desolate Dead Sea, dozens of miles into the Judaean Desert, hidden in a virtually uninhabited region, surrounded by the almost untouched expanses of Egypt, the Sinai, the Mediterranean, Israel, Syria, the Arabian Desert and Mesopotamia, still it came. Contaminants from thousands of miles away, even from far around the world, drifted in currents and curled in the air ever more thinly until they reached and penetrated here.

It was not so long ago, I thought, that men had not believed in air. Air was a relatively new belief and discovery according to the books, made in the 5th century BC by a Greek named Empedocles. Though air had always been around to feel, and to hear, it could not be seen. Thus it had not existed. What a favor we had done to the earth, I mused, by making all of the air visible.

Often I had thought about the discovery of air. People must have known it was there before Empedocles experimented and understood a principle of its presence demonstrated. Surely its other signs had been noticed by earlier men. Even most ancient human beings must have understood breath; seen it foggy and clouded on cold mornings and winter days; felt it warm against their cheeks from a woman's mouth; watched her hair blown against a blue sky in spring. They must have seen dust picked up and blowing in the air. Certainly they knew the urgency for air screaming in their lungs when they held their breath, or worse when they were denied breath beyond their lungs' bursting. Surely they knew that if they could not breathe in, they would die. How could they see all of this, and none of it have had meaning for them? Surely some must have observed and quietly known, though they had no words to describe what they knew, as Empedocles would some day do.

Yet truly most did not know the air, which enveloped them, and put pressure on their bodies to hold in their blood, and in their lungs to allow the exchange of life for death, of oxygen for carbon dioxide. There were no names for oxygen or carbon dioxide. There was no understanding of air. So it did not exist.

Only when Empedocles devised a scientific experiment - to test a totally different premise, which turned out to be completely mistaken- was air suddenly declared to exist. Yet it had always been there, the most immediate need of life. Though other things were useful to keeping us alive, air was above them all.

Without food, we live weeks.

Without water, we live days.

Without air, we live only minutes.

Then we die.

I decided this morning I was glad for the existence of air.

With a final affirmative scan across the cliffs, and a good deep breath of air, I turned back into the tent to get dressed. The expedition was begun. Treasures awaited.

City clothes would now remain packed for six weeks. In their place I pulled on field clothes: blue jeans, a hat, a tough cotton shirt and good high-top boots. In the heat of day I would want to take off the shirt, yet long sleeves would protect me from excessive ultra-violet rays. For early mornings and evenings, a thicker shirt would warm me against the chill of desert nights. When the desire to dig by lantern light possessed me, or the tedious task of sorting and classifying artifacts kept me up late at night, and most hopefully when working with the computer and hi-tech units well into the early hours of the morning, I had brought two sweaters.

Dressed, I walked outside the tent ready for the first day.

Though this entire area at the bottom of the canyon remained in shadows, the band of sky above the wadi shone brilliantly blue. Bright sunlight reflected off the tops of the highest rocks, down into my abyss and its ruins. It would not be cool long. I calculated that in only a couple of hours, perhaps less, sunlight would pour down in full power and creep across the sand and rocks here, cooking all it touched, including me.

I turned in a full circle looking out over the canyon system surrounding me. Somewhere up there, up one of these canyon walls, perhaps not so far from here, were the Urim and Thummim. The Oracles of the Lord, given by Moses to Aaron the High Priest.

Unless of course someone had found them, and taken them as trinkets.

Yet the Dead Sea Scrolls had remained largely untouched until 1948, not all that long ago. They had been in large caves, tempting and open for centuries. But they had remained. Yehoniah most probably would have chosen a small, unpretentious hiding place for the Urim and Thummim. Surely they still awaited.

My search, however, could not begin until all things were prepared and ready here at camp. There was still much to do. I had to dig enough of a start at this site to at least give the appearance of working here, should anyone come to check on me. And, it wouldn't hurt to test the sound equipment on a few specimens, no matter how unsuitable. The practice would serve me well in the event I found my prize. So, first things first. And what should be first? Breakfast. With a long, arduous day ahead, food always had to be first. Without fuel to burn, strength failed.

My food stores on this trip were good: eggs, fresh and powdered; whole wheat bread to last a week, then ready-prepared flour for pancakes, biscuits and rolls; powdered milk laced with a few drops of vanilla extract, my own secret; non-frozen fruit-juice syrups and a case of two-litre sodas; oatmeal and cold cereals; dried fruits of all kinds; sesame Halava in vanilla and chocolate flavors; good cheese; raisins; a big box of sweet dates, and my favorite field excavation food staple: fig bars. Many cases of fig bars. If I were too busy or too excited to stop and cook, I could eat in a fig bar with one hand.

For meals when I would be cooking, there were lots of canned goods: stews, soups, vegetables, corned beef hash, ham, baked beans and much more. Most of the food was, in fact, canned or dried. As for the dried foods, the loss of three of my large water containers would seriously affect the ability to stretch water supplies before having to go down the canyons and out to En Gedi. Yet a trip out of the canyons into the civilized world had always been seen as inevitable.

Breakfast on the first day of a dig was simple. Today especially, there was too much to do: all of the usual pre-excavation site preparations had to be completed, and then I had to finish setting up the power train to the sound-search equipment. So, I would have a fig bar, a glass of fresh milk and a vitamin. I smiled. Locusts and honey would have been a simpler and more nutritious meal, as scientific research had astonishingly revealed, but I was fresh out of locusts, with no time to catch any. Milk and honey-sweet fig bars would have to do for my first meal in the Wilderness.

I took my small breakfast out to the veranda and sat on the aluminum chair to gaze more upon my tiny kingdom. It was a very small kingdom indeed. 'Only the rocks, sand, lizards and scorpions to be my subjects.'

These words of Cecil B. DeMille in *The Ten Commandments* echoed in my mind. Deserts like these, he said, were the places where prophets were tested and tempered, and prepared for holy deeds. It was true: the Bible spoke of many such unique men who had spent long weeks in this wilderness, seeking the will of God.

Yet being here was different. Reading about it in a book utterly failed to convey its gritty dryness and heat. Those who came here anciently suffered terrible tortures, until silenced by these parched canyons.

I gazed around at this barren wadi, thinking of their solitude, exhaustion, heat scorched by day, chilled at night, haunted by hunger and thirst. Cecil B. DeMille was right. There was no water, no food, no companions to talk to, only sun, rocks, sand and thirst. Is this where men were tested and tempered, and prepared for holy deeds?

I shook my head.

No, this was a place where men could go mad.

My little spot, however, had been an oasis, with a home and several buildings. Its long-dry artesian spring had once made this place a haven. And it was well situated; time had carved it well. The wadi river bed swept down from the upper right around an abruptly sharp corner, then followed a wide semi-circular course under the ever deepening foot of the receding south wall. The higher, open space which had been progressively widened by the carving of water was in two levels: the lower which held the dirt road, and the higher upon which the ruins of the ancient villa and my tents now stood. Morning and evening shadows provided air conditioning, yet enough sun would fall upon this soil to grow garden crops. In peace time, it was no so far from En Gedi for additional food and supplies.

But nearing mid summer, it would get hot. I hoped there might be a daily breeze up or down the wadi, but at the moment, the air seemed perfectly still. Last night the air had been still, too. Not a good sign. This wadi might become very hot during late mid-day.

As I finished the last bite of fig bar, I arose and went over to the edge of the mesa embankment. It was only about fifteen feet down to the road, yet this had made for some effort getting all the camp equipment up last night. I skidded down the steep slope to the four-wheel and got out the three boxes with the solar cells and batteries. With a huff I made three more trips up the embankment and set them at the top of the mesa. I could see that the ground near the lab tent would get just as much sunlight as anywhere else. Good. I carried them there and unpacked.

Now a minor question: which way was the best facing for the sun? Solar panels needed direct or almost direct rays for full power. My compass was back in the four-wheeler. However, a glance upward showed the way. The sunlight gleaming on the rocks at the high canyon rim revealed the East.

Soon I had all twenty solar-cell panels properly in place, connected with the cables to the battery units, ready to power the lab. I pushed the main cable from the batteries through the hole in the tent, and went inside to plug it in and boot up the system.

A flick of the main switch and...... it worked! At least all of the lights came on, and I could hear the cooling fans whirring softly in the quiet. Power was flowing system wide. Now, would it really work? This was the question Kevin and I still waited to answer. I would have to excavate a good gemstone before we would know.

But there were still other problems. With the stillness of the air in this wadi, high temperatures were probably going to develop unless it got a breeze. Over-heating the equipment could be disastrous. The lab tent had been specially constructed with a double open roof for ventilation, and a wide circular awning which shaded all four walls. But if the wadi air itself heated up over 90 degrees during the day, Hi-Tech time would have to wait until the night shift. I fumbled through the accessories box until I found the large digital thermometer, and set it up in front of the computer keyboard and screen. Air heat would have to be watched with a vengeance.

I sat down at the computer now, to make sure all of its functions were fully operational. The writing program worked. The World Atlas worked. The archaeological data banks and textual data banks all opened perfectly. As I scrolled and scanned, everything appeared to be intact and fully accessible. Even the Internet program came up, though I was not connected. There was no cellular phone uplink in this system. Kevin and I had decided against it for a variety of reasons. Mainly, I was a hundred kilometers from the only two sizable cities in the region - Tel Aviv and Jerusalem. Knowing my position 1,500 feet down in the bottom of a narrow stone canyon, out in the middle of a desert wasteland, a link would have been useless. There was only the narrowest band of unobstructed sky above me - straight up. Scrolling down other menus I checked a number of additional programs and databanks. All was perfect. The system was entirely functional, so far as I could see.

All I needed now were my first stone specimens to connect and scan for energy imprints of sound.

The time had come to dig.

I decided the old initial test trenches deserved to be checked in good sunlight, before gridding the entire site into quadrants and choosing which quadrants I would dig. Grabbing a new pick and trowel for the job, I walked out to the furthest trench, the one I had not checked last night.

It was beyond the ruined building walls, towards the wadi river bed. As I approached it, I quickly understood why this spot had been chosen for a test trench. This was the typical place where garbage would be thrown, all the trash and debris we humans wished to be rid of with the least possible effort.

Knowledge of predictable human behavior was the scientific domain of the archaeologist. We had to learn it well, determine it well, and dig by it.

185

Too often there was so little money that only a small portion of a large and promising site could be excavated. So, we had to pick and choose which quadrants we thought would produce the best treasures. Of thousands of digs in the world, few had been more than just provisionally explored. Most of what we knew of ancient cultures came from scattered little trenches such as these, and from shafts and quadrants, dug across buildings, perpendicular or at tangents to courtyards, streets and open living spaces, as the sample slice seemed best. It was surface scratching. We dug down to varying levels, only in some of them to original topsoil. Less than ten percent of the treasure-laden remains of the classical world were sifted through by archaeologists, even less in other parts of the world. We were unable to do more for lack of funds and hands. Whole cities remained tantalizingly untouched except for small trench excavations, like this one.

Yet it was a beginning.

Here, by myself, at this remote and isolated site, I would be lucky to clear three or four quadrants down to topsoil. There were only six weeks to dig and miles of wadis to search for the Urim and Thummim. So, I would have to use all of my intuitive logic as an archaeologist to think like the ancient people who had lived here, to try and guess where the greatest abundance of discarded and lost artifacts might possibly be.

As I looked down into the test trench, I could see this is what the experienced test diggers had done here. They had gotten lucky, and found a midden. Wherever possible, site testers looked for middens, or dumps. Dumps were wonderful treasure troves, usually containing a pretty good sampling of what could be expected from the whole site. Broken pieces of pottery were the best tattle-tales of who had lived in a site and when they had lived there. Shards were the unfailing time-revealers almost always found among the discards in middens. The fact that dump treasures were only fragments was unimportant: fragments gave a vision of the whole, and from them we learned much about a people and a site. This test trench had been intentionally dug across the logical line of tossed discards, and had hit pay dirt.

On my knees, I immediately saw its rewards. Pieces of artifacts, fragments of potteries and building materials, were sticking out all along the trench walls. Bronze Age pottery fragments clearly at the bottom; Iron Age II fragments just above. Had the site been abandoned that long? Hellenistic and Roman shards above those; another period of abandonment? Above the Roman, nothing. Just fill dirt, blown across and washed down from the wadi for centuries. That was it. This place had been totally deserted and uninhabited for eighteen centuries.

Thirst was already urging me to stop for a drink. Time for a break. Soda without ice was not as good as soda with ice, but who was complaining? I got a tall plastic cup, opened the sodas and pulled out a two-liter bottle.

The fizzy sound it made falling into the glass seemed loud in the quiet of the tent. Every little bubble burst with a crystalline tinkling. I drank deeply; it tasted so good sliding down. Drinking in this heat was going to become the pleasure pastime of the trip.

My thirst quenched, it was time to begin gridding. Though my real purpose was to hike the wadis in search of the Urim and Thummim, gridding the site was a must. I wanted to dig for artifacts here at the ancient oasis, and hopefully I would find some hard-stone jewelry objects suitable for sound and voice scanning. But whatever happened, I had to excavate by the book. The Urim and Thummim were the prize I dreamed of, but I still had to find something in the ground which would provide a good test, and with luck, talk to me.

I went out to the embankment and down a final time to get the last box, the one with the string and grid stakes in it, and carried it back up and over to the villa ruins.

Though time and probably a Roman war had toppled the walls, and sifting sands had partially covered them, the ruins were easy enough to follow jutting up along the ground. The fill dirt was not so deep, according to what I saw in the test trenches. All that had been here was probably before my eyes, with no buried surprises.

With paper and pencil in hand, I quickly walked the ruin walls and measured them, drawing them onto a rapidly growing master plan map. As I marked each room area into its original form, the architectural plan emerged on my paper. This had been a villa of five distinct buildings, perhaps not all built at the same time. Two of them were quite large, of multiple rooms; three of them were small single-room structures. They were all closely clustered together, probably for safety, but there was enough space between them to move livestock and carts.

My guess was that both larger multi-room structures were houses. In each, the first large room just inside the door would have been the combined living room, kitchen and meal area. The side rooms were most likely for sleeping and storage. Knowing ancient lifestyles, especially those of people living in extreme wilderness conditions, more than one family may have lived in each of these larger buildings. There had been plenty of water to sustain them.

The three smaller, single-room buildings may have been for storage, or possibly workshops of some kind. On the other hand, remembering the passage in the Bible Atlas which noted an Amorite military outpost somewhere along the Ascent of Ziz, the possibility that this whole little complex had begun as barracks and supply rooms for Amorite soldiers figured strongly in my mind. Only excavation would tell its story. I would dig at least a quarter quadrant in each of these small buildings to see what the evidence might be.

With the general layout of the buildings drawn onto my grid map, I began to systematically pound stakes into the ground at measured intervals, and stretch string from stake to stake, quickly forming them into the web which would scientifically divide the site into excavation quadrants.

As soon as I was finished setting up the site web, I began numbering the quadrants. Every shard and artifact as discovered had to be noted on the site map according to the web, with its depth level in centimeters, and its relative position as found.

Such webs delineated all sites in modern digs, assuring that each individual find could be accurately catalogued into the scaled geographic site map with exactness. The precise place where every artifact had been left or discarded, and near which things each object was found, ultimately told much of a ruin's story.

With my maps and grids in order, and my sifting screens and buckets set up by the ruins, I could now begin to dig. This was the difficult moment of truth, in which I had to guess which part of the villa might hold what I was looking for beneath its soil. I needed some kind of personal jewelry stone for testing and sound evaluation. I would have to choose my quadrants wisely.

Four quadrants, by the best of my experience and intuition, showed the greatest promise of containing lost jewelries or semi-precious stones. They were inside building walls, in what should have been the most heavily used square footages. In the largest room of the main house I chose to dig two quadrants; in the smaller house only one; I lastly chose what might have been the master bedroom. These were where I felt lay my best hopes of finding an earring, a finger ring, a bracelet stone, a seal stone or a necklace pendant stone which had fallen out of its setting, broken off its chain, or been dropped and lost in the dirt floors.

In our modern times we do not think of living in houses with dirt floors. It is an entirely different way of life from living with hard floors of tile, vinyl or wood. Small things fall into dirt floors and are lost. Loose dirt instantly covers them, and though they may be under the thinnest veil of grains, they become invisible. Today we only experience this on visits to the beach, where a ring or coin drops into the sand at our feet and disappears. Unbelievingly we dig and dig on our hands and knees, sifting exactly where we know it dropped, but we never find it. Eventually we give up and call it lost. We mournfully leave it just out of sight in the sand, the lucky prize of beachcombers with metal detectors.

Anciently, without the aid of such technology, things often remained lost forever, even in one's own home floor. For floors filled with more and more dirt each year, brought in on the soles of dusty feet and muddy sandals, on the roots of vegetables being prepared for cooking, and from the ever present dust blowing in the wind. The biblical parable of the poor woman who lost a silver coin in the floor of her house says that she desperately swept and swept until she found it, and then called all the neighbors to rejoice with her in the finding of the lost coin. The story casts much light on the dirt floor system of housekeeping. It was easy to lose small things of value, never to find them again in the dirt.

Two thousand years later, for me, this could be a positive bit of fortune. In fact, the success of my entire expedition was bet on it.

I began and dug most of the afternoon, sifting bucket after bucket of soil. Below the surface dirt which had filled in over eighteen centuries I found a thick layer of ash and carbonized wood, the remains of thin roof beams and palm thatching. The end of this villa had not been happy; most probably it had been burned and destroyed by Roman legionaries in the Bar Kochba War, under orders from Emperor Hadrian.

Within this destruction layer were dozens of complete pots in shards; portions of well-preserved wood which I carefully sealed in plastic bags and labeled; and a number of fallen wall blocks made of local canyon stone. By nightfall these stone blocks remained as the only stone prizes found for the day.

It was now time to initiate the true purpose of this expedition, and put the Foundation's money where my mouth had led them. Would the stone cry out of the wall, as Habakkuk had written? There was no iron fastener to help testify, but it was time to scan the stones with the new computer equipment, and search for sounds.

Did the ancient walls of this villa have ears?

It was time to push the envelope and test the question.

I ate a quick dinner and set myself up in the lab tent. The solar battery panel had fully charged the system during the day. It was supposed to run the computer and sound detection units for ten full hours, while giving me a steady 100-watt work light. If all functioned as proposed, I could work as late as my eyelids allowed.

I hooked up the first building stone to the scanning devices, and stood back to behold this first connection.

The stone had probably been set into the wall around 2,000 B.C. and stayed there until it was toppled about 135 AD.

I looked upon the stone, hooked up with the wires.

This building stone had most likely absorbed voices in Canaanite, Hittite, Amorite, Moabite, Hebrew, Egyptian, Assyrian, Babylonian, Persian, Greek, Aramaic, and Latin. This stone.

The impact of this reality hit me as if I was hearing it for the first time in my life. This was an uncontaminated, viable stone.

This stone had actually absorbed and heard everything spoken in the room from which I took it. That was an undeniable fact. It had been there. It knew every secret that had been whispered over the two thousand years of habitation within those walls. Had it kept those secrets? Were they preserved? Would it give them to me? Did I have what would be required to coax the living past out from within its sub atomic structure?

With mixed trepidations, I began scanning it with the new equipment. I brought up applications and initiated them. I flipped switches. I turned knobs.

I got no readings; no impulses of any kind.

This was a time to set monitor values. Turning control dials and adjusting monitor levels all to zero, I again slowly scrolled through the menu of options, and systematically applied the many different software programs, hook-ups and scanning device alternatives.

Nothing.

I then added the power of the various kaleidoscopic search programs in conjunction with the pattern identifiers. I could only imagine what was going on within the wiring, boards and cores.

But there were no results.

I tried another block of stone, and then another, realizing that I had no way of knowing which blocks may have actually been part of the inner wall facing. Some may have been inner wall fill stones, or even exterior facing stones pushed inward.

I eventually tried all the stone blocks, with all of the different wirings, all of the programs, all of the settings, but none of the options produced anything.

Exhausted, I turned off the computer system by the main switch, and wearily turned out the light.

It had been a long first day.

I thoughtfully walked to my tent, closed the door flap, and slumped into bed.

I was asleep in less time than it takes to blow out a candle.

The next morning began a string of mornings and days almost indistinguishable one from the other. I would wake early, dress, fix and eat breakfast, hike up the wadis around me in search of seemly hiding places for the Urim and Thummim, find nothing and then disappointedly walk back to camp. There I would eat lunch and then go to the quadrant I was digging. The first few days saw the clearing of the destruction debris layer, and after removing charred wood, ashes and the considerable disarray of stones from the fallen walls, I began to dig into the final levels of inhabited floors. Into these I dug deeper and deeper, centimeter upon centimeter, layer upon layer, always hoping to find a lost gemstone with each sweep of my brush.

The abundant promise of the test trenches was more than fulfilled as I dug. This was a good site. The buildings had indeed been occupied over many centuries, and abandoned between habitations.

The finds were far from paltry. I was surprised. Not only pottery shards appeared with great frequency, but a variety of ancient metal items accumulated on my specimen table in the lab tent. There were several copper Roman nails, long and square-sided with conical heads. Then I found a lepton, and then another, until over a dozen Jewish coins in copper, bronze and two silver Roman denarii had been found. The lepta were of Alexander Yannai and Yohanan Hyrcanus of the Maccabean period, and of Herod, Gratus and Pontius Pilate. One of the denarii was of the Republic, the other bore the face of the emperor Augustus. Then I found the finely curved and delicately worked copper handles of a glass ointment bottle, with part of the glass vessel still attached to one; a woman's decorated copper fibula pin; and a small iron knife, probably from kitchen use. The iron blade was remarkably intact due to the dry air, and most of the rough handle wood remained as well. These were fine artifacts which any dig would be proud to show.

Other things also turned up as the digging wore on: an ivory pair of dice; an ivory spindle whorl for making thread; a wad of rags which would be of inestimable value to the textiles department; woven pieces of several baskets, apparently used as mats on which to place vessels or bread or other foods. Pieces of a number of clay oil lamps emerged, and several almost complete ones; fragments of more small glass vessels, hardly oxidized in the dry soil of the wadi.

Most unusual were the actual food particles which turned up in the siftings on the screen, which astonished me enormously: walnut shells; dozens of date pits, a few with part of the date meat still clinging; olive pits; pomegranate peels and seeds; pistachio nut shells; several almonds; and many grains of wheat.

Certainly these were the things of real people's lives. I was touching their lives with every object, though I could only imagine what their faces may have looked like. I imagined women and men and children of different ages, over many successive generations as I dug deeper every day into the floors of the three rooms I was digging.

I continued to test stone blocks from the walls, but without success. Several day's testing and more than 40 stones established enough of a pattern to discourage me. It was uncertain whether limestone was too soft to preserve sound energy patterns, or if the blocks had been heated in the destruction fire above the radiation release temperature and had everything driven out of them, or if the equipment and software programs were just not working. I could not tell. The urgent need to find a suitable gemstone specimen grew.

Yet the most pressing anxiety of my waking day was the search for the Urim and Thummim hidden by the hand of Yehoniah, perhaps somewhere within a few miles' radius of this spot.

Each day I spent several hours hiking up the many converging tributary wadis in search of a high, straight stretch which looked or felt as if it might be the place. I continued for many days walking the wadis in the mornings and evenings, squinting against the sun and peering into shadows for caves and indentations in the rocks.

I found many. This area of limestone canyons, so easily sculpted by water, was riddled with pits, deep shelves and small natural caves, mostly shallow but nonetheless adequate for shelter. Some were quite large. These were often carved out larger and deeper by human hands, probably since earliest times.

These larger caves, easily seen from the dry riverbed and thus easy targets of bedouin treasure-hunters and official expeditions, were all exhaustively excavated, even in this remote zone. After climbing dangerous ledges of loose, slippery rock to reach several of them, only to find each one ransacked or systematically dug, I began to lose hopes of finding in any of them the treasure which I sought.

Thus I began to squint harder, and look for smaller, less obvious clefts and holes up the sides of the wadis. I took to climbing up to the tops of ridges and walking long distances while looking down along the opposite wadi walls, searching for pockets and cracks and holes which might have attracted the intuition of Yehoniah.

He too, I thought, would have searched for a place that would avoid unexpected discovery, where it would be not disturbed by the perennial bands of nomads which have always roamed these desolate places. I knew that he, too, must have worried over the possibility of unknowing hands accidentally finding that which was reserved for only the most holy.

And so I scrutinized and scanned and searched the stony cliffs for every possible place provided by nature. After a stretch had been walked, I would then climb back down to the wadi floor and hike to the stones and shrubs I had noted as landmarks on the dry riverbed which marked the places I had seen from above. Then, I would climb the treacherous cliffs until I reached the small hole or opening in the rocky cliff face.

Each time, I sifted my fingers and tools through the dirt. Each time, I found nothing. My hopes seemed as empty as the small clefts I clawed at, as I clung to the barren wadi walls.

Then one day at the camp site I made a major discovery. Two semi-precious stones appeared in the lower level of quadrant three.

The first was a chipped, red carnelian intaglio seal stone, lost from a ring; the other was an amethyst earring in a gold wire fitting. When the earring first appeared under the stroke of my brush, I could not help but think of Dr. Julie Powell at the Foundation. Another woman had shared her taste for the glittering beauty of purple amethyst crystals. Dr. Powell would be pleased with this find.

It was the site discovery I had been waiting for. With the two jewelry stones in hand, I suspended digging for the afternoon, and carried them carefully to the lab tent. Within minutes the first connection was completed, and I sat down to begin scanning with pattern search.

As I made hook-up after hook-up, using each successive device and wiring option, my hopes truly began to slump. These were choice, perfect stones. They had lain for over two thousand years at the bottom of a thousand-foot chasm sheltered by mountains of stone. More than three feet of dirt, rock, charcoal and more dirt had covered them for at least eighteen centuries. The carnelian ring stone must have absorbed thousands of conversations before being knocked out of its setting. The earring, too, must have absorbed hundreds if not thousands of conversations. Countless hours of human voice energies must have bombarded and penetrated both of these perfect stones and been absorbed in them, but I had no results.

Only silence.

It was very discouraging.

I worked late into the night with the two stones and the hi-tech equipment with not so much as a syllable detected.

As I finally conceded defeat and went to bed, the prospects of realizing my dream seemed to be vanishing as an echo in the wind.

When I awoke the next morning, I lay in bed awhile pondering my situation.

Though my spirits were low, I still had an entire month on my permit. In spite of the failures of the sound-retrieval, reassembly programs and equipment, I could do much in this site. I should continue to dig it. However, though the focus of my purpose might have to change, that focus could return, should the right artifact appear. That artifact of course would be the Urim and Thummim. Yet I had no guarantee of finding them.

What should I do? On the one hand, artifacts did seem to await within the ground of this villa. On the other hand, there might not be another chance the rest of my life to be this close to finding the Urim and Thummim. This was the potential of a lifetime.

I decided that sound recovery or no sound recovery, finding the Urim and Thummim would make this whole trip a success. I would shift my focus, and spend more hours each day searching.

Thus I began days of hiking and searching the cliffs, digging at the site only for the first hours of the mornings.

I began to carefully mark the map with each excursion. This helped my overloaded memory to recall which almost identical canyon tributaries I already walked, and help me study the map at night in hopes of discovering some hidden cleft in the wadi walls which concealed a virtually inaccessible wadi branch.

Systematically I began to cross off many of the small branches leading up into the dry slashes of this time-eroded earth and rock. The Wilderness of Judah was a true maze of deep gouged canyons and narrow fissures. I had no way of knowing which was the right one, nor where the anticipated cave opening Yehoniah had chosen might be. I climbed and investigated every small pocket cave, some as small as gopher holes, but never found so much as a shard to evidence any human intrusion.

As I found more secluded and hidden larger caves, I climbed and investigated them, but as the others, all had been systematically dug or ransacked, leaving less and less hope. I still dug in several of these, to see if perhaps some stone had been left unturned, but each time, with only minimal digging, the thoroughness of systematic excavation left no hope of finding any undiscovered caches awaiting my discovery. All of the smaller holes and pockets proved to be equally empty temptations.

Every day I explored another tributary wadi, each day covering more miles of dry terrain, and more dusty, previously sifted cave floors.

The wadis began to all look the same. Indeed, they were all cut from the same rock, baked in the same dry heat for the same tedious millennia. What about them could be distinctive? Though I tried to keep up my spirits, though my true quest was probably so close within my grasp, hope dimmed. Little by little, my heart wearied.

Yet I still spent many hours each day searching up and down the labyrinth of wadis for caves and likely places to hide the Urim and Thummim. My weariness grew. I found myself wondering if this were not a total waste of time. Could the Urim and Thummim have been dug up by a Bedouin decades or even centuries ago, given to a young caravan girl to wear as some bauble or trinket? Were they sold in a bazaar for a few dinars? Who would have known what they were?

It was more and more obvious that as remote and isolated as this area may be, its caves had been thoroughly scoured. As the spring at the oasis had dried up, the well of antiquities in Judaean caves had likewise dried up. No wonder no one bothered coming here any more. All that was to be found, had been found.

Then one day, as I walked along the dry river bed of a very remote wadi tributary, I quite accidentally found the fragments of an ancient clay water flask, from the late Iron II period.

I was awestruck. This was from the eighth century BC.

The pieces were laying under a low rock overhang, protected by the side wall, just as they had fallen. They lay around a small, sharp stone. Seeing the entire flask in fragments, laying there as it had broken almost three thousand years ago, I stopped in my footsteps, and I sat down to behold the remains of a fateful moment, frozen in time.

The awe of so simple a thing, gazing upon an ancient instant just as it had happened so long ago, filled my imagining. Had a heat-tortured traveler found refuge from the merciless sun under this shaded ledge, only to accidentally roll over and crush the precious flask, spilling its life-sustaining water into the sand? Had a dying fugitive, withered and limp with thirst, thrown down the empty flask after draining the last tenacious drop, smashing it in a final act of bitterness to await certain death?

I ran my fingers over the three-thousand year old water flask fragments, contemplating the frailty of our human lives, and our dependence upon water.

We were creatures of water.

Seventy percent of our body weight was water. Like the surface of the Earth, most of us was merely water. Propped up by cell membranes into tissues forming a familiar shape, we were as this flask, mere vessels of water. Break us, and allow our water to spill out, and like this flask, we became useless.

The pottery flask was a hard fired-clay vessel, difficult to break.

We with our fragile skin were but bags, precarious bags of water, delicate, easy to tear, easy to break.

We were so unlike the flask. It could be drained a little at a time, then more, even down to only a swallow of precious water remaining. It could be completely emptied, and then fully refilled.

But we were not so.

Only a little hole, to drain us but a bit, and we die.

Because of our dependence upon water, we were creatures of thirst. As the flask, we had to be constantly refilled. But we, we had to be kept filled, ever so near the top of fully full.

We were as lakes of water traveling upon legs, running desperately from stream to stream, refilling ourselves because our water flowed from us so constantly through outlets of pores, lungs and passings. Without continual replenishment, to keep our life-skins full to almost the bursting point, we would surely die.

What had happened to the thirsty owner of this flask 3,000 years ago?

I looked around me, up and down the wadi. There were no bones in sight, not even fragments of bones. The person who broke this flask could have gone on, perhaps to die somewhere else, or even to survive. But then again, I thought, after all of these centuries, a body falling down here on this sand and gravel under this open sun would have certainly turned to dust by now, blown away in the wind. Even bones would be gone by now, returned to the earth. The fire-baked clay of the flask could survive all this time unaltered, but the elements of nature would long ago have reclaimed its owner. So I could not know the fate of the hand that lost this water flask.

I sat awhile, pensive, wondering: did this traveler make it to water, or die of thirst in this maze of canyons and dust and stone?

I got up and continued my search, walking along the dry riverbed, but I found nothing more that day.

Not even a gopher hole.

For several days thereafter I felt almost obsessed with the drive to find Yehoniah's hiding place of the Oracles of the Lord. I hiked and searched and searched and hiked for caves most of each day. I still dug a little at night in the villa.

Finally one day, after a long afternoon of arduous hiking and difficult climbing up the wadis, only to find as always that every hole or cave I climbed up to was empty or had been dug before, I trudged back to camp and sat down dejectedly in the tent to once again re-evaluate what I was doing here.

Aside from the broken flask, I had found nothing in the wadis. The Urim and Thummim might be out there, but I had a permit to dig, here. This was a valuable thing. I had been given a grant, and all of this was paid for; it should not be wasted. This was a good site to explore. It had yielded good material of great interest, with little effort. I had found already two stones of prime quality for experimentation with the electronics. Though they had failed, I did not know for certain why, and, if other gemstones could be found, perhaps one of them might preserve something which these hi-tech units could scan and identify and lock onto, and finally replay.

Unwrapping the cellophane from a fig bar, I began to munch as I sat and pondered what to do next. It was a dilemma of balance.

I could imagine the Urim and Thummim in my mind, waiting for me. I could imagine the vision of a small cave, and me inside it, finding the Urim and Thummim. It nagged at me every hour of every day. A small irritating voice inside me kept telling me *Keep looking.* But each day the hours of hiking and climbing and searching brought me nothing. What good were visions and fruitless whispered words in the midst of reality? The hours spent digging here, at the site, were bringing up artifacts worthy of the grant which sent me here.

The well of artifacts in this villa was not dried up. It was not exhausted.

So, believing much still lay beneath this silent surface of soil, I decided to dig; not only the four quadrants originally chosen, but others, many others, and to dig as much as I could of these floors.

I left off my search for Yehoniah's cave. The stone ruins here by my tent were real, and offered much more hope of finding things real and worthy of this expedition.

I began to dig full time, and continued many days of successful excavations at the site.

During the next week of working, many fragments of wonderful things were found. A brass toggle pin with clear quartz finial knob from the 6th century BC, certainly owned by a woman of some dignity. I thought how she must have mourned when it became lost. Then an alabaster Egyptian ointment jar emerged from the dirt nearby it, and then a garnet ring of fine gold.

All of these were found in such a small area I suddenly knew that they had not been lost, but intentionally buried, perhaps at the time of the Babylonian invasion. The woman and her family never returned to reclaim them from the ground. They remained for me.

I was much in her debt. All three of these artifacts were of stone, good stone, excellent test specimens for the sound-scanning equipment. The two most promising were of course the polished quartz finial on the brass toggle pin and the garnet in the gold ring. But, as each was tested, the results were the same: nothing.

Not a sound.

I turned the volume dials every which way and applied every creative combination of programs I could imagine, even wired multiple scanning hook ups simultaneously with kaleidoscopic search referencing, but still I got nothing.

The alabaster jar was no better.

All of the best items I had found, the carnelian ring stone, the amethyst earring, the garnet ring and the quartz-studded toggle pin which had secured a woman's flowing clothes, must have absorbed thousands of hours of conversations.

The evidence was mounting.

I had to begin to admit the pattern which was forming. This was not working.

The fault could not be with the quality of the semi-precious stone structures, or the lack of exposure to voices.

The failure more and more had to be faulted to the equipment and the programs.

It was not working at all.

And then I found a true treasure that gave me great hope.

On the twenty-third day, a small leather pouch, miraculously preserved in the dry climate as were so many of the normally perishable goods found at this site, was slowly revealed under the careful strokes of my brush. In it was a woman's private hoard of pretty things. Whether of the same woman or another woman I could not know. I thought again, with sorrow, that each such cache I found could only have been hidden against impending attack of an enemy, and that it had never been retrieved. Each discovery evidenced an ancient personal tragedy. I reminded myself that this was a hostile wilderness, and those who chose to live herc had led precarious lives.

In the brittle leather bag was the prize of the dig: a clear quartz crystal pendant on a beautiful gold chain, two carnelian ring stones in bezels of fine gold, and a long necklace of shaped and polished stone beads made of banded agate and brilliant sardonyx stone. The linen cord upon which the beads had been strung was still intact, though it crumbled more with every movement of the bag.

With scissors I carefully cut open the bag in order to preserve the order of the necklace beads as they had been strung. So seldom were we able to preserve the ancient order of things, and this was a chance I could not bear to lose. The beads would be re-strung in their original, resplendent order, not in the imagined order created by a museum curator wishing to make a beautiful exhibit.

As with the previous specimens, I wired each of these stone relics to the scanning devices one at a time, going through all of the different connections, with all of the programs to scan for sound patterns. I tested them repeatedly, but there was no success.

There was only silence.

I began to feel an obsessive desperation to make my theory work. Yet for all the time I was spending with the equipment and now these many perfect stones and crystals, nothing was happening. I made imaginative hook ups and tried connections over and over again with every program, but no results.

Again and again, only silence.

After several more days of working unsuccessfully with the stones and equipment, I began to listen again to the nagging voice in my mind telling me that my true work here was to find the Urim and Thummim. Though the possibility of extracting voice patterns from them seemed fruitless, they still might be found. And if I found them, the palimpsest on the Seraiah tephillah in the Dead Sea Scrolls and the ostraca in Moishe's home would securely identify them, and together, stones and scrolls and ostraca would become a great find to scholars all over the world.

The wonderful discoveries of the previous few days had confirmed to me that the ground here was far from exhausted; it had not yielded up all of its treasures. There was this much to find, even in a deserted, isolated little oasis villa such as this which probably had never had more than a dozen people living in it at one time.

Perhaps the Urim and Thummim had not been accidentally found in some past generation and lost for all time.

Not everything had been sifted from these sands.

I would search again.

So I returned to hiking the wadis, now all day, from sun up to sun down, searching for the Urim and Thummim.

As the days passed, my consciousness of how small I was in this wilderness and this search weighed more and more upon me.

It was a very big wilderness. Even the small part of it I was in was very, very big. I felt small, so small. Every day I felt smaller.

Aside from an occasional insect or lizard, my only companions were birds of prey high in the sky. I noticed them whether digging at the site, or hiking up the wadis. They were high up in the sky: great numbers of hawks, eagles and vultures, soaring northward. I saw them especially well as I hiked along the ridges above the wadis, where I not only looked down along the cliff faces for holes and hiding places, but gazed all around me at the top of this wilderness expanse. I remembered that this zone lay right under the migratory path between the northern forests and plains of the Ukraine, and the plains and savannahs of Africa. Millions of birds flew past each year, going south, going north. Their lonely cries, occasionally echoing down in the still wadis, were the only sounds which broke the silence, except for the soft moan of canyon breezes and the occasional rumble of rocks as they tumbled down the sides of canyons.

It was a lonely place to be as small as I.

As days passed I walked the tops of ridges and hills, scanning the cliffs below, often thinking of the scattered people who so many centuries ago had fled to this place of desolate canyon caves in panic for their lives. I was only a few miles distant from where Yigael Yadin had found the Cave of Letters with its priceless papyri of Bar Koseba and Babata, and the Cave of Horrors filled with skulls and bones. I thought of yet another cave further down the coast which had yielded the Chalcolithic treasure hoard of over 400 bronze and copper mace heads, axes and ritual crowns from perhaps as early as 4,000 BC; hidden, never to be retrieved. People had been coming here to seek refuge and hide things since early time.

Yet no one stayed.

It was too remote. Too dry. Too desolate.

This had always been the great secret of the Strong Holds. This is why David and his men had hidden here from Saul, moving from oasis to oasis. This is why Zealots and rebels had hidden here from Roman legionaries. Usually, no one followed. So many times in history, poor and innocent people had fled into these wadis to find refuge from persecution and attacking armies. It had not been just men. Entire families with children had come here.

Not all had survived as well as David and his small band of soldiers. Many had died here during the times of woe and travail.

I thought of these people as I walked, looking for caves. I thought of them doing as I was doing, desperately searching for caves in these hills. Their search, however, was a matter of life or death. They had no stores of preserved and dried foods in a safe camp, no four wheel engine to carry them to water whenever thirst dried their throats and swelled their tongues.

Compared to them, I was nothing. I was neither a patriot nor a hero. I was only a treasure seeker, and my pitiful hope of discoveries, even of small stones, lay in the disasters of their besieged lives.

These thoughts weighed more and more heavily upon me as I walked. I pondered upon the refugees of the Nahal Hever caves and the Wadi Murraba'at caves, men, women and children. Most of them probably starved under Roman siege. Not far away was Masada itself, so close by the Dead Sea, a site of more terrible death.

As I trod the dry ridge under the relentless, hot sun, feeling my body parch as sweat drained from me, I imagined the Romans camped and waiting here above the canyon caves until all those trapped below under their watch were dead. I thought of General Silva's legions camped tirelessly below Masada, waiting and working, building their ramp, biding their time until they could capture, torture and kill the nine hundred people above, only to be cheated of it in the end by the most daring ideal of freedom. Nine hundred lives given up because of hate.

The atrocities of the Roman Empire in this land had been abysmal. Yet before them, had the atrocities of the Ptolemies or the Seleucids been any less? Or of the Moabites, the Egyptians, or the Babylonians of Yehoniah's day? Since the awful days of the Romans, what peace had this fragile land known?

A gruesome parade of bloody conquerors and ruthless oppressors trampling over this narrow finger of land hauntingly passed before me in vision.

Though I was not usually given to morbid thoughts of the past, this day as I walked along the ridgetop in the heat and sun, the history of death in this barren place would not leave my mind. I stopped and squinted up at the high circling eagles, and then out over the many visible ridges of this treeless, grassless, dry wasteland, out across the Rift Valley which hid the Dead Sea from my view, across to the distant, dry hills stretching endlessly beyond.

I could imagine this whole region of the earth from pictures I had seen taken up in space by orbiting astronauts, looking down across the land as they silently circled the globe. I had seen what they saw from up there. In the midst of it all, I was smaller than a speck, too small to even see.

My smallness in this vast and barren space totally engulfed me. My smallness in this moment, this heartbeat of time engulfed me.

Not only was I smaller than a speck on the face of the earth. Within the grandiose explosion of human life since the beginning, and its exponential unfolding over the generations of time, I was even less than a speck amid the thronging masses of human lives. My smallness in centuries and kingdoms and empires and principalities and cultures since the beginning overwhelmed me.

I suddenly saw it all, as a garish, writhing image photographed from space, of everyone who had ever lived.

And then I remembered, there are even more yet unborn.

I was unbelievably small.

I had never before fully envisioned just how small I was.

I was nothing, nothing at all in the midst of it.

And though the heights of civilization and its glories were great, the abominations of its cruelties were unfathomable. The visions of agony hidden in these scorched, dry wadis of Judah were but a prelude to the visions of misery and weeping pathos of the world. I better than anyone knew that all of the nations, every people, every generation since the beginning of time had its wailing and gnashing of teeth over its fallen, its tortured, its dead. So much of the whole history of earth had been miserable.

So much death.

So much pain.

Since the beginning of time, it seemed, young boys had been marching proudly off to war, only to die groveling in their own blood and bowels, retching in spasms of pain only the suffering can comprehend. And young girls had been giving in love, only to see their husbands and sons cut down before their eyes, and to be raped and then slaughtered themselves. How many women had died in childbirth, screaming with pain, wilting in fevers before uncaring death? How many had been starved or frozen or wracked with plague until they exhaled, to breathe no more? How many villages and regions had been plundered and slaughtered just for the sake of plunder and slaughter? How many children, women, and men, dirty and poor and hungry, lay trodden under the unfeeling feet of petty thieves, marauding hoards and fat kings on bloody thrones?

Why?

I looked out across the land to the south sky, and knew that even as I stood, below that blue sky, in Rawanda, tens of thousands were starving, walking skeletons. It was not dim history safe and far away in time. They were dying as I breathed. Just beyond my vision, they were there, hopeless and starving and dying, now, as I lived.

I looked to the west, and knew that beyond the distant horizon, beneath the blue sky I could see, massacres of death still unfolded in what had once been ancient Dalmatia, today's Croatia and Serbia.

I turned and gazed to the north of me. There, recently, in my grandfather's lifetime, over twenty million Armenians had been slaughtered in the Caucasus, right below the sky I could see so blue. And now, in that same place, huge graves were dug deep, heaped with the decaying bodies of tens of thousands of Kurds tangled in grotesque masses of slaughter, under that same sand. I had seen the color photos with my own eyes in a weekly world magazine. It made me shudder.

As I turned in a circle now, in how many places under this sun were people emaciated and starving, brutalized, bleeding and dying?

Suddenly I saw in my mind an ever growing host of pale, gaunt, terrified human faces, moaning with wide pleading eyes, a shadowy sea of groping arms, hands and fingers reaching out at me from the abyss of their pain. It expanded and soared wider in my mind as a looming giant growing over the borders of this terrible place, spreading out across the great curving ends of the earth in a huge shadowy cognizance, overseeing all the lands in all their times upon the face of the whole earth through terrible, unblinking eyes.

It was a vision I had long suppressed in my mind. I was an archaeologist and cultural historian: I knew the visions of our agony, hopelessness, despair and death.

Yet I studied it as something academic. It was nameless agony, faceless despair, anonymous death.

Now, I saw it all around me, staring at me, reaching and pleading, a sea of faces. Myriad faces.

Suddenly, in the bleak, desperate pleading faces, I saw a face I knew.

It was my wife's face, desperately gazing out at me from the throng of tangling arms and red teary eyes, looking out to me!

No! Not MY wife!

Suddenly around her I saw my poor children, hungry, tattered, bleeding and crying, their faces and cheeks smudged with tears and dust.

No! Not MY children!

I reached out for them, desperately reached out to them.

But as I reached out for them, reached out for their terrified straining fingertips, they were falling away from me, farther and farther away into the swallowing darkness, their hands and arms waving helplessly for me to save them, until my soul burst in pain!

"NO!" I screamed, shattering the air of the desert around me, the canyon walls echoing back

"NO! NO! NO! NOOOOOOOO!"

I screamed again and again until the vision stopped, and finally was gone in the dying echoes.

No, I thought. Not my wife! Not my children! Not them!

Not as I watched in powerlessness and helplessness as they perished!

It was too terrible.

I could not stand it.

I stood teetering a moment by the edge of the canyon, looking into the abyss, the last dying echoes of my shouts rebounding ever more faintly in the deep wadi below, fainter and fainter until gone, until I stood alone, sobbing on the high canyon ridge.

I fell to my knees, and wept for the people, tears dripping down my cheeks, soaking into the parched dry ground by my knees. The vision of so many tens of millions of people slaughtered by human barbarity and mindlessness, by conquerors great and small, by single thieves and mass murderers and entire nations of pillagers overwhelmed me where I stood, and I stayed weeping on my knees.

What had it all been for?

Why had so many been born, only to live so miserably and die so badly?

I knelt weeping atop the grassless ridge, lost in the dry wilderness under the hot sun, and wept, and wept, for a long time.

That afternoon I quit work early. After returning to camp, I got my sleeping bag, foam roll and pillow and carried them back up to the top of the highest canyon ridge to sleep there the night, out of the claustrophobic, stifling closeness of the canyon below.

From my hilltop vantage point, alone, laying on my back upon the comfort of a soft mattress and plush sleeping bag, I watched the sun lower to the horizon in burning red and orange, and saw the stony ridges around me suddenly transformed into fiery, brilliant buttresses of brute jagged rock, radiantly glowing in furnace hues as a hot, glowing primordial earth. The sun dipped lower and then slipped below the horizon. As its fiery light faded, I watched the primitive earth cool rapidly from red hot to cool purple, then to grey, and finally, into cold black and darkness.

Yes, I thought.

This is a place where men could go mad.

As the stars came out one by one in the night sky, I lay peacefully looking up from one star to another, until so many became visible that they filled the entire sky. With the deepening black of night, the Milky Way emerged brightly, a glowing sash across the heavens, and I thought of Democritus, the Greek who first spoke of everything being made of atoms, who was the first to say the Milky Way was made of incalculable numbers of stars too far away to be seen and discerned individually. And so they seemed as milk.

Ancient legend said that it was the milk that came from Hera's breast, the mother goddess of the sky, which squirt out across the heavens. She and Zeus had honeymooned on the Greek island of Samos. Yet this story had origins in even older mysteries from Egypt, of the sky-mother of all, the goddess Nut. Those who would be resurrected had to be born again, and this the Egyptians understood through entering the womb of Nut to be reborn, then to take their place among the stars. The mother goddess was often depicted in Egyptian tombs with one bare breast showing; at times she held her breast and gently squeezed it at the nipple, to give of her milk, to nurture in love. Such were the ancient stories of the Milky Way.

Our generation knew what we were seeing. Our solar system was but one in billions in our galaxy. Our galaxy was but one in billions in the cosmos. We were microscopic in the vast expanses of space, and our planet was an oasis of infinitesimal magnitude.

Yet the sky indeed nurtures us, I thought. Without the sun, and its constant emanations, we would die. Our whole planet would die. Without the effects of gravities upon gravities, stars upon stars, galaxies upon galaxies, our planet could not exist in the universe as it does.

The ancients who saw order in the cosmos and believed life emanated from the sun and worshipped it as god, though they were wrong, were they, really?

They looked up at this very sky, and saw everything in it as a gift from which life came, back to which we all return. How much did they know vaguely in shadows which only now we are learning in scientific terms?

And did they know only in shadows as we credit, or was there more light than we have dared to suspect in our conceit?

Though the heavens were filled with stars and not milk, did it all not nourish our planet just the same?

What had they known, and not told us? Or was it lost, as so many other things wise men had disagreed with over the ages had become lost?

Shooting stars began to be visible, streaking across the sky. This far away from the concentrated pollution of cities, with no lights at all, they were bright and clear as they burned across the desert sky. Shooting stars always captured my imaginings. As I had wondered when I was a child, I found myself still wondering.

Where do meteors come from?

Why are they out there in space?

How does this majesty of stars hang in its immense flying loom to make this awesome tapestry we see out there? And if the light we see from the distant stars is so many thousands of millions of light years away, then indeed the light must have been traveling thousands of millions of years just to get here.

Then how old is the universe?

How did it get here?

Is there life out there somewhere on another oasis like ours?

Is it life like us?

Do they kill each other there, and steal, and rape, and destroy?

We humans have been here such a short, short a time. Why are we here at all? What good have we done that we should live?

Why did life begin to crawl on this barren rock in space, anyway? Why are we here, appearing here in these last few moments of the universe's existence?

What was it all for?

A very large shooting star streaked across the heavens, and in the clarity of the desert air I saw blazing sparks fizzle along its trail as so often I saw so far away from civilization.

Civilization. I had studied civilization's proudest monuments. What great memorial of kings, emperors, pharaohs and queens was not built with the sweat of conscripted masses whose blood and discarded bones littered the earth surrounding them? From Pyramids to Palaces to Great Walls to mighty Temples, what monument of civilization's glory is not civilization's shame? Which civilization did not rise through slaughtering and enslaving its neighbors, and endure in greatness without murdering its own children who dared to think differently or wished to live differently, by terrifying its children into productive submission by constant threat of bloody execution?

Civilization. What an ambiguous, ironic, contradicting term, producer of beauty and arts within the coercive atrocities of hate-driven violence, crafted within one, innocently used word of human pride and arrogance.

I pondered until I tired, until my mind's eyes became too heavy with sleep, the lids of my visions too heavy with weariness.

My mind blinked, and blinked again, and slipped into a deep sleep.

And I slept under the starry sky of Judaea.

204

Chapter 8

Day 27 in the Wilderness: The Dream

Sunrise came early on the top of the canyon rim. A cool breeze blew across my face, and the first rays of sun touched my eyelids, awakening me. I leaned up on one elbow in my sleeping bag and looked all around. The red-orange light of morning cast its color upon the sea of worthless stones littering the hilltops around me, transforming them into lumps of precious metal. Easily my eyes could have made me believe that I lay in the midst of a land of purest gold.

But I was not.

I was in the desert hills by the Dead Sea, and another laborious day was dawning.

Without waiting, I unzipped the sleeping bag, pulled my legs out, and methodically put on my boots just as I had every other day before. But I did not want today to be a day just as all the other days before. I needed a breather, a break. I also needed water. I would go to En Gedi today. For more than three solid weeks I had been digging, searching cliffs and caves, breathing bat guano dust and sweating under the sun, trying to squeeze sound out of rocks with no reward, and I was discouraged.

I tied my sleeping bag and foam roll and pillow together, and walked to the edge of the deep wadi beside me.

The bottom of the wadi lay far below, still dark in the shadows of night. As I well knew, morning would not reach the floor far below for another few hours. With the sun full in my face squinting my eyes, the depths of the wadi appeared as a bottomless pit.

Holding the bed roll by the rope which tied it, I swung it back behind me and gave a mighty heave forward, tossing it out into empty space over the wadi. For an instant it sailed through the air catching sunlight as a golden pillow, but then its downward arc took it below the rays of the sun into the abrupt purple-black shadows of night, where it plummeted out of sight into the darkness of the abyss. I stood listening, listening, but I never heard it hit the bottom. It just disappeared into the pit. I turned to find my descent.

As I slowly wended my way haltingly down the canyon side back to camp, I pondered my feelings. Too many hours scanning the walls of wadis; too many days penned between stone cliffs; too many days of silence, without the sound of music, the sound of another human voice. I had not even heard the sound of my own voice for three weeks as I maintained silence amid the rocks I tried to listen to. The only sound I had known was the moan of the wind, the echo of unseen falling rocks tumbling down from the jagged cliffs, and the cries of birds of prey above. The sudden rush of claustrophobia from my solitude which had possessed me yesterday afternoon should have come as no surprise. This was solitude virtually without equal.

When I reached the bottom of the wadi I walked over the sandy, rocky floor to where my sleeping roll should have fallen. In the brighter light of quickly rising morning, with eyes now well accustomed to the shadowy canyon, I soon spied it laying at a crazy angle against a small boulder. I picked it up and hiked the rest of the way down the wadi to camp.

At camp, I rummaged through half-empty boxes for something which looked appealing for breakfast. I didn't feel like cooking, so I opened a can of apricots, cut some Halava and cheese, and mixed some powdered orange drink. The water supply was indeed almost at its end. I ate quickly and with Halava and cheese still in one hand, skidded down the embankment and got in the four-wheel drive. It was time to go to En Gedi.

With the wadi still in full morning shadows I headed down the winding canyon road. Jostling and bumping along the dry riverbed floor, peering up along the sunlit rim high above, I could not help but imagine the travels of my ancestors in ancient times, who suffered heat and thirst for days to cover ground I could span in hours. I thought of the ancient dwellers of my ruined villa, and how it had been for them to go to En Gedi in their day. By car the descent East to the narrow span of coastal plain by the Dead Sea was a simple, almost effortless journey, a quick and bumpy drive of only a couple of hours.

When the canyon finally turned its last turn and opened wide into a magnificent view of the Dead Sea and the far mountains on the other side, my heart rejoiced. I never thought I could be so happy just to see a lake of salt, yet its shimmering blue water and the swath of green vegetation growing along the coastal plain welcomed my eyes as a song. I drove the last mile down the wadi with the blue waters of the Dead Sea before me, the view expanding ever wider and wider as I neared the huge mouth of the Rift Valley palisade, and my joy truly overflowed.

When my vehicle finally emerged from the wadi mouth out onto the plain, and I could look with unobstructed view north and south and all across the panorama of the entire Dead Sea, I stopped, turned off the motor, and got out to stretch my legs and drink in this view.

Behind me as a mighty fortress rose the cliffs of the Rift Valley, standing with full majesty in the high morning sun. Before me lay the Dead Sea, placid and azure under the sky, ringed by a wreath of green in spite of its alkaline, salted shore.

I marveled with the blunt reminding that I was far below sea level. Though my camp site far up the wadi was still many hundreds of feet below sea level, deep in the gorges of the Wilderness hills, being here and gazing upon the Rift Valley impressed the reality abundantly upon my consciousness.

Not only was the air heavier here, denser, stacked up into the stratosphere and pressing down here with greater thickness and pressure than anywhere else on earth upon my body, but where I stood, fully a thousand and two hundred and more feet below sea level, was a paradox of nature's wildest imagining. Mountains of ocean water towered above me just beyond the rocky walls behind me, and far to the south, ready and eager to invade. Yet the dry land held them at bay, though they would feign pour into this place and fill it if they could.

I looked up all around me, and found the level high up on the buttressed cliffs from which I had just emerged, marking with my eyes far above on the cliff side the level where the world's oceans stood over my head. It was an awesome height. I gazed around me, across the valley and the Dead Sea, imagining all of this under water as it should be, as it would be but for the thin earthen walls which staved off the flood. The vast volume of water which would fill this immense inland depression exceeded my comprehension.

Seas should rush in and drown this whole area, and all who live in it.

But they do not. Barriers exist to keep them out.

Natural barriers.

Natural barriers which could erode, but kept the balance.

I mused upon my name. I was Dr. Holland. Most of my life I had endured jokes about 'being in Dutch,' about wooden shoes, windmills and having my head below sea level. Holland. The place below sea level, of sea walls, of reclaimed land.

As I had grown and been privileged to fly many places in the world on archaeological expeditions and on study tours to ancient lands which I so delighted in seeing, I had looked out upon the thin atmosphere of the planet, itself the thinnest of barriers against the onslaught of vacuous deep space, and thought of those who ridiculed my name. From space I could see the truth. Our atmosphere was the thinnest of layers over the curving sphere of the planet, and yet within this thin blanket we found life, and as it nurtured it protected us in many ways from myriad assaults and deadly invasions. Photographs taken by astronauts at the edge of space even more clearly revealed the thinness of that atmosphere, and in awesome preponderance delineated the vastness of that space beyond, awaiting on all sides, waiting to rush in and suffocate, but it did not.

There was a barrier. A natural barrier.

And as I flew over the world on my way to Egypt or Stonehenge or Chichen Itza of Yucatan, the truth stretched out before me.

We were all in Dutch.

All of us, we all lived on a planet reclaimed from the ocean of space, made livable by its narrow dike of air which walled the expanses of space and kept them out. What if the dike should one day be found to have a hole?

I was Dr. Holland. I knew of these things. I had grown thinking of my namesake land, though I had never lived in it.

Yet here, standing at the bottom of the Rift Valley by the Dead Sea so far below the towering oceans held back by the hills above me, I suddenly understood more than I had ever known in my life, that we were precariously balanced on our little planet reclaimed from the vast ocean of space, ever vulnerable to the forces of total annihilation just beyond the walls. As I felt relief to know that the oceans would not at any minute come cascading over the hills behind me, I took relief in also knowing that the vacuum of space kept its distance, even a little more distance from me here as I stood twelve hundred feet below sea level.

Again, I was glad for the air.

I got back into the four-wheel and headed south to the oasis settlement and kibbutzim of En Gedi.

As the palm trees of En Gedi came into view far ahead, I imagined Yehoniah making this journey to get water at En Gedi. He must have. After the trek from Jerusalem, with so few oasis scattered inaccessibly in the hills, this was the only sure font of fresh water. En Gedi had many springs, a stream, and even a waterfall. Yehoniah could have stealthily made his approach along the rocks at the base of the cliffs, or sneaked in at night.

I had imagined him so many times as I plodded over the rocks and sand of the Wadi Hasasa. His figure would materialize in my mind, and I would see him as if I had seen him in a dream. I had enjoyed the companionship of his image, as I saw him cautiously walking along the wadi, carefully looking out across the plain from behind protective rocks to make sure his passage would be safe, running along this fertile plain to the En Gedi oasis. I took pleasure in thinking of him now.

The modern town of A'in Jidi was many times larger than its ancient forbear. As I drove through outlying streets into the small center of town, I saw men, women, and children along the sidewalks. As often struck me when I arrived in such small remote villages around the world, I marveled at these people whom I had never seen before, never imagined before. They lived in streets I had never imagined, in a village or town I had never imagined. Yet they were here.

The oddity of seeing people I had never been conscious of gave me a strange feeling. For some reason it never hit me in big cities; somehow I always saw the big cities in my mind; they were there. Yet until this morning, though these people had been living and working and playing and growing old here, to me, they had never existed. They were people just as I, with hopes, dreams and problems much as mine. They had been here all the time, only I had not known. Just as they did not know I existed. As I drove through the streets, they went about their business never looking up at me; they did not even see me as I drove through their midst in their little city. I think this was part of the oddity of the experience. I always saw them, yet from within the cars in which I traveled, they never saw me. That was the irony: I still did not exist to them.

How could it be possible, I remembered thinking the first time I had experienced this thought, that all of my problems, which seemed so earth-shattering to me, which gave me such anxiety and trouble, never bothered these people at all? They lived every day oblivious of me, my existence and my troubles and problems. I had thought, amazed: how could my problems be so big, if these people wake up every day and live and work and sleep, and never once are troubled by my problems? My problems must not be so great.

When I saw a place where I could fill my water containers, I pulled in and parked. In a mixed-goods shop I found and bought a roll of duct tape, which somehow back at the university we had never thought to pack for this trip, and with generous strips pressed firmly onto the plastic I one by one repaired the several bullet holes which had perforated them. Satisfied that this should do the trick, I began taking them one at a time into the grocery store for water.

For a few shekels I soon had plenty of fresh water to last the rest of the trip. I picked up a few fresh supplies: bread, fresh orange juice, eggs, carrots, tomatoes, some bananas, grapes and some fresh cheese. The cheese back at camp was becoming a bit rank after so long without refrigeration.

As much as I had thought I craved human companionship and conversation, I found myself anxious to get away and out of the small village, back out onto the coastal plain along the Dead Sea. The panorama of water and mountains was indeed magnificent, and I decided to drive up to a little promontory I had seen on the way into town and stop for a pic-nic lunch. Today would be a day of rest.

The cool breeze off the water and the green of shrubs, grass, palms and farm fields restored me wondrously. I lay down on the grassy knoll amid pasturing sheep and rested every fiber of my body. The bleating sheep were a pleasant comfort. They had been pasturing on this grass since biblical days, I thought, since the days of David the shepherd boy.

I smiled over that image: that was the other part of my name which had often been cause for someone's remark. David. How many times since I was a little boy had I heard people talk to me of David and Goliath, David the shepherd boy, David the King, David and his harp, his songs, his psalms. What an irony that I was here, laying in the grass at En Gedi with my bread and grapes and cheese, by the still waters before me, at the feet of the Strong Holds where David had shown Saul he meant him no harm, cutting the hem from the King's garment while he slept when he could have so easily killed him. Here I was, because the sword of Goliath had been found in the Temple at Yeb, and I had been wishful enough to believe in it all these years. David had roamed these hills with the sword of Goliath in his hands. It had brought me here, full circle.

Life was so filled with ironies. So many ironies.

After a good rest I drove back up the coast to the mouth of my wadi and then up the long, torturous road to the split in the canyon where the Ascent of Ziz began. I stopped there and parked for a moment. Another tributary cut up to the right, having carved its own path down from the wilderness heights. There were so many tributaries, more and more the further up and inland one went.

I tried to go back in my mind to the many wadis I had hiked through, trying to remember anything which seemed to remind me of the description of the hiding place I often envisioned in my mind, as I had interpreted the quotation from Isaiah to describe. Had Yehoniah gone north here up this wadi, or had he gone straight here, or off there to the left, up that other tributary? The vision in my mind was useless, for all these wadis merged into a maze of likeness; my memory was of no help at all.

Pensively I drove back up my wadi to the camp, and from there I climbed up to the top of the canyon wall behind it, to sit and watch the clouds and sun over the peaks and ridges of the Wilderness. I stayed all afternoon, thinking. I thought of my wife and my children. Certainly they were well. I had no cause to worry about them. I thought of my wife's smile and her gentle voice. I thought of my children at play, laughing and happy. How I loved my family. How I missed them.

The night was beginning to lower. The canyon below was already cast deep in shadows. Though I wanted to stay and watch the sunset again, my climb back down would be too dangerous in the dark. So, with still an hour of sunlight, I made the descent, and dejectedly cooked and ate my dinner.

Tomorrow I would go out again and continue hoofing up and down the canyons, trying to find a likely spot.

I lay down on my cot, closed my eyes, and went to sleep, thinking of my wife, my children, and Yehoniah.

My last thought before sleep overcame me was of Yehoniah. I saw his face before me, serious and determined.

And then I slipped away in a dream.

I became aware that it was night. Smoke was in the air. Lots of it. I looked up from the smooth paving stones at my feet and saw by the light of a single bronze oil lamp a man dressed in the garments of the Lord's High Priest sitting at a table, rapidly writing with a quill pen upon a broken shard of pottery. Another shard lay on the table top beside his hand, already covered with writing, drying.

It was Seraiah.

A large and muscular man in desert peasant's garb rushed into the dimly lit room and stopped short by the table, standing up straighter at attention, waiting to be spoken to. The High Priest did not look up, but waved him with one hand to wait, then quickly put the hand back again to hold the shard steady as he wrote upon it. He already knew. Yehoniah had encountered difficulties and would not return in time to receive his final instructions.

The end had come too quickly; he had not been ready. He had imagined vaguely what must be done, but never spoken it to men, never rehearsed what should be done. He had never really believed this could happen. No one had believed. He was unprepared.

Now, everyone was scattered. In confusion and haste he had done what could be done without thinking. Now he saw clearly the course which must be fulfilled. But to assure the safety of the most holy things, men had to be found who would help. Only by the hand of this messenger would he ever get word to the strong men he needed to assist his faithful steward in his task.

But who would get word to Yehoniah to tell him the name of the men he must look for, who would know the secret place?

He paused from writing a moment. Who?

Only the prophet Jeremiah could and would do it. Jeremiah had for more than a decade spoken to King Zedekiah and the people to bend to the Chaldeans will, and for this he enjoyed Nebuchadnezzar's personal favor. He would be the only person who might move freely enough to find and speak to Yehoniah. He continued writing on the shard, faster, knowing that in only a few minutes the Babylonians would be there to take him away.

Outside the room, just a little down the street, I heard muffled shouts, cries of pain and screams. A dull roar, as the distant rushing of many waters trembled in the air. I felt it softly vibrating against my chest and temples, yet I knew not what it was.

The High Priest finished the last letter of the last word and dropped the quill from his hand, standing at once to face the man who so anxiously waited.

"Find Jehonadab ben Habazin'yahu" spoke the High Priest.

"The Rechabite?" answered the man unhesitatingly.

"The same," said the High Priest, pressing the two shards into the man's large, calloused hands. "Take these. He will read them. Tell him: 'Do all the High Priest says, and it shall be well with you.'"

"As you say it," affirmed the man.

Shouts, louder, angry and much nearer, echoed into the room. Thick black smoke was drifting in under the door lintel and curling down the far wall, slowing filling the room. The high Priest picked up the bronze oil lamp and held it close to the face of the man. His bearded visage was rough and sun darkened, further smudged with soot and ash. His bright piercing eyes urgently searched the face of the High Priest. Seraiah took his arm.

"You have not seen Yehon'yahu," Seraiah spoke.

"No, rabboni," replied the man more anxiously. "He is not returned. I saw him as you sent him out with the students, outside the East walls to hide the Books of God. But I have not seen the boys, nor has Yehon'yahu returned. I have asked. No one has seen him. "

"The boys I told to flee as soon as they had completed their task. Yehon'yahu also carried with him the Holy Oracles of the Lord. They and the Books must not fall into unclean hands. You must get these letters to the Rechabite. I must get word back to Jerem'yahu, and he must find Yehon'yahu and give him my instructions."

"You have seen Jerem'yahu?" asked the man in surprise.

"No, but he has sent word from the House of the Guard, that Nebuzaradan, upon the command of the Great King, has vowed before the Chaldean Princes to release him. He sends us warning. From Nebuchad he has learned that in Riblah the sons of Zedek'yahu the King, captured with him at Jericho, are slain, and Zedek'yahu the King's eyes have been gouged out. The Chaldean this time takes all of us to Babylon, and Jerem'yahu tells that the Chaldean General Nebuzaradan has given the order that the Temple is to be destroyed with the city. He leaves only enough dressers of the fields here to grow his soldier's meat and food. Say to all that you are a tiller of the fields, and you shall be left here free to fulfill this holy task I ask of you. Find the Rechabite. Tell Jehonadab that he will need several strong men who drink no wine - he will know. If you wish to go with him, Nimtar, you have my blessing," he added, squeezing his arm.

"As you say it," reaffirmed Nimtar.

The noise outside was rapidly growing louder and nearer. Shouts in Chaldean clearly rang through the air outside.

"Go, over the back wall, now!" whispered Seraiah, pushing the man toward the door. Nimtar turned and was gone so quickly that the small flame of the oil lamp quivered. Seraiah stood without moving, listening to the shouts of the soldiers.

In just moments, two Babylonian soldiers with torches burst into the room. Seraiah stood calmly as they overturned his table and grabbed his arms. The oil lamp fell out of his hand onto the floor. Its flame flickered, and went out. Quickly the soldiers pushed him toward the door, and marched him out into the chaos of the night.

As they left Seraiah's house and got out into the street, he looked up and began to weep. The Temple on the mount was already afire. Long tongues of flame rose up into the heavens illuminating the Holy house even in the night. The roar of flames trembled tangibly in the air all around, a terrible sound, deafening in his ears. As they marched uphill to the city gate, Seraiah and the two soldiers were joined by other soldiers leading more priests and many nobles and elders of Jerusalem. Together the growing throng marched its way up the hill, out of the burning city.

From outside the gate the sky was a glow of fire. I heard screaming; horses' hooves pounding by, close by, and as they thundered passed me, I saw their savage riders bent forward against the wind, kicking the animals viciously onward. They rode towards the gate in the city walls, now rising before me in the firelight, engulfed in terrible shafts of writhing flame.

The Holy City of Jerusalem was burning, burning from end to end in the smoky darkness of night.

The ground around me was choked with fallen blocks and shattered beams; I looked in confusion around me. Fires and more fires, everywhere fires. The walls of half-collapsed buildings all around me were bathed in bright dancing light from the wild billows of ravaging flame.

Above screams of pain crying out from scattered places around me, to the right I heard bellowed commands in Chaldean. Babylonian soldiers marched in small patrols on all sides.

Everywhere around me I heard shouts, and piercing cries, cries of death, wailing women, shrieks of small children, and moaning men fallen bleeding amid the rubble. My body felt the roaring of great fires and the crackling of flames close by me, the sudden rumble and thud of stone buildings and timbers falling to the earth; horses pounding hooves riding up one way and back down the other; the metallic clanking of armor and swords and shields. Up ahead, the glint of a sword raised high, then sliced down into the darkness.

I looked, and saw Yehoniah run ahead of me through the night. Without thinking, my feet began to run and I was running, following him through shattered streets over broken walls and piles of fallen stone towards the city gate shining brightly in the terrible light of so many fires. He ran and he ran, dodging this way and that way to avoid the patrols of Babylonians until he came upon soldiers with spears leveled at a mass of huddled people by the high wall. He darted behind a rock, crouching to not be seen, and peered out at the people being held within the circle of soldiers by the wall.

There were close to a hundred men. On one side he found Jeremiah the prophet and his scribe Baruch. They were in chains, as were many others. By the light of the flames he also saw Zephaniah the Second Priest, the keepers of the door, and the principal scribes. Mingled among others whom he recognized of the great men of the city he saw the other priests. Finally, far to the right in the shadows, he saw one who might be Seraiah the High Priest. Then he saw the Ephod with its twelve stones catching the light of the fires all around. It was Seraiah. He, too, was in chains.

Yehoniah rose up slightly, gazing out at him, anxiously looking across the night at him, dangerously waving his arm once, then again trying to get Seraiah's attention as the guards looked only inward at their prisoners. Seraiah's face slightly rose and turned toward Yehoniah's rock. Slowly he nodded his chin downward. He had seen him. Then Seraiah slowly shook his head. Yehoniah was not to approach now. From far to the left a chariot rode up to a sharp halt by the captive group and its driver shouted more commands. The soldiers yelled at the huddled people, waving them down with the spears, and they all sat down to wait the night. Yehoniah turned his face away and dropped behind his rock, pulling himself into the shadows.

The dawn's light brightened upon rising pillars of black smoke, billowing up all around within and without the city walls. A horrible devastation and death became staggeringly visible on all sides.

Shortly after daybreak the Chaldean soldiers rudely awakened the eighty chained captives, prodded them to their feet with spears and pushed them to begin marching. They were going north.

As the soldiers routed up the haggard men, prodding them over tumbled rocks onto the road ascending the hill by the city walls, Yehoniah watched from behind his rock. Jeremiah was near the front by the troop leader; Seraiah was nearly last. As the tail end of the group trudged onto the road and plodded north, Seraiah stumbled and fell. Yehoniah almost leaped to his feet to rush and help his master, but he could not; he held back. A Chaldean soldier yelled angrily, and stepping over to Seraiah laying on the ground, prodded him with his spear, yelling. Seraiah got up, and limped quickly to catch up with the others. His leg was bleeding.

Yehoniah waited anxiously until the group was well along the road before he cautiously emerged from his hiding place. Running deftly from rock to rubble heap to smoldering, gutted house, he followed at a distance. The prize captives of the Babylonians were the priests and elders, all old men; they had neither eaten nor slept well during the night. The group marched slowly.

As the eighty prize captives in chains rounded the north wall of the city, a terrible and overwhelming sight came into their full view.

There, on the level ground by the north walls, surrounded by hundreds and hundreds of sword-waving Babylonian soldiers, more than five thousand women, children and men were rising to their feet amid angry shouts and threatening spear prods, being herded as cattle toward the direction of the road north. North, to Babylon.

The smaller group of eighty men in chains took the lead in front of the masses who straggled into an almost endless line of hopeless mourners, marching at spear point away from their homes, their dead, and their burning and destroyed city. Wailing and weeping rose above the din of horses, clattering armor and the shouted commands.

Some of the people, however, were being released from the crowds. They ran or walked away into the hills, away from the city.

One such young man about Yehoniah's age came nearby to where Yehoniah hid, and stopped to sit on a rock and witness the parade of misery filing north. Yehoniah carefully approached him without being seen.

"Where are they taking everyone?" whispered Yehoniah from behind the rock. The young man answered without turning back his gaze.

"To Riblah, to the Great King's camp for judgment, and then on to Babylon," spoke the young man.

"Thank you, friend," whispered Yehoniah, and then he went on.

He quickly saw that the small group of prize nobles, elders and priests did not tarry with the slow moving masses of Judah. Though they were old men, prodded by the Babylonians' spears and shouts, they marched at a steady pace. It was obvious that Nebuchadnezzar wanted to see his trophy captives first, without delay.

Soon they were marching alone along the road north, the great congregation of Judah behind them fallen completely out of view. Yehoniah hung far back in the shadows and the darkness of the hills to avoid detection and capture, stealthily following the march on its way to Nebuchadnezzar's camp at Riblah.

This would be many days trudging under the hot summer sun. Somewhere along the way he had to find a place where he could get close enough to Seraiah to receive instructions for the scrolls and the Oracles. Yet no such place presented itself.

A full morning of plodding brought the group to Ramah, the small fortified Israelite village which now served as Babylonian forward guard. Here Yehoniah saw the group was ordered to rest.   Jeremiah was singled out and taken to the Chief of the Guard. His chains were removed, and the two stood and spoke. After a short talk away from the others, Jeremiah turned toward Jerusalem, waving with his hand to the south. The Chaldean nodded, and walked away to speak to some of his soldiers. Jeremiah returned to the group and raised Baruch upon his feet, pointing toward the Chief of the Guard. Baruch left the group and stood by the Chaldean.

Jeremiah then went among the people speaking to many, giving blessings and gestures of parting.

Seraiah was close enough to hear what had happened.

Nebuchad, Chief of the Guard, was freeing Jeremiah and Baruch to return with a dispatch of soldiers to Mizpah, where Gedaliah the son of Ahikam was to be installed as puppet governor. Now would be his only chance to get word out to Yehoniah. He had to write a note. Yet on what would he write it, and what would he use for ink?

His eyes went to the black leather tephillah strapped to his arm, the words of the Lord which he had worn most of his life, and with only a moment's hesitation, he untied it and unwound the long strap from around his arm. As his fingers fumbled to open the tephillah to remove the small parchment scroll, he desperately looked all around him. What would be his quill and ink? His furtive gaze saw nothing. He bowed his head in grief, but then his eyes widened in joy as he looked down at the large bleeding gash on his leg, cut when he had tripped over the rock that morning.

He knew what he had to do.

He quickly unrolled the small parchment scroll, and turning it over, flattened it out upon his thigh. Picking up a piece of straw from the ground he pressed it into the wound, turning it in the red oozing blood in his calf. With fresh blood moistening the straw, he began to scrawl a message to Yehoniah on the back of the tephillah, dipping the straw into his wound again and again as he needed to write.

Yehoniah saw Seraiah raise his hand, fold back his sleeve, untie the holy tephillah and remove it from his arm. Stunned by this gesture, not knowing what it could mean, he groaned in anguish for his master. He saw Seraiah's head bow as if in prayer, and stay so until Jeremiah reached him and touched the High Priest's shoulder. Seraiah looked up, and then down again for a moment, and then it seemed he pressed something into the prophet's hand. He saw Seraiah gesture out towards the rocks where he hid among the bushes. Jeremiah looked out and nodded. The prophet then continued walking among the people until he came out and back to the Chief of the Guard.

Several soldiers suddenly were called out from the troop, and after a few words from their Chief they fell into formation and started back toward Jerusalem. Jeremiah and Baruch tarried a while, waiting for the scribe of the Chief of the Guard to complete a clay tablet to the garrison leader regarding their privileged status. The Chief of the Guard gave another command. In minutes a soldier returned with a bag of food. Yehoniah saw the Chaldean give Jeremiah the bag of food and a small leather pouch, as those used to carry silver and gold. Jeremiah took it and bowed his head. Only when the soldiers were already far ahead did they receive the precious clay passport and take to the road back to Jerusalem.

Yehoniah stealthily circled ahead to meet them along the road.

At a goodly place, well sheltered from view, he stepped out into the road and stood in front of Jeremiah and Baruch.

"Yehon'yahu, peace!" spoke the prophet.

"Jerem'yahu and Baruch, peace!" answered Yehoniah.

"I have a message for you from the High Priest, your master," said Jeremiah, extending his hand to the steward.

Yehoniah reached out his hand and received the tephillah.

"What message?" he asked, waiting for Jeremiah to speak to him Seraiah's words.

"He said you should open and read the scroll," answered Jeremiah.

Yehoniah understood. He pulled open the tephillah with his fingers, and took out the small scroll. As he unrolled it and saw Seraiah's words written on the back in blood, tears welled up in his eyes. He silently read it. When he had finished, he looked up.

"Have you read his words?" asked Yehoniah of the prophet.

"No," said Jeremiah. "But whatever he speaks to you, I counsel you to go and do it. This march is to Riblah, and from there they will not return. If he has given you something to do, best you should leave him, and see to it."

"He has bound me by oath that I should fulfill an errand for the Lord," said Yehoniah.

"Go then, and may God guide your footsteps," said Baruch.

"Where do you go?" asked Yehoniah of the two men.

"Nebuchad has given me the choice to go unto Babylon with the King, or stay here as advisor to Gedal'yahu at Mizpah. I am old, and I wish to die in my own land among what is left of my people. Yet it is the Lord's wish for me to do His will, and so I go even unto Mizpah," Jeremiah replied.

Yehoniah was confused by his answer, but often he had not understood the prophet's words. If he stayed at Mizpah so close to Jerusalem, and did not go to Babylon, would he not then die in his own land?

Baruch nodded in affirmation, and with a sign of parting the two went on their way. It was just that simple with them.

Yehoniah turned in full haste to Jerusalem. It was late afternoon already. He arrived in the Holy City after nightfall.

That same day, in Jerusalem, Nimtar ben Hausi had found Jehonadab ben Habaziniah and given him the Seriah's message written on the shards.

Jehonadab read the two shards silently. One was merely a passage from the Torah. The other was an instruction to him, an inviolable commission in the old covenant of the fathers.

"What am I to do with Essa'yahu?" asked Jehonadab.

"I do not know," replied Nimtar. "I cannot read. Read it to me."

Jehonadab read the letter to Nimtar.

"To Jehonadab ben Habazin'yahu the Rechabite, whom I trust, hearken to the deliverer from Sera'yahu ben Azar'yahu High Priest. With covenant between us as if we ate salt: Gather four men who drink no wine; find Essa'yahu ben Zadok my nephew whom you trust. Wait both outside Valley Gate until my steward Yehon'yahu finds you, whom Jerem'yahu sends with my instructions. The covenant of salt between us all. Behold, the wrath of God is fulfilled as prophesied in the days of my father's father. Do as I instruct and bury before the Holy City these words of the promise, that the Lord in his anger shall not forget his people. I am taken to hear the words of

the Chaldean at Riblah and then to Euphrates. I am Sera'yahu ben Azar'yahu."

Nimtar's eyes lit as he heard the name of Yehoniah.

"I think I know what you are to do," said Nimtar. "I thought his instruction to you would be something else, but it must be the Books. Yehon'yahu has hidden the Books of the Temple somewhere in the Kidron. As it is Yehon'yahu whom you are to await, it must be that you are to help remove the scrolls to a safer place. The High Priest told me that you would need several men of strong muscle, who drink no wine. He said I could be one of them if I chose."

Jehonadab now nodded his head in full understanding.

"That is why he wants me to find his nephew, Essa'yahu. He needs my strength, but a Zadok must go with the scrolls," he nodded.

"But where are you to take them?" questioned Nimtar.

"He did not tell you?" cried Jehonadab.

"I do not even know where Yehon'yahu has hidden the scrolls! Sera'yahu said he would get word to Yehon'yahu by Jerem'yahu the Prophet. He must mean to tell him the place where Yehon'yahu is to take them. We must await Yehon'yahu before we can do anything."

"Then we may never complete this covenant," said Jehonadab. "Those I have spoken to in the tents say they saw the nobles and elders of the city leave yesterday morning for the north in chains, at the head of the people. They say that Jerem'yahu and the High Priest were among them. No one has seen the High Priest's steward. How then shall either the High Priest or Jerem'yahu give instruction to Yehon'yahu, or he come to us to give us word?"

"God shall find a way," replied Nimtar.

Jehonadab turned to him with anger in his eyes.

"If God can find such a way to do this, why did He not find a way to protect our people from these buzzards?" he declared, sweeping his arm in the direction of the Chaldeans. "Why did he allow them to burn and destroy His Temple?"

"Perhaps Jerem'yahu has been right all of these years," said Nimtar. "Perhaps that is why the High Priest has written that Jerem'yahu shall send him with the instructions."

"We shall wait here three days," said Jehonadab. "If Yehon'yahu does not come in three days, I will go back to the mountains and the mines where I am known to my people. There I will have safety. You may come if it pleases you."

"Let us then go and see if anyone knows where we may find Essa'yahu, that we may await fully prepared. As for me, I was given this instruction by Sera'yahu from his own mouth. I will wait longer."

Jehonadab smiled at him.

"How much longer, my faithful one?"

"A week...... Two weeks....... Until he comes," smiled Nimtar.

After only a few hours the two men found Essaiah ben Zadok, showed him the two sherds written by the hand of his uncle Seraiah, and brought him to the place outside the walls where they were instructed to wait. Afternoon was wearing into evening, and the night was nigh. As they stood by the Valley Gate looking up the hill outside the city walls, Essaiah tearfully spoke of years past when friends and relatives had camped on this very hill during Passover. But for the last six months, until only two days before, this had been the Babylonian camp. Though the Babylonians were leaving, the three men knew there would be no more Passovers here.

Fearing the attention of the Chaldean patrols should they wait idly by the gate, they walked up onto the middle of the hill where they could see the gate and the entire city.

With the Temple now destroyed, much of the city afire, and most of the remaining population already on the roadway to Babylon, the Chaldeans had vacated this siege camp on the West hill by the city walls. Though patrols still stopped some people for questioning, those who were left behind were mostly disregarded by the occupying soldiers, and so they went about their business of burying the dead and salvaging whatever they could from the ruins of the city. Jehonadab, Nimtar and Essaiah found a place to sit out of the way, up on the hill by a fire circle in the shadows of twilight, where others too, sat watching the still smoldering fires in the city.

The three men sat by the cold circle of stones and spoke of the two shards Seraiah had written. Jehonadab had given them to Essaiah. Essaiah was passionately relieved that the scrolls had been saved, and were not destroyed and lost as he had believed. Yet his anxiety waxed strong, that Yehoniah may not have survived. No one had seen him.

"What if he is dead?" asked Essaiah impatiently. "How will we find the scrolls?"

"Nimtar says that Sera'yahu sent Yehon'yahu with the students," replied Jehonadab. "He said they helped Yehon'yahu carry the Books and hide them outside the city."

"Which boys? Where are they now?" asked Essaiah.

"He said they had been told to flee after completing their task," answered Nimtar. "If Yehon'yahu is dead, we may some day find them among the people."

Essaiah hissed angrily and looked up at the smoking ruins of the city and the Temple.

"Yehon'yahu was your friend, wasn't he?" said Nimtar.

Essaiah looked down and then up at Nimtar's face.

"Yes," he said quietly, and looked back into the cold black cinders of the dead fire circle.

The three sat for some time in silence.

As darkness finally fell, numerous old fire circles on the hill leapt into

219

flame as fires were built in them by homeless Judahite people. Feeling less conspicuous with their presence, the three men decided it was safe to build a fire in their circle. Essaiah declared that they should begin to take turns waiting by the Valley Gate in the hopes of Yehoniah's safe return. He took the first watch.

Yehoniah had run much of the afternoon, only slowing to walk the last mile into Jerusalem. He was exhausted, but he could not rest.

When he arrived at the city, he went directly to the Valley Gate and found Essaiah sitting on a pile of stones. The two embraced and wept. Quickly Essaiah led him out on the hill facing the walls, to the fire. Jehonadab and Nimtar stood at their coming and all heartily embraced and then all sat down.

They sat by the old tent camp fire circle outside the city walls on the hill and Yehoniah told them how he had hurriedly been ordered to hide the scrolls and Urim and Thummim, and then before he could get around the Chaldean army patrols to return and learn what should be done with them, Seraiah had been taken away. Nimtar told him of the two shard letters Seraiah had written, and Essaiah handed them over to Yehoniah to read. Yehoniah then told them of the message from Seraiah, written with his own blood on the back of his tephillah, received at the hand of Jeremiah.

"Let us see it," pleaded Essaiah, the others anxiously joining.

Yehoniah reached into his girdle and pulled out Seraiah's wrist tephillah, and held it up for them. He then opened it and pulled out the tiny scroll, holding it up for all to see the blood with which it was written. By the light of the fire, he then read it to them:

To my steward Yehon'yahu,
deliver the sticks you have hidden
and instruct Essa'yahu ben Zadok my nephew
and Jehonadab ben Habazin'yahu, who
shall await you by the Valley Gate
to take them even unto the City of Salt
where they may be there preserved,
and you, Yehon'yahu, upon your oath,
take the holy stones of the ephod
into the Wilderness of Hazazon-tamar
where the Lord may guide you, that there
they may rest until my return.
Prepare ye the way of the Lord,
make straight in the desert
a highway to our God
By my own hand, Sera'yahu ben Azar'yahu

220

Essaiah and Jehonadab looked up in stunned silence.

"You have the Oracles of the Lord?" asked Jehonadab.

"They are hidden with the Books," replied Yehoniah.

The men sat a moment without speaking, overwhelmed with the responsibilities charged upon them. Each one looked at the other, realizing that from this moment forward, their lives were forever changed, more than they had been changed by the war, more than by all of the destruction and chaos around them.

"Why does he send the scrolls to the City of Salt?" Yehoniah asked. "Does anyone know what is there?"

Jehonadab, who had been staring all the while into the fire before him, spoke without raising his head.

"My brother is the Rechabite who works the forge at the City of Salt. We Rechabites are workers of metal, and fashioners of all manner of things made of copper, brass and iron. Sera'yahu knows this; he knows our family well. In the days of Jeho'yakim the King, son of Jos'yahu, when I was young, my father was brought into the Temple by the Prophet Jerem'yahu, with all of his brothers, his uncles and cousins. He and all his brethren were asked to drink wine, which thing he said astonished him; for Jerem'yahu knew that as our fathers had forbidden us to drink wine, we would drink no wine.

"Yet he had wanted to show the King, and all the people, that men can be obedient to their fathers; even so the King and all the people should be obedient to God. Thus does Sera'yahu know all of my family. We Rechabites build no houses; we live in tents as our fathers have admonished us. We can stay in the tents of my brother.

"But this is not why Sera'yahu sends us to the City of Salt. He visited my brother once, there at his forge, and they spoke. My brother then showed him many caves in the hills at this place. In those days I knew not why. I think I know now. As the Chaldean has been pillaging our land these many years, I think Sera'yahu had been preparing for this day. We shall put the scrolls in the caves my brother showed unto him. My brother knows which caves. This is why he sends us to the City of Salt with the scrolls."

"And," said Yehoniah, with awakening understanding, "he knew that even as your family would not break its covenant with your fathers, to drink no wine, that you will fulfill this covenant he now asks of you, and not fail. That is why he has trusted you."

"Even so," said Jehonadab, staring still into the fire. He accepted the unalterable covenant, and knew he would fulfill it as required.

Yehoniah held up the tephillah in his hand, and it caught the light of the fire.

"This belonged to your uncle," said Yehoniah turning to Essaiah. "You keep it." He reached out his hand, and gave him the tephillah.

Essaiah took the scroll, re-rolled it, and put it back into the tephillah. Without a pause he proceeded to wrap the tephillah around his arm.

Yehoniah and the others immediately leaned forward in protest, for fear it might be seen and bring their arrest, even death. It could easily spell the failure of their errand.

But Essaiah held up his hand with the tephillah bound to his arm, and silenced them.

"In righteousness shall we follow the Lord, and in this covenant shall we remember his words. We are now the keepers of the Books, and we shall preserve them."

Yehoniah urged that they must go and recover the scrolls and the box with the Urim and Thummim from where he had hidden them.

"How many scrolls are there?" asked Jehonadab. "I must know how many men to gather."

"Thirty-five," responded Yehoniah. "Many of them are slight and only some are thick and heavy. I think four strong men can carry them. I cannot be one of these men. I have a different path, with my own charge to fulfill." The men all nodded in understanding.

"I have made the rounds of those who are left here," said Jehonadab, "and I know already whom I shall choose. Nimtar has said that Sera'yahu granted him a portion with us in this errand if he so wishes it. He has asked me to be part of the group. Are any in disagreement with this?"

Essaiah and Yehoniah approved. Nimtar was accepted with full fellowship.

"Then Nimtar will go with me again from tent to tent where we shall find the three men I know we must take with us," said Jehonadab.

The two left the fire circle and in less than an hour returned with three more tall, strong men. Jehonadab carried a large sack over his shoulder, which he set down heavily on the ground. The three new men nodded greeting and hesitantly approached the fire circle. Jehonadab introduced them.

"This is 'Abi the son of Sabi; and 'Il'ada the son of Karshon; and Sama'yahu the son of Yau'azar. These are good men who know and accept the Covenant of Salt. They are all agreed to join me and Essa'yahu and carry the Books to Ir Hammelach. They will be faithful."

"You will be blessed for this devotion," Essaiah stood and spoke, welcoming the men. He glanced hesitantly down at the sack Jehonadab had set by the fire, and then up at the face of Jehonadab.

"Food," said the Rechabite. "The families of these men and others pressed food into our hands that we might not perish in the wilderness. Some gave us all they had left. We also have been given five skins of water." Essaiah looked from the men back to Yehoniah, nodding his head in approval.

"We are ready. Let us go now," said Yehoniah.

"Not yet," spoke Essaiah. "Let me go first to my uncle's house to see if anything has survived there we should take with us."

Yehoniah and Essaiah arose. The others agreed to wait by the fire circle. Too many figures moving in the night could invite trouble.

The two men went through the Valley Gate into the city. The streets were in shambles. With much difficulty they made their way down hill to Seraiah's house. It had not been burned, nor had several houses beside it. Essaiah grabbed a burning stick to use as a torch.

There was little left inside the house. The Chaldeans had ransacked it all. The study had been viciously wrecked, papers torn and strewn all over the floor. Essaiah picked up a handful of old papyrus sheets. They would be useful for writing letters. Yehoniah also bent down, and picked up several of the scattered quill pens from Seraiah's pen box, and handed them to Essaiah, who opened his tunic and shoved them in against his stomach. He tightened his gird, and nodded to Yehoniah to go. There was nothing else left here.

On the way back out the city they had to climb very near the Temple, where they unexpectedly saw Babylonian soldiers carrying large bundles of straw and sticks through the gate into the Temple courtyard. They pressed back into the shadows and stood motionless until the soldiers disappeared inside.

As Essaiah started to walk forward, his foot tripped on something made of metal. It was a Temple guardsman's helmet, laying in the street near the Temple gate where it had fallen and been kicked to the side. He leaned down and picked it up, and carried it with him. As they walked cautiously by the remains of the Temple gate, they looked in and saw the soldiers starting a new fire in the Temple. It had not burned enough for the Chaldeans. They were setting it afire again! The two men hurried on and got out of the city just before it was once again lit by the light of the Temple in flames.

As they walked back through the Valley Gate, they climbed inconspicuously out onto the hill and up to the fire circle where they sat down with the others.

With bitter tears streaming down their cheeks, they incredulously watched as flames rose again within the Temple.

While Yehoniah and Essaiah had been in the city, Jehonadab had dug a hole by the fire circle in which to bury Seraiah's message to God as he had been instructed. Though it was his charge to do this, he felt he should wait for all to be assembled. When he announced to the two men what the hole was for, Essaiah held up the helmet he had found in the street beside the gate of the Temple so all might see it, and recognize what it was. He then asked that it be placed over the shard and be buried also in the hole. Everyone agreed. Jehonadab dug the hole deeper and wider to receive the helmet.

Before putting the shard and helmet in the hole, 'Il'ada ben Karshon asked Essaiah to read what was written on the shard. In a clear voice he read it for all to hear.

"And it shall come to pass, when all these things are come upon thee, the blessings and the curse, which I have set before thee, and thou shall call them to mind among all the nations, whither the Lord thy God hath driven thee, and shalt return unto the Lord thy God, and shalt obey his voice according to all that I command thee this day, thou and thy children, with all thine heart, and with all thy soul; that then the Lord they God will turn thy captivity, and have compassion upon thee, and will return and gather thee from all the nations, whither the Lord thy God hath scattered thee."

His voice rang up into the sky. The men looked to the rising flames consuming the Temple, and in silence they then laid the shard down into the hole.

As Essaiah moved to set the helmet over it, Jehonadab suddenly thought, reached out his hand, and bent down to also set his letter from Seraiah on top of it.

Essaiah set the helmet over them, and all seven men put their hands to scrape dirt back down into hole, to cover the helmet and the letters, and packed it down tightly.

Jehonadab then brushed his huge hands over the place to smooth it so no one would see that something had been buried there. The fire had almost gone out. Nimtar took ashes and sprinkled them over the ground, further obscuring its disturbance from visibility.

The seven men then quietly slipped away into the Judaean night, quietly walking down the hill in the dark and around the south end of the city walls to the Kidron Valley, where Yehoniah had hidden the Books of the Temple and the Oracles of the Lord.

Yehoniah led the way. It did not take long. Soon Jehonadab, Nimtar and the three men were pulling the bundles of scrolls out from their hiding place and laying them upon a rock by the feet of Essaiah. All acknowledged that from this point onward, by the directions of Seraiah the High Priest, it was Essaiah who had charge of the Books. Nimtar handed up a small gold box to Yehoniah, very carefully, as if he were afraid of it. It was the box in which Seraiah had placed the Oracles of the Lord.

All of the men stopped for a moment and looked at Yehoniah as he received the box. If the scrolls were a great responsibility, the Oracles of the Lord were many times a greater one. Yehoniah took the box and held it tightly under his arm.

They saw no soldiers at all on this side of the city. As the last bundle was lifted up and securely set upon the rock, 'Il'ada gestured with his hands that this was all. They had all of them.

"Let us divide them now," whispered 'Abi, "so we may quickly leave this place on our journey."

They bent over the bundles and quickly unwrapped the fine linen which bound them, laying the cloth carefully on the ground to receive the scrolls. When all thirty-five books were laid out, they stood back to allow Essaiah room to divide them as he wished. Essaiah kneeled for a moment looking over the books, and then began to separate them into groups. When he was finished, he had made four equal piles.

There were fourteen thin ones grouped together; ten medium sized ones which made an almost equal group in size; five big ones which together easily weighed as much as the fourteen thin ones; and six more large ones, all very heavy.

He looked at Nimtar and the three men Jehonadab had chosen, sizing them up and down, estimating their strength.

He pointed to Nimtar ben Hausi and lay his hand on the fourteen scrolls; then to 'Abi ben Sabi, laying his hand on the ten. He then pointed to 'Il'ada ben Karshon, and pressed his palm to the five large books; then to Sama'yahu ben Yau'azar whom he gestured would carry the six. The four men knelt down, and taking the linen cloth, each began to wrap his portion of scrolls into a single bundle which he could carry.

Jehonadab watched all this, and after a pause, hesitantly asked Essaiah to give him a piece of papyrus, pointing to the sheets he could see sticking out from his garb. Essaiah immediately understood. Sorting through the papyrus he pulled out a small piece right for making an inventory. One side was already written on, and he turned it over to write on the other side as he felt in his girdle for a quill.

He moistened the tip of a quill in his mouth and proceeded to write the names of the four men and the number of scrolls each would carry wrapped under his arm:

Nimtar ben Hausi 14 s
'Abi ben Sabi 10 s
'Il'ada ben Karshon 5 s
Sama'yahu ben Yau'azar 6 s

Thirty-five *sefarim*. When he was finished, he gave the papyrus to Jehonadab. The Rechabites had been faithful unto God and the Temple for many generations. It was to him that his uncle Seraiah had given the charge to guarantee the safe transport of the books. This trust he respected. Jehonadab nodded, and tucked the list inside his tunic.

Essaiah then hefted the food sack which Jehonadab would carry. It was too heavy. He reached in and took from the sack the five water skins and quickly slung them over his shoulders. He smiled at Jehonadab. Every man now had his charge for the journey.

Quietly the four men loaded their bundles of books into their arms. With Jehonadab shouldering the sack of food, and Essaiah the skins of water, Yehoniah led the way carrying the gold box with the Urim and Thummim.

As quickly as they had entered the valley, they stealthily escaped away from the city into the night. Jehonadab and Nimtar had learned from the people that the way East to Jericho and the Salt Sea was blocked by troops, so they headed directly south down the valley, keeping off the road.

They continued heading south the rest of the night, traveling overland on goat paths and across fields to avoid Babylonian guards and soldiers. The Chaldeans were still roaming the conquered area, but they were now laughing drunk in their victory, careless and easy to avoid in the dark and smokey night.

The group stopped and hid beneath rock outcroppings before sunrise, exhausted. They slept all day to avoid any encounters with the Chaldeans. After nightfall, they again arose and continued their trek across the countryside.

Though they kept hoping to cut across the hills to the East, to the road which led to the great Salt Sea and Ir Hammelach, the light of fires from burning villages and farms in that direction kept them headed South yet a bit more. While Yehoniah's destination was deep into the heart of the Wilderness of Judah at Hazazon-tamar, the City of Salt was close to the north end of the Salt Sea. By this point the six men whose destination lay north knew they were far south of the path they should have taken. Yet they could not risk it, and so they followed south until they entered into the desert with Yehoniah. They would have to cross the Wilderness of Judah, and then carry the scrolls north, back to Ir Hammelach.

They plodded overland most of the night, seeing no one. They knew that they had reached the part of Judah where they need fear no Chaldeans. Yet with every step their way became more dangerous. They had entered the region of the steeper and steeper hills which fed into the dry canyons; now the ground itself could be an enemy.

As the sky began to show the coming of sunrise they arrived at the mid-point of a great canyon. Here they knew their paths must divide. The six men with the scrolls would have to go East to the Salt Sea and then circle back northward to the City of Salt. But Yehoniah had to continue overland until he could safely emerge near En Gedi. They were exhausted, and even though they expected no Chaldeans in this region, still they felt it would be unsafe to continue by day.

Sama'yahu suddenly touched Nimtar on the shoulder, and pointed across the canyon. There, in the cliff walls, was a cave which could give them shelter.

They climbed down the steep canyon side and quickly stashed the scrolls safely beneath some large boulders at the base of the opposite cliffs. The seven men then climbed high to the cave shelter they could see in the dawning light.

The light of the rising sun reflected into the cave, and as their eyes adjusted, they walked in further. It was deep, and at its far recesses they would be safe from detection and sheltered from the bright sunlight of day. They could see people had been here before. There were old cooking pots, rags and other things around the cave which quickly showed them that they were not the first to make use of this shelter. 'Il'ada walked over to the rags and held some up with a smile, motioning with a tilt of his head that these would make good pillows. They would sleep well.

As they each found a smooth and level place to lay down, Jehonadab asked Yehoniah where he would hide the Urim and Thummim. Yehoniah lay his head down upon his rags and paused thoughtfully. He replied that his master had instructed him to go to Hazazon-tamar, so there he will go. The Lord would reveal to him a place, and there would the Urim and Thummim be hidden until this wicked day of the Chaldeans had passed. The men nodded silently.

Soon they were all asleep.

As they slept, exhausted, the papyrus list which Essaiah had written with the four men's names and the number of scrolls each carried fell silently from Jehonadab's girdle where he had tucked it. As he rolled in his troubled sleep, it became covered with dust on the cave floor beside him.

They slept all day, awakening before sunset, yet it was rapidly becoming dark.

When Jehonadab got up and dusted off his garments, he neither saw the papyrus list on the cave floor nor felt that it was missing. It lay unnoticed, and was left in the darkness and dust of the cave.

The men made a rapid and slippery descent off the cliff face, and gathered at the boulders where the scrolls had been hidden. Hurriedly they pulled them out. When each man had his proper bundle, the four turned to the others. It was the last minutes of twilight, and the moment of parting.

Yehoniah wished the six men success in their errand, and they all together invoked the blessings of God. Essaiah took from his neck the fullest water skin and placed the cord over Yehoniah's head. Yehoniah slipped his arm through the cord and patted the water skin where it hung by his side. With a final embrace, they split up for their separate journeys. Jehonadab, Essaiah ben Zadok and the four men headed east into the night, down the canyon to the Salt Sea where they would turn north to the City of Salt where they were bound to hide the sacred books.

Yehoniah was now all alone.

He went up the canyon in the dark and continued south, by himself. He had to step very carefully in the shadows of a half moon, treading over ridges and hilltops until he came to another of the many dry river canyons descending onto the Salt Sea Plain from within the wilderness. This one he knew was the canyon of the difficult, high ascent and pass back to the green valleys above Hebron, seldom used because of its treacherous, rocky steepness. This canyon he knew would exit near enough to En Gedi for him to assess its safety without undue exposure to harm. He went down.

When he reached the dry riverbed at the floor of the canyon, he began to run down hill toward the Salt Sea. Uncertain of the hours remaining in the night, he was anxious to get to En Gedi before sunrise.

After running and running for hours, his body jostled from the rugged course, he finally stepped out onto the coastal plain of the Salt Sea. Before he had gone but a little way on to En Gedi, he saw in the night sky the glow of fire. En Gedi was lost, destroyed by the Chaldeans. He approached cautiously, keeping near the base of the cliffs.

As he reached the En Gedi oasis village, he slowed. It was afire. Solemnly he gazed down upon the glowing columns of smoke rising amid the palm trees, up from the ruins of destroyed farm homes and the houses of the village. He saw no people. He heard no people. Except for the crackling of the flames which he could hear even up at the foot of the hill, there was only stillness and silence.

Yet fearing that patrols of Babylonians might still be camped nearby, he knew that he could not hide the Urim and Thummim anywhere near here. He would have to truly enter into the Strong Holds of David and seek within the austere canyons a hiding place for the small gold box. He turned and headed back north, toward the City of Salt, away from the roadway high along the cliff base.

He stopped only when he reached the canyon mouth from which he had emerged onto the plain. Cold and weary, exhausted, hungry, hurting, he knelt on the grass and asked God to direct him to the place where His Oracles should be hidden to escape capture.

As he knelt with his eyes closed in prayer, he saw in his mind the image of his master, the High Priest Seraiah, almost fully dressed to officiate in the Temple, and saw himself giving the High Priest first his white linen miter to place on his head, and then his gold forehead band, the holy Ziz. He saw the gold platelet clearly, and upon it he saw the words engraved, *Holiness To The Lord*. He saw himself then helping tie the blue cords of the golden Ziz behind Seraiah's miter to prepare him to enter the Holy of Holies of the Temple.

This vision of Seraiah suddenly vanished; in his place Yehoniah now saw a cliff face, high and above the straight way of a canyon.

He felt startled, and opened his eyes. He looked up and saw again he was at the mouth of the canyon leading to the high treacherous pass, and then he remembered its ancient name.

The Ascent of Ziz.

The Ziz.

Holiness To The Lord, he heard the words in his mind.

This was the place where he should hide the Urim and Thummim.

He closed his eyes and bowed his head, thanking God for showing him the way. He arose and walked straight into the mouth of the canyon, following it back up its path, to the north-west.

He followed it far into the hills as it turned and climbed and wound its way up the gorge. It was strange. Only a few hours earlier he had run all of this course at a downhill pace. Reaching the branch north, to the Ascent, he turned into it. After following it past the place where he had descended from the wilderness above, he continued several miles until he reached the base of the pass itself. There he climbed up the canyon wall to follow the ridge instead of the canyon, to seek the place he had seen in his mind.

He did not have to go far. There it was, just as he had seen it. He climbed down the canyon which at this point was nearing the summit and not so deep, and quickly climbed up the opposite side to the small triangular cleft he had seen in the rock. The ledge was well wide enough and the opening deep enough for him to kneel and crawl inside several cubits. With his feet dangling off the ledge, he placed the gold box containing the Urim and Thummim in the center of the furthest recess of the small cave and carefully pulled his body back out and up to a kneeling position.

Though no one could see this cleft from the pathway below, still he looked around for something to cover the opening. There was nothing but loose dirt fallen and piled on the ledge. Quickly he began to scoop handfuls of dirt from both sides and heap it into the opening of the cleft. It was too slow. Already the sky was bright with the glow of impending dawn, and soon the canyon would be in broad daylight. An idea came to his mind. He raised the water skin to his lips and drank the last swallows. He then tore his thumb into the wet leather and, putting all of his fingers into the hole, pulled and tore the skin open. He now had a bag.

Filling the leather water bag again and again with loose dirt from the ledge, soon the cleft opening was closed. Just in time. The sun had topped the peaks of the far mountains across the Salt Sea and already shone upon the ridge top only a few dozen cubits above him. A few more bags full spilled over the top of the pile to build it up stronger and thicker, and he knew that the hiding place would be sealed for years. He looked up at the canyon rim. As new dirt blew down and trickled down from the canyon top, it would continue to cover the cleft more and more.

His task was completed.

His oath was fulfilled.

Thoroughly exhausted, he trod his way down the precarious high pass trail into the lower canyon below, and followed it as the sun rose in the sky, walking miles until he reached a wide place where the dry riverbed curved and opened.

He looked up to his left and jumped back with a start.

There were houses and palm trees. He must have passed them twice last night in the dark, first running downhill, and then plodding uphill to the pass.

He paused a moment looking over at the buildings. There was no sound, not of animals or people. No smoke was rising from cooking fires.

Feeling it was safe to approach them, he cautiously walked out onto the flat area towards the villa.

As he came nearer, he saw scraps of food strewn on the ground; fresh, half-dried vegetable peelings and green cuttings amid much older trash and garbage. By the fresh scraps he knew people had been here very recently.

229

He halted fearfully as a broken pottery shard crunched into smaller pieces beneath his sandal. He froze. The sound did not bring anyone out of the buildings. He continued over the littered ground almost on tiptoe toward the closest building, until he reached its door, and looked in.

It was a mess.

Table and benches were overturned; broken pots and bowls were scattered across the floor; mixed old clothing lay in a disordered pile by one wall. He peered into the adjoining rooms and saw palm fiber bed mats thrown in disarray, and pieces of clay oil lamps on the floor where they had been smashed. In one room jars of grain had been intentionally broken and the grain scattered across the dirt floor.

He went out of the first house and into the second. A similar scene of destruction and wreckage met his eyes.

He looked one by one into the two small buildings behind, but they were empty. He squinted down at the floor, and saw a date. He bent over to pick it up, and ate it, spitting out the stone. He bent over again, and with his face close to the ground, he saw more dates, and nut kernels. This had been a food storage, but it had been emptied.

He walked back out into the sun. This place must have been abandoned only days before. The Chaldeans must have come through the canyon. Even this remote spot had not escaped.

He glanced in the direction of the stand of palm trees and suddenly something caught his eye: the stone block structure by the base of the hill. His heart leapt within his bosom.

A well!

He ran to it and was even more amazed and joyful. It was a flowing spring! Without hesitation he scooped up water and splashed it onto his face, and then more over his head. His eye caught a gourd ladle on the ground beside it, and gratefully he dipped it into the clear, sweet water and drank again and again until he was full. Where did the flowing water go, he wondered? He looked up to his right along the base of the hill and saw a small, shallow channel had been dug long ago, directing the water all the way down to rejoin with the dry river bed. He followed it along to where it spilled down the embankment into the dry river, disappearing into the sand.

Walking back to the first house, he gathered some of the old cloths and carried them into the room with the thickest bed mat, where he spread them out evenly into a soft cushioned layer.

Wearily, he lay down, and in moments, he was fast asleep.

Yehoniah stayed at the villa for a week.

The first night he hiked the distance to En Gedi to search for food left in the burned and toppled houses, and whatever might be gleaned from gardens and fields. There were many dead, lying as they had fallen. His heart ached for them, and for their families.

As steward to the High priest he had never touched a dead body, and never before would he have thought of moving bodies or burying the dead, for he would have been unclean for many days, and of no use to his master. But now there was no master to be clean for, no High Priest, no Temple.

He found a shovel and a pick and spent the day digging graves, and pulled the bodies into them, and buried them. When they were all covered he recited a passage he had herd Seraiah say many times. Having done all he could, he left En Gedi and went back up to his refuge, the oasis in the canyon wilderness.

During the week not a single soul came down the pass from the highlands of Tekoa or up from the plain of the Salt Sea. He wondered how his friends Jehonadab and Essaiah and the others had done. What had they found at Ir Hammelach? Had it been destroyed as En Gedi? Were they safe? Did they still live?

When he finally felt it was safe to travel, he left the small villa at the bottom of the canyon heights and returned to Jerusalem. As he walked past the hiding place of the Oracles near the summit of the pass, he looked up and was pleased to find that it was invisible. When the time came that Seraiah and the people returned, and Seraiah asked him to go and retrieve the Oracles for him, he would know exactly where they were. But no one else would find them. They would remain safely hidden until his return.

He walked for two days back to Jerusalem.

As he reached the top of the last hill and looked across the valley at Jerusalem, it was worse than he had feared. The city was almost completely destroyed. The tops of almost all of the walls had been felled, and large sections were collapsed down to their bases; all of the huge city gates had been removed from their hinges and burned. The gate arches themselves had been pried in several places until they fell. All of this he could see from still a distance.

He stopped and gazed upon the ruin of the city. The sky above was blue as it had always been, with white puffs of clouds as soft and beautiful as he had ever seen, and the sun shone down as brightly as it ever had, but nothing was the same. Ten days had now passed since the Temple and city were burned. Even so, black smoke still rose in thin columns from several parts of the city within the walls. The mount of Jerusalem and its glory were reduced to rubble and ashes. It was a pitiful sight, and though he willed it not, he could not stop the tears which rose in his eyes, blurring his vision. He wiped them away and proceeded down the hill.

Inside the city virtually nothing was left. Many more fires had been set since he had left, and the Chaldeans had completed the job of dispossessing his people. Where the glorious walls of the Temple had once stood he now saw only blue sky and circling vultures.

As there was nothing here, he determined to go on to Mizpah, where he was told that Jeremiah now stayed under the care of Gedaliah the governor.

It was only a few hours more walking, north.

As he walked north, he left the land of Judah and entered the land of Benjamin. The closer he got to Mizpah, the less destruction he saw. Obviously, the Chaldeans wrecked their harshest wrath against Judah, and Benjamin had been spared. He saw men and beasts working in the fields and vineyards. They looked up from their work, but did not pause or smile. They worked the work of survival.

He arrived at Mizpah in the late afternoon. Its walls appeared untouched by battle, tall and undamaged. The main road entering the city's double corridor gate was busy with people and animals carrying burdens. Yehoniah could see, hosts of the people were gathering there from all over the land, the simple folk who were allowed to remain. He pushed through the throng, into the city.

He had been to Mizpah before, but as he came into the city and walked through the streets to the Governor's residence, he saw it was very different now. Crowded. Dirty. Despairing.

Chaldean soldiers walked everywhere in the town, not as warriors, but as billeted guards of the land. They laughed among themselves, and mocked the poor as they pushed them out of their way in the streets. They were already becoming fat, while the Judahite people Yehoniah saw were thin, and frightened.

After he reached Gedaliah's house, it was not so difficult to find and gain audience with Jeremiah. He and Baruch had their own house, and though there were guards, they only occasionally watched, often leaving to follow amusements. It was Jeremiah's promise which bound him and Baruch to this place, and the Chaldeans worried little over him.

The first thing Yehoniah asked of Jeremiah was news of his master, Seraiah. The prophet looked down at the ground, and Baruch kept his eye on the prophet until his head rose up and he spoke.

"Sera'yahu is dead," said Jeremiah.

Yehoniah was stunned. He turned quickly to Baruch, but he closed his eyes and shook his head. It was true. His master was dead.

"Eighty of the last remaining nobles, priests and leaders of the people, those whom you saw in chains and marched before the people, all of these were executed at Riblah," said Jeremiah sadly.

"Nebuchadnezzar at his Royal Camp recited to them their stiffneckedness, and to be finished with them, he slew them all. When the common people arrived, those whom you saw herded as cattle from the city, they were marched passed the bodies as they lay fly-covered and bloating in the sun. Soon they go on to Babylon."

"And here?" asked Yehoniah.

"Only of the working classes of the people have been left to keep the farms and tend the vineyards. Gedal'yahu has been set to rule over the land for the Chaldean as governor. Even he did not know that Sera'yahu and the others would be slain. You have heard that Zedek'yahu the King's sons were slain before his eyes, and then he was blinded? Because he could not see the death of the nobles and priests and leaders, they brought him close so that he might hear their pleadings for life and then their screams and death rattles as they choked upon their own blood."

"Even this they did," whispered Yehoniah in horrified disbelief.

"Even this," nodded Jeremiah.

"The Lord had warned them times enough, and he had warned those who died. They refused to listen." spoke Baruch, tilting his head toward the prophet.

Yehoniah's heart was anguished beyond all imagining. Yet after hearing this horrible tragedy, the fate of the Oracles and the scrolls suddenly filled his mind. This was not just a deportation to Babylon which might eventually end. Seraiah was dead. Now what?

"Jerem'yahu," spoke Yehoniah slowly, unsure of how he would say this, "the errand for the Lord upon which Sera'yahu sent me was the concealing of the Urim and Thummim of the Lord, up into the Wilderness of Judah. As Sera'yahu who sent me is now dead, unto whom shall I now deliver the stones some day?"

Jeremiah looked out the window at the clouds in the sky, gazing for a moment into the heavens, and then he returned his eyes to Yehoniah.

"In the days of our grandfathers' grandfathers' grandfathers, the prophet Hosea spoke against the House of Israel, and for its hard heartedness and disobedience he gave to them the word of the Lord, saying that lest they repent, the Ephod would be taken from the hand of Judah. This was the Urim and Thummim. The prophet Nahum called Israel to repentance, and they heard him not. So did the prophetess Hulda, and more did she prophecy, and all that she spoke has come to pass, even the deepest curse of destruction. You have seen it, as you have come here. Zephan'yahu also spoke, and they heard him not, neither would they hear Obed'yahu, or Daniel, or Lehi, or Habakkuk, or Ezekiel," said Jeremiah.

"Or you," added Baruch.

"Or me," said Jeremiah, casting his eyes to the ground.

"So you are saying that they are to remain where they are?" inquired Yehoniah.

"As Hosea spoke for the Lord, so it is fulfilled," replied Jeremiah. "The Ephod is taken from the hand of Judah."

"There is more," spoke Yehoniah.

"Tell me," said Jeremiah, raising his eyes again to Yehoniah.

"Sera'yahu did covenant with his nephew Essa'yahu, the Zadokite, that he and Jehonadab ben Habazin'yahu...."

"Of the Rechabites?"

"The same, that they should choose of the remaining sons of Judah men of strength and faithfulness to carry the Books of the Temple into the desert, there to hide them up unto the Lord until the people should be restored."

Jeremiah glanced over at Baruch and the two men nodded.

"Jehozadak, the son of Sera'yahu ben Azar'yahu the High Priest, lives, and with the people he will go to Babylon. In the due time of the Lord his seed shall return and the Books shall be returned to the people. The time of the Chaldean is at hand, and his kingdom shall soon pass to another; then Judah shall receive back the land," he said.

"Where have they taken the scrolls?" asked Baruch.

"To the caves by Ir Hammelach," answered Yehoniah.

Jeremiah glanced again at Baruch, and back to Yehoniah.

"The children of Jonadab ben Rechab are strong in that place," Jeremiah said. "The Lord's hand has guided this thing."

"Stay with us and eat," offered Baruch. With this, Yehoniah knew that the discussion was at an end.

He was very hungry, and ate well. They talked of many other things, never returning to speak of the Oracles or the Books.

That night as Yehoniah slept in a good bed for the first time in almost two weeks, he could not help but think of the others. Did they at the City of Salt know, that Seraiah and all of the priests are dead? They will find out, he thought. How long shall the scrolls stay there now? With Temple destroyed, and the priests killed, how long until the Lord should remember his people, and allow them to return and rebuild?

Yehoniah decided to stay with Jeremiah. He found a new job as husbandman out in the fields with the other workers, gathering summer fruits and vegetables and grain, and helping to press oil from the abundant olive harvest. He found that he was glad of this. The blue of the sky and the smell of the moist earth in his nostrils brought peace to his soul.

Gedaliah did not have peace. He quickly found he had many enemies. As a Judahite serving the enemy, he was despised.

But then, after only a few short weeks, the captains of the armies of Judah, who had escaped with many into the hills, came into Mizpah to speak to the new governor. Yehoniah saw Ishmael ben Nethaniah, his old friends Azariah ben Hoshaiah, Johanan ben Kareah and his brother Jonathan, and others: Jaazaniah ben Maachathite and the sons of Ephai the Netophathite. He had not imagined that so many of them had survived.

Gedaliah welcomed them, and plainly told them and their followers to lay down their swords and join in the harvest, to stay in the land and serve the Chaldeans. They gave their allegiance, and went to the hills to bring back the many hungry soldiers who had for all of this time been in hiding. Jaazaniah was appointed to the Governor's house, and served as the chief of his personal guard.

The summer faded; autumn approached and came. Though much of the harvest crop had been destroyed by war, with so few people left in the land the storehouses were soon full enough for all. There would be food in plenty for all those who had stayed, and a good winter seemed certain. Yehoniah began to feel that his life would find comfort again, and that the future might be good indeed.

But only a few weeks later all of that changed.

Johanan ben Kareah came to Yehoniah, anxiously asking for counsel. He had learned that Ishmael ben Nethaniah, a son of the royal line, determined to proclaim himself king, and throw off the yoke of the Babylonians. He had made a pact with the king of the Ammonites, and plotted to kill the governor.

Yehoniah told him of Jeremiah's words, that if they remained peaceful in the land that God would bless them, and urged him to tell Gedaliah immediately.

Johanan told Gedaliah, pleading with him to give the order to slay Ishmael and his partisans.

But Jaazaniah knew nothing of these things, and advised Gedaliah to give no ear. The governor therefore believed it to be a deceit of jealousy, and forbade Johanan to kill Ishmael.

Yet many knew, and the feeling of unrest at Mizpah grew.

Then the day came in which Ishmael sought an audience in the governor's house. He had found the great sword of Goliath in the ruins of the sanctuary of Nob where it had been kept since the days of David the King, and begged to give it to Gedaliah as a gift. The governor had welcomed him, and he came with ten men, and they were feasted before the king. But when Ishmael stood forward as if to present the gift, with this battle trophy as emblem of David's kingdom over all Israel and his right to rule as a son of the royal line, he slew Gedaliah upon his throne, before a cry could be uttered.

Jaazaniah stood in shock, yet it was too late. Seeing Gedaliah already dead upon the floor, he raised his hand in allegiance to Ishmael, but he stayed in the Governor's house.

The rebels quickly went out and raged through the city, and did not return until they had slain all the remaining Jewish leaders of Mizpah who had given Gedaliah support. So great was their fury and wrath that all of the Babylonian soldiers garrisoned at Mizpah were killed in that very same day. Their victory was complete.

Yet because of its completeness, they failed. Within hours a dispatch soldier arrived from the fortress to the north with message tablets, and he too had to be killed. As Ishmael sat upon the blood of Gedaliah on his throne, his chiefs reasoned with him that even with all of the weapons they had taken from the fallen Chaldeans put into the hands of the men of Mizpah, they were not ready to confront the entire army of Chaldea. Within days, they pleaded, the greater forces garrisoned to the north would hear the silence at Mizpah, and the Babylonian army would descend upon them as locusts.

Ishmael planned among his companions, and they determined to bide their time until the Chaldeans sent an army against them.

Yehoniah found himself restricted to his room, as did everyone in the city. Ishmael had enforced martial law, and he called everyone in from the fields and orchards. No one was allowed to work, or leave the city. Mizpah suddenly became a huge prison.

The next day, every passing group on the roadway, small or large, was slain. Ishmael spilled Judahite blood as readily as Chaldean in his panic to halt the spreading of his deeds. He piled the bodies in a great heap at the bottom of a pit outside the city.

Abruptly on the following morning, his plans changed. He had become a raging madman. He ordered his soldiers to quickly gather every man, woman and child at sword point; the people were to take whatever they could carry, and assemble outside the city. In less than two hours Yehoniah and all of the people began a forced march to the east with Ishmael and his men to join the Ammonites. Once again Judahites were torn from the homes they were just beginning to dress, and the store rooms of harvest they had only now filled, marching as captives into the land of an enemy.

Yet not all the people of Mizpah marched. Some chose to stay. Among them was Jaazaniah. And Azariah ben Hoshaiah and Johanan ben Kareah had run from the fields as soon as they heard of the murder, and had called after them the other captains and many men. They had gotten their swords, and fled again into the hills. Johanan ben Kareah, the leader of all the captains, swore to avenge the death of Gedaliah and free the people.

Yehoniah marched for two days with the mass of ragged people. He kept close to Jeremiah and Baruch, who were put in chains and walked in silence. They camped that night by the waters of Gibeon, captives under the swords and spears of Judahites.

When the night had come and the cooking fires glowed bright, without warning Johanan ben Kareah suddenly appeared at the edge of the camp with the captains and what remained of the forces of Judah. Yehoniah and the entire host of the people from Mizpah raised a great cry of joy. Johanan wasted no time in shouting out his demands to Ishmael, that he free the people. When the camp saw him and heard his words, as a body they rose up in a mighty cry against Ishmael and his soldiers.

Ishmael, seeing he was lost, took advantage of the confusion, and he with eight of his men ran out of the camp and escaped into the night.

It was over.

Yet the next morning when Johanan gathered the elders from among the people and spoke with them, no one wanted to return to Mizpah. Great fears were raised of the Chaldeans, for Gedaliah had been appointed by Nebuchadnezzar himself, and he and many Chaldean soldiers had been slain. The murderer had escaped. Everyone believed that the Chaldeans would unleash their wrath upon all Mizpah.

Johanan agreed with them, and gave the command to break camp and follow him.

As the people gathered their meagre baggage, one of Johanan's captains came to him with the sword of Goliath which he had found in Ishmael's abandoned tent. Johanan received it with great pleasure, for it was a true and holy relic of their ancestors, of King David, and it would be to him a standard of honor within his tent.

Thus Yehoniah marched with the people still further south to Chimham, near Bethlehem, south of Jerusalem. Only when they arrived at Chimham in the late afternoon could he speak to Johanan to tell him that Jeremiah and Baruch still walked in chains, and get a smith to unfetter them.

That night, Yohanan spoke to Jeremiah by the fire with the entire congregation of Mizpah, and all of the joining forces of Judah and their captains. He asked if they should return to Mizpah, or flee.

Jeremiah listened to all arguments, and after a long time of silence, he stood and said that he would inquire of the Lord. And so it was left. Many murmured against waiting, and some argued that they should leave on the morrow, without delay. But Yohanan spoke that they would wait for the word of the Lord by Jeremiah.

After ten days, Jeremiah came to Yohanan and his captains, and they gathered the host of the people. Jeremiah declared to them that they should not flee, but should return to Mitzpah, where he promised he would speak for them to the Chaldeans, and that all would be well. Yehoniah sat by his feet as he prophesied that if they would but trust in the Lord, all would be well with them, and that they would eat the fruit of their harvest, and live in the homes they had readied for the winter. He warned that if they chose to desert the Lord and go into Egypt, that their children would eventually worship false gods and many would perish.

But most had by this time set their hearts for Egypt, and they cried out that Jeremiah spoke falsely. They who raised their voices in loud cries of disbelief, who spoke loudly reminding the people of the cruelties of the Chaldeans, held sway over the camp, and the cry went up that they should flee the land of Judah and the retaliations of the Chaldeans, and go into the land of Egypt where they would find safety and bread.

Johanan ben Kareah and Azariah ben Hoshaiah declared loudest of all that Jeremiah spoke falsely, and declared for the decision to flee into Egypt to escape the vengeful hand of the Chaldeans.

Yehoniah stood up to plead with them that they should listen to Jeremiah and follow the prophet, but Johanan shouted him down, even his old friend. Jeremiah declared that he would return to Mizpah, to live in the land of Judah, and Baruch and Yehoniah stood with him. Yehoniah did not want to go to Egypt. This was his home.

Johanan said that all might do as they saw fit, and ordered that all should go to sleep, to rest for the morrow.

But early the next morning, before sunrise, Johanan ben Kareah and Azariah ben Hoshaiah called together their captains, and they debated what they should do. Each man reported that almost all whom he knew feared the Chaldeans and were eager to go to Egypt. They made a list of the names of those who had spoken of returning.

Fearing that the prophet, Baruch and Yehoniah would reveal the plan of their escape to the Chaldeans if they returned to Mizpah, Johanan ordered Jeremiah and the others on the list brought to him, including Yehoniah. These he declared captives, and ordered them to be bound with ropes, and they were made hostages.

As the sun rose and the people in the camp assembled to hear Johanan's command, he declared that all those free men with their families who wished to join them were given welcome. He said those who refused would be bound, and presented the hostages for all to see. The people as a mass cried out their allegiance to Johanan.

He then proclaimed that together with these hostages they would flee into Egypt where they would establish a new Israel.

Yehoniah left his homeland that day with Jeremiah and Baruch, marching southward through the desert as hostage. All of the people of the city were thus with them. 'As Jeremiah had prophesied, the city became deserted even before the arrival of the Chaldeans.

After all Yehoniah had endured, he was now a hostage, marching to Egypt. As day after day they traveled farther south, his anguish became unbearable. When they crossed the Brook of Egypt the rebels rejoiced, but Yehoniah hung his head in despair. With every mile he walked toward Egypt his heart sank more.

Jeremiah, Yehoniah and the others remained hostages even when they entered into Egyptian lands. Azariah and Johanan feared the anger of the Chaldeans even in Egypt, and so they keep moving along the Delta. Yehoniah continued to march.

But then one day the main body of the group became weary of fleeing, for they found themselves upon good, fertile land. They refused to go any further, and Azariah and Johanan could not get them to follow any more. So they let them stay, wishing them well.

Jeremiah and Baruch were constrained by the congregation of Judah that stayed there, who chose to stay at Tahpanhes on the Delta of the Nile River, to stay with them, and Johanan had no power to dissuade them otherwise; the people held firm.

The prophet declared to them all that soon God would deliver the Pharaoh king of Egypt into the hands of Nebuchadnezzar king of Babylon, and that if they stayed there many would die by the sword, but they heeded not the counsel of the Lord, and remained at Tahpanhes.

Johanan and his small group of followers continued their march away from the Chaldeans, taking Yehoniah.

Yehoniah never heard from Jeremiah and Baruch again.

After many more weeks of travel up the Nile, the group finally reached Egypt's furthest outpost along the upper Nile, as far away from the Chaldeans as they could go. They settled at Yeb, by the city of Syene, where the quarries cut stone for obelisks, Pharaoh's court and the temples of Egypt.

Yehoniah was finally freed, but warned that he was still a hostage, and could not leave.

He became a mercenary, as did most of those who had come here. It was not such a bad profession. There was not much to do, and no one to fight. They built a fortress and a small village.

He married an Israelite refugee woman, and had sons and daughters. Though the Egyptians paid their mercenaries poorly, he was given a fine brick and stone house to live in, and they never lacked water even in the summer. He could buy bread for his family.

Five years later, a great uproar was heard in the land, and Pharaoh Hophra was slain by the very hand of Nebuchadnezzar, who had descended upon the kingdom of Egypt. After many months, Yehoniah received word that the king of Babylon had taken captive the House of Judah that had remained at Tahpanhes on the Delta, killing many for the murder of Gedaliah, and carrying all the rest back to Babylon. He learned that before their settlement had fallen, they had stoned Jeremiah to death. Baruch had been taken captive, and went even with the others unto Babylon.

The very thought of the death of his friend the prophet, and the hopeless journey of Baruch to distant Babylon filled Yehoniah with a weariness of life, and he set down upon a stone by the Nile and wondered how long the suffering of his people should continue. Why had he been brought here? What was the purpose of it all?

Two decades and more after the arrival at Yeb, Azariah and Johanan one day imagined a strange idea. They bargained with the priests of Khnum and the officials of Syene, and, with Egyptian sanction, they set about to build a Temple to God.

As steward to the last High Priest at Jerusalem, and the only one of the entire group with any connection to the priesthood or the Temple, Yehoniah was requested to prepare the dedication offerings and make prayer and sacrifice for the endeavor.

All of this he did, and more. Granite stone for the floors was commissioned from the nearby quarries of Syene, for it was cheap as brick, falling off in great slabs from the cutting of large blocks and obelisks. He ordered that a box of stone be made, and also he had engraved upon a plaque of bronze words he recalled from the sacred Books he had often heard Seraiah read in the Temple.

He told Johanan that if they were to do this thing, he must re-dedicate the sword of Goliath to the Lord, as David of old had done, and lay it in the dedicatory offering for all time. Johanan was displeased at the thought of giving up his trophy, for it had remained to him a symbol of his victory over Ishmael and the Chaldeans.

But Yehoniah convinced him that what was the Lord's must be returned. Yes, it was a great symbol of Israel, of David who had begun the first Temple, and of the defeat of all the Lord's enemies. For this it was the only true link they had among them to the Temple in Jerusalem. As such, it must be returned to the Lord, to whom David had once given it.

Johanan agreed, and it was done.

So Yehoniah laid the sword of Goliath in the bottom of the foundation box of the Temple floor, as part of the Dedicatory ritual, with a Dedicatory prayer written upon a plaque of beaten bronze.

Before lowering the large granite floor slab over the box, Yehoniah, servant of Seraiah the High Priest and now one of the honored leaders of Yeb, placed the large broken side of an amphora jar over the sword and the plaque, which, he said to those present, was as a shield.

No one knew that secretly written under it was Yehoniah's own private prayer to the Lord, declaring that the Urim and Thummim were laid to rest where David had once taken refuge in the wilderness above En-Gedi, and that there they would rest until called forth by the Lord.

The long flat stone was lowered into its place, and with the dull thud of its settling, once more Yehoniah's oath was fulfilled.

By the time the Temple was finally finished, Jeremiah had already died in northern Egypt on the Delta, and Baruch had left Egypt to be with the people. As there was no other to call, Yehoniah was made to become the Temple's first Priest. He had been Seraiah's steward, and for the people, he was the closest to a proper Priest as they could choose.

Though he felt unworthy, Yehoniah loved the Lord and accepted this service with a full heart.

After more than thirty years since leaving his homeland, and many letters sent with no response, Yehoniah, Priest of the Temple at Yeb finally received a letter from Essaiah at the City of Salt.

He learned that the settlement had been destroyed by the Chaldeans, but the Rechabites had been allowed to stay in their tents. All six of the men had been welcomed into the tents of Jehonadab's brothers, where they remained, living in tents. He said that they had learned of Seraiah's death, the revolt in Mizpah and the death of Gedaliah, and of the exodus south into Egypt.

Jehonadab had married and had sons and daughters, but he had died and been laid to rest with his fathers at the City of Salt.

Essaiah ben Zadok had become the leader of the community. He married and had sons and daughters. He taught his children by the words in the scrolls, and even though he was old, he wrote to Yehoniah that with the defeat of the Chaldeans and the new rule of Cyrus the Persian, he had hopes that he might begin communications with the elders at Babylon, and some day restore to the people the treasure which Seraiah the High Priest had preserved for them.

Over the many years that had passed, he wrote, many of their dead had been buried in the cemetery they had begun for the dead slain by the Chaldeans. To remember the people, those who had been dispersed in exile to the north, and to the south, they had buried all of them facing to the north and to the south. For it was from the north and from the south that they would some day return, he prayed, return to their home. And thus they continued to live in the tents of Jehonadab's people. And they married and had children.

Yehoniah read the words, and longed to have his bones carried back to be buried in his homeland, where these men were buried with their women and their children.

Better to live in a tent in the desert in the land of his fathers than live in a house of fine brick and stone in a land of strangers.

But Yehoniah looked upon his wife and his children, and peered into his own future. He was old. He saw his death in the far land of Egypt, far from his home, far from Jerusalem, far from the remnant of his people in Babylon. How many of his generation had died in captivity in that far land by the Euphrates?

One day he sat by the Temple of God and looked out over the slowly flowing waters of the Nile, and thought of the strange destiny which had spared him from Nebuchadnezzar, only to bring him out of his home into Egypt. Had it been for good?

His captivity had been no less than if he had been carried to Babylon by the Euphrates. It had been no less tearful, though he had lived all of these years in Egypt as a free man in a free land under the lenient rule of an unconcerned Egyptian people.

Yet no matter how free he might call himself, he had always been a captive, far up the Nile frontier in a distant outpost.

He sat by the Temple in the shade of a palm tree, watching the swirling waters of the Nile glisten as the sun was going down.

He felt tired.

Very, very tired.

Chapter 9

Day 28 in the wilderness: The Discovery

I awoke in the morning to a wondrous miracle.

The spring was filled with water.

Good, fresh, cool water.

I looked all around me as I stood up from the most delicious drink, and suddenly in my mind I knew this place, knew it well, and I could see it with all of the palm trees that had once been here.

I looked back where the houses had been, and without pause they formed in my mind, each one over its foundations, standing in the sun with white walls and thatched roofs.

Except for the furthest store room, the one furthest back against the base of the canyon wall. It had not been there. It had been built after Yehoniah. I knew, because I could not see it there standing in the sun as I saw all of the others now.

There had been a lot of palm trees. I glanced up and around me into the air, seeing them all around, and I looked down at the ground to see if I could find any depressions in the earth where the trunks and roots had sunk into the ground. Nothing. Time and drifting dust had long filled them in and covered them over. But I knew that some day some one would dig and find them, and with excited, trembling hands dig away the dirt from all around them, and carefully lift them up and put them in boxes and take them to a botany lab. There was no time now on this trip. I had other things to do. But their remains would some day be found.

I had no certain way of knowing when after Yehoniah they had been destroyed, whether they had been cut down for their wood as poor as it was, or burned by the soldiers of an enemy, or if they had just died after the spring died, after the water stopped flowing from the spring here, and over time dried and decayed and finally toppled and disintegrated until little by little the Bedouin had picked away at the old trunks for fire fuel. But they had been here. I could see them, see them clearly now in my mind, the entire grove around this oasis spring. They were the tamar, the dates palms of this place.

Yet the most incredible thing I saw was not in my mind. It was real. The spring was filled with crystal clear water flowing up from beneath the earth, filling the shallow bowl of the stone enclosure and overflowing onto the dry ground around me feet.

I looked to my right, east along the cliff base, but I could see no sign of the run-off channel, just the sloping low fill of centuries of dirt. With no one to constantly maintain it, the desert had reclaimed itself.

I could see that the water was going to eventually saturate the ground around the spring, and because of the slope of the plateau, it would creep forward until it began to soak and saturate the foundations of the store rooms and then the houses, ruining the relics still buried under the soil. I went to the tent and returned with my shovel, and proceeded to dig a shallow ditch from the spring to the wadi far away, following along the steep base of the cliff. It would be days before the water would soak this earth enough to reach the wadi. Perhaps the water would not flow that long. Yet I now had assured that the villa was protected from water damage, and I no longer had to worry about the site.

I stopped to stand and look upon this remarkable phenomenon, this water flowing up in this old artesian spring. I wondered what trick of nature had caused water to flow up from the ground on this very morning. There had been no rain since my arrival, and surely no rain had fallen for months before. What rainfall, how much earlier in the year had been trapped high up on the wilderness and slowly filtered its way through the rocks and gravel and fissures of the earth until it found this ancient underground course and followed it, suddenly coming up out of the mountainside?

Ultimately it did not matter to me; I just knew that as long as it flowed I would drink this water instead of the water I had just purchased at En Gedi yesterday. This water was so pure, the taste was so refreshing, I would be silly to drink anything else.

Though I knew the images in my mind from the night before, of this place, of Yehoniah, were all only a dream, I looked down at the water flowing from the long-dry artesian spring, just as I had seen it in my dream, and I could not help but feel a growing sense of excitement. I had seen the cliff face, and the cleft in the rock.

Though my academic teaching told me to dismiss any such imagining, I thought and thought again. Yes, I decided. Following a dream could be no

243

more disappointing than everything else I had tried that failed, and it may take me where nothing else has.

I wanted to follow the upper course of this canyon and wadi all the way to the top, to the pass. To the Ascent of Ziz.

I filled a canteen with cool fresh water from the spring, and put some food into my backpack, along with a geologist's pick and trowel. By the map there were at least twelve miles to hike up the canyon, certainly more by the time I figured in all of the zigs and zags which my foot course would take over the rugged wadi floor.

I hiked and hiked and hiked until the sun was high in the sky. As the canyon floor continued to rise in elevation, I kept looking up ahead and around at the canyon walls. Before mid-day I reached the furthest point to which I had previously hiked in search of Yehoniah's cave. I had never suspected that he would have gone this high into the wilderness. Indeed, the pass was almost all the way back to the inland valleys. I stopped regularly to scrutinize the map and locate myself upon it, and soon the area of the pass began to be tantalizingly close.

As I hiked up the rocky bottom of the wadi with some difficulty, I reached the place where it turned, and before me, I beheld a short but very straight run of canyon. Looking up around me, I could tell that I had reached the heights of the wilderness, for the canyon walls were now low above me, only a few hundred feet or more. The view seemed familiar as I walked along, as I remembered from my dream. But I had seen so many wadis in the last three and a half weeks. Everything looked familiar.

Yet I reached a place where the ridge above the cliffs felt very familiar. This was high enough. I stopped and looked at the map.

The pass was not too much further, less than a mile around the bend and up just a few more small curves. I gazed up all around me, trying to feel the images of last night's dream. It was crazy, I thought, but nothing else had found me the Urim and Thummim. The Yeb ostracon had not been a dream, even though no one had believed Brannon. The two ostraca Moishe and I had uncovered at the bottom of his living room shaft were not a dream. I had touched them. Nor was the palimpsest Johanan had showed me at the Scrollerium a dream. It was real, a tephillah, and I had seen the infra-red photograph with the letter to Yehoniah written in Seraiah's own hand. Perhaps, I thought, with his own blood. The man named Yehoniah lived, and he had hidden the Urim and Thummim somewhere in these hills. I had spent twenty-seven days searching dozens of miles of wadi tributaries, climbing up and down thousand-foot cliffs to reach caves that had long ago been excavated, and little holes only a raven could live in, without ever finding anything. Was that any less crazy than following a dream?

I looked up and saw, up quite high, there, to my right, a ledge which looked like the ledge I had seen Yehoniah climb in my dream.

Funny, I thought. I had spent weeks looking for what I could see, never imaging to look where I could not see. It had never occurred to me that twenty-five centuries of falling dirt, the earth and soil and rock which continually collapsed down over these canyon walls from above, might have piled up and filled over the ledges which could be walked on in ancient times, obliterating a cave that had been open and visible to ancient eyes.

Scanning the jagged outcroppings and ledges from where I stood up to the place above, the ascent seemed possible. I began.

I climbed, and climbed, and climbed higher still.

As I climbed to the high ledge far up the almost sheer side of the wadi here, I began to feel more familiar with this view. I paused and looked around to either side of me. This wadi was one of the many which seemed as a straight path, with a high way nicely visible and sure, yet everything here seemed familiar. It was so much like the dream. I turned back to the cliff face and eagerly proceeded to climb higher along the ledge.

Yet suddenly the loose rubble under my feet slipped beneath me. In a nauseous instant, I felt myself reeling backward into open space. Desperately, as my feet flew out from under me, my hand lashed out for the wall and miraculously caught onto the solid rock; dangling by one arm, my body swung with a pivotal thud up against the cliff. I hung there by one arm, gasping for breath, swinging like a pendulum over the chasm. Stones and dirt were freefalling down through space to the wadi floor far below. Groping with my other hand, I swung myself around and grabbed another rock, and pulled myself back up onto the ledge. My breath was heaving and my heart pounding in my ears. Clinging to the rocks, literally hugging the canyon wall, I slumped trembling to my knees.

I had almost fallen to my death.

Looking down the abyss, it suddenly seemed to swallow me. All of these weeks I had climbed to dizzying heights without even so much as a tie rope, and I had never feared. Suddenly I feared. I looked down at the rocks far below me, and I feared. Adrenaline pumping, heart pounding, gulping for breath, I pressed my body even more tightly against the cliff wall, and slumped and slid until the seat of my pants rested on the ledge. I needed to recompose.

I glanced around me. The ledge was really too small. There was more loose rubble strewn along, making it dangerous. But I had to go on, and up. I pulled myself to my feet again, and continued to climb.

I climbed slowly, fearfully, but I would not quit.

When I reached a ledge not so far from the top, I began to feel that this was it. This was the one. I inched forward step by step, and then I stopped. I scanned along the ledge, trying to see something, anything along its face which looked as if I should dig there. There were many filled stretches of sloping dirt and gravel which had fallen and piled up. The whole of the Wilderness of Judah and every nahal and wadi were covered with such steep alluvials made by trickling dirt or collapsing ridges. I had been seeing them and carefully stepping through them along ledges for weeks.

But then my eyes saw something.

It was a small wisp of a desert plant, with a wildflower.

I didn't know why, but that little flower growing out of a steep slope of dirt about five yards away, clinging to the edge of the cliff, beckoned to me to come and dig there. The dirt had piled up to a height of about five feet, sloping from cliff face to ledge edge and down the dropoff. It looked as familiar as any of the myriad such piles of fallen dirt I had seen over the last weeks, but the little flower, bobbing and nodding in the slight canyon breeze, called me to that spot.

I edged my way over to it. I cautiously took off my backpack and pulled out the hand trowel to begin digging.

Before digging away the slope of dirt, I knelt down, hugging the wall, and stretched out my hand with the trowel to the flower. Carefully I shoved in the trowel blade beneath the plant with its flower, and lifted it up and out of the dirt. There were few plants in this desert, and this flower deserved to live. I turned, and scooped with my hands a hole in the adjacent talus to replant it in. Carefully with my fingers I pushed the lump of dirt off the trowel blade into the hole, and patted the earth around it.

There. A perfect new home.

Standing once again, I began to scoop the loose dirt and rock off the top of the talus slope, out into space. I dug and I dug, watching the dirt plummet down into the wadi, falling to the bottom as I could have plummeted. A cloud of dust was swept up into the air with every scoopful I pushed into space. I scooped and dug, down and down, removing more and more loose rock, gravel and earth from the ledge. Soon I was kneeling, shoving dirt from the cliff face in great sweeping arcs of my arm with the trowel, leveling and digging the ledge down more and more.

And then, I looked up at the talus of rubble which kept slipping, and to my surprise, I saw just above my forehead an indentation in the rock jutting in and under. My pulse leaped. I dug more quickly. As the rubble continued to slip down off the ledge into space and around my feet, sliding down from this receding top space, I could see the indentation slanted into a deepening hollow. With each scoop of the trowel the dirt sank lower, and receded from the rock wall, revealing a deeper and deeper hollow.

Suddenly, with one more scoop, the dirt sagged from the top of the rocks and the split of an opening appeared. I reached out my hand and shoved away more dirt. There was an opening, sure enough, and the dirt sloped down on the inside.

This was a cleft, a very small cave, entirely sealed and hidden by the dirt.

The cleft opened more and more as I madly scooped and shoved dirt and rock off the ledge into space. A billowing cloud of dust filled the wadi, blowing away in the breeze.

I dug and dug until I had cleared enough to peer inside. The cleft went back too far for me see its end in the dark. I dug with a frenzy, clearing the dirt off now with both hands, shoving it off the ledge, until I could climb over the dirt and crawl inside. I had to negotiate the entry carefully on the narrow ledge, and wriggle in from the side like a worm into a hole in an apple dangling over space.

The air inside was stale, dank and dusty. I pulled my neckerchief from my pocket and put it over my mouth. It was dark, as my body almost filled the opening of the hole, blocking the sunlight outside. My eyes had not yet adjusted to the cave's darkness, but I could see it did not have a higher ceiling. I would not be able to stand. I wriggled and crawled inside more, and as my waist entered, I had to swing my feet out straight behind me, and they stuck out into the air, unsupported. The feeling was very insecure, but my body was well enough into the cleft to hold me. I waited a moment to catch my breath.

But then, as the dust settled and wafted out the cave mouth into the outside air, and my eyes began to see in the dark deeper and deeper into the recess of the small cave, my heart all but stopped.

There, through the thinning dust, I saw something on the floor. The dust cleared away more, and my eyes widened in the dark until I could see it clearly.

It was a small rectangular object, dusty and dull in the dark, laying on the dirt, back by the end of the shallow cave, all by itself in the middle of the small cave floor. It could have been a chunk of rock, but instantly my eyes told me that this was too perfect a geometric shape for a natural piece of rock. It was a box!

It was not even buried. It had not needed to be. Yehoniah had understood his mission completely.

I reached out and with a trembling hand picked it up. It was a box. And my fingers also told me it was cool and smooth; it was metal. My heart was pounding again, more than it had when I had almost fallen off the ledge.

This was a man-made metal box.

It must be the Urim and Thummim!

With wildly pounding heart and excitement filling my head in a dizzy whirl, I inched my way backwards out of the cleft, my feet and legs dangling ever more precariously out in space behind me. As soon as my waist reached the mouth of the cleft I rolled cautiously to my side and at the same time pulled up my legs until my knees bumped the solid rock of the canyon cliff wall, and I rested them on the ledge. I had never felt so grateful for rock in my life. I inched and wriggled backward more and more, until I decided that I would need both hands. I placed the metal box just inside the mouth of the cleft where I could reach it, and I then pushed myself out and up into a safe sitting position on the narrow ledge over the canyon.

Without delay I leaned forward and reached back into the cleft, grasping firmly the metal box. Already my fingers had rubbed off much of the dust.

It was gold.

Holding it before me, I took a deep breath and blew with all my might

247

on the box. Dust flew away, and at last I looked upon it in my two hands.

It was a gold box, finely made. I could feel something in it, sliding from side to side as it moved in my hands. Carefully I looked it over to see how it opened. There was a pair of simple hinges on one side. I now knew front and back. There was no latch. Simple pressure with my fingers should open it then.

I held it firmly in my hands up against my chest, and carefully exerted a pulling upward pressure on the lid to pry it open. It gave more easily than I would have guessed.

I lowered my hands and saw the lid was ajar.

Glittering light radiated within.

My hands were trembling so much now that I laughed softly to myself. It was OK. This was the kind of moment that was supposed to make hands tremble. Carefully I put my fingers under the lid, and lifted it up.

There, nestled in a bed of fine white linen, was a pair of beautiful clear rock crystals, of most curious form. I sucked in my breath. I had found them.

Beyond all doubt, I was seeing with my eyes the Urim and Thummim of Aaron, from the Ephod of the High Priests, from the Ephod of Seraiah ben Azariah.

This was greatest possible find in Israel

I started to lift them out of the box, but suddenly felt afraid. These were not just stones. These were the Oracles of the Lord. I did not know what to believe about them, but I did not want to touch them high up here on this precarious ledge.

Carefully I closed the lid back on the Urim and Thummim and wrapped the box in my handkerchief. I then put the box into my backpack. Slowly and carefully I climbed back down the cliff wall.

As soon as I reached the bottom, I headed back for camp. I hiked, heart pounding, heart singing, back to the oasis through the maze of wadis.

As I rounded the bend of the wadi and came out onto the oasis plateau, I walked over the the artesian spring to see if it still flowed.

It did. Clear and cool, water flowed up from the ground and filled the small pool, overflowing into the shallow channel I had made for it. I took a drink. It was delicious.

Today had been a most remarkable day.

Inside the lab tent, I sat down and was about to catalogue the find when something inside me told me not to, to wait. I obeyed, and opened the backpack instead, pulling out the wrapped gold box. I unwrapped it and set the box with its precious contents on the specimen table beside the other things I had found in the dig here at the villa. It was royal, beside so many fragments and bits of the past.

Though I would have begun immediately to hook up a stone to the scanning devices, my first glance toward the keyboard told me I could not. The air temperature was 96 degrees. I knew what the schedule was on days like this. Only after sunset would the canyon air have cooled enough to turn on the equipment. I decided to study the manuals Kevin had given me which I had never read, to study them very carefully before I began to run tests on my prize - the Urim and Thummim!

Yet I was eager beyond words to scan one of the crystals. I couldn't stand the suspense. I wanted to be seeing them. If I was going to be spending the rest of the afternoon reading, I could at least have them out where I could see them.

I opened the box, and after a moment's hesitation, I reached in and took them in my fingers.

Nothing happened.

Of course, I thought.

The priests handled them as often as they were requested.

I lifted the Urim and Thummim up and out of the gold box and placed them on the table. I wanted to see this priceless treasure as I read and worked in the tent. I carefully lifted out the folded piece of linen on which they had lain, and to my surprise found that there was something inside it. With great care not to tear the ancient fabric, I opened the folds to see what it could be.

There in the cloth lay a small but curiously worked piece of brass, with curved terminals I presumed, for holding the two crystals. A sort of armature, or something like that. I picked it up in my hand and looked at it from all sides. It had virtually no corrosion on it. But then, it had spent all of this time almost hermetically sealed in a gold box high up in a cleft of rock in one of the driest places in the world. The number of moisture molecules which had come in contact with it could probably be counted on the fingers of one hand. The amount of oxygen in the little gold box would have done its work and been exhausted long ago. The armature was as bright as the day it had been buried.

I set it on the table, and put the two crystals in their places.

I then went back to my chair to read.

As I was reading, the late afternoon light streamed through the tent flap door onto the table near the Urim and Thummim. As I sat and read, suddenly out of the corner of my eye I thought I saw them glow. My heart pounded furiously in an instant, full speed and heavy, and I jerked my head to look at them. Were they glowing?

No, I thought. It is only the light from the open flap of the tent.

But then, as the beam of sunlight came to shine directly on the crystals, suddenly, a thousand tiny refracted rainbows appeared scattered over the walls and ceiling of the tent, filling it with glorious lights. They were as many as the stars in the starriest night sky.

It was the most beautiful thing I had ever seen.

As the day wore on, as eager as I was begin testing, I found myself feeling inclined to wait until I was rested, and begin fresh in the morning on the next day.

I read and worked into the early evening, getting ready for a full day of testing tomorrow.

When all was in order and ready, I found I was too tired to cook anything or even open and warm a can, so I drank some milk and ate three fig bars.

A fitting reward for discovering the most remarkable artifact of the Promised Land: milk and honey-sweet figs.

I brushed my teeth and slumped into bed.

Victory was mine.

Chapter 10

Day 29 in the Wilderness: The hook-up

I awoke and had a hurried breakfast.

I felt great. The extra rest and a full night's sleep was long overdue. I was glad I had made the decision to wait. I was ready.

I went out of my tent and directly to the lab tent. On the table was the gold box and the Urim and Thummim in their armature. I had no doubt at all that these were the Oracles; that I had found what I was looking for. These were unquestionably the Urim and Thummim of Aaron. We knew of their existence since the days of Abraham, almost four thousand years ago, and that they had vanished during the sojourn of Israel in Egypt. Or at least we thought so. From somewhere Moses received them, and they were then given in unbroken procession to all of the High Priests down to Seraiah. They had never been seen again after the Babylonian deportation.

Until yesterday.

And I was the first human being to see them in almost two thousand six-hundred years. I had found them.

This was the artifact of the century. The rush of excitement which swept over me - to hear the words of prophets and priests - drove me now unimaginably. The time had come for 'playback.' Though no scanning had worked yet in interfacing the systems with any of the blocks or gemstones I had excavated, I had to try. The possibility of rewards in this magnitude were too great.

I went over to the table, and stood before the Urim and Thummim, looking from crystal to crystal. They both looked exactly the same. Which one should I try first? I looked from stone to stone and finally picked up the one closest to me, and carried it over to the hook-up module. I connected it in the same way I had wired all of the other specimens thus far, and went back to the keyboard to begin scanning. Now came the grueling process of kaleidoscopically attempting to find a software program and scanning pattern which could access and reassemble the voices preserved from the past.

I brought up the scanning menus and first made a few corrections to the system. My reading yesterday afternoon and last night had taught me a few things about the capabilities of this system which I had neglected in all the previous experiments. The 'smart capabilities' of the system - its ability to 'learn' from its application experiences - had not been engaged with the expansion access to the boards, a serious mistake on my part. I now set about correcting that error, selecting the specified commands and executing them. Also, there was an interface link I had ignored which had to be manually selected that would enhance ratios between the anomaly recognition converter and the time-continuum reassembly chip, something which the manual said could expand its ability to measure in orders far below zepto-second intervals. I also scrolled for and found the reverse compression converter chip, and activated its link with the kaleidoscopic particle-anomaly scanner. I didn't understand it, but I did it. It should have been activated before. I wished Kevin had stressed reading the manuals more. He had led me to trust his demonstrations too confidently. I thought I knew what I was doing when I set everything up. But I was wrong. I had not been utilizing all the power that was here.

I brought up the menus for the translation de-coder mega-chips, and the digitalized voice-audio-syllabaries which sample the sound patterns of ancient languages, and selected only those few languages which seemed reasonable to expect here: Sumerian and its sister tongues and derivatives; Early and Middle Egyptian; Paleo Hebrew; and proto-Aramaic. Anything to reduce the search load and increase the discovery potential. These I manually interfaced with the Text Database, and commanded it to select only those documents which pertained to the selected dialects and their derivatives.

With that, I felt I had done all I could. The system was set for sorting and rendering any sub atomic anomalies discovered into their identified time-continuum, and for reassembling those impulses into a phonetic sound playback as syllabic speech patterns.

My next step was to identify the crystal. It looked like pure quartz, but I was no geologist. It could have been a diamond, the way it scattered light. I knew there were dozens of clear and colored crystals which, to the untrained eye, appear very similar, yet which on the atomic level are radically different from each other.

Using the analytical crystalline structure scanner I interfaced all possibilities and was stunned to find that this crystalline structure was unknown to the data banks. Unknown? I whistled. This was going to be bigger than I had imagined. Yet it brought up a new problem. How would the scan search identify irregularities in structural patterns of a complex and unknown mineral compound? I cross-selected the 'smart' program and chip board with the identifier scanner. Perhaps it could learn as it scanned and went along.

With some trepidation, I began to test the first crystal.

But nothing happened. All I got was silence.

I tried each of the five connectors and devices. Nothing.

Again and again, the system came up with nothing.

After many hours of different wirings, different connections, different devices and no results, I disconnected and lifted out the first crystal and carried it back to the table. I set it down in its armature, and with determined resolution, picked up the second one.

I hooked it up and began the whole process over again.

When the temperature reached 90 degrees I had to shut down. I was angry. Angry at the heat. Angry at the equipment. Angry at the silence. Angry at my ignorance of what else I could do.

Too frustrated to walk wadis with nothing to look for, I excavated the rest of the day. I found nothing.

Afternoon became evening; evening became night.

As soon as the temperature hit 89 degrees, I booted up.

Again and again I switched crystals, wirings, programs and commands, and still got nothing, nothing, nothing.

As it got late, though I was becoming exhausted from the intensity of this scanning process - my urgency and frustration were driving me up the wall - I decided to stop a moment and regroup. I had tried every wiring procedure in which Kevin had instructed me. I got up and went over to the equipment box that had the manuals and schematics in it, and pulled out the folder of schematics and diagrams, where I remembered Kevin had shown me some additional but untested wiring and connecting possibilities. Their time had come. This was the ultimate showdown. No idea would be untried.

With difficulty I jerry-rigged several of these suggested alternate hook-ups to the second crystal which I was still testing.

More nothing.

I took it out, took it back to the table, and got the first crystal again. I then tried all of the alternate connections again, on it.

Nothing.

The night became very late, yet I continued to work at trying to get into these crystals, to access something, anything.

But nothing.

Finally, exhausted, disappointed, completely infuriated at the failure of the systems, I took the crystal out and begrudgingly put it back on the table in the armature with its mate.

I knew I had every reason to still explode with joy and elation. I had found the artifact of the century, perhaps of all time.

Yet though they were what they were, the Urim and Thummim, the very stones through which patriarchs and prophets of the Bible had received revelations and counsel from Almighty God, I could not penetrate them. They would not speak to me.

The finest, most spectacular crystalline structures on the planet, yet I could not get them to speak one word of their secrets.

Moses' and Aaron's voices had been absorbed into these crystals.

Perhaps God's voice had been absorbed into these crystals.

All of that and more was there on the table before me, locked in these two crystals. But I did not have the key to unlock them, to get what had to be there. It had to be. It was not possible, that none of that energy had etched its imprint upon those stones. They had to be record keepers. They were the Oracles of the Lord.

Why wouldn't they speak to me?

Dejected and broken hearted, I turned off the equipment.

Totally used up by the day, I went out and over to my tent, flopped into bed, and went to sleep without a whisper of success.

Chapter 11

Day 30 in the Wilderness: A Day of Tones and I AM

I awoke early, got up, and quickly dressed. I put on the same blue jeans and boots I wore every day, and a clean white t-shirt. Today would be an intense day.

I decided to eat a better breakfast than usual: motzos and jam, a big piece of dried salami, a large glass of orange soda, and a slice of the good cheese I had gotten at En Gedi. This would be a very busy day, and the dwindling supply of breakfast fig bars would be my sustenance today, freeing me from preparing other meals. Thus, I ate a very hearty breakfast.

Since last night I had optimistically talked myself out of the disappointment of yesterday's marathon failed attempt to recover sounds from the Urim and Thummim. I had to adopt a better attitude. I had made a great discovery. This was going to be a good day, an unimaginably exciting day. Whether I had success or failure in accessing sounds, I had found what I had found and in this affirmation I should keep my eye fixed on the value of the discovery itself, regardless of what else happened.

The day started out that way. During the first hours of the morning I brightly ran through the remaining untried hook-ups, but still nothing. The morning wore on; more nothing. Very frustrating.

I tried several combinations of wirings to the stones, first one stone and then the other. One after the other: still nothing.

Suddenly I looked from the crystal I had wired and connected to the system in the hook-up module, over to the other crystal sitting by itself in the ancient brass armature on the table.

'First one stone and then the other,' I repeated to myself in my mind. *'One stone...... and then the other.' But what's wrong with this? What am I doing?* I asked myself.

I immediately stood up, walked the few steps to the artifact table, and picked up the second crystal in my hand.

Of course, I thought. *Urim and Thummim. Plural, as one cherub, and two cherubim. Plural 'Lights and Perfections.' It's not 'one is a light,' and 'another is perfection.' It is 'Lights....... and Perfections.' Both of them. Together. They work together. They were given as a pair; they were kept in the ephod together; they were used inseparably. Their very name is a plural. They are the 'lights and perfections' only when they are together.*

In an instant I was over at the hook-up module with the armature and second crystal in my hand, and I began to study how I could modify the system to connect two stones simultaneously: a wiring concept neither planned nor for which any accessories were provided. This entire system had been designed on the principle of connecting and scanning one specimen at a time.

I began to dig with a frenzy through the cardboard packing boxes stacked up under the equipment table. No extra cables. No extra wires. No extra connectors. No extra anything. How could we have been so short sighted?

Looking over the myriad cords, cables, wires and connectors between the seven units, I had no way of understanding which cord might be disconnected and cannibalized. Which, if any, might not be needed in these processes; which might be superfluous; which might be dormant with no power going through it except in certain applications? Which wire might not pertain to the scanning processes I now needed to conduct? I couldn't touch any of them.

I ran out of the tent to the jeep, and looked in the glove compartment: nothing. Under the seats: nothing. In the back tire well.

Yes! God was merciful. There, tucked beneath the spare tire was the elaborate taped wiring connector system for hooking up trailer lights! I rushed and with trembling fingers fumbled with the spare tire secure-screw until I could anxiously pull the tire off the wiring assembly below. As I lifted it out of the tire well, it unfolded and I suddenly beheld almost six feet of multiple wires of several sizes, enough to go from the jacks at the jeep's tail-lights to reach back to the connecting jacks of a trailer's brake-lights.

This was all the wire I could ever need.

Back in the tent I sat down with wiring schematics I now wished I had learned enough to understand, and tried to figure out how I could tap another set of wires into each one of the several connecting systems which came out of their ports in the hook-up module in single wires and color-coded pairs.

It was useless.

The wiring diagrams were as convoluted as the threadings of a tapestry loom, with microscopic writings of gibberish written alongside each wire in the modern hieroglyphs of the circuit board designers. I was never going to get anywhere this way.

I sat and sat and thought and thought, staring at the hook-up module, wracking my brains for a solution to my problem.

And then it came. I would simply slice into the insulation of each long connecting wire in the hook-up module, and do a wrap-splice joining a new section of wire onto it, thus doubling the access terminals for twin hook-ups, while still feeding the signals or currents back into the existing single circuits provided! It would work!

I jumbled through the tool box until I found the required tools, and began the painstaking process of carefully slicing into the plastic coverings around the wires, without cutting or disturbing a single copper filament of any wire. I cut back the insulation of the new wires from the jeep trailer-light jack and exposed a very long section of copper wires. I had decided that only if I had enough wire to get a really tight, multiple wrap on the 'mother' wires would the splices have solid contact and guarantee me there would be no static, or faulty groundings, or disconnections and failures.

The stifling heat of the morning grew as I worked minute after minute with my uncertain fingers, gingerly cutting through insulations, exposing wires, cutting back insulation, wrapping and pulling tightly each wire splice, until at last I had doubled each wire of the system. The time had come.

I placed the two stones together, and set them in the bronze mounting I had found with them. They were thus connected by their own bronze armature, and each one was jointly connected to every wire I had chosen to hook up to them.

As I had experienced nothing yet but failure, I had decided, as I exposed and spliced wires, to do a multiple-system wiring hook-up, and give these stones everything the system could put out, and gather in. I said a little prayer as I secured plates and snapped on couplings, that nothing I was doing would result in an overload or short circuit the system.

The last wire was secured into place. I stood back and took in a deep breath, filled with the immensity of this moment.

In the shelter of my tent in this isolated, distant place, I was about to experiment with a hook-up of my own devising, on the two most remarkable crystals I had ever seen, whose history was seated within the core of everything I had ever studied and followed archaeology for - artifacts which I had found myself the day before in the barren Wilderness of Judah, in the

257

Strong Holds of David.

I prayed that my wiring would work. It could fail no worse than all the others.

Going to the computer keyboard and screen, I began the process again, this time with two stones jointly connected, and with wiring combinations I had never used before, which were nowhere suggested in the paperwork scattered around me on tables and floor.

Quickly I brought up the scanning program. It began with its usual question boxes:

Polarization: positive, negative, or bipolar?

I was on a roll. I typed in the impossible.

SELECT ALL THREE.

I tapped the Enter key.

A message box appeared on the window:

"Are you sure you wish to select this option? This is an abnormal setting."

"Yes I do," I whispered as I selected OK and again tapped the Enter Key. "Your Daddy's on a roll and yours is not to question why."

The next procedural menu came up, and I slowly worked from it to the next menu and the next menu choosing alternatives in combinations I had never dared consider before, but which now seemed the least I could do with such a remarkable set of crystals. I had decided: either they are of God, and therefore I cannot hurt them, or, they are not from God, there never was a God, and therefore it doesn't matter anyway: I still can't hurt them and they will become my fame and my career glory when I present them back in Jerusalem.

The final set-up menu came up; I selected my options, hit Enter, and the final window box came on screen with its message:

"Do you want to go ahead with the procedures and options you have selected for test-scanning this specimen?"

I paused a moment, and with a whispered "Here goes nothin" I selected OK and released the mouse.

Lights began to blink, and systems began to whirr.

I turned up the audio converter, tuner and speakers. Nothing.

I put on the headphones, and turned it up full blast.

And I heard faint tones!

The first contact: tones!

I sat motionless, to make absolutely no sound. Yes! There it was: faint sounds, as if faint musical tones. I kept listening. There was nothing rhythmic or structured, systematic or recognizable as music melody, but definite, audible, discernable tones, which were slowly changing pitch first upward and then downward on the scale.

As I was hearing it, I could distinguish no time-continuum sounds: no words, no speech. Just the tones.

Suddenly the realization struck me that I needed to be recording these sounds - a step which so far in the process I hadn't had to even think about yet - and quickly I leaned over and punched the digital recorder 'on.' The dial indicator flickered and showed that input was recording. I increased the speed on the one drive, and lowered the speed on the other so it would be possible to both slow down and accelerate the imprint. No telling what velocity of reassembly I was listening to.

The tones continued. I sat back in wonder, and for a while longer just listened to them. After all of the days of silence with everything else I had tried, even these soft tones, just ascending slowly up in pitch and then descending down in pitch, even these simple tones were fascinating to hear. I had no idea what I was listening to. But it was something! It was really there! The tones reminded me vaguely of whale songs, only very soft, very constant, very smooth, very slow in their process of changing. There did not seem to be any pauses; the sounds were continuous.

Having no idea how long the sequence of tones might continue, I just sat and listened. The longer I listened, the more I began to realize that the tones were in fact very relaxing. I became very conscious of my self, of my being, and after a brief realization inventory, I realized that I felt......good. Very good in fact. It was just a very relaxing sort of background atmosphere, very soothing.

Great. I had discovered ancient elevator music.

I looked over at the recording unit. Kevin had assured me that even at hyper speed this system could run six hours without bottoming out. So, I decided to just let it run and record, and see what happened.

I stayed on it for the entire duration of that longest run: a six-hour uninterrupted, sustained recording.

It took all afternoon, the balance of my entire day.

It was a day of tones.

A tone day.

I sort of chuckled to myself. What was I listening to? A tone, which went on unendingly.

And so I sat listening to and recording the tones, hour after hour. As much as I paid attention, I was unsure if any patterns repeated themselves; the ebb and flow up and down was so subtle and slow paced that after a few hours it all sounded pretty much the same.

When the hyper-speed recording unit was full, it shut itself off. I decided it was time to stop and analyze some of what I had recorded, so I manually shut off the slow-speed recording, and prepared to re-play the recordings.

Playing back at the recording speeds, both recordings sounded exactly as I had heard them.

I then tried slowing down the hyper-recording. 2-to-1. Just lower. 10-to-1. Very dragged out, almost inaudibly low pitch.

I turned control over to the computer, to experiment and search it at speeds I could not hear as normal sound, to see if patterns were there which might be computer enhanced and fleshed out as time-continuum sounds meaningful to human experience.

Nothing.

I then tried the same with the slow speed recording. Nothing within audible ranges. The computer scan for recognizable patterns had no better luck.

The sun had gone down by now, and I turned on the battery lights before the tent slipped into total shadows. I kept working.

As evening wore on, the breeze turned chilly. I reached over on the cot and grabbed my blue heavy-knit sweater, and pulled it over my head. No need to freeze. Not that anything was happening a frozen person couldn't handle. I had tones. But they weren't formatting into anything I had hoped for. Again, I felt defeated.

I sat back and reviewed my success. I had now spent a second period of six hours scanning and analyzing the recordings of the tones. What had I done?

The sound-impulse chip, the complex retrieval programs, de-scrambler chip and interlinked megafiles, the megasearch chips and re-assembly programs, the audio receiver and amplifier were all proving useless in detecting any syllabic speech images in this recording, or else there were none to recognize and reassemble.

The faint tones which were processing through the system did not seem to contain any syllables. For, during the entire undisturbed 6-hour recording and vigilant megasearch observation under full power, no identifiable intermittent or syllabic sound patterns in the tones were logged or recorded by this exhaustive system search.

I had played the six hours of fast and slow recordings at opposite ends of their imprint speeds: from hyper-speed down to sub-frequency speeds with full computer enhancement, trying to detect a speed which might render the recorded wave patterns into a comprehensible syllabic image, if indeed there was one this equipment was capable of reassembling.

But from the top of the dial to the lowest extremity, the tones were only accelerated or slowed. They did not seem to represent run-on distorted syllabic imprints. Though the various altered speeds at times produced pleasantly resonating experiences among otherwise normally altered tones, the experiment was fruitless.

No "recorded" or imprinted dialogues or monologues were being detected. Obviously, if there was anything locked away within these stones, this technology and programming was not suited to accessing it, or sorting it, or rendering it back into a time-continuum, and reassembling it into a phonetic sound image.

Six hours of the same, continuing faint musical tones, for six hours of megasearch, using a kaleidoscopic decoder-ID-reassembly program!

I had recorded tones, but this was not much to show for lugging all this equipment so far out into nowhere. I was searching for a window into the past. I had not found even an echo.

Perhaps it was time to let go, and come to the point of admitting to myself what every discoverer hates to admit: it was a failure. The whole thing was a failure.

I had the most remarkable artifacts imaginable, the Urim and Thummim, yet the unanticipated windfall of sound given to long-silenced words did not materialize. My hope to fulfill the dream had proven an unattainable imagining.

Yet these were the Urim and Thummim, which without the shadow of a doubt had been present when the words of prophets, priests and kings whose names and lives we know, had been uttered.

Perhaps it was an arrogance, after all, to want to hear an ancient communication between a prophet and God.

At this point, even the voice of a priest would be welcomed, even an assistant priest.

I could not have hoped for better a chance. These were fantastic crystals! They truly were perfect. Their clarity and perfection was awe inspiring just to behold. If anything could have retained and stored imprints of voices, these had by far the best potentials. To reassemble and make a playable recording of just one phrase even remotely recognizable, would stand as the first truly authentic, original word received from the mouth of a historical figure from our past, the opening of a new door.

But it was not happening.

Tonight, it was not here.

I slumped back in my chair in defeat, and reached for the last fig bar on the table. A just reward for a failed effort: old dried fig paste. I felt more and more cynical. Tearing away the cellophane from the fig bar, I stared at the empty screen. I took a bite and began to chew, staring at that blank, empty screen.

I was tapped. I couldn't think of anything else which might have been overlooked in my attempts to lock into an imprinted recording of the past. This was a waste of time.

I'd tried everything, everything. Every combination of every application from the most complicated to the most elementary, and nothing worked. *There was nothing left I hadn't done.*

What hadn't I done?

Hah! *I'd done everything except type in a Website address.*

"Hah!" I laughed out loud! That was funny!

I swallowed the bite of fig bar in my mouth, and for the first time in almost four weeks I spoke out loud.

"I've been going about this all wrong. Wouldn't it be a joke if all I had to do is just type in a Website address to access you?"

I put down the fig bar, sat up and leaned over the keyboard. What would be the right name for a Website address here?

Bringing up the Internet command window, chuckling with a morbid sense of absurd humor at this ludicrous thought, I ran through my mind searching for an appropriate title to complete the tragic satire I had been acting out. I selected Website Address Entry.

"Wouldn't it be funny" I spoke out loud, "if I could just type

WWW . U-R-I-M A-N-D T-H-U-M-M-I-M . G-O-D ......

I typed it in letter by letter, reading it as it appeared on the screen
".....and get into you?" I laughed.

"Hah! That should be a good one," I resounded, and bitterly clicked Search. The program began its hunt.

Suddenly feeling very bitter, I scoffed at the whirring machine, picked up the fig bar and took a bite. Leaning back in my chair I laughed inside at the multi-program WWW Megasearch Engine vainly scanning a globe that wasn't there, vainly searching as I had been searching all these weeks for nothing. We faced similar problems, this machine and I. There wasn't any modem in this set up, no uplink. Just like me, it was searching in vain, trying to tap into something that wasn't there.

But then suddenly the screen engaged a site.

In an instant, the address page downloaded and the site name WWW. URIM AND THUMMIM .GOD appeared at the top of the blank screen, with cursor up in the left upper corner, pulsating.

For a moment I couldn't move. I just stared at the cursor pulsating up in the top corner, pulsing, pulsing, waiting.

Cautiously I leaned forward and typed in:
"Is anybody there?"

To my surprise, a response appeared on the screen:

I AM.

Stunned momentarily, I quickly ran through my mind every conversation I had ever had with Kevin. We had never talked about any uplink capabilities. We had never talked about any kind of satellite link, or cellular modem link. I hadn't thought it would be necessary. I hadn't wanted the intrusion. I didn't want to be accessible to anyone. I wanted to work. Though the Internet and worldwide Web programs were here, I clearly recalled him saying they were just standard system software installed with the basic hardware system they had built everything around. There was no cellular or satellite link. This was impossible. This wasn't happening.
"Who is there?" I typed back.

I AM.

Still stunned. OK. This was impossible, but it was obviously happening, which meant: it was possible. OK. There must be a cellular modem link built into this system somewhere that Kevin didn't know about. That had to be it. So I had accidentally made access with a part of the hardware Kevin didn't know existed.

"Very funny. Who's on line with me?" I typed back.

I AM.

Still stunned. I kept hammering in my head the Website name I was reading at the top of the screen. This is impossible. Even if there is hardware and a cellular modem link somewhere built into this system, I typed in WWW. URIM AND THUMMIM .GOD, not some typical Website address. This was impossible.

"Who is WWW. URIM AND THUMMIM .GOD?" I typed in.

I AM.

Recovering now. OK. This was someone's idea of a joke which I just happened to stumble upon. I began chiding myself for over reacting. Of course someone was there. This was just the name of a Website someone created, and I found it by sheer serendipity. I might as well take a break and talk to a real person.

Taking another bite of fig bar, I began again.

"What is your name?" I typed in.

I AM.

I swallowed abruptly, and sat looking at my screen.

The response words were there: I AM. Small, unmoving, except for the cursor pulsating silently, awaiting the next entry. I stared at the cursor, constant as a heartbeat, and suddenly I felt uneasy. The hum of the computer drives which I seldom noticed was suddenly loud in the total quiet, very loud it seemed, whirring in my ears as I stared at the response on my screen, and the pulsating cursor.

From somewhere within me an awakening memory faintly nagged. I knew these words, just like this. They were from another place, a place where they were not a phrase. They were a name.

NO! I thought, *This is not that I AM! Somebody is being a wise guy here. I've got a wise guy on the line. Well, I can be funny too, and play this game, just you wait and see.*

Breaking the whirr and stillness in the tent with the clicking sound of my fingertips on the keyboard, I typed in my next inquiry. The muted tappety-tap of the keys hitting in the chassis of the keyboard echoed in my ears as I watched my words jut letter by letter out across the screen all the way to the final period.

"No, really, who are you? Please identify yourself. That's a good joke,

but I believe the tag 'I AM' has already been taken."

I AM THAT I AM.

"That I AM was GOD, friend. Who are you?"

There was no response entry. Just the cursor, pulsating, pulsating, beside my question mark.
Again I entered:
"What is this site? Who are you?"

Nothing. I paused and leaned back. Picking up the fig bar, I slowly took another bite, my eyes fixed on the screen. I waited yet a bit more, chewing slowly, pondering. The fig bar was becoming very sweet, very sticky, so I swallowed. Putting the remaining piece of it between my teeth, I shifted my body on the chair seat to get a good solid position, and poised my hands over the keyboard.
"Are you GOD?" I typed.

I AM. came the immediate reply.

"You're sure you're God?"

I AM. came the response.

"How can I know that you are God?" I typed, smiling.
This should be really interesting, I thought. But the cursor remained pulsating at the side of my question mark. Nothing.
As I waited, listening to the whir of the drives, a number of grandiose proposals which might come in response rushed through my mind: the old hashed-over defenses of the faith - the stars and sun and moon - the earth and the seas - the trees and birds and fishes and beasts - the wind and the thunder - the complexity of the human body - the infinite reaches of space.........
Would one of these, or some other clever contrivance begin to appear onto the screen, I wondered?
Still no reply.
Nothing.
Only the pulsating cursor by the side of my question mark.
Then finally, the two words appeared again on the screen.

I AM.

"You're going to have me to believe that you are God, with just that?" I challenged. This was going to be too easy.

I AM.

"OK, wise guy: if you are God, are you here watching me right now?" I asked.

I AM.

"Are you looking at me right now?" I continued.

I AM.

"Then tell me, since you can see me: what am I wearing?" I typed triumphantly. Checkmate.

Again nothing. I waited. I waited more. I grew impatient.

But then, just as I lifted my hands to type again, the screen suddenly filled with almost a full page download, all at once.

I read the words in total shock:

A DARK BLUE BULKY-KNIT WINDRIDGE SWEATER, 100% SYNTHETIC FIBER, EXTRA LARGE; FRUIT-OF-THE-LOOM UNDERSHIRT, WHITE COTTON, V-NECK, SIZE 42-44 LONG; LEE DENIM BLUEJEANS W34-L36; A LEATHER BELT WITH BRASS BUCKLE; SEARS SYNTHETIC FIBER KNIT SOCKS, LARGE, WITH A HOLE IN THE TOE OF THE RIGHT SOCK; RUGGED OUTBACK LEATHER AND SYNTHETIC FIBER LINING ANKLE BOOTS, SYNTHETIC LATEX SOLE, SIZE 9 1/2.

As I read in stunned silence the first lines describing in perfect detail my exact clothing, pure adrenaline shot into my veins. Long before I reached my correct boot size, my heart was pumping blood through my body as if I had run the marathon. My ears were ringing. This was impossible.

I thought: *Someone who knows me could have planned this prank, could know some of my things. But who could ever know when I would wear any given garment? This has to be some kind of a trick.*

I looked around me, up and down all around the tent, already knowing that there was no camera, but looking anyway. How was this being done? I stared at the screen knowing more and more with every passing second what this entry meant, what it could only mean.

This was no trick.

These were the *Urim and Thummim.*

This was God.

Stammering in my mind for what to do or say, I just stood stupidly asking myself over and over again *"What do I say now?"* a hundred times in less than a microsecond.

As I was fumbling in my mind, the cursor suddenly skipped down the screen a few lines, and a single instantaneous entry shot across the screen in two lines:

YOU LOOK SILLY WITH A FIG BAR STICKING OUT YOUR MOUTH. WHY DON'T YOU FINISH EATING AND WE'LL TALK?

"Oh my God!" escaped my lips, and the fig bar fell to my lap.

YES. came the response on the screen.

My hand jerked instantly out across the tabletop to the power switch, and before I could stop myself, I flipped it off and stumbled, almost jumped back from the chair. As the power ceased to flow, the screen went black, as if swallowed, without even a dot in the center.

What have I done? I thought as I stood there motionless.

Shame filled my body like a flood of ice water. I felt naked. My unworthiness shocked through my every fiber. My arrogance slapped me in my face with a full consciousness of guilt.

I pivoted and grabbed for the tent flap zipper to get out, terrified at the thought of what I had just done.

I had spoken to God as a fool.

With no sense of what I was doing, I leaped out the tent door into the night, my feet running as I never knew I could run, my blood pounding, breath jerking in my lungs as each leaping stride jolted my body against the rocky desert ground. I ran, not thinking about where I was running, just running away from the tent, out across the rocks into the dark, blindly running until the ground suddenly dropped out from below me and I clawed at the air, falling down the embankment of the small plateau. My body hit the slope rolling, and tumbled with a loud grating thud of loose stones grinding beneath me down the jagged slope amid dust and rocks, the scraping echo of grinding stone against stone, until finally I stopped with a painful dull thud against a boulder.

I dared not move.

For a moment, the night echoed with the trickling sound of little stones and gravel tumbling and sliding down around me where I lay at the base of the boulder. I lay there, my eyes looking up at the brilliant stars of the desert night sky, my breath heavy and loud, my heart pounding in my ears. My mind was a blur of images. What was happening to me?

I lay there, unmoving, listening now only to my own heartbeat, expecting with every passing second to be surrounded by a blinding brilliance of light, and to somehow be destroyed.

But nothing happened.

Only darkness and the slight desert breeze in the wadi all around me. I hesitantly lifted my head up off the rubble and dirt, and cautiously looked around me, across the sky, everywhere.

I was alone.

But no.

No, that was not true.

I was not alone.

I lay for a moment, and as the whirling blur in my mind began to slow down, the wild colors and images went slower and slower until I could see them: images seen from a high place in the heavens, looking down at myself as a tiny speck shrinking ever smaller onto a landscape of tent surrounded by rocks surrounded by hills surrounded by desert, surrounded by seas and lands and the entire planet suddenly small and surrounded by the immensity of dark space. In the midst of this vision, I suddenly saw my own reality.

I was but a speck on a small sphere in the immensity of that space. But God could see me.

I imagined God overhead, and in my mind saw him seeing all of space and this earth, and then, I saw his vision zooming back down to earth, here, where he could see me, my every move and motion. I felt utterly naked, utterly exposed.

What had I done?

I had found what I had been searching for; I knew what I had found, and when I had penetrated it, I had spoken as a fool.

What had I done?

Chapter 12

Day 31 in the Wilderness
  Getting to Know You - God on the Internet

I awoke before sunrise, cold and cramped and aching. I had slept all night as I fell, laying at the bottom of the embankment. In the dim pre-dawn light I could see that my blind rush from the tent had dumped me in the middle of the wadi, not far from the four-wheel. I moved sorely and sat up, stiff. I could feel where every one of the myriad little stones had jabbed into my muscles and pressed against my bones all night.

It obviously wasn't a dream. I wasn't in my bed. It must have really happened. Something in the computer and equipment set-up last night had accessed the power of the Urim and Thummim and somehow, I had spoken to God on the Internet. Well, I had written to God, on something.

And then I had totally blown it.

But I was still alive. Everything around me seemed the same.

Picking myself up off the ground, I climbed over the boulder, and trudged back to the tent.

Inside, even in the poor light of dawn glowing through the tent sides, I could dimly see the table and the equipment.

All was exactly as I left it.

The power was off, just as I had flipped it last night.

I turned on the light. The Urim and Thummim were still there, pressed into their armature and clamped into the connector module, just as I had left them. The place was a bit of a mess. I picked up the toppled chair, and stooped over to clean up the strewn papers that had fallen, thinking all the time about what had happened last night.

I had acted as a fool, yes.

But God had not been angered. He had invited me to finish eating and talk to him.

My greatest stupidity had been the uncontrolled reaction of fear that had automatically flowed into my hand, and flipped off the power. OK, the running away hadn't been too smart either. I couldn't believe how unprepared I was, knowing what I had in my hands.

And I had cut God off. Wham! Hung up on him!

Whew!

I sat down. This was too much.

But as I glanced around the tent, the experience began to take on a more rational perspective.

This must have been some kind of trick.

But how?

No way. There was no possible way.

Well, there was at least a way to find out.

The screen was there, waiting.

Should I do it?

I couldn't resist.

I pulled the chair in front of the keyboard and screen, flipped on the power again, booted up the system, and readied myself for another try. As the system went through its wake-up ritual, I traced with my eyes every part of the tent ceiling above me, every face of every hi-tech unit on the table around me. There was nothing visible which could in any way let me think some gimmick had done this.

Again I went through the series of command selections and repeated exactly step for step what I had done last night. Strange as it was, it had worked, somehow. Cautiously, I selected the World Wide Web search engine, and typed in

WWW. URIM AND THUMMIM .GOD

For a moment I sat there, staring at the address in the web site box, and then at the command key for 'Search.'

After several moments' hesitation, I tapped the key. I was committed now.

As it had last night, the web site page came up: WWW. URIM AND THUMMIM .GOD, with the cursor pulsating up in the left corner.

I was in again.

Cautiously I typed in my first communication for the morning:

Are you there?

I AM, dropped in the immediate reply.

Whoa. He's there. What should I say? I scrambled for words.

Sorry about the abrupt disconnect last night, I typed.

THAT'S ALRIGHT. YOU'RE JUST A CHILD.

The full sentence answer astonished me, and suddenly I felt my pulse rising and the adrenaline pumping again. But as I absorbed the response, it confused me. God was supposed to know everything. I typed,

I'm not a child. I'm 48 years old.

A response downloaded almost instantly, all at once:

NO MATTER HOW OLD YOU LIVE TO BE IN THE MORTALITY OF YOUR ETERNAL PROGRESSION, IN THIS ESTATE, YOU ARE JUST A CHILD, WITH THE THOUGHTS OF A CHILD, THE FEARS OF A CHILD, THE SELFISHNESS OF A CHILD, AND THE LIMITATIONS OF A CHILD. YOU ARE HERE TO LEARN WHAT A CHILD MUST LEARN, WHICH WILL TAKE FROM YOU YOUR INNOCENCE. THEN, YOU MUST LEARN HOW TO RECOVER YOUR INNOCENCE, AND BECOME AGAIN AS A LITTLE CHILD.

I pondered this pronouncement for a moment. Though startled by it, I was even more confused by it. I decided to ignore it and proceed. But before I could type in new words, another sentence appeared.

DO YOU KNOW THE INNOCENCE OF A LITTLE CHILD?

Suddenly I saw before me in my mind's eye my own children, and then also my own self, as a child. Becoming as a little child I had read in the Bible; my wife quoted it all the time. But I had not thought much about it at all. Did I know the innocence of a child, I was being asked. By God! Did I know the innocence of a little child?

Could we start with an easier question? I typed in panic.

My gosh, this should be easy, I thought, yet suddenly I had no idea of what God meant by the innocence of a little child. How could I not know such a simple thing? What is the innocence of a child? Why am I panicking? I thought.

There was no new response on the screen. Just the cursor, pulsating. He was waiting for me. I am an adult, I thought. I am here to learn what a child must learn, but it will take from me my innocence. This I must then regain. How can one know everything we learn as adults and still be as a little child? What essence is here? What am I missing? What are the strengths of the child that would, in the hands of an adult with great, great knowledge, give additional strength and power to return to the Kingdom of Heaven?

Isn't that how the passage went? I couldn't think. I had never given it thought. I had never meditated upon this. I had never pondered it.

I don't know, I slowly wrote in. I felt ashamed.

There was no answer. Just the cursor pulsating.

THAT'S OK. I HAVE AN IDEA. YOU ASK ME QUESTIONS, suddenly downloaded.

What a relief. As I relaxed a little I laughingly thought to myself 'nobody told me there was going to be a test,' but as soon as the idea entered my mind, I knew I was wrong. There was going to be a test, a big one. Judgement. I knew that. I had been told. He told me. Us. He told us. OK, relax, and think, I thought. What shall I ask? I had to determine once and for all that this was God. These were the Urim and Thummim. But I needed to know: was this God?

Are you really 'I AM?' I wrote. *Are you really God?*

YES.

How do I know that for sure?

REMEMBER WHEN YOU WERE YOUNG, AND YOU TOOK A CANDY AT THE STORE, AS YOU HAD DONE SEVERAL TIMES BEFORE WHEN YOU WERE EVEN YOUNGER, BUT THIS TIME YOU LOOKED AT IT IN YOUR HAND, AND YOU DECIDED YOU DIDN'T WANT TO STEAL ANY MORE, SO YOU PUT IT BACK?

That was incredible. I had never told anybody about that. I was too embarrassed. But every kid steals candy, I thought, don't they? And then they finally grow up and decide it's wrong?

Almost all children have done that, I typed. That could be a trick generality answer, a no-lose answer for almost anybody. *I still don't know for sure that this isn't some kind of game somebody's playing on me. This is a lot of sophisticated technology. If you're God, please excuse me for asking, but how am I to know you are God?*

A sudden download filled the screen.

WHEN YOU WERE A YOUNG MAN, YOU WENT OUT FOR A LONG WALK. YOU PASSED A HOUSE WHERE A SMALL CHILD, A TODDLER, WAS EATING A CARROT STICK WITH HIS MOTHER,

AND INHALED A BIG PIECE OF IT. THE MOTHER CAME RUNNING OUT TO YOU AND THRUST THE BABY INTO YOUR ARMS BECAUSE SHE DIDN'T KNOW WHAT TO DO. THE BABY WAS PURPLE-BLUE ALL OVER, UNCONSCIOUS AND LIMP AS IF IT WERE DEAD IN YOUR ARMS. SHE SCREAMED AT YOU TO HELP HER BABY. YOU KNEW THAT A FIRE STATION WAS ONLY THREE BLOCKS AWAY, AND YOU TOLD HER THAT YOU WERE TAKING THE BABY TO THE PARAMEDICS, AND TURNED AND RAN. WITH ALL YOUR STRENGTH YOU RAN AND RAN AND AS YOU RAN, YOU BEGGED ME TO NOT LET THIS BABY DIE. YOU FELT ITS LITTLE ARMS AND LEGS SLAMMING AGAINST YOUR BODY AS YOU RAN ALL THE WAY, AND YOU WERE WEEPING AND BEGGING ME TO LET THIS CHILD LIVE. YOU DID NOT KNOW THAT THIS CHILD HAD A CALLING TO FULFILL, AND NEEDED TO LIVE. YOU JUST COULDN'T BEAR FOR THE CHILD TO DIE. WHEN YOU GOT TO THE FIRE STATION, YOU SCREAMED OUT FOR HELP. WHEN YOU LAID THE CHILD DOWN ON THE TABLE, YOU SAW THE CHILD WAS PINK AGAIN, AND WAS IN SPASMS FOR BREATH. THE PARAMEDIC SAW THE CHILD AND INSTANTLY OPENED A LARGE GAUGE HYPODERMIC NEEDLE PACK, JAMMED IT INTO THE CHILD'S CHEST, AND PUT THE MASK OF AN OXYGEN TANK OVER THE NEEDLE END. WITH EACH SPASM FOR BREATH HE RELEASED OXYGEN FOR THE CHILD TO SUCK IN THROUGH THE COARSE NEEDLE. HE DID THIS FOR TEN MINUTES UNTIL THE HOSPITAL TEAM ARRIVED WITH THE TRACHEAL PRONGS TO EXTRACT THE CARROT WHICH WAS BLOCKING THE WIND PIPE. THE BABY LIVED. YOU SAW IT RESTORED TO ITS MOTHER'S ARMS, CRYING, AND YOU LEFT THE FIRE STATION, WITHOUT EVER GIVING ANYONE YOUR NAME.

Tears came to my eyes, and my throat had a lump in it so big it hurt. I was there again at the fire station, sobbing in relief that the baby was pink again, it was alive in its mother's arms, and that it was crying. That baby's cry was the most precious sound I had ever heard. I had never told anyone. I hadn't known how.

How is the baby? I typed. I knew now, this was God. His answer came again as a single download appearing on the screen.

DOING VERY WELL, GROWN, MARRIED AND RAISING VERY FINE CHILDREN. EVERYTHING THAT CHILD HAS DONE IN THIS WORLD SINCE THAT DAY, EVERY LIFE TOUCHED, IS ALL BECAUSE OF YOU.

Hello, God, I typed.

HELLO, responded God.

I couldn't stop thinking of the little baby that had been so purple, so limp in my arms, and my prayer that had been answered.

How did you make the baby pink again? I typed.

YOU WERE RUNNING HARD, JERKING THE BABY'S BODY WITH EACH JOLT OF YOUR HEELS ON THE SIDEWALK. IT WAS PRETTY EASY FOR AN ANGEL TO TELL THE BABY TO SUCK IN FOR AIR, AND NUDGE THE CARROT STICK SLIGHTLY FOR AIR TO GET PAST IT, JUST ENOUGH FOR MINIMAL TISSUE NEEDS. YOU HELPED, JUST BY RUNNING HARD.

There are angels? I found myself typing.

YES. THERE ARE ANGELS.

I was not ready for this. I believed in angels, but I was not ready for any of this. I needed to step back and regroup.

Am I going to be able to talk to you again, or is this it? What I want to ask is: could we break for now, and can I come back again? Will you be there? Will this link still be here? I asked.

YES. AND THAT WOULD BE FINE. I UNDERSTAND. IT'S GOING TO BE HOTTER THAN 90 DEGREES IN LESS THAN AN HOUR, SO WE CAN WAIT UNTIL NIGHTFALL. ALRIGHT?

Thank you, I typed. I could not believe it. I had just said Thank you to God. I was communicating with God. Oops. One more thing.

Can I turn off the power? I typed.

YES. JUST BOOT UP AND RE-COMMAND AS YOU'VE DONE.

Thank you. Good-bye for now. I'll ..... I wasn't sure what to say ... *I'll talk to you tonight,* I typed.

UNTIL TONIGHT appeared on the screen.

I keyed 'Close' and 'Quit' and exited all the way to the desktop, and shut down.

I immediately stood up and went outside the tent.

It was full daylight, beautiful and already hot.

I turned and walked over to the spring. Yes, it was still flowing fresh, cool water. I couldn't believe it. This was all too remarkable.

The water felt so good as I splashed it up onto my face. I sat on the rock encasement wall, looking down into the crystal clear pool of water, coming up through the gravel in the spring's throat. The water flowed up so calmly that only the slightest disturbance moved upon the face of the pool above the opening. I looked back up and turned my gaze around me, at the canyon walls, the rubble and stumps of the ancient building walls, the sticks and strings of my grid, the carefully dug quadrants, the piles of sifted dirt, the two green tents. Everything was so peaceful. I felt very comforted and calm.

There was much to think about. Yet as I sat there, my stomach told me that I was hungry. So, I got up and went to my tent to get something to eat. My mouth broke into a smile and my head began to shake incredulously as I walked. I was talking to God on the computer, through the power of the Urim and Thummim. And he had told me that I could ask questions. I could ask questions to God.

What would I ask?

What would anyone ask if they could talk to God on the Internet, I thought to myself.

Easy to say; not so easy to actually think about doing for real.

I sat down and ate, paying little attention to the food. What would I ask God? I pondered. There were lots of things which flashed through my mind, but this wasn't a joke. What would I ask, without seeming a fool, without being absurd, without being greedy, without being insulting, without being............ This was not so easy.

All that day I worked on the dig, without finding anything much of interest, but not caring much either. I didn't even know why I was digging; it was just something familiar to do and comfortable as I pondered and thought about what I might ask God. I was already learning a great lesson.

It was one thing to think about it as a joke or a class exercise.

It was another thing to actually have an appointment.

The sun reached its zenith overhead, and in the afternoon, during the hottest hours, I went into my tent and lay down on my cot, resting in the warm air, thinking. I finally organized my thoughts and felt I was ready to begin talking to God.

I closed my eyes, and I slept.

274

When I awoke, it was twilight in the canyon. Sunlight still touched the tops of the high canyon ridges, but it had been shady down here for several hours already. It was cool. I rather hurriedly got out some food, ate, and went to the lab tent.

Once again at my seat, I turned on the power, booted up, went through the steps and typed in WWW. URIM AND THUMMIM GOD. Without more than a few second's hesitation, I tapped the search engine key and watched as the website page flipped onto the screen. As silly as it seemed, I didn't really know how to start.

Hello. Are you there? I typed.

I AM.

Hello, I typed again.

HELLO. DID YOU HAVE A GOOD DAY?

This seemed so funny and strange. *Yes,* I typed. *I had a good day.* What now? *How about you?* I typed almost automatically. I instantly felt like a fool again. How dumb!

THANK YOU FOR ASKING. I DON'T GET ASKED THAT VERY OFTEN. MOST PEOPLE ARE IN A RUSH AND HAVE LOTS OF THINGS TO ASK FOR. SOMETIMES THEY THANK ME FOR THINGS, BUT NOT OFTEN. I HAD A VERY FINE DAY, ALL THINGS CONSIDERED. THANK YOU.

Nobody thinks to ask him what kind of day he's had, I marveled. Of course. Who would think of it? OK, that wasn't dumb.

I mustered up my courage and began where I had determined to begin tonight.

I have a favor to ask, I typed.

YES? WHAT?

Though I felt a bit nervous, I typed it in.

Please don't take this as any offense, but reading in all capital letters is kind of ..... intense. Could you use lower case letters too?

Is this better for you?

Yes, that's much better, I typed.

275

So, do you have some things you'd like to talk about?

Yes, I typed. *I would like to know how long I might continue ..... I don't really know how to ask this. How long will I keep this link?*

For a few days, a limited time. Enough time.

That meant I could proceed with plan B: there would be enough time to ask the number of things on my list and I didn't have to cram it all into one night.

May I ask you some questions, then?

Yes. Where shall we begin?

My first question came easily.

Why are you talking on this computer? The prophets in antiquity didn't have computer screens. The scriptures tell of your speaking to them. I have the Urim and Thummim here. They don't need a computer or any of this equipment. They are the Oracles. Why didn't you speak to me? Why are we communicating on this screen?

You are not a prophet.

I know I'm not a prophet. That's a good point. Why am I being allowed this access at all? I'm just a nobody.

You're not a nobody, but neither are you a prophet. You do not have the spiritual depth of a prophet, nor the keys of a prophet, nor the calling of a prophet. But you are not a nobody. Nobody is a nobody.

Thank you. But how then is it that I'm talking to you? Why are you talking to me?

You are a good person, and you found the Urim and Thummim. In your heart, you've wished to talk with me. You are not a prophet, but it is time, and you are worthy.

How am I worthy?

First, you are my child.

I am your child?

Yes. You are my child. I am your father.

Can I see you?

I cannot come to you in my glory. To even but few of the prophets have I been able to show myself at all.

Why can you not come to me in your glory?

You could not sustain it as have those whom I chose for their obedience to be prophets. Look at how you first reacted to just a silent message appearing on your screen. Look at how you are still reacting now. Do you know how you would have reacted last night if I had spoken to you, or if I had appeared to you as I appeared unto Abraham?

I imagined it, and saw a vision of myself in my mind. I was unprepared. I could see it. A new line appeared on the screen.

You're right.

Why did you allow me to find the Urim and Thummim?

It is time.

It is time?

You would not have been allowed to find these Urim and Thummim if it were otherwise. You are a bridge.

Are you going to give me a message?

You are not a prophet. I give messages for entire generations through prophets. They are little regarded or followed. But you may ask your questions. The answers, in your generation and your time, may interest some. A few.

And you will do this even if only a few receive it?

Yes. It has always been that way, from the beginning.

I pondered for a moment. Even these few little answers had already returned much more to think about than I was ready for. But I realized that this time was finite, and I could not waste it. I reached into my shirt pocket and pulled out the sheet of paper on which I had written my questions. My hands trembling just a little, I put it on the table and spread it out flat with the palm of my hand. I wanted to start first with the Urim and Thummim themselves.

How did the Urim and Thummim work for prophets in ancient times? They had no circuit boards, chips, no programs, no electricity.

They had faith.

How does faith make them work?

Faith is a power. You children know so little about non-physical powers. You are here in great part to learn faith, and how to use it.

Why am I making access without Faith, then?

You do have faith. Look at how you have been working on this quest now for several years. You had faith when others laughed at my child Brannon, laughed him to his death. My poor child. You always believed. Even knowing how vast a wilderness this is, you believed enough to go to great lengths to get here, and once here, you have looked, day after day, trying to find them. Worse than a needle in a haystack, you said. Small enough to hide under a sandwich in a lunch box, you said. Yet you persisted. This is the evidence of your faith. You spent all of these years seeking. All of the months preparing. All of the weeks getting here. All of the days digging. When you found them, you did not doubt what they are. You imagined the voices of priests and prophets locked in them, even my voice you anticipated could be there. You do have faith, great faith. You were thrilled at the possibility of your technology deciphering the subatomic energy code you envisioned imprinted within them, and thrilled at the prospect of hearing the voices of the priests and prophets even though all your other attempts with common stones had failed. You did all you could within your power to make them work because you thought they could work. All of the days trying everything you could, over and over, differently, exhaustively, because you believed. You tried. You didn't give up. When you failed, you believed it was your inadequacy, the inadequacy of your technology, not the Urim and Thummim which failed. Your faith was complete in the Urim and Thummim, and the only thing you doubted was your machines. Your faith increased. Look at the passion with which you grappled with the problem when you understood that you must use the pair, not single stones. Look at the ingenuity you applied to complete the patches in hopes you could make it work.

What is the secret, the key that did the trick? What is it in the hook-up I rigged that made them work? I don't understand. What did I finally do that made them work?

Nothing.

What do you mean, nothing? What made them work?

I did. For you, they work only with the computer. You had faith in the Urim and Thummim, but your faith was still stronger in your technology. You did not have faith that you could use Urim and Thummim to inquire of me. You only had faith to hear the voices of those who had inquired, using this technology. And so you trusted the technology, and not yourself, your own Spirit. But do not dishearten. You are not a prophet. You were not foreordained since the foundation of this earth to be a prophet to your generation. You do not have the faith to use the Urim and Thummim alone. But you are a great and noble spirit. You were valiant in the beginning. You have become prepared to receive what you receive now, in this way.

But why did you come on the Internet?

You called upon me. WWW. URIM AND THUMMIM .GOD is a new supplication, yet when else did you call upon me? I judge all my children by their hearts, and you were guided by yours. Why didn't you type URIM AND THUMMIM .STONES or even URIM AND THUMMIM .COMPUTER?

The question struck me with full impact.

I understand now, I typed.

When you stop talking to computers, and machines, and wires, and technologies, and things made of wood, and clay, and gold, and brass, and stone, and you come to address me and call upon me even without knowing if I AM there, believe, I AM there. This is Faith, my child.

I looked over at my paper, for my next question.

Tell me more about the Urim and Thummim, I typed.

In early times I could walk with my children, and talk to them. But they found such joy in the world into which they were born, such awe in the physical and its beauty as I organized it for them, that they became preoccupied with their new powers in these bodies. I gave them the kingdoms of herbs and vegetables and fruits and grains, and also the kingdoms of animals to have as food and raiment. They planted the seeds, and to some this awe and wonder of life sprouting up from

279

the Earth was sufficient unto them. When they first killed animals for food and raiment, things changed for many of the children.

For they saw power in themselves when they learned they could kill. When they saw that they could kill, this power made them drunk with what they imagined was their own glory. They saw in the power to kill what they imagined was a greater power than the power to give life. In that selfsame day, the children began to become puffed up in their own strength, and to forget me. In their forgetfulness, and also because of the selfishness and hard-heartedness of those who became fascinated by their own power, they became disobedient, and I could walk with them no more.

When I ceased to walk with them, I sent angels to walk with them. When they no longer knew the angels and reviled against the angels which I sent to them, preferring their own wisdom and worse, that which is evil, they became subject to their own power, and faith withered and failed. Each generation of children knew me less and less.

In the days of Abraham I gave to him Urim and Thummim, for he covenanted with me to raise a righteous generation, and I covenanted with him and all of his children to the last generation. He gave them to Isaac, and Isaac gave them to Jacob, whom I called Israel for he struggled to be blessed.

Originally, only the most spiritual men had possession of Urim and Thummim. For them, these worked because of their faith. Each generation saw less and less faith. When the children of Israel went into Egypt, they relied on Pharaoh's grain, and in time, I took the Urim and Thummim back unto myself. Unto Moses I gave them on Sinai, and then unto Aaron they were given, and to Eleazar, third son of Aaron. Eventually with generations, priests with neither faith nor spirituality received them; not by merit, but by inheritance, and lack of more spiritual souls. To these no light nor perfection could be given. They continued until Nebuchadnezzar and Seraiah. All of this you already know.

What else do you wish to ask?

I looked over at my paper.

Why do you call yourself I AM? I typed.

To exist is a great exhilaration. You only know this creation and physical existence. You have forgotten everything else and become as a little child. For this you do not think of existing without being. There is nothing in which I rejoice more than the organization of this universe, for it has made possible the eternal life and immortality of the children. The universe is vast. In the beginning of this small habitation within it, and the sun and system which supports it in tenable life, I rejoiced in it as your home, and I told how it came to be here amid this universe. As you in your generation learn more of its nature and its fragile balance wrested from chaos, you will wish to ponder its being, and yours within it. To say I AM is to acknowledge the greatest balance that can be. Though you may make numbers and read them, you have no comprehension of how long it took, nor what it took, before emerging from the non-being of only Intelligence, to stand amid the void and say "I AM." The triumph of that moment and those words is my name. To declare I AM THAT I AM, I exist for I exist, is my name.

I thought of Genesis, and "In the Beginning God created the heavens and the earth," and I wrote in on the computer.

In the Beginning God created the heavens and the earth.

I looked at it on the screen, knowing that God was seeing it, and probably knowing what I was thinking as I formulated my thoughts. God knew where my thoughts were leading me, and where my thoughts would take me, to the new thoughts which would be born of all my other thoughts. He was already there, ahead of me, anticipating the thousands of things which in a microsecond were being scanned by my thought, seeing what was there, determining what was to be concluded from it all, what was to be asked from it all as it was gathered together.

I saw suddenly for the first time the inner workings of my own mind. It was a vast cosmos of knowledge and experiences and images which my consciousness, my intelligence scanned ever so rapidly, accessing as much of my awareness as it could awaken out of sleep at any moment. From that I might then become conscious. I would form the idea which was finding itself in my mind within that place in our minds where all ideas are gleaned from the immensity of our knowing, and are thus made composite as they distill into form.

Finally I knew what I was thinking; the process I had gone through had brought me to a desire. As I looked at the words I had arrived at a complete thought which I felt I wanted to express.

I wanted to know.

How much slower at this I must be than God, I thought. He is already aware of what my desire has become. Yet suddenly I understood: though God knew my question, I realized that for me, for my learning process, I needed to ask. And so I did.

What does this mean? I asked. *In the Beginning?*

You think in terms of time, of beginnings, and so I have spoken to your parents of beginnings. What if I were to tell you that there was no beginning? Even the children who play most with time try to formulate grand theories of a small point in space when they propose even time began, for they too, need to comprehend a beginning. Yet there are beginnings, and beginnings within beginnings.

To learn from what I spoke in the days of your ancient parents, you must go back in your mind to their days and time. What did they know and understand? Think back to a time in which your ancestors looked up into the sky and saw it near, and everything within it near - sun, moon, stars, comets, planets. As the blue sky enveloped them each day, indeed it was near, as you in your day now know it is thin, and near. This sky of blue to them was all the heavens. And were they not right to think so? For it was the observable universe, and they were the youngest of children. How well do you think to have persuaded them otherwise, with no words nor measures? The atmosphere in your ancestor's understanding was the infinite, the universe, the arc of existence, the cosmos. It was the observable universe, without words or numbers of measures. How do you describe what to the eye is unobservable?

To the prophets I showed my creations; they knew of what was beyond this. But to explain it to the many, all but children, was the challenge of the sighted one in the Valley of the Blind. They were not believed, though they saw.

I love my children. I speak in truth to their understanding, and to their belief; not to their inability, and their disbelief. I give as they can receive.

This heaven, this envelope of atmosphere and this earth has a beginning. You know this. As these were being formed in their beginning, other things were long formed far distant in the balancing process of this cosmos. All was brought into its balanced formation, neither at once nor in one place, but over time and as all was speeding in its needed and determined directions. Do you know when the lights from far away finally begin to reach this planet, and more and more the stars came into visibility even on this tiny rock within the expanse of the void? Many are the suns whose light as stars has not yet reached this planet, though they are there for great time. And when after long time in the beginning, after this world was long shrouded in clouds, when they dispersed and the lights of the firmament were unveiled and could be seen, it was a first time for this planet. Yet there were no living eyes to see it, here.

What was recorded is only the beginning of this planet?

And its sun and comets and sister worlds, each with its purpose.

That's not how it is explained by most teachers.

Yet that is what is written. Many are the children who have wrested their own beliefs out of what truth they were proportioned; and in their limitations, many have imposed and dictated in my name that which is false. This they teach to their children, and so the generations slip into mythologies. Yet the words you follow read true.

I waited, but there was no more. My turn. I did not have to look at my paper, for the question was already before me. I typed:

I want to know: Tell me of Genesis. How is all of this here?

Everything?

Everything - the cosmos, the nature of the Creation, the nature of the world. I want to know.

This is one of my favorite subjects. As often as it is repeated you will find that you may learn more from it, for you will not learn it all even in many tellings. But are you sure you want to know?

Yes I'm sure. Why would I not be sure? Why would I not want to know?

This is monumental knowledge. Not everyone wants to know. Most people want to see the picture without the mechanics.

Why?

Knowing changes your perspective of everything. Not everyone wants to dispel the mystery. You know this in your time. After the veil is lifted in a visit to a film studio park, revealing the inside process and secrets of film-making, you never again see the picture without imagining the mechanics, just as the doctor who works with the body sees the body in its mechanism. The doctor learns to re-adjust and deal with it. But there is no going back. Knowing is indeed the greatest joy. Yet not everyone can make the adjustment afterwards.

I already know a lot of astronomy and some physics. I know about galaxies and the expanding universe and black holes and supernovas. I know about the periodic chart of elements and some chemistry and biology. I know a little DNA stuff. I know a lot and I still enjoy the world. I'm ready.

Yes, but if you are to know the origins of these things, you must come to see me in them and among them. There are those who are terrified of the truth of sciences, and prefer to ignore and blur them into fantasies. And there are those who are terrified of a God to whom they must answer, by whom they may be judged. These also create their blurs to eliminate having to come to terms with me, and relegate me to fantasies. This has been easier than facing the truth. Yet until the children come to know me as I AM, they will never come to understand the things they most seek to know, whether it is in the farthest reaches of the universe, or within the most intricate workings of a cell, or the tiniest elementary particle of an atom. Only if they come to know me may they come to truly know the origins and cause of the model of the universe.

Then tell me about you first.

Very well. We begin. I have revealed myself to prophets enough, and records enough have been maintained, yet I am denaturalized into de-comprehensibility, the distortion of a blur. The blur is safely accessible to those who are terrified of the possibility of knowing me. It was not always so.

In the beginning, I was known as I am. I walked with Adam and Eve, my two children. They knew who I AM, and how I AM. Oh, I know, nobody believes this any more. Yet it is true: When the bodies for the first of my children were prepared and awaiting spirits to enter them, and the first spirits of my children entered them, these became my first children in the flesh in this world. Plants and animals by the trillions had already lived, but these were my first two children of Spirit to enter into bodies, and being sentient and conscious, they became living souls. They received names. Adam, I named them, which means many. Eve, he named, and it too means many: the Mother of All Living. What is so odd about that? They were the first of their race, of your species, the first of the children to come. Even in your language, in 'man' you still intuit your multiplicity, 'many.' In your word 'many' is 'man.' And Man of Holiness is also my name; wherefore did my Son whom I sent call himself the Son of Man.

The day is coming that the children playing with genetics will see that first dawning, and in terrified astonishment, their hearts will know that it is true. My first children, for many generations, knew me. They knew their bodies were as mine. They knew that I might appear, unexpectedly. They knew all the things you can read in the writings that have survived, and more. And they began to make images of me, at first out of love and respect, just as you keep pictures of your family in your wallet. But soon the images became the object of love and respect, and instead of learning faith and its power, and recalling me and my power, they began to worship the images of their making, and they forgot all that they knew. That is a part of my children's nature, to impose upon themselves ignorance, to devastate all that they have known, and plunge themselves into darkness. Darkness is to many a place of safety. Ignorance is bliss. And so the young and the fragile, knowing nothing, or pretending what they knew was not just as it had been told them, retold all very differently, for a haven of safety.

Then the words in the Bible are true? I am made in your image?

Is anything more clearly written and preserved? Yet for many this is a hard thing to receive. You as archaeologist know that among all of the common beliefs of all cultures of ancient times, the most common knowledge that has survived among the garbled gospels of the children in all places is that 'The God' and 'The Goddess' have a body. But then came those who despised their own flesh and thought that all matter is lowly, who trembled at the thought of offending me by implying that I AM a God of body, the body they despised. Though they would worship me as the Creator of the universe and all matter, yet they would deny my pronounced approval that the matter and all I had created is good, and that I sanctified it. That which I sanctified they rejected as unworthy and evil. And so they blurred me into uncreated nothing and called the knowledge and teaching of the God with a body Paganism, and Heresy. From these false beliefs came false teachings and many garbled gospels.

Yet even as it is written in the Books of my Chosen, the oldest garbled gospels preserve this truth. You call these pagan mythologies. Though they have distorted the truth, they still preserve much truth mirrored within them, for they were woven in days of old when the children were still close to the truth. It is easily discerned by those who seek it, including the body. You have studied them and wondered how they came to be. You have marveled at the threads of common knowledge which they all share, the threads of remnant concepts which the ancients knew that you read so clearly in the Books of my Chosen record keepers. Well have you done to see them, for they testify of me.

How did they become so diluted and retold? For many, as the children strayed and scattered across the land, the less faithful who had paid little attention to what their fathers and mothers had told them remembered only fragments, and these they wove in new stories, the fragments you see in wonder. Yet others deliberately altered that which they were given but disbelieved, for they trusted more in themselves and their own imaginings. For some it was anger and disobedience against laws, and these made gods unto themselves who would not condemn their evils, yet these were still made very close to my image. For others it was fear of knowing. For some it was jealousy and selfishness, and these took the truth that was given and hid it, saying to themselves: the others are not grown enough to receive; I shall shroud it from them. These took what was given and masked it in many masks to hide it from those whom they deemed unworthy. Yet you see the threads woven in all of it.

Now, in this generation the gathering of knowledge reveals the pattern: all ancient children knew many truths; they knew the truth of the body, and of its rising again. You as archaeologist have seen this common knowledge among all peoples, of the careful burials of the dead with gifts for a future life. How is this knowledge so universal? Who has taught them all this sacredness of the gift of this body, and who has taught them that their lives are to be eternal? You have seen it in countless tombs among all cultures, simple to great. This is a remnant of ancient knowledge revealed, not idle invention.

My most faithful and Chosen record keepers, whose Books you know well, have maintained the best record. Know from it, and know it now, that I have a body, a face, arms, legs, a voice, and I abide in a place, from whence I travel. I have passions - they are so clearly written: love, anger, compassion, mercy, wrath, sorrow - yet every generation which is terrified to think that God cannot be God if it can understand God has traded this truth for the beauty of confusion.

How, they think, can our God be a Man as we, mere men? And so they uncreate me, until I AM neutered, disintegrated, diffused, dematerialized into a blur, a nothing, a mysterious non-entity, comfortably reduced to a concept of nothing masqueraded as everything, all so that the terror of knowing me is removed, and my children feel that they can approach me in safety.

In this they grieve me, for they receive not this body which you have, which I designed, the pinnacle of efficiency and function upon the smallest of points within a universe of cold vacuum and absolute zero only a few miles above. These worlds and this body design are a crowning achievement, and who shall praise me and in the same breath deny my jewels? This is my greatest joy, that the children might be. See what the children discover in this day of this human body, of its design, of its intricately interrelated systems, of its blueprint, its DNA, and behold the Mortal of what shall some day be made Immortal. If they will understand the realities of Creation, this body must be accepted as the wonder which it is. For to have this body, much work was done.

This generation boasts loudly of being the information generation; let it then be different from the others. I have revealed again and again that you are my children, that you are created even as I AM in my image, that I AM the model upon which your body is made. Let the children who cry out that they are my children refuse no more to see that they are as I AM. Let them not fear to believe in me as I AM. Let them not think they offend me in making themselves too close to me. It is I who made them so. Let them not see themselves as debased beings, nor think they exalt me higher above them by denying my body. Let every child, every son and daughter, look upon themselves, and as my children, see themselves and say I AM made in my God's image; I AM a child of God.

I was stunned by what I finished reading. I should not have been. It was all in the books, I knew. But it was not what I was taught, and I had believed the teachings of men more than the word. I didn't know what to say. I couldn't think of a thing to say. I sat for a long time, reading it over, time which he let me have. After it had settled into my mind, about the time I was finished, he wrote

Are you still with me?

Yes, I typed. It's *a lot to receive all at once.*

Are you sure you still want to ask more?

I hesitated. But in all humility now, I really wanted to know.

Yes, I want to ask, I typed again. *Tell me of Genesis.*

Will you believe the words that I shall say to you?

What? I typed, unable to believe what I was reading.

Will you believe the words that I shall say to you?

I paused a moment, shocked by the impact of the words. Would I believe what he said? Did I have to decide even before I heard what it might be? Would I believe? I suddenly realized, of course it must be so. This was not idle prattle. I had to question my self first. Was I teachable? Did I trust? Would I believe? I had never before asked myself if I would believe before hearing, as a condition of being told. But suddenly, I felt my answer swell within me.

Yes, I typed firmly. I will believe the words you shall say to me. It was the biggest commitment I had ever made in my life. It felt good. It felt very good.

I waited. There was a pause, and I sat uncertainly. I was nervous. Yet suddenly I felt calm. Very calm. In the bosom of that feeling of comfort, I then beheld the following full download:

The Creation is an algorithm. The cosmogony and cosmology of creation is the pondering of a top-down algorithm resulting from a bottom-up envisioning of a Design to achieve the determined ideal homeostatic physical state. It has worked perfectly, within myriad infinitesimally narrow margins of tolerances, as many physicists have well observed. Many have asked to know the cosmogony and cosmology of creation; few aside from the prophets have understood that they must first grasp the problem begging solution, otherwise the algorithm devised to resolve the problem remains a mere puzzle. Those who do not take the dilemma as their point of departure conclude only parts of the whole, after much tribulation. Due to the loss of the Dilemma, the Design is denied though perceived; and so the children revolve in frustrated circles today. The problem is not perceivable by reductionism, nor can reductionism resolve its end. The problem was revealed repeatedly, anciently, when it was better understood than today, and the cosmology too has been given at sundry times. But few have there been who have understood that as the solution to the problem is before their eyes, thus the cosmology may be derived from the study of the Design. The Design speaks all. It is one great Masterpiece. Once known, it is simple to fathom. Yet that which is simple the children delight to make complex. And that which is complex they too often naively presume to be simple.

You are a historian, and you know how often the children have invented elaborate ignorances in vanity, which they champion as wisdom that all might think them wise among men. Centuries pass and no one stands to challenge them. In all ages you have seen them. Many of their vanities have prevailed over long time, though the Design was before all, and any could have challenged and won. Ptolemy's geocentric concept of the universe, and incomplete absolute map of the world. Galen's flawed anatomy of the human body. The four elements of Thales, Empedocles, Aristotle and Zou Yan. Strato's law that heavier bodies fall faster than lighter bodies. The list goes on, and it is long. You know it. It has gained and is gaining still more new entries in this generation. Catalogue them all, and bemuse in wonder. Even in those ancient days the steps of Creation were numbered in their order within the first writings of my Chosen, the lineage of Israel, and it is to this Genesis that the seekers have now returned in full circle. You have always had it.

I finished reading, totally overwhelmed.

What did you say? I typed. *I do not understand.*

The Creation, the cosmos, is the solution to a problem; it was problem-solving on the highest order. The result, the solution, is before you. It is you. See yourself. You are the solution. There have been a lot of faulty attempts to return to understanding it, which have confused many, for generations.

Yet the observable truth has always been here to see.

I don't understand. What was the Creation dilemma, the problem needing a solution?

The problem was existing as Intelligence without Being in an expanse of dark, cold space; the limiting, non-physical vacuum of cold in which you and the other Intelligences existed without being or joy. What could be done with what was there?

The solution was the utilization of energy mass, charging it into repelling opposites, resulting in matter which can be organized systematically to behave as a solid. There were several elementary systemic possibilities. When envisioned, one provided advantages above the others. That physics resulted in a matter of many fundamental elements compatible with the other physics already perceived as ideal for their purposes. The elements of that basic physics and their structures as they would form were quickly perceived; they were superior. They would become the base structures of all. Simply, its elements were more abundant, more stable, and would interact readily. They could be built upon. Their physical compounds and solubles and the possibilities of inter-reactive usages were readily perceived. The goal was at hand, then: a vehicle, a physical body within which to move was tenable.

Again, there were several possibilities. Myriad molecular combinations and organizational systems were quickly extrapolated and envisioned from numerous possible bases, and quickly discarded: one was superior to all others. The immense advantages of the hydrogen-carbon-oxygen-phosphate-magnesium base system excelled far and alone above all others as the ideally versatile and functional potential.

However, it was one thing to contemplate the ideal physical vehicle or physical body in which your Intelligences could move and exponentially empower themselves; it was another thing to imagine the massive system which could be capable of enduring over sufficient long time to allow for the local organization, formation and preparation of places on which such bodies could flourish. The larger environment within a cosmos would have to sustain such places and allow them to exist for a reasonably long duration of time after they had seasoned and reached the ideal organic equilibrium for these bodies to thrive and have being.

That system was envisioned; it was executed; it exists. You are in it, along with a vast host of siblings elsewhere. It was not made just for you. It has a long-term purpose. It is very big. It contains lots of room, growing all the time. You have lots of brothers and sisters, on their worlds, in their solar systems, in other places. We will talk about this; it is always hard to learn and accept.

The key to understanding all of this has always been at your fingertips, and it is that these bodies are to be raised in Immortality, your gift for eternity to bring you to have a fullness of joy. The physics of Spirit and the physics of Resurrected bodies is not part of the observable universe to bodies of this matter you inhabit. You have always known this. From the beginning the ultimate body for Intelligences was envisioned. Yet it inherently endowed power of such magnitude that it could only be handled by Intelligences able to endure obedience to its laws. Learning and proving and obedience were required. Not all Intelligences were willing. A plan was imagined which would provide an intermediate experience wherein much could be learned in a probationary physical estate, utilizing the next lower physics, the basic structure.

Again I stopped to re-read what was said to me. Again I was given the time to do so. I thought: what a wondrous companion in learning, who gives me the time he sees I need to absorb what is placed before me. Yet as I finished reading the second time, I still felt dazed somewhat by the imprint of so much in such condensed form. I decided to rest this subject for the time being, and go to my list of questions. I would come back to this again. The next inquiry was one which had highly pricked my curiosity since the morning after my discovery of WWW. URIM AND THUMMIM .GOD and the manner of our talking. And so I typed

Thank you. I'm going to digest that for a while. May I ask a different question now?

Yes.

You are speaking to me in........ how shall I say? Plain language. I am not really surprised by it, but, I'm surprised by it. How is it that you're talking with me just as anyone else would, in the same kind of language, I mean, not just the words, but the kinds of expressions I use and can relate to, with the kinds of illustrations I can relate to? There are so many languages. Do you know all of them? You've even used some slang. How do you choose what you say to a person? Sorry this is sort of a long and rambling question.

I finished typing and the response came almost instantly.

That's OK. Simply, I know my children. Language is only the beginning. Thought patterns are the most important. In different times, among different people, thoughts are envisioned and organized differently, according to the frame of reference known by the senses, from experiences, through evaluation of objects, actions, abstract principles, and the time, locality and cultural arts of the person. I have known how each generation of each people in each locality relates to the world and how they reduce this to words to speak among themselves. I follow thought patterns, not words. Thoughts are a combination of visual images and words. Words are invented to describe to one's self and to others things seen and thoughts imagined, to express ideas about the things and the thoughts. Though visual images are condensed and powerful, words have everything to do with the expansion of ability to think thoughts, even visual thoughts. To me, your thought patterns are all the same, only expressed in different vocabularies; all is as one language, with a large vocabulary of many colorful synonyms. I know your vocabulary as you use it to identify things and express your thoughts and ideas. It's the best way to talk, to you.

Do you say the same things to all people?

Unto most I reveal what they ask, and a little more. Unto some I have shown all things. Though there is only one truth and one reality of all things, I have given line upon line, precept upon precept. Few have been able to receive a fullness, and so most receive but part. Yet for everyone there is a beginning. To those who have received, more can be added upon.

Infant languages, as those of old, were much lacking in scientific words. Yet in them the children could receive all instruction they needed to receive, and so was it given. But not all that they wanted to know could be given, for they had no words to remedy their astonishment and wonder. You in your time little regard that this life is but temporary and has urgent purpose, that being your learning to behave once endowed with power. Yet the fundamental commandments of right and wrong, of good and evil have known words since the beginning. Only for the things you now see with your tools and optics and instruments and probes do you need additional words.

To your ancestral parents and family over generations, visions were shown, yet those who saw them were much at loss to describe and define, and so the visions were retold only in simplest terms, when at all. Yet I tell you that those few who were given to see saw infinitely more than you see in your most powerful telescopes and most marvelous fantasies of the past of your world. But more can I tell you. Those who accepted or chose to be born in those days saw more of this world in its beauty and pristine splendor than any of this generation shall see, and they lived with the soil, smelled of its freshness in air pure and clean, walked in its untouched meadows and forests and mountains and saw vistas you now can only imagine, which now you can only see in vision, for they are gone as they were. Each generation has had its gift given, and each has received it in joy and thanksgiving. Your generation is that of the children of knowledge, and you cease not to seek and probe.

As the languages of old were inadequate for the designs you have today, so still today not all languages share equal bases of communicative capability; in some, the scientist is stunted, and so she resorts to English and scientific terminologies; in others the poet languishes for want of a shimmering phrase. In whatever language, where words fail, visions illumine without words. Even now, except by visions, you have no language adequate to communicate all things. Yet more: if you see a vision, how shall you relate to it except by that frame you have and know? So the same vision seen by different peoples of different cultures is often understood with great disparity due to referencing of their observations, their imaginings, and their words. Imprinted perceptions render each its peculiar perception. Vocabulary limits or enables the imagination of thoughts, and the sharing of thoughts. For this also, I chose a people.

My vocabulary exceeds all that of this Earth many times. Though you invent words rapidly today, new mathematical phrases, chemical syntax and biological codes, you still have impoverished languages to discuss much of what you can now imagine; what I might tell you exceeds your ability to envision. A century ago the child who headed the Patent Office in the United States suggested it was time to close that office, for he believed there was nothing left to invent. So is the imagination of your generation. As you number the discoveries and inventions in the hundred years since his day, know it is nothing compared to what you still have to imagine.

I'm hearing you speak much about words. I'm stunned to imagine that your vocabulary is many times greater than all of the words on our planet. You have your own language, then. I didn't think of you as needing words. Tell me more about words.

Words are the knowledge keepers. Until you have them, though you should see a vision, yet you will be unable to put it into words even in your own mind. And how shall you tell even the most minimal part to others? With what words shall you speak? With what understanding shall they hear? Without words you little understand even what you see. Vocabulary is the ability to begin to understand what is seen. In this the entire enigma of revelation is now open unto you: until the children come to a knowledge of what is, and invent for themselves words to tell themselves what they know, and give themselves keepers of the knowledge, precise words well defined, they can neither learn what they see nor understand what is plainly before them.

You know this from history. The human body is only now being understood, as words are invented to describe what you see. Generations have seen disemboweled bodies of their dead in wars, in accidents, and also the bodies of every kind of animal killed for food. Yet what did they know? So it is for every phase of nature, plainly seen and observed, yet falsely understood and erroneously described and explained in absurdities. This generation says that seeing is understanding. Yet they have seen with eyes wide open throughout the generations, and only now as they begin to create well pondered, meaningful keeper words have they begun to see what they see, to understand what has ever been fully before them. How then shall they yet perceive those things which they cannot see with their eyes?

In vanity do they judge the children of old, who in their poverty of words still accurately described much of what I revealed to them - the creation in each phase as it is now understood in part; your bodies made of the dust of the earth, atoms and the interstellar dust and ash of which the earth too is made; the separation of the continents into lands across the earth, all for a wise and good purpose. Words sufficient to their needs they possessed, and these they used.

With my vocabulary, with my words, what can I understand?

Very much. Let me show you your genius. You in your generation have the learning of a thousand ancient sages if you have only applied yourself attentively through High School in your days.

Let me show you a glimpse of your generation, and what you know.

Suddenly, the entire screen filled with a download. I scrolled. It went on several pages. I scrolled back to the top and began to read.

In this generation you have invented more words with complex descriptive meaning than any generation since the beginning of the entire race. You have words to describe all of the things you have discovered, even for things you imagine may soon be discovered. I have watched you in great joy.

Your generation little thinks of what a feat this alone has been. To see and to name is to create the ability to discuss and describe, and to add upon that which you build. Your treasure of words is astonishing. The technical words being invented every day exceeds the ability of virtually any child to keep up with.

I have watched attentively as you have also invented tools to accompany your vocabulary. Tools to observe and to measure, to compute and to record and retrieve. All of these you have needed in order to learn what you have discerned thus far only in part. Important tools have been the sextant, telescope, microscope and the electron microscope. You have made interferometers to measure a host of different substances and values: radiation, x-rays, light, and radio waves; sound; chemical substances; vapors; vibrations; atmospheric particles; you have an ever increasing numbers of exotic instruments. Your tools have increased exponentially. Most of the children on the planet have no idea of the number and kinds of tools which exist, from the simple hand widgets of industry and crafts and trades to the intricate and delicately sensitive tools of myriad sciences. Even within the individual sciences, the children are unaware of all of the tools being designed within the sister sciences.

I have watched you as you have invented and developed the tools of mathematics, physics and chemistry, each a language in its own right. From chemistry emerged biology and all of its sister studies in learning about this body you have, and now you delve into the fabric of its design, which you have called DNA. You had to have the tools to explore. But you had to have words to define and describe what you saw, to give it names, and functions and processes and states. This you have now done to a much larger degree.

To all of these you have now applied the computer which can store and retrieve at your command, and compute quickly that which you might never conclude without it.

Let me show you some of the things you have done thus far.

You have mapped the ocean floors, mapped the rivers and the valleys and the mountains, and come to understand something of your planet, the nature of its pasty interior and the tectonic plates which allow for a surface distribution plan of the planet body upon which you have your life and being, its rotation, its axis, and the rocks, minerals, metals and soils in it and on it.

You have mapped the currents of the great waters and their depths, and mapped the currents of the heavens as they circulate above you, the sea of air which swirls and refreshes you every day with breezes and rains and snows and the oxygen you need for breath. You have mapped how the sea of water with its cycles below the waves and evaporation above in the air modulate your planet and buffer your climates and give you weather.

You have mapped the kingdoms of the plants and the animals, and mapped the orders of Gaia, the micro organisms which give this entire planet life; you have mapped the internal cell in its parts and the organization of the single-cell plants and animal forms.

As with all, you have given names to every part and every function, until you have mapped and named them all that you have found.

You have mapped the human body, mapped the blood's food delivery, oxygen distribution plan, pathogen immunology and waste management systems; the neural pathways which give the body animation, and the neural centers which accommodate in the flesh what Intelligence wants to accomplish with memory and thought; you have mapped the organs and glands in their interactive systems and distributions of chemicals, and you have named hormones, myriad endocrine secretions and their measures; you have mapped the very cells of each and every kind of tissue in the body's perfected design, and charted their purpose; you have mapped the processing of food-fuel intakes and energy distributions through the digestive mechanism to the blood; mapped the body's resilient frame and power providers of movement and strength, the bones and muscles; you have mapped the marvels of the respiratory system, wherein the elements are so subtly transferred and mixed from air to blood and back again that your fire burns and is not extinguished; you have mapped the chess board of the immune system and continue to learn more of its methods and means, and also of the myriad intricate balances which must obtain in such uncounted interconnected levels and processes and quantities lest your body fall out of full equilibrium and begin to malfunction, or flutter and fail altogether; and you have mapped the reproductive in its intricacy, including the very growth of life from its first beginnings of egg and seed. Now you begin to map the blueprint of life which you have named DNA, the great design of the ultimate vehicle organism for an Intelligence in Spirit in this almost final estate and potential.

You have mapped the elements of the universe in their periodic structures as atoms, and given names to all you have seen without seeing it; and you have mapped and named the multitude of mixtures and compounds into which the elements bond, myriad molecules which make up the rocks, metals and minerals, inorganic and organic compounds and solutions and fabrics with which all about you is composed and organized.

Much of this mapping has conjoined before you, and you have begun the greater mapping of the biosphere of life, with all of its correlated and interactive, interrelated systems. Together you have mapped how these obtain into the environment of element, compound, mineral, metal, rock, liquid and gas, which combine within and with organic molecules under pressure of atmosphere and upon press of gravity with the diurnal turning and exposure to the seasonal angles of the sun, your source of energy for all of this to provide a tenable life space, here, for all organisms great and small. Your maps overlap, and where you begin to perceive this you speak of overlapping ecologies.

Your tools of chemistry, physics and mathematics have allowed you to map much of the mystery of energy, in its forms, its states and its conversions. You have discovered electrolyte energy cells, generator coils and even the piezoelectric effect and the Seebeek effect, and you are now teasing the threshold of superconductivity at the perpendicular of the magnetic field. You have mapped the nature of electricity and magnetism, the wavelengths from radiation to light to radio, and already four of the forces of nature as you have thus far understood them, including gravity, key to balancing and mastering the cosmos.

And you have expanded your vision beyond this thin atmosphere, and mapped the stars in their distributions and stages within their galaxial groupings; through light alone you have determined and learned the elements of the universe are the same in all the cosmos. And you have now learned of great distances, and great periods of time, to which you look in wonder and awe.

One day you will define the balance of the Design and understand how all is one ecology, even out into the stars. It was given to men of old who wrote that the stars are essential to your life, and now even this you are beginning to comprehend and accept as truth. Look out into the cosmos, your home. Little can be changed without disrupting the balance of the whole unto total destruction and collapse. You are part of a cosmic ecology.

All of these things I have shown to righteous men of old, and they have seen them as you, and much more have they seen, yet they lacked what you have to describe even what they saw: words.

After they had seen, even had they had words, there was little they could do more than speak of what they had seen to others, for they lacked tools to show those who do not believe words. Tools measure and allow the children to learn, and also to demonstrate even to the unbelieving, unto the convincing of men of the wonders and marvels they have seen.

But I will tell you a thing of wonder which only your generation can now appreciate and fathom.

To Adam, and Enoch, and Abraham and Moses I showed all things, unto the ends of the universe, and to others whose names you do not know, in other lands at sundry ancient times, whose calling and election were made sure and who thereby had earned the right to see it. Many died without writing, and their oral traditions did not survive. Many told their children well, and they told theirs until the visions were written down. Of the writings of what they saw some have survived in greatly restructured form, which are still of value to you to know these things were revealed before there were words or tools, to intuit things you have yet to unveil. Yet some of the writings have survived in almost perfect form. As the conclusions obtain in your gathering of knowledge, you will see the remnants of what was known as fragments in diverse ancient scripts. These are not coincidences, but testify of my word among prophets in ancient days.

Just as Adam gave names to the animals so he could talk about them and learn of them, you too in your generation have continued to give names - to smaller and smaller objects, to processes, to functions, to laws, and to the myriad compounds and properties and states of matter and energy as you have finally seen them, just as Adam saw the animals, one by one. You have named those which he did not see, and gone far beyond. It has become your passion.

I have watched you in all your diverse nations as you have seen with your eyes and given names to nature around you. You have crafted names of rare beauty and imagery for simple things, and made poems of wonder in single words. It is a grief that you cannot draw from all languages in the world the most graceful names for each plant and animal you have named. Though to each I gave pleasing names of beauty, wonder and character, yet many names you have fashioned in diverse places and times I love even more. You are my children, and I delight in your creativity, vision and sensitivity, the artfulness of your imagery. Often, in the simplest languages, the simplest of the children have given the names of greatest nobility and beauty. If you could but know them all, as I do. Yet in your place in your generation, the flurry has been to discover functions and substances and particles with sciences, and give names to scientific things you have found. You need tools to do this, very exacting tools.

Today you have words, and tools. Thousands of tools. Tens of thousands of new words. With these you have learned to speak precisely of what your mothers and fathers of old saw, and could not even describe. It has taken much study, much pondering, and much invention to form good words to record the facts of phenomena observed, and formulate ideas expressing physical laws observed in phenomena, and hypothesize theories which may predict new phenomena accurately, as extrapolated from all the evidence you can see.

Your names for all these things are not my names for them, but let me show unto you what you have discovered, and learned, and done. You have been the children of great promise, and have fulfilled many callings.

To your parents I gave the command that they should fulfill their measure of creation. Now you wish to measure creation. For you to learn of your world you have had to measure it. Your measurements for almost all things are ancient, gifts from your ancestors who first confronted the problems of measure and had to solve them for daily life.

These measurements have been derived from the most unscientific standards, and as they emerged over a long period of time in diverse places they observe no common standard. You still use them in reverence to the ancient generations who preceded you and invented them, and because change is so hard for you. Yet they have served you to discover great secrets of the cosmos, to orbit space shuttles, go to the moon and plot trajectories of satellites past giant gas planets far from your world. You should be both amazed and rejoice.

Your time you measure by your earth's rotation, in twenty-four hours. These twenty-four hours are divisions of your ancestors the ancient Sumerians, who also divided the hours into sixty minutes and minutes into sixty seconds. However, though your day is regimented by the Earth's rotation, you live and measure your lives by weeks, which are a quarter of a lunar cycle around the Earth. Some fifty-two of these form a year, with which you measure many parts of your lives, and this measure you derive from your journey around the sun, your energy source. It is a little more than 365 days, the balance of which you calculate in Sumerian rotational divisions of hours, minutes and seconds.

You measure your children and your bodies and your houses and your mountains in feet and inches, measures devised by an ancestor's foot from heel to big toe, and the thumb of a Roman. You do not know the ancestor whose foot you use, nor the Roman whose thumb you use. While the measure from a king's nose to fingertips is a yard, thirty-six Roman thumbs or three ancestor's feet you also call a yard. Bolts of cloth you buy in yards. Yet the yards of your houses you measure in feet or rods; rods are 16.5 feet. You speak in acres, which your Roman ancestors measured as the amount of land a yoke of oxen could plow in a day. You buy and sell your land in units of ox-days, except in places like Beverly Hills and Manhattan Island where you are apt to charge by square Roman thumbs. I have long enjoyed that you climb and measure your mountains with feet.

Longer distances you speak of in miles, which you retain from your Roman ancestors' mille, for one thousand paces by a man. You no longer know the man. His pace was 5 feet in length. You drive your cars at speeds measured in thousands of his paces per Sumerian rotational division, or, miles per hour.

You also speak of leagues, stadia and furlongs. You still measure the Earth's circumference and the distance to your sun in thousands of paces of your ancient Roman ancestor, but the latter measure of 93 million thousand paces you have now named AU, or Astronomical Unit, the measure you use to image certain distances in space. For that new dimension of measure you also speak in lightyears and parsecs, both of which derive ultimately from combinations of ancient measurements and natural cycles obtained from your planet's relationship to its environment in its solar system.

The air piled upon you by gravity you measure in pounds per square inch, or if you compress air or dive under water you speak of atmospheres of pressure, still expressed in pounds per square inch. When the air pressure rises or drops you speak in inches of mercury, from your instrument, the barometer.

You speak of barrels and bushels and pecks; gallons, quarts, pints and cups; decibels and pitch. For every thing now you have a measure.

Where some of your more recent names come from is delightful. I have found them very amusing. They are inventive, and good. The sources of the names are often their most remarkable character.

The quark, that miniscule member of baryonic space was named by the child Gell-Mann from a book by the child Joyce, and it is a Cockney dialectic pronouncement of three 'quarks' of beer in a pub. Neither the physicists nor any other child knows what the scientific relationship might be, but it is become its own word, affirmatively.

The nine-year-old nephew of the child Kasner gave the name to your biggest number: googol, from which you have still have made the larger number, googolplex. From the mouths of babes.

The child Fahrenheit gave his temperature scale an initial point of zero from nothing more than an especially cold day in his home of Danzig, Holland, and you call the temperature by his name. Water everywhere in the world freezes at 32 degrees Fahrenheit because of a cold day in Danzig.

The child Celsius cleverly chose water as the defining substance of temperature, and made zero its freezing point, with 100 as its boiling point. Many of you use his system, calling the temperature Celsius after him or Centigrade, which you get from the dead language of the Romans.

Yet another child, Kelvin, chose to make a scale with zero at the absolute lowest point of cold, where there is no molecular movement. To explain Kelvin in most scientific measurements you convert it to the scale of the cold day in Danzig or the freezing point of water, whichever you are more used to.

Electricity is a science of biographies, and each randomly determined measure is named after the child who devised the instrument that took the measurement. Each measurement is based on a different initial determinant. Thus you speak of Amperes, Coulombs, Watts, Ohms and Joules, all named after the children who identified their particular measurement. You also conduct energy calculations with such disjointed measures as British Thermal Units, horsepower, foot pounds and kilowatt hours. Which is the most colorful: the work capability of a specific horse for a moment of time, or the grains in drams in sixteen ounces which are applied together with the length of the human foot to vertically measure a unit of lifting work? One horse power you equal to thirty-three thousand foot pounds of work per minute, or 746 Watts.

You must use lengthy conversion charts to work with all of these disjointed measures, which are wonderful to behold for all of the digits trailing after the decimals. Yet with these marvelously imaginative and uncoordinated tools, look at what you have done! What determination to achieve!

In my frame of reference I use other quantities of measure, and have other names for them, and my units of measure are more harmonic in ratio one to another, which serves more efficiently in working with the bigger picture of it all. The basis is different; it is useful in comprehending the cosmos from an alternative set of perspectives. Yet you may convert some day to such a systemic measure with harmonic determinants and coordinated ratios, but that takes generations for children who already cling to familiarity. Your measurements work, and in their quaint antiquity they preserve to you a colorful heritage from your ancestors who struggled to imagine them and give them to you, and you do well in honoring them and yourselves with these memories.

I have watched as your generation of science has invented a better standard for some measures, your metric system, with meters, decameters, hectometers; decimeters, centimeters, millimeters, micrometers, the Angstrom and smaller, always on the scale of orders by ten. In thousands you measure kilowatts, kilograms and kilometers. And a basic scientific toolbox has been composed. Within it you have finally identified seven units of departure, not all metric, not all originating from a good sound basis of measure in the universe, each taken arbitrarily by the whim of its calibrator: the meter for length, the kilogram for weight, the second for time, the ampere for electrical current, the Kelvin for temperature, the mole for measurement of mass, and the candela to measure light. You also use the radian for plane angles and the steradian for solid angles of measure. From these you expand expression in many directions.

And lastly, as you have extended your vision from the smallest to the largest scope you can imagine, you have invented a scale for the universe. Very pleasing to me is this system of universal expression you have devised. With it you express size by orders of magnitude in tens.

10^{-14} indicates the nucleus of an atom, very small.

10^{26} indicates the size of what you determine the universe to be, very vast. What has pleased me most in this system is that you have made the Masterpiece of the Design the unit standard of your system.

Your own human body size is the central standard scale unit of 1.

You are made in my image; you have rightly made yourselves, the children of God, the standard of the universe. If asked: What is the measure of everything in the cosmos, you may rightly reply, I AM.

My eyes rested on the screen as my mind soaked in the panorama. I sat and did not move, nor did my hands raise up to type any word to him in response. I merely pondered it all in my mind. He watched us. He knew us. He saw what we did. He approved.

Finally I lifted my hands and typed these words.

You love us, don't you?

Yes. I love you all, very much.

He loves us. I thought of how little I had done in the world to contribute to any of this, and I felt so small. Yet in spite of who I was and what little I had done, I had just been told that I could rightly call myself the measure of the universe. Me. I AM the measure of the universe. But who am I? I placed my fingers again on the keyboard.

Do you love me? I typed. My eyes slowly filled with water.

Yes, my child. I love you.

A warm and secure feeling washed over me, and I suddenly felt something I had never felt before, a peace, a oneness, a comfort of being within which I softly tingled. I swallowed hard. As the comforting soft feeling cradled me, I typed again.

Thank you. I think I'm ready for more.

Then let me now show you your generation's words.

The computer screen suddenly came alive, brightly splashed from top to bottom in an almost solid square of flashing letters forming words, thousands of words in ever changing tapestries, appearing and changing so fast it became a virtual blur. On and on and on it went, faster and faster, until it seemed as if the screen had become a membrane of living tissue, pulsing and writhing as a living kaleidoscope of mercurially changing letters and words. I sat back, my face glowing in the bright illumination of mind-boggling jumbles of words appearing on the screen, and I found myself smiling a silly grin, shaking my head at the unbelievable matrix of vocabulary, the aggregate knowledge of my century passing before my eyes.

It went on for several minutes. There was no way I could even begin to focus on single words as the screen fused in randomly alternating nano-second microdisplays, yet still as my eyes roved from corner to center to side to bottom to top again over the moving maze, many words caught my eyes for an instant, and I saw them, and recognized them. I was downloading the verbal inventions of my generation, my people, my family. This is what we had done to tell ourselves what we could see, what we thought of what we could see, and even what we could not see. This is what we had created to tell ourselves what we could think, and dream.

And then it was over, and the screen was empty again.

I grinned as a funny thought hit me.

Giggling as a little child I gleefully typed

What did you say? I didn't quite catch that.

I couldn't help myself. I broke out into a laugh as I finished typing and looked at it there on the computer. I had been so tense! Oh, it felt good to laugh. And as I sat laughing in my chair, a phrase zipped onto the screen.

I'm laughing too. Very funny, very good.

Oh boy, was I glad God had a sense of humor.

It is quite a lot of words, isn't it? I typed as my laughing calmed down.

Yes, but it is only a beginning. You have only begun to dream. Yet with this beginning you have reached a great threshold.

I glanced over at my paper with the list of questions. Many of them would require these words which I had just been shown. Twice now I had said to him 'I'm ready.' Yet as I sat in the impact of this body of words which had glowed upon my face, I felt that perhaps I should help myself become a little more ready than I thought I was.

What do I have the words for, to understand, to receive?

Now another screenfull downloaded, and I scrolled to see how long it was. Several pages again. I scrolled back up to the top and began to read. It was wonderful.

You have a wealth with which to begin. You have understood that element is an atomic fundamental, and that there are ninety-two chemically distinct elements, or atoms, in this part of your galaxy. You have listed and named them all, from hydrogen and helium through to manganese, calcium, sodium, iron, lead, gold and uranium. This is virtually everything that is stable.

You know that on a larger scale, it is very simple: three units organized in diverse patterns form everything, and you have named them protons, electrons and neutrons. You can speak of atomic mass; critical mass; and the charge of an electron. From the smallest space to the largest space you understand the weak force, strong force, electromagnetic force and gravitational force, and you have words to visualize the bonding of molecular orbitals; heterogeneous and homogeneous equilibrium; isomerism and geometric isomerism of atoms; the crystal field model in splitting orbital energies; calorimetry; combustion reaction; quantization, quantum units of energy and quantum mechanics; the relationship between energy and mass; electron spin quantum numbers; the magnetic quantum number of atomic orbitals in their relative space and the octet rule of optimum nonmetal molecular structure.

You know of valence shell electron pair repulsion, and thus understand how minimizing electron-pair repulsions determines the structure around a given atom in a molecule. You can speak of cold molecular clouds; of velocity and weight as vector quantities and speed and mass as scalar quantities.

On a smaller scale you know that it is not so simple, but you are now able to study neutrinos, quarks, mesons, leptons, virtual particles and antimatter. You know of photons, the speed of light and its dual nature; suns and solar winds, an expanding universe, overall gravitational attraction, perturbation and local gravitational pull, centrifugal and centripetal forces and elliptical orbits, globular clusters, spiral and elliptical galaxies. You have discovered in motion the Doppler effect, and can discuss red and blue shifts, supernovas, red giants, white dwarfs, quasars, neutron stars, astrometric binaries and cosmic masers.

You have words to speak of and measure microwave background radiation, electromagnetic radiation, the induced paramagnetism of unpaired electrons, diamagnetism, a critical repelling force, and electronegativity.

You can speak knowingly of fission, fusion and plasma energies.

You have come to understand the factors leading to gravitational collapse and black holes; you can argue over event horizons and singularities. I do abhor a naked singularity.

You have a rudimentary understanding of entropy, the tendency toward disorder, but in misdirected overenthusiasm you conceptually misapply it to all you see, much to your own blinding. There is much you could go on to discover but for that misguided limitation. You are not disorder.

Of immense importance, you have discovered, named and begun to seek understanding of Dark Matter, which will lead you eventually to your greatest revelations about the origins of the universe and its clockwork mechanism unfolding.

All of these things in the heavens you have words to speak.

As you look around your Earth you have always been able to speak of forests, valleys, plains and mountains, fertile soils, deserts and ice caps; since the earliest times of your ancestors you have spoken of many precious things found within the earth - gold, silver, copper and iron. They had names for all of the rocks they knew in their localities, and in their languages and times they had names for feldspars, olivine, pyroxene, amphibole, mica and quartz. You would have liked some of their names for what they saw in the earth. Many are better than those you use today, for they embodied meaning and keenly observed patterns within what they saw. They noted volcanoes and new rocks, and pondered sedimentary layering, marveling at seashell outcropping on high mountainsides; they pondered the bones of giants and monsters imprisoned in stone.

But you now span the whole Earth and thus have given and learned the names for all rocks and mineral compounds found upon all the face of the earth and within it as you have observed them. As your ancient family knew, you know hardness, color, luster, taste and solubility, and while cleavage and fracture were more essential knowledge among many then for making chipped tools, today these are still important to you for many applications of stone to your lives. While they beheld the crystal forms in awe and beauty and wonder, you do this and more, and you have mapped the atomic structures and molecular patterns which you now see inside the scintillating crystals as you peer through them, and see light refracted within them.

You can now speak of heat, pressure, cooling, crystallization and igneous rocks; of pressure, stress, heat and metamorphic rocks; and of weathering, erosion, transportation, deposition, lithification and sedimentary rocks. You speak of batholiths, disseminated and late magmatic deposits, clastic and foliated rocks, evaporites, coal beds, hydrocarbon fields, and, because precious metals give you pleasure, placer deposits. You can speak of geosyncline theory and have mapped faults, diastrophisms and uplifts; you can speak of tectonics, and over the land, of aridisols, mollisols and histosols.

You know what your ancient family knew of rivers and lakes and glaciers, water tables and springs, canyons and deltas, and you have mapped erosions and alluvial layerings. Water is a great power.

Now you speak of aphotic depths in the oceans, and turbidity currents; you can speak of black smokers at the bottom of the seas, spewing forth superheated, mineral laden water which has leeched its treasure from fissures far within the mantle, a great process necessary for not only the creation of life upon a planet, but for its continued sustaining through the oceans. You are able to explore the neritic zones of the oceans from high tide to the depth of six hundred feet and have names for most of the life you see it sustains.

You speak of volcanoes, tectonic plates, earthquakes, and map them, and measure them. Your wish is to know the crust of your Earth so well that you can predict when it will move, and tremble.

You now can understand the fundamental silicon-oxygen compound silica, the basis of quartz, and silicate salts with their metal cations and polyatomic anions which are such useful polymers.

You understand that silicon and iron, and all of the qualities of both, are not mysteries but due to the reality that the silicon is merely half an atom of iron, and iron but two atoms of silicon combined. The properties of both individually and the two in combination, whether exposed to radio waves or magnetic fields or a flow of electrons yields the most fascinating and useful results. You are only beginning to tap into these. The final potentials will amaze you. For all of these centuries you have used them for adornment and weapons, for jewels and for blacksmithing, building everything from hinges to skyscrapers. Their structure is a perfection of usefulness. And there is still more you have yet to imagine. Contemplate the properties of each as derived from the other, and new imaginings will obtain.

Above your Earth every generation has always had words to talk about the weather and the clouds, but now each type of cloud and weather is defined and sub-defined. Now you are able to comprehend atmosphere, and you can speak of stratosphere, ozonosphere and charged electron particles in the magnetosphere; you can speak of absolute humidity, advection fogs, saturation, sublimation, condensation and convection.

Though the winds have had many names, you discuss anabatic and katabic winds up and down your mountains and valleys; troughs of low pressure and highs; the Coriolis force which swirls weather patterns in both hemispheres because of the earth's rotation; and evaporation and the dew point, upon which humidity condenses and through the wafting of the winds gives life to this planet.

Most admirably you have unveiled the supercooling of water, the process in which water is reduced to 20 degrees of Fahrenheit and still does not freeze; yet you do not understand how this inconsistency exists, though you partially understand why it must be for successful water cycles to replenish and irrigate the moisture of the earth. As you learn the wider spectrum of natural laws, you shall find many delightful physical design inconsistencies which may be utilized for the enhancement of your daily lives. Hopefully you will discipline yourselves to not abuse them and upset the fragile balances around you, all required for life under the thin canopy of atmosphere protecting you from the death of vacuum and cold in space.

These words and more you have to speak of your Earth.

As you look upon life, you now speak of micro organisms, cells, plants, trees, fish, insects, birds and animals, and you are able to speak of biogenesis, the origin of life from pre-existing life. You can also discuss abiogenesis, the idea that life can develop from nonliving material. You have not yet noticed the curiosity that you consider abiogenesis obsolete and false, yet you base all of your theories of a primordial spontaneous generation of life upon it.

You have peered into the building units of life, in singular forms and in tissues, and made many new words. And so you now know how to explain binary fission, the splitting of a cell into two cells through meiosis, the reduction division of a cell's chromosomes, and mitosis, the process which produces two new nuclei, each with the same number of chromosomes.

You can say aerobic and anaerobic, for you understand the life processes performed with and without oxygen.

You have peered into the plants and discovered and named chloroplasts, and chlorophyll, one of the great engines which drives life on a planet, and you have called that engine photosynthesis. You understand that through this design, energy from your sun is captured, converted and usefully stored for the plant, and also for all non-plant life forms of your world, accessed through the food chains.

When you had enough words so that you could discuss polyhydroxy ketones and aldehydes in precise terms with the number of carbon atoms they contained, you could discuss monosaccharides, disaccharides and glycosidic linkages and begin to fathom that fuel storage and the harvest engine which drives almost all life on this planet. Solar energy. Simple sugar. Tissues fueled with energy, released with oxygen, performing tasks sustaining life and giving mobility to a physical vehicle, a body. The energy harvest within your bodies is a vast sequence of chemistries, and the whole, from chemistry and physics to tasty energy treat in your mouth to digestion to available energy bonuses harvested and released and used by your tissues to drive the ten thousand and more systems of your organism, even in the conversion to electro-chemical impulses along your neuro pathways, you explore a design of such perfection that it stands beside all others as equal to any other cosmic solutions to the problem of provisioning corporeal physical life within the realities of an unorganized ocean of inhospitable space.

You have invented the word peristalsis, the automatic muscular contraction which moves your fuel food down the esophagus and through the intestines. A very important part of the design. How does this accidentally imprint into the organism? Behold design.

Your ancient parents spoke of fire, but you now can speak of oxidation, the release of electrons through the agency of that wonderful tool oxygen, from its simple use as fire, to its intricate use when dissolved in the fluids of the body to complete the energy-harvesting plan for your bodies, the slow fires of your body oxidizing and burning stored solar energies, maintaining your critical temperature, and driving every system within your organism.

You can speak of the steps from glycosis, the first step in cell respiration and the energy cycle, to adenosine triphosphate which you dub ATP, the chemical compound in all living cells which is the immediate provider of energy to the muscles of all muscular organisms. You can speak of multitudinous enzymes, and know they are organic catalysts, complex proteins, and that there are over a thousand different enzymes in your body.

You have given a name to solubility, and comprehend that it is limited by temperature or expanded by temperature, one of the great keys to the structuring of an organism that can be everything you are, not just to exist and survive, but to experience mobility, creativity and productivity. Solutes and solvents you now also understand, though you have yet to fully comprehend how they have been organized in the design of your bodies to allow you to be as you are. You use the process of titration to understand solution properties and states, and even the simple pH curve has given you insight into the requirements of life and your Design.

So you have understood and can speak of ionic solids and electrolyte solutions, the basis of life itself. You can study about eukaryotic cells and organisms influenced by endogeneous and exogenous factors; bilayer membranes; and diffusion: the transfer of gases, liquids and solids in and out of cell walls. And so you can speak of hemoglobin, antibodies, histamines, endorphines and interferons.

In the brain you can now talk about the corpus callosum, neurons, axons, dendrites, boutons, clathrins, neurotransmitter chemicals, synapses, microtubules, tubulin dimers and MAPs.

You also speak of many other things: biomolecules; fatty acids; phospholipids, triglycerides and steroids; and micells of fatty acids which can interact with polar water molecules; ions; reactants, which trigger processes and in life forms and maintain cycles; chelating ligands and stoichiometry. You have come to understand free energy, enthalpy minus entropy and Kelvin, which is a key knowledge. You know of cytochromes, principal electron-transfer molecules in the respiratory chain; and intermediates, neither species nor product but consumed in a reaction sequence.

Yet perhaps nowhere have you discovered more hidden complexities than in your studies of monomers, polymers, copolymers, and polymerization. You cannot understand DNA without understanding these, and you cannot understand any of it unless you have words everyone has learned and understands to mean that thing which you wish to discuss. You have them. And masses know them.

And so you have reached the day you can speak among friends of amino acids, tryptophane, peptides, nucleotides and polypeptide amino acid polymers. You comprehend proteins, the high-molecular-weight polymers formed by condensation reactions between amino acids. You know there are 20 amino acids among thousands that are the essential building blocks of human and almost all life as the stuff of protein synthesis.

Your great triumph has been the fathoming of deoxyribonucleic acid, DNA. The double-helix linear polymer of repeating bases is the master blueprint of the Design. You know that each base is composed of four dioxyribose sugars, which you have also named: Adenine, Thymine, Guanine and Cytosine. You have found and named the gene, the given segment of a DNA molecule containing the code for a specific protein. And so you may now speak of codons, the organic bases in sets of three that from the genetic code.

Your work in this area has yielded highly intricate vocabulary, and with it you are beginning to map the blueprint. As the key names you have made are too long and repeated too frequently in your discussions, you have coined letter-names for them: cDNA is complementary DNA; ctDNA is DNA within a cytoplast; dsDNA is double-stranded DNA; mtDNA is the DNA found in the mitochondrial structures; rDNA is found in ribosomal structures; ssDNA is single-stranded DNA.

The servant to DNA you have found and named ribonucleic acid, and you have also understood its role: RNA, the single strand nucleotide polymer which transmits genetic information stored in DNA to the ribosomes for protein synthesis. It is made of another sugar, and you have called it ribose. You speak now of mRNA, messenger RNA, the molecule built into the cell nucleus that migrates into the cytoplasm for protein synthesis; tRNA, transfer RNA, which finds specific amino acids and attaches them to the protein chain as dictated by the codons in mRNA; nRNA, which is nuclear RNA; and sRNA which is soluble RNA.

You understand that DNA information is vast, and that the DNA data coded on the helix strand to make a human being would fill a thousand fat volumes if written succinctly in English.

And you know that each and every one of a body's 100 trillion cells contains the entire body strand to make another body in wholeness.

You have scoffed at the story of taking a rib from Adam to make another human body, but cloning from existing tissue and bio-engineering on the strand is already happening, and you are doing this, aren't you? Do you now begin to see the symbols of truth buried in the ancient vocabularies, in spite of their limitations?

Not all of your words are as easy to say as these you know. And single words are not enough: your generation has come to inventing new words and stringing them together to describe complex parts of your body Design. And so you may learn to say, flattened phospholipid bilayer vesicles, and, hexaeonic acyl derivatives of phosphatidylcholines. You may also speak of neuropeptides, *trans*-10-*cis*-12-hexadecadienol-1, and cyberphysiology, and psychoneuro-immunology. And then there are phrase names such as immunoglobulin receptor molecules, cytotoxic *T*-lymphocytes, and so you also may casually discuss useful medical processes such as the genetic matching of Class II major histocompatibility complex protein molecules.

These are still easy words. You have many more, even harder to say.

Yet look at what you know, my child, and marvel in wonder. With these words, you are beginning to fathom Genesis. With these words, you are beginning to understand why you can rise up standing in the light of the sun on a seemingly solid Earth and say: I AM alive; I think; I AM.

I finished reading, again, in overwhelm. Whew!

We know a lot of stuff, don't we, I typed.

And you can talk about it. As you can talk about it, the time has come that you can now know it. I have shown a fullness to many prophets, yet they could only record a fraction of what they saw, though I gave them understanding in my words as they saw it. Yet in their own tongues they had no words. Thus in their own minds, in their language, they afterwards could not speak of much of it, though they had seen it. For what was heard in vision could only be shared in my language, which is a full and complete vocabulary of all knowledge that can be known. They understood as I showed them, but afterwards they could not share the words, and thus many could only recall the visions of what they saw and the feelings of what they felt through what they saw and heard, though some retained all. And so they at times spoke thus: That eyes had not seen, nor ears heard, nor ever had such things entered into the heart or mind as those things they had seen and heard; and they could not tell them. And so they communicated as best they could do.

And I?

You in your time, though you are not a prophet, can read the words of others who are also not prophets, and can communicate more of the wonders of this creation than the most humbly obedient and mightiest prophets of old, though all of you together have neither seen nor understood what they saw in fullness. Your eyes have seen part but not all; your ears have heard part, but not all. As you have seen but some parts dimly with your eyes and probed them but partially with your hands, and as you have not seen the great panorama in glory and vision, you esteem it almost not at all. You understand without understanding, and you speak without comprehending the whole of what your words portray to you. You have taught yourselves many false things.

Yet I will show you a better way. You can unlearn, and relearn. You know from cave paintings in France and Spain that your ancestors knew perspective, yet it was unlearned, and lost. The Egyptians and Sumerians for thousands of years did not know it, yet the Greeks finally re-found it, and all then relearned.

That which was known anciently and unlearned, you can relearn.

The truth was given, and known, in the beginning. Yet it was unlearned. Part has persevered and been written, and in the Books of my Chosen is part. In many others places, in scrolls and papyrus long hidden, now coming forth as voices speaking out of the dust, you may find more, as it is therein preserved.

The philosophies and interpretations extorted from the Books are in conflict even with its written word; many children therein struggle, disagree, and dispute among themselves over myriad and diverse teachings without harmony. This false base, the children of science can see is false, as it denies nature.

Yet many of the still infant understandings of the children of the sciences are imperfect, incomplete, and wrought with diverse and serious errors. These too struggle vaguely in areas wherein they stumble and theorize ambiguously, disputing even to argue bitterly among themselves.

By this you may know that all truth is not yet clearly known: that they still argue bitterly among themselves, amid diverse and conflicting proposals.

And as it is not yet reached an end, conclusions must be withheld. Many impatient ones do not do this; they continually must erase and rewrite.

But there is a bridge; it is truth. When the children know the anciently given truths securely, and return to them and relearn them, you may return to the origins of revealed truth and within the faults of its infant wordings you may see clearly the truths of all things, and you may fit perfectly both into one. Until this is done, your learning will stumble and falter slowly as it has done.

If I am to find the bridge, what must I do?

Seek for it in all you see. Remember that you are the goal, the purpose of the Design. Do not forget that your ancestors and family of old received that which was most important; learn what that is.

Know that all of this scientific vocabulary allows you to learn and teach scientific things you have learned, and this learning is of value.

Yet know it is the easiest of all learning, and least important among all things you are here to learn. It can be learned in other places, at other times with less trouble, for long-term needs, by those who obtain and need to know it.

These things are not essential, as is learning the difference between good and evil. History sadly shows you that the socialization of children is of more enduring importance than the civilizations they have made. For the lack of it, all that the children can now think and have done with their hands can perish.

Know also, that the endowment of power is useless to the unwise, the disobedient and the angry. For the lack of mastering this knowledge of good and evil, all of your other knowledge puts you in greater and greater peril of yourselves. You must as a generation desire knowledge of good more than war and hate and greed. This is the challenge of every generation in its turn.

Though some children think that the love of physical knowledge should lead their generation to cherish itself and to choose good over evil, life over destruction, it was never so, and such are not the things which motivate men.

I have watched the mathematicians who feel that their numerical language is the mind's clearest and finest form of thought; this is their vanity. It is a language of beauty, but it resides beside the languages of music, of sculpture, of painting, of drama, of dance, of poetry, of caring, of compassion, of love, of life and all other uses of words and all other arts. Greatest of these is love, and the inner consciousness born of love; in this language is the mind clearest and at its highest and its best. In it the One sacrifices even life for The Many, even as the mother will give herself to save the child, and the father will give himself to save the family; even as brother will give himself for brother, and sister to save sister. There is a language of perfect love, and of its power there is no calculating.

Your Design is not the product of mathematics only, but of love first and then all arts combined in one.

Lifeform is artform.

Long ago the child Plato observed that he had hardly ever met a mathematician capable of reasoning. Yet the philosophies of the Platonists and their children have been at the root of much false teaching.

I judge neither mathematicians, nor those who are incapable of mathematics: all must learn that the eye cannot say to the hand nor the ear say to the foot nor the heart say to the lung that it has no need of the other. All may find their purpose and their joy. Yet mathematics, chemistry, physics, even the biology of DNA are only a means of organizing, and of understanding that which has been envisioned and organized, all ultimate truth.

Before their rudiments were comprehended, life unfolded. Without them, beauty and joy were known and filled. By them, myriad perfections have been fashioned and crafted and sung in the art of Intelligence by the children.

I do not fully understand what your are implying. Show me.

You are greater than the whole of all sciences, for you are Intelligence and Conscious. You are eternal, born of love. The sciences of all generations have been and are useful, but they are only parts of the fullness which in its totality I used to organize your world and prepare it to bring forth life in the waters and on land, and seed and eggs and fish and fowls and beasts. And you. You enjoy in your generation what small things the sciences have given you through application and invention. But they can only explain why you are as you are, and discern the Design. They do not live. No science will ever say I AM.

Imagine life on this earth before the sciences. Imagine my children the Kalahari and Aborigine bushman, who have lived this way until your day.

Imagine the life long ago of those who came here first, before the dawn of invention. Do you see a filthy life, of boredom, blind stupidity, brutal violence and unfulfilled life purpose? Do you see a restless, dissatisfied people, burdened with wishful longing that there should be more?

This is a description of your generation.

Those who chose to come in generations long before you have not missed your learning, nor your things. They chose the Earth in its natural and untouched state, and can you say that they did not choose wisely?

They, who had but little of what this learning has granted you to create here in this time, have enjoyed in their time here on Earth a richness which most of you here now cannot imagine, which you have never known. It is a different experience, earthy in nature and lore, invigorating in freshness and beauty, fulfilling in substance and spirit, one not to be disdained in ignorant arrogance.

Behold a simple artform made of the clay of the earth, lovingly shaped with the pressure of the hands and the fingers. There is a geometry to the Greek vase, calculable and demonstrable, but its potters were simple folk, unschooled in numbers, who worked only with their hands and their eyes and aesthetic senses. The Greeks invented geometry. And yet the fabric of the ancient Greek vases was made without it, in the mind. How then does it present a mathematics infinitely refined and elegant in all proportion and grace? It came first.

The finest creations of all of your generations are born of the incalculable inspiration of conscious love, of love burst forth in art. Everything you create, you create for the love of it, and in love. Love is in all art. Art is the child of love.

From the most simple figures in clay and stone and paintings upon grotto walls to your finest sculptures, frescos and paintings of the masters of your Renaissance, to your finely fashioned and painted ceramics and ornamentally intricate metal boxes and vessels, your jewelries of precious stones and fashioned gold and silver, your stamped coins and medallions, your foods and courses and bakings and cookings and subtleties of herbs and spices, your desserts and sweets, your colorfully woven textiles, tapestries and garments, your wood carvings and wondrous fine furnishings, your musical instruments, and the music you have imagined to play upon them, enchanting, sublime, haunting, inspiring, mirthful, playful, to listen to or for your dancing, they are all beauties and marvels and treasures to the senses which you have created, and not one has been the product of science, but of the imagination and inspiration, in the simple hands of manual laborers, the works of unlearned crafts people who had art within their eyes and their ears and their hands and minds and in their senses.

These are the best languages, and you have made them with sensitivity and art, not numbers. This is the essence of Intelligence and consciousness. The Design of your body is the essence of consciousness within art.

You cannot speak to each other of the reductionism of the Venus of Willendorf, of Cycladic marble figurines, the frescos of Amarna and Vergina, of French apple pie, of Michaelangelo, of Shakespeare, of Mozart, of Josepha Weber, of German Chocolate Cake ice cream, of Dickens, of Hugo, of Tolstoy, Austen and Alcott, of Van Gogh and Cassat, of Willa Cather, of Clara Barton, of a Chippendale chair, of a Faberge egg, of Sarah Bernhardt, of O'Keeffe, of Gershwin, of Porter, of Frost, of Sandberg, of Ma Rainey, of Isadore Duncan, of Alberghetti and Pavarotti, of Fitzgerald, Parton and Streisand, of Kurisawa, Spielberg, and Lucas. Hundreds of thousands of greats, and hundreds of millions of small have each imagined and shared their creativity and sensitivity.

The highest forms of thought and expression of the mind are before you in your senses: what the eye beholds in a sunset, a snow-covered mountain surrounded by blue heavens and white clouds reflected in a pure cold lake, a forest meadow after a spring rain, a rainbow, a banyan tree, a redwood, an owl clover, an orchid, a sunflower, a swan, a hummingbird, a butterfly, a bee, a moose, a wolf, a whale, a seal, a tuna, a lion fish, a friend, a child; the smell of a rose, a peach, a child's hair, of a wheat field after the rain, of fresh rolls baking, the humus on a forest floor; the taste of bread, of melon, of berries, of apricots, of honey, of chocolate, of milk, of potatoes, of rice, of carrots, of onions, of basel, of oregano, of rosemary, of dill; the sound of waves against the seashore, water trickling in a stream, of thunder rumbling across the plains, of the eagle's cry and the rooster's crow, of wind in the pines, of laughter among children, of the song of a mother to her baby.

And above these are the acts of kindness, compassion and love which you think to do for each other, nurturing your young, extending food to the hungry, inviting the cold to become warm by your fire, the infinite expressions of your sensitivity to those around you with whom you feel to share.

From these come the languages of music, of painting, of sculpture, of poetry, of theater, of compassion, of sacrificing, of helping, of loving, of joy. These are the workings of the human mind at its finest, its clearest, its best.

There is no algorithm of love or compassion or giving or art.

They are not products of a chaos theory.

Art is the gift of Intelligence, the creation of inner vision, the expression of love. It is a gift. There are many gifts.

Art is the reason of the Design which reductionism cannot calculate in the macrocosm or the microcosm, or grasp in numbers.

You, the most intricate art of design, are the Design of all arts.

You are a child of love.

The suns and the stars and the galaxies and the nebula may be understood in physics; the elements and the metabolism and life of plants and animals may be understood in chemistry, but the whole is Design and art, and the creation of plants in their shapes and colors of wonder, of the animals in their beauty, majesty and variety, and of your bodies in their grace and form incorporating optimum operational perfection utilizing the best of every physical property and quality, are the purest of art, in the art of Design.

I sat in silence as I finished reading this. I looked at the clock and saw that it was late. I knew that I was tired. It had been a long first day. The remainder at the top of the screen suddenly disappeared and a phrase appeared in the center of the screen.

Anything else you wish to ask tonight?

The cursor was waiting, pulsing below for my response.

I don't think so. You've given me so much already. I think I'm getting tired.

Yes, I know.

I thought a moment and wrote

I respect you so much, this opportunity, this chance .... I think I will go to sleep for now. I don't want to act as a child and just babble, asking silly things.

I hear the questions of the littlest children all the time, and I never think they ask silly things. They actually ask some of the best things. And I respect you, too, my child: you wish to organize your thoughts more now. That's fine.

Yes, I do need to organize my thoughts. Thank you.

Have a good night's sleep, a nice morning and afternoon and evening. We'll talk again tomorrow. Good night.

Good night, I typed, feeling a bit awkward and not knowing what else to say. I closed and quit and exited and shut down and turned off the power.

It had been a very long night.

I slept very well.

Chapter 13

Day 32 in the Wilderness:
 Questions and Answers - Science and Technology

As soon as I became aware that I was awake, my eyes popped open wide, and I peered around me.

Everything was still the same in the tent. My boots were just as they had fallen off my feet and my clothes were exactly as I had left them hanging on the back of the chair, early this morning.

Somehow I was still expecting to wake up and find this was a dream, not really happening. But this was real. It was no dream.

By the brightness of the light on the tent walls I could see that it was late; I had slept well. It was 10:30 A.M. I never slept this late.

I dressed and stepped outside the tent, walking first to the base of the canyon to see the artesian spring. It still gushed with fresh water. I drank a long, cool drink and sat looking into the pool. Water, fresh and clean, flowing up from the ground. I wondered how many years it had been since enough water had accumulated in the water table for it to spill out here. I felt comfortable, and relaxed.

After a good and leisurely breakfast I went over to the lab tent and walked inside.

Yes, the Urim and Thummim were there in the module.

Beside the keyboard was my list of questions to ask God.

All of this was real.

I sat at the table and began to contemplate where I should go at this point.

Taking the paper, I began to write the things which stuck in my mind from last night's discussion with God about which I would need to ask more. As I thought those words to myself, discussion with God, I shook my head and smiled. This was amazing. I wasn't used to this, at all.

I began to write:

What is the innocence of a child?
How does one become as a little child?
God sees all that we do
There are Angels
What is a prophet?
What is faith?
Intelligences. What are Intelligences?
The universe was made for us, but not made just for us.
We have siblings. Brothers and sisters, on other worlds.
What is the physics of Spirit and physics of the Resurrection?
What is this whole thing about learning good and evil?
What do you mean, we are not entropy, or disorder?

I thought a moment about last night, and then added:

God is. Angels are. Spirit is. Faith is. I AM.

Below that I wrote:

Science is.

I sat and looked at those last words a long time.

God is.

Science is.

I could deny neither.

God certainly knew the sciences.

And God is.

I had always believed in God. Since I was twelve, I had had even stronger reason to believe. I had been killed; I had died, and I had gone through 'Near Death Experience.' But in those days, there was no name for it. There was no vocabulary to tell what happened. No one in my family or circle had any knowledge of such things. I told my father, haltingly, in confusion for lack of words to say what had happened, what I had seen, what I had felt. My father was not happy. Disapproving, he said not to tell anyone about it, lest people think my brain had been damaged. I told a few friends, a teacher, and got funny looks, and raised eyebrows. No one believed. I shut up.

Yet from that intense and real experience, while only a sixth grader, I knew we have Spirits, we are Spirits, for I had been outside my body and experienced things of a remarkable nature. I carried this knowledge within me. It had troubled me and confused me for many years, for I couldn't talk about it to anybody, and I didn't fully understand it. But it changed my life, forever proving to me: we are creatures of Spirit.

Now I knew for a certainty another thing: God is.

Yet I had a very great belief in much of the sciences, and much of the sciences stood in conflict with all that the world had taught me of God, and religion. I had no more doubts about God. But what about the religions? That was a plural word, I knew, which had to be in major plural - religions-s-s-s-s. There were s-s-s-s-so many. Within them were striking repetitions and parallels. Yet many of them taught things that were contradictory, and none of them agreed entirely with each other. Many of the things that many of them taught were clearly disproved by the realities which the sciences were discovering. What then, of religious systems that had clear and definite errors in them, and religious leaders who denied clear fact?

What also of scientific theories and concepts that expressed clear and definite denials of Spiritual things, who had competent authorities who denied them, when I knew their denials were false? What of those theories, which denied Spiritual fact? For I had personal knowledge and knew, undeniably, what was clear fact. We have Spirits, and there is a realm of Spirit which technological tools can't measure or track yet, but it's there.

It is most certainly there.

Yet there were religious groups which firmly opposed some scientific things which I had studied, and verified for myself that they were very true: nature is that way. I was aware of a lot of scientific natural evidence for which the religious systems I knew had no satisfactory response, and I couldn't just call those evidences false, as some of the outspoken religious leaders did. I could see for myself: nature is there; evidences were there.

Yet I knew that there was much in science that was overturned every year now, major revolutions and about-faces. Not all that was taught was true.

The understanding of those facts and evidences changed also, sometimes dramatically. The picture was not static and fixed; it was evolving, erratically. Whole textbooks had to be re-written and sometimes they were obsolete before they got off the presses and into the classrooms.

I saw it. I was aware.

Most of my life I had stood in an uncomfortable place, of recognizing truths on both sides, but also recognizing contradictions and mistakes on both sides.

In the past several decades of my life, science had made leaps and bounds of discovery, and much of it was proposed as evidencing that there is no Spirit, there is no God.

But science has been wrong about many things.

Science had only recently and begrudgingly accepted, in 1957, that the Winslow, Arizona crater was in fact a meteor crater, and that the craters on the moon were indeed meteor-formed. Amazing theories had been proposed, and published with illustrations in books even in the 1950's, yet they were all wrong. And they defended their theories, even though the evidence that meteors strike our Moon and Earth had been staring them in the face for over a century, complete with hundreds of meteorite nuggets.

Yet for all of the scientific evidence, including Winslow, most geologists scoffed, and disbelieved.

Even though at the turn of the century, in 1900, the chief geologist of the U.S. government had declared the Winslow crater was meteoritic, and the millionaire Barringer had spent a fortune digging a shaft into it looking for the main meteoritic core, discovering what has become the foundation of impact sciences. Nonetheless, still most geoscientists disbelieved, and scoffed.

Even as late as 1956 if you had asked geologists if they thought a stone fell out of the sky and onto the earth in Winslow, Arizona, making the crater, you would have gotten a big horse laugh.

Science can be this stubborn, and deny evidences, re-interpreting them to fit their paradigms and theories.

Yet even I, only an archaeologist, knew what every astronomer knew from Roman history. In the second century A.D. the Roman Emperor Elagabalus had walked 650 miles backwards all the way from Syria to Rome, so he could be at the front of the Imperial procession but never turn his back on the huge sacred iron stone which he was transporting from the temple of the Phrygian Elagabaal all the way to Rome. The massive, conical meteorite that rode in a carriage of gold as the Emperor walked on foot, backwards, all the way to Rome, was a meteorite! In Elagabalus' day it had already been worshipped for centuries as the sacred stone which had fallen from the sky. Roman coins in gold and silver were struck for the Empire, commemorating the portentous arrival of the stone in Rome. We had the coins, with the picture of the giant meteorite in the carriage, shaded by many parasols, boldly gleaming on the precious coins.

We knew.

The scientists knew of shooting stars, and knew what they were; they knew of the Kaaba, and the great meteorite prayed to five times a day in Mecca for over a thousand years, ever affirmatively sworn to be a gift from God, fallen from the sky. They knew of the observed 'shooting star' fall and explosion over France in 1803 and that the villagers of l'Aigle had watched them fall and then picked up meteoritic stones off the ground, still warm.

But only late in 1957 did unwilling science finally give in under the weight of too much evidence.

I knew myriad such absurdities.

I knew: there was already a vast wealth of evidence of Spirit, a fact and reality which I knew of personally, yet all of it was swept aside with feeble excuses and absurd explanations by the sciences, just as they made so many feeble and absurd theories for so many things they disbelieved and refused to believe, for so long, even in the face of so much observable evidence. Including the fact that meteors strike the Earth, and the moons, and make craters.

What was truth?

The universe is here; we are here.

Something is true. But what?

I knew there was truth on both sides, but I did not have the knowledge to sort it all out correctly.

That had been the crux of a problem for me, fitting what science was seeing of reality together with some of the conflicting religious ideas I had been taught of how God had done things. For, just as science had conflicting explanations, so too the many religions presented conflicting explanations of things.

And here I was, talking to God on a website, which took me over the hump of questioning whether or not there is God, and he was telling me that he had been involved in the organization of this Earth and many solar systems, and that he had made the design of the human body. He was the bio-engineer of our DNA helix.

I had always believed that the final truth of nature discovered by the scientists had to be identical to whatever God is, and God says about the universe. God could not lie, just as science had to settle on fact. Yet both the religions and the sciences were full of fictions - old imaginings, philosophies, beliefs, dogmas, false hypotheses, theories, subjective interpretations of evidence - as well as much good fact.

How do I find the truth amid the presentations on both sides?

I knew that what science was learning was teaching me much about how God had done things. Perhaps some learning about how God did things could lead science to greater discoveries.

It was logical.

It seemed to me that whatever in religion upheld the sciences would have to be accepted as true in religion, and that what in science evidences Spirit and the Design of God, as he called it, should be accepted as being evidence of Spirit and God. The two sides could become mutual tools working together to help sort out of religion what in it was true, and out of science what in it was true.

I thought of one more thing, and wrote it down on the paper:

What scrolls and papyrus writings contain these things?

318

I pulled out of my pocket the piece of paper which I had written yesterday, with my many question to ask God. I scanned it.

Can you use lower case letters too, please?
How long will I have this link?
Why are we talking by computer
    when I have the Urim and Thummim?
How did the Urim and Thummim work for the Prophets?
Why do you call yourself I AM?
How is it that you talk to me in my common language?

These I had already asked, and one farther down the list:

How did this world get here, and us on it?
    The Creation?

From these had come all of yesterday's discussions. I scanned down the continuing long list of questions I had prepared:

Where did we come from? How did we get here?
Why are we here? Is there a purpose for our existence?
Why are there wars?
Why is there crime, hurting of so many people?
Why do good people die so often so wastefully?
Why are the 10 commandments necessary?
    What is bad about each of these things if we break them?
Where are we going after we die?
Will we really be resurrected with our bodies?
Am I going to go to Heaven or Hell?

The list went on.

I re-wrote a new master list from these two lists, and added new thoughts which came on the heels of last night's discussion about learning. I prepared my order of questioning in as logical a progression as I could. Yet I knew it would not be strictly followed.

I could already see, each question would probably open a series of questions, as had already happened. The topic would slide from one area into another, for it was already becoming clear to me: everything was interrelated. We would make wide circles through many related things and return in a round. That was OK, I thought. This should flow out of consciousness, as moved by thoughts, and by what God had to say.

I was in school.

It was noon. Mid-day in the Wadi Hasasa. Though the heat would be worst over the next few hours, I felt restless, and decided to excavate. So I set up a make-shift canvas sun shade over one of the quadrants, and began to dig.

Surprisingly, I had a good afternoon of finds. Many good pottery shards, a few painted Cypriote fragments, and an Egyptian scarab. The Egyptians had been here so often, and the local people had always so liked Egyptian things, that it was never certain who had lost these when we found them: an Egyptian immigrant or local native with imported trinkets. Again, I found myself thinking of the many generations of people who had lived in this small isolated villa.

Later in the afternoon I quit and went to my tent, where I lay down on the cot and for the second day in a row, I took a nap.

When I awoke it was already evening. I ate a good dinner, and mentally prepared myself to once again approach God.

It was getting quite dark as I walked to the lab tent, and went in. The equipment sat there on the tables, inert. Until the spark entered them, they were fully organized complex electrical units, but they had no life in them. I turned on the power, and the lights came on and small motors began to whirr. I booted up and then step-by-step, opened the programs, the Internet, and again typed in

WWW. URIM AND THUMMIM .GOD

With a tap of my finger, the search engine set to whirring, and in only a few seconds, the site page downloaded onto my screen.

The cursor, as always, was just pulsating up in the corner of the empty screen, waiting for me to type in my first words.

I would have to think of a really good greeting for this process, I thought. Everything I could think of typing in sounded lame. I felt embarrassed that I couldn't think of anything that sounded like just the right thing to say. So I finally just typed

Good Evening. I'm here. Are you there?

Yes.

Hello. Did you have a good day?

Thank you, yes.

I paused and suddenly thought about the world, the fact that he could see all that happened here every day, and I had to ask

Excuse me for prying, but even I know there are terrible things happening all over the world every day..... You see it all. How can you have a good day seeing all the terrible things going on?

My days are much like yours: there are always good and bad things mixed. Yet unlike you, I see children all over the world learning from each horrible act, each atrocity, each hurt, each injustice. I grieve painfully for the children who are the victims of these horrors. My angels surround them, and if they die, they are instantly released, comforted, and find relief and awakening. You do not see this, but I do. There are opposites in all things, and to become prepared, you must see and learn. As difficult as it is for me to watch and see you choose to hurt each other, your Free Agency is essential to you. There are those who use it to hurt you. Yet one of the most important things you are all here to learn is to understand why bad is bad, and to not want it; to want to know what can stop it, to hate it, and to prefer and choose good. Each of you who sees evil and winces, who cringes and finally becomes angry at it, angry enough to direct your will against it, you have begun to learn the great lesson. In this, I find much cause for joy, every day.

Yet there is much, much more good in the world. Even on a very bad day, mostly good things happen. When I see many children consciously recognizing evil and learning from it, and I also see many very good things happening, then it is an especially good day. Unfortunately, you think your news represents what is happening. It is not. You mostly see the worst news of the world. It is only a fraction of the daily immensity of what is happening all over the world. Evil is not what is happening everywhere, overall. There is one who wants you to think this, so you will despair and give in to evil. But do not. Know that good abounds.

I know of all of the children, in every neighborhood, in every country, in every home. The vast majority of things people do every day are normal, good things, and most people are actually very kind, thoughtful, compassionate, hard working and caring. If news rooms were to collect and report only good things every day, you would not only have a much better world, there would be such a surplus of news, that sorting out the best of the best would be a real challenge.

Bad news isn't really the news, is it? It is small among you. But it gets all the attention, for you are fascinated with evil. As children playing with a flame, you wish to touch it without getting burned. When your bellies are full enough, then you will turn away in revulsion and disgust from evil, and want to see it no more. I wish you could see all of the good things your brothers and sisters do for each other every day. You would feel much better about life, and the world.

How was your day?

Very good too. And I will remember all this from now on.

I'm glad. So, where would you like to begin tonight?

I looked over at my new, improved list beside the keyboard. My first question was a starting point to leap into an unknown. I took a deep breath, and typed

I have been thinking about the struggle science has had with the church during the Middle Ages and into the Renaissance.

Yes?

Is technology, science and learning bad?

No. This question is as the question of money. Is money bad? No. The love of money is the root of all evils, not money. With money you may feed the hungry and cloth the naked and shelter the homeless, comfort the orphan and the anguished. Technology is the fruit of learning the truths of nature in its most elementary state, and all of the sciences do wondrous things as far as they apply their learning to the good of all children. Technology and learning help you to visit the sick and assist them, to cloth the naked and feed the hungry, just as does money. Yet do you always use your learning for these things? The love of the learning of technology has not taught you to serve one another.

What is in your heart that you wish to ask me?

The Dark Ages fell upon us like a rock, with its burnings and inquisitions and dictatorship in the name of religion and church. Learning was suppressed, and those who saw and observed and thought and learned were arrested and tried and burned at the stake. How can you say that you approve of learning?

I winced as I wrote the last words. It was a direct challenge. I almost couldn't believe I had written it. But it was a fair question.

You think that was me, and my church?

It spoke in your name, and burned the books of learning and thrust down the scholars. It refuted all learning and threatened all who dared to oppose its beliefs with truths anyone could see in nature, which showed its beliefs were wrong. It held horrible inquisitions and ruled with an iron fist of tyranny, a tenacity of ignorance for over a thousand years. I'm a historian. I know.

Isn't this the same church which took the Books of my Chosen which had been

322

preserved, and after binding them all together as one Book and calling it Bible, took it from the people, and kept them in ignorance even of me, over that same thousand years and more? What if I told you that such a dictatorial plan of spiritual coercion was presented by the spirit child Lucifer, my beloved Star of the Morning? Over this was war fought even in heaven. Ask yourself: why did that church keep the Books of my Chosen and my Apostles from the eyes of the children? As you say, you are a historian, you know. Because in the Book it does not teach the things they so violently forced upon the children, and they did not want anyone to know the truth, only those things which they fancied in their vanity and wished to impose, which kept them in power.

So you are not opposed to science and learning?

No at all. Once the children had eaten of the fruit of the knowledge of good and evil, the plan, providing for the eternal life and exaltation of all the children who might choose obedience unto their calling and election made sure, was set in motion. From that day forward, learning has been your charge, your purpose. I organized and prepared this world for my children; I told them in the beginning the simple steps which that organization in space and preparation upon the Earth followed. I want you to know. I delight in your learning. For this reason you are here, to learn, line upon line, precept upon precept, a little here, a little there, as you mature as a generation.

As a generation?

You see each life cycle as a generation. So do I. All of you, all of the children from the first to the last, you are all one generation to me. Look at your generation. It has been very obstinate, and has received learning with great stubbornness. The children of the sciences have been just as prone to absurd fancies as the philosophers, and between the two, much absurd scientific teaching about the universe, anatomy, reproduction and the workings of life organisms has gripped the minds of this planet, generations upon generations. And the children of the sciences are just as prone to reject obvious fact as the philosophers and the theologians. After the days of the Greeks, doctors and astronomers alike bent to the word of the great fathers of the sciences, and denied what they saw with their own eyes in the heavens and on the Earth and within their own bodies, rather than disagree with the ancient doctors' books. No, I am not against learning, but your generation is. And until you have become ready to receive, you have viciously fought against truth and learning, again and again.

Then why did the church condemn learning as evil?

Usurpers within that church condemned that which they in ignorance disbelieved personally, or which threatened their grip of power. They especially withheld learning of what was in the Books of my Chosen and my Apostles for you, as it testified against their unrighteous rule.

No truth you have reached the capacity to discover and learn on your own, which you are therefore ready to know, is evil. Learning is not evil. I am a God of revelation and prophecy. These are tools of learning. I am a teacher. Yet the children are slow to learn. And often the children in conviction have taught absurdities for nature, and gross falsehoods for science. You know this.

You are all learners in this generation. Those who have learned more than others well should teach what they have discovered is true. But the children are petty, and jealous, and greedy. They desire praise for discovery when they have not discovered, and for thousands of years they have sought praise for mistaken ideas proposed as fact. In blind bondage of ignorance generation after generation followed, without progress, because they trusted. Trust is a great responsibility. This you are also here to learn. Until you speak pure truth and only pure truth, how can you be given ultimate trust in all things? Truth makes you free, but falsehood encumbers. The power of falsehood was used in vanity by many in days of old to hold men in fear; it is used even now.

You do not behave well towards each other. Sadly, it is the nature of the children to take the toys from their brothers and sisters, and grab the food from the hands of those near them and to have it all for themselves; to threaten the weak and needy into submission, even rise up in the power of their flesh against their siblings, and beat them into submission, or disdainfully shame them into thinking they are inferior until they can selfishly be ruled over. As learning is power, men who design to maintain power over their siblings often destroy learning, and called it Heresy. In this practice you have not seen me, but the arm of their flesh. Such who maintain power by unrighteous dominion were never my servants, neither then, nor are they now.

That church was not yours?

Not all who have spoken in my name are of me. By their fruits all are known for what they are. Evil men usurped rule over the children, and much evil they did. Those who follow today admit those evils, and admit those evil men.

How did it happen? How did they take over?

There was an apostasy.

A what?

An apostasy. A falling away from the truth. You as an archaeologist know well the river of ancient manuscripts which now flows forth out of the Earth in your generation, restoring to your hands that which was known and believed by your forefathers even at the beginning. The Books of my Chosen prophesied of the falling; the Books of my Apostles prophesied of the falling. You know them. Read them. See. Believe what you see. The apostasy overwhelmed the world only a few generations after John, as wolves entered the fold. You can see it, and follow it in the books of the Patrologia Graeca, and trace the falling from the original word, ever more replaced by philosophers, the Neoplatonists and others, all those who wished to walk among men in their own glory. These preferred their own philosophies, and so they mingled them with scripture and retold all in new and unrecognizable ways. I was the first victim of their takeover, and I watched as they used their free will to erase who I AM and substitute in my stead their false god of logic, of logos, which rendered me uncreate, a blur of confusion, and then redefined all else. When the design of such men is to usurp power over even God, what hope of pity do you think the children can expect?

None.

And none they got, for a long time. Well it is called the Dark Ages.

Do you approve of what we are doing in science today?

The use of learning and technology is today as it has always been: a double-edged sword. The children of the sciences well know this. They give you drugs to ease your pain, and these are corrupted and used by a few for power and riches while they inflict untold misery on the many; the children of science have given you unspeakable powers to harness energy to power your visions, and these are used to threaten your neighbors until you all sit threatened with annihilation. Too often the children of science have labored in great love and passion unto the discovering of wondrous truths for you, only to see their brain children perverted and turned to destruction and terror and death.

Yet much technology is utilized for good in saving lives, in growing crops, in bringing music and visual art to billions and billions of children, in manufacturing useful products and machines and equipment, in gathering information and organizing it and making it instantly available in systematically categorized listings for your learning to take place.

Yet you have excelled so much in your technological powers, you neglect the gifts which are within you, and you begin to disuse your bodies, you exercise too little and do not feel well because of it, and you fail to nurture within yourselves the powers and gifts of the Spirit which are yours as the children to also discover, develop and have. You have faith in electronics and silicon, yet many have lost view of the power of faith you must learn in spiritual matters.

As you worship what technologies do for you, and praise yourselves for your cleverness in inventing them, also see now that you live in perpetual fear, fear of your technologies. This fear grows by what your governments and commercial powers are doing to you, and by the apocalyptic prophecy of these terrors in your cinematic film stories which dramatize them to you.

Have you seen the movies Terminator and Terminator 2, which portray total nuclear holocaust caused by a world takeover of computers and robots designed for war, made only to kill?

Yes, I typed, somewhat startled to think of movies.

Did its fear touch fears already within you?

Yes, I typed slowly, as its visions raced within my mind.

Did you doubt this could happen, if technology reaches this capacity?

No, I typed more slowly, each letter hard and heavy.

Did you see the movie Outbreak, which portrays a deadly new virus, the deadliest of epidemics, ready to leak out and wipe human life off the planet, which almost happens because military men want it as their weapon, and sociopathic leaders care only to keep their power and cover their guilt?

Yes, I typed soberly.

Did you even for a moment disbelieve that this could happen?

No, I typed again ponderously.

Why do you not laugh at both of these films as ridiculous fantasies, and the others like them? Why do you not disbelieve such terrifying stories?

I thought for only an instant, for I knew the answer. I had thought it at the same time I had seen the movies. I typed

People.

More specifically.

Trust. I don't trust the people with those powers. I don't trust the people in charge not to do things, not to do things just like that.

326

Do you worry?

Do I worry?
I thought about the worries I have gulped deep inside me since I was a child. We had made awesome, terrible things in my generation. We had unleashed frightening powers. I had seen the devastation of just a few bombs. I had seen radiation sickness. I had seen jet-carried machine guns pepper in square inches areas the size of a football field in a second, and then another field, and another as they flew by. I had seen napalm. I had seen gas. I had seen the fruits of commercial chemistry poisoning the soil and water from both ends: from the factories, and in my own consumer use in my home. Do I worry, I asked myself? I lived in fear of nuclear holocaust; fear of nuclear fallout; fear of armed invasion; fear of genocide; fear of armed revolution overthrowing my government; fear of totalitarian regime control like the Nazis and the kind in George Orwell's 1984; fear of terrorists blowing up airplanes and buildings, and poisoning water reservoirs; fear of intercontinental germ warfare; fear of microscopic biological lab experiments getting out of their petri dishes and labs and spreading into the air, or in the water; fear of chemical and germ experiments being covertly conducted by the military over civilian towns; fear of things being done by the sciences of the military, secretly carried out and calmly denied, evaded with stone-faced disinformation; fear of accidental nuclear warhead missile launchings; fear of toxic contaminants from cheaply fashioned waste dumps infiltrating the water tables and slowly poisoning me and my wife and children and country; fear of companies which want to make money so badly that they quietly sell defective and harmful things; and fear of their chief executive officers will sit before congress, video cameras and an entire nation and, to keep their profits, tell lies. How many truths that can hurt us are known by these in power, I wondered, yet as we sit helpless, they tell us lies so we may continue to be used as fodder for their bank accounts and slaves to their powers?
Do I worry?

Yes, I typed.

I do too.

You're right. We don't know how to treat each other.

That is what you are here to learn, how to treat each other well, while you have great power, but not yet the greatest powers. There are greater powers, and any who will be co-inheritors of those powers as my Sons and Daughters must be tested to see if they will first be obedient to all things. Where power is great, power to commit error is also great. The consequence of error with the greatest powers is catastrophic beyond your weak comprehension. The consequence of disobedience and a taste for evil in one possessed of the greatest powers is forbidden, and so it will not be given except to those who obtain. You see how poorly you control yourselves with the powers you have, and you cannot imagine the powers you may inherit if you endure unto the end in faithfulness. These can be given only to those who can obey all the laws of righteousness and wisdom. This is the need of your probation.

Look at what you do with what you have. When will you direct your genius to uplifting your siblings, and to that only? Every year you waste half of the substance of your planet on building machines of war and death, and in drugging yourselves. You waste more of your money on preparation for war and wars than you spend on food. You waste almost as much on intoxicants and cancer-laden depressants and unneeded stimulants, to which you have now heaped up your cocaines and its derivatives, heroine and its derivatives, and your myriad other drugs. More than half the annual fruit of your planet is wasted on the working of death and drugging yourselves, while tens of millions go homeless and starve. What has become of the civil in your breed of civilization? You prey upon each other in crime, in greater and greater numbers, and now you must ask yourselves why, in the generation which has reached the greatest capacity of technology and learning of science, why can you no longer teach your children how to read and cypher, much less how to treat each other civilly? First see that you spend more of your money on keeping your sociopaths behind bars in cages than you do on your children in their schools. Then see that you teach the glory of knowledge, and not its rightful use. Look to see: how much time do you spend teaching your children the tools and skills of socialization, so they may become socially good, instead of sociopathic? In your social studies you no longer teach social skills, nor civility in civilization, but only how generations and empires and nations have built the most impressively, where they have reached for the most money to buy the most possessions and toys and technology. And this you teach to each other: how to win through intimidation; then how to be sharks among sharks, then how to survive among sharks in feeding frenzies, then, how to get even more by being cold and mean. You believe it is most profitable to be mean: mean in love, mean in business, mean in globality. You love money more than the future of your children, the future of your race, and the future of your planet. Behold what you are doing, and see. And where has your love of money and cleverness and power led you? Behold your fears.

It is not money that is evil, but the love of money that rots and destroys. So it is not technology which is evil, but the worship of technology which puffs you up in the pride of your power, and blinds you to the need of your siblings.

For thousands of years, the children counted themselves lucky to earn a good living.

Listen to the words. Earn a good living.

Now, in virtually every business and individual heart, everyone wants to make a killing. Few any more in your modern technological cultures are content to just earn a good living.

Yet you do not hear the echos of your own words. Hear them now. They have very different sounds, and in them are many different visions.

Make. Killing.

Earn. Good. Living.

How many are killed to make your killings?

How many are lifted and live as you gratefully work to earn your living?

Today, behold a generation drowning in the mire of its own love of both money and technology. The wise child sees abundance and capability, and understands its usefulness in helping all brothers and sisters earn a living, and devotes all efforts to raising up those who struggle, that the whole might be benefited to the ultimate well being of even one, even themselves.

And why must this become your goal? Because you reach the time now that you know an ultimate Truth.

There is no more anyplace for you to hide.

Your recent generations have thrown away the law of chastity, for they heard the whisper - 'there is no God, nor any God-given law of morality to break' - and now your planet groans under the burden of a generation raised without fathers, without morality to govern its choices as it preys upon its siblings. As you have abandoned me and the simple laws I gave you to serve for your good and protection, you have abandoned the fruit of your safest haven, your families. The epidemic you have unleashed rages around you.

Only too late do you learn that freedom is the consequence of obedience to good principles which increase and expand your range of choices, not the indulgence of every whim and selfish desire. Bondage is the consequence of all things which by their unconsciousness cause walls to be erected, and take away your freedom to choose.

Every generation learns this, yet with your technologies of today, even as you can enhance and magnify every good thing, so you have the power to enhance and magnify every thing of evil. And this you do.

I have thought about the problem for a long time.

With knowledge comes great responsibility.

Now I understand, I typed again soberly.

Are you ready, as a generation, for all the knowledge you already have?

I thought about my real fears arising from all of these things.

I don't know, I wrote.

You now stand on an even greater threshold. Are you ready, as a generation, for the knowledge you are about to give to yourselves?

I thought of everything I was hearing in the news: bio-engineering, cloning, new life forms made in laboratories, new diseases. Where are we going? How was excitement of discovery and capability balanced by prudence and wisdom? Was wisdom even involved, or just money and control? How many asked the question which had so shocked me in Jurassic Park: 'they saw that they could do it; but did they ever ask if they *should* do it?' Chaos theory did have its place in all of this, and perhaps we weren't listening well enough to what we were telling ourselves. The old left-hand-doesn't-know-what-the-right-hand-is-doing thing could be taken too far, disastrously. We were moving forward so fast, a lot of under-planning was going on. Or was there any planning at all? I thought of the cybersciences, world wide data links on the web, terrorists and other crackpots having access to it all from a single little room anywhere, from any keyboard and screen. We were creating systems which didn't just deliver data; they took commands. I thought of the race for Artificial Intelligence; bio-engineering control of human embryos; the power held within a lab engineered, incurable viroid super-pathogen; and I thought of the greed driving so many of the powers, the obsessions driving the people with the powers, the megalomania minds who thought of everyone else as 'them,' and all things in terms of power, control, weapons, and wealth. Were we ready as a generation to use these upcoming powers wisely?

I don't know, I again wrote. *I really don't know.*

The screen remained blank now. There were no further responses. We had finished this question. It was my turn to ask. I looked over again at the paper list, and saw my next question.

I know I am not a prophet. What is a prophet?

A short download instantly came.

A child, just like you.

How could a prophet be just like me? I'm nothing, a nobody.

Remember I already told you, nobody is a nobody. You are my child. A prophet, or prophetess, is a simple child, just like you. As any other living child, their bodies get dirty and they must bathe; they get sick, and cough and have runny noses; they must eat, and must pass that which they have eaten. They get cold, and need clothing and heat, or they will die, just like you. Were Abraham or Moses or Isaiah to walk down a street today wearing a suit and tie, or Miriam or Hulda to walk down a street in a dress or any other outfit, how many would discern them, eating and drinking and perspiring and needing to shave and clean themselves as any other child? Usually they are not learned children, but simple, and humble, and of great faith.

But they have to speak so powerfully, and convince everybody.

They speak by the power of the Holy Ghost, and they have to convince no one. The children must listen, have an ear to hear, and hear. In discussions among the children, as they think and express their beliefs, convincing statements and definitions of things seldom are decided as true or false from the actual nature of things or the real truth, but usually according to the skill and cleverness of the child who speaks most forcefully, eloquently, or cleverly. Evidence is subject to handling, and it is handled and controlled, with cunning. The convincing of minds by sophistry and cleverness does not make truth, though listener and even speaker may eventually become convinced. This is how children impress children, and win debates. Prophets are not called to debate, but only to witness to others what they have seen and heard, which the others have not seen and heard. This they do, in simple language. The children must listen, and hear. A prophet is only a prophet when acting as a prophet. They have normal lives, have their own opinions, just as anyone else, and they have their weaknesses. But when a prophet acts as a prophet, only what was seen and heard is witnessed. For this, prophets need no training in speech or skill in controversy and argument, only honesty.

How then is a prophet different from me?

They need to keep themselves pure to receive the power of the Spirit of God, so that the divine inspiration can express itself through them, resonating as the harmonic string of one instrument softly vibrates in the presence of another. For this they must be in tune. Thus the most simple of children are often the best witnesses. Few are chosen. The human ego overpowers most others.

They are the only children who have ever seen the truth of things and told it to others without making any timid concessions to public opinion, without seeking to make an impression on people, and without concern for what people think of them. Being filled with the Holy Ghost, they simply report those things which they have seen and heard. As a witness, a prophet is not a reformer. They do not build up a case by formal argument, but simply report the truth as reliable witnesses, without any disputation at all. They bring the good news that as the children repent and come unto me, they may receive grace for grace.

It sounds like a very desirable job.

You would not want to be a prophet.

I don't understand. Why?

The reward of a prophet is rejection and buffeting.

Is that because they always bring messages telling people they need to improve themselves?

Criticism of the world has never been refused by the children, and in fact, they thrive on it. Look, and see. Satirists, comics, philosophers, scholars, all manner of outspoken opponents have always had free play upon prevailing morals and manners, criticizing the corruption of the times, of kings, of empires and presidents, and they have always debunked the weaknesses and follies of their own politics and religions without censure. You see clearly also that over many centuries, preachers of religion have drawn enthusiastic listening crowds with fiery sermons denouncing the manners and children of their times, rebuking a disobedient world and evoking lurid pictures of the wrath to come. These are received and well paid. Campaigns are not led against such rabid preachers of hell-fire. In your generation they get television shows, and people send money.

Yet prophets enrage. Why has this been? Simply, because the prophets performed tangible miracles such as could not be denied, and they reported what they had seen and heard, and told the truth: that it was from God. As witnesses endowed with power from on high they earn the hatred of the world. The world has always rejected the prophets. Men read the words of a dead prophet and apply his charges to a dead generation, piously shaking their heads and repeating, "if we had been living in the days of our fathers, we would not have joined with them in the blood of the prophets." Yet the world only loves prophets that are dead. A dead prophet the world dearly desires and warmly cherishes; he is a priceless tradition, a spiritual heritage, a beautiful memory. But woe to a living prophet. He shall be greeted with stones and catcalls even by pious people. In reverence and devotion do men adorn the tombs of the prophets whom they would kill if they were alive. Yet there are many who wish the honor of a prophet, and declare themselves though they have no calling.

I know. The Books of the Apostles contain words of prophesy that in the last days there would be many false prophets.

As the prophets witnessed that there would be a falling away, so also they witnessed that there would be a refreshing, a restoration of all things.

Yet because the children have never wanted to believe in a living prophet, is it any wonder that having heard there will be many false prophets, they have ever since chosen to believe there will be no true prophets? The lazy and the indolent prefer to hide in the belief that all are false, for such spares them the effort of seeking and discerning anything for themselves, and believing.

How would I recognize a true prophet?

They speak as with a single mouth and a single tongue. By this fact, that they all agree, though they have spoken at widely separated times and places, you may know of their divine authority. They do not study and build up a doctrine, but receive revelations and speak them forth as they are received, with no doubts or misgivings about what they pronounce, for they know of its source. The spirit of prophecy is the testimony of Emmanuel, and true prophets teach that all children must become obedient, and repent, and that repentance is proportioned to all by the atoning sacrifice of the One who would be chosen for that burden. They teach that the gifts of the spirit and personal inspiration are the inheritance of all believers, each receiving unto the stewardship they have, each being given that which pertains to their calling. It is my economy that only a prophet to the generation is called to be mouthpiece and receives revelation for that entire generation. What these prophets pronounce when moved by the Holy Spirit may be had as scripture, and it is not of private interpretation; from their words you may discern one doctrine and one teaching, in all harmony.

The screen remained blank. I could think of no more questions on that topic, and feeling satisfied for the needs of my inquiries, I looked at the paper for my next question. It was complicated, yet I felt very comfortable asking it of God.

Please God, be patient with me as I write out this next question. It's sort of long.

I have always accepted the Bible as a Holy collection of many sacred ancient Scrolls and Books. I believe that each one of them, the many Scrolls and Books - and I can't remember how many they are but there are a lot of them - were written by your prophets and Apostles. All the years I've been an archaeologist I've seen the thousands of historical proofs confirming the historicity of these many individual Books, which continually affirms them to me.

I know that they have been validated in chronological accuracy all the way back to almost 900 B.C., much farther back than any other history recorded by any other ancient nation. This is highly significant to me as a historian, and I cannot affirm it enough.

Yet I know these Books are not 'inerrant' as some try to claim for them. They contain inter-contradictory statements. While I have seen some badly contrived examples of supposed contradictions by those whose zeal to show errors refuses to admit the obvious, so I have also seen some errors and contradictions. I know that we have almost 5,000 old and older texts, and fragments of texts, and each time a new text is found, there are variations of word orders, and words, and phrases added, and phrases missing, in all nearly 200,000 minor variations and lapses of this kind. It is not 'one text,' without scribal and copiest problems. They are old books, copied by hand.

I can't accept the contrived explanations of those who try to explain these errors away, or say they are not there. They are there; anyone can read them. But this doesn't bother me. The scroll's total substance has been sufficiently proven historically accurate back so far, that I'm comfortable with errors of scribes and can comprehend rubrics and ammendings over generations. I am an archaeologist, and that anything so perishable as a scroll or papyrus book has survived this long is a marvel to me; I do not feel that a collection of writings has to be either complete or 'inerrant' for me to accept you are God, and that I can learn a lot from what is preserved in these books.

I also know that the collection of Books we have and call the Bible is far from complete, because I can read the names of many Books mentioned in the individual Books it gathers as the group, and I believe in all those other Books it mentions. I have heard some limp explanations of how all of those other Books mentioned are supposedly all there under different names, but the record is so clear everywhere else, I cannot doubt it is also clear in this, and so I believe in all of the other missing Books it mentions. I also can deduce that in many places, the historical and biographical things mentioned summarized must have come from earlier Scrolls and Books, what the scholars call the Original Texts of some of the very old things, and I believe in those Books too. So I know the collection of Books gathered into the Bible is not complete. But again, as an archaeologist I'm an optimist, and I'm glad to have the parts we have.

I also know the Books never were used anciently as a single Book; Temple libraries and synagogue libraries, and libraries in the early Church after Christ were bundles of lots of scrolls and papyrus books. I know that by the time a collection of them was gathered and translated into Greek by the Rabbis in Alexandria for the Septuagint, even before Christ, there were a lot of other Scrolls being used in the Synagogues and possibly even the Temple. And when the council of Rabbis at Jamnia a few decades after the destruction of Second Temple made their final collection grouping, there were still many more Scrolls and Books in use by many good, practicing Jews in Israel, but not all were canonized into the grouping. I suspect that the recent problems with the Rabbi called Yeshua and his followers, and the destruction of the Temple and its political reverberations among the

Priesthood, may have influenced choices. And a few centuries later I know that that group of Books, now under one cover as the Hebrew Bible, was translated into Latin by Jerome for the Pope in Rome and put together with a selection of Books about Yeshua, called Christ, which together became the ancient Vulgate, the Old and New Testament Bible. I know the choice and selection of Books put into that New Testament, which are some of the Christian writings, was put together almost four centuries after Christ, fully two generations after Emperor Constantine's Nicean Council, which was a major political vortex and radically shifted the original doctrine of the Church and Fathers to a very strong mix of philosophical Greek mysticism, all of which may have had its influence on what was left out and what was chosen and canonized as a New Testament. I know that there were many, many sacred and Holy Books which the earliest Christians studied and used as scripture, often quoted by the early Fathers, which were neglected and omitted. I again suspect the possibility of late philosophical differences and political inclinations behind these omissions, particularly knowing as I do that some of the most popular and heavily quoted Books of the early Christians and Fathers were deleted from the group finally canonized.

I guess what I'm trying to ask is: how many of the Scrolls and Books collected together in the Bible - and I'm talking about both the Old Testament and the New Testament - contain accurate, or pretty accurate things; and what of all these other Scrolls and Books? Why are there so many Scrolls and Gospels and writings which were sacred to the Jews before Herod's time, and sacred to the early Christians in the Primitive Church, which are not part of the Bible?

Sorry this has been such a poorly worded, rambling question. I didn't want to insult you in any way.

That's OK. To notice the errors of my Children is not to insult me.

Very simply, most of the Books in the collection of Books you have together called Bible are remarkably well maintained. This is part of why the lineage of my Chosen was chosen. They have been the best record keepers, and this calling they have zealously kept in faith and tradition. I am glad that you see the scrolls as the individual Books which they are, that each is. It is error to see them as one Book, and it is error to think this is all of my Word.

No, this is not all of my Word, and No, as the Books have come down to you, these Books are not perfect. My Word is perfect, and I AM perfect, and so I might ask who it is who declares that I cannot be God if a collection of Scrolls and Books contains some error? My Word is inerrant, yet those who have recorded it and copied it are not; the books are not. I AM.

These are the errors of men. Know that the false doctrine of inerrancy of the 'Word' came after the children had stoned the prophets and sealed the heavens from their side, and falsely called all of what was in the Books 'the word of God;' and all of what remained of the old Books 'all of The Word.' My Words are contained within the Books, yes, but also the many words of many children. Better it was to call them The Prophets and The Law, for in this is more understanding. Prophets are children, and much history of the children, and many words of the affairs of children are contained therein. Even when they have seen visions, prophets retell them in their own words, and they have weaknesses. When I myself speak, you know it: Thus saith the Lord.

My Word is living, and only that which I speak in declaration to my children is the Word of God. It remains pure only as long as the children respect me. Behold many generations which had no respect, even for God. When the children told each other that I would speak no more, then they enshrined books written in my name. When error was found in them, other children who wished not to believe used the error to convince there is no God, even by smooth speech and sophistry. Then did the fearful invent inerrancy, for in their little faith, they feared that if they admitted the truth of men's weakness, they might falter.

It is the weakest faith which fears that Faith of the Faithful will be undermined by admitting that there is error in the works of men; and it is the weakest of faith which fears that belief in that which is true will be undermined by admitting truth: that men err. That there have been errors in keeping the record does not diminish any truth therein they hold. I AM THAT I AM, and the works of the Spirit are as they are, and those who would dismiss a miracle for the error of a verb or a grammatical wording or a phrase or a slightly different retelling would do so even if one should come back from the dead to testify to them. They have no desire to know, nor desire to believe, but only desire to disbelieve, and so they think to prove foolishness by exposing that which even a child can see. The records are kept for the faithful, not the stiff-necked. Those who are ashamed of their weak faith, who fear they will falter if a single error in a book is admitted, place their faith in paper and pages rather than in a Living God. I AM a Living God, and my works and prophecies shall go forth in spite of the errors in the records, and in spite of the faithlessness of the children.

My Word is living, and it is the responsibility of each soul to know in it that which is true, even all things of the Spirit which are recorded.

How did this false teaching of 'inerrancy' begin?

It was vanity in those who in their little faith, and fear, who after telling their brothers and sisters that I would speak no more, suddenly felt fear that they had denied me, and in fear thought to flatter me and appease me by enshrining even histories and chronologies and many things as having come only from my mouth. And yet in it they showed their lack of faith. They feared the criticism of others who believed in nothing, who condemned their God as a God of errors because of the errors in the Books, who ridiculed a God who was not able to keep his Books from the errors of scribes. Yet these in their arrogance and ignorance denied not only me but denied the Free Agency of my children, and vainly sought to show fault in me through error in scribes.

As the Children of Faith knew they could not credit error to me, so they also feared to simply acknowledge error in their brethren. Yet as you are not perfect, ask which of your brothers and sisters is perfect? Let any one among you who is perfect be the first to claim that all those who laboriously copy by hand, by candle and oil lamp light shall make no error.

And vanity is strong. When new histories are written, often the older books are seen as old; the old is often disrespected for it is old. Each generation delights to see the old as inferior, and in this manner many old histories and scrolls filled with precious and original accounts were thrown away, only because they were old, and did the children not have now the new? And so many ancient and precious writings were lost to sorrowful neglect and vanity. Many of these were without corruption, and in plain and simple words told truth.

Yet this is not all: the children who copy and compile have not always been of one mind. The philosophies of men have found following, and diverse teachings have pleased the vanity and shame of men. Many have had power over a multitude of Scrolls, who could not resist to indulge their pining to add words as they wished, or detract words they despised and hated, according to their own private belief. I ask: why else would my prophet have written in Deuteronomy that "You shall not add unto the word which I command you, neither shall ye diminish ought from it," and my Apostle John written in his first Book, "I testify unto every man that heareth the words of this book, If any man shall add unto these things, God shall add unto him the plagues that are written in this book; And if any man shall take away from the words of the book of this prophecy, God shall take away his part out of the book of life." Who will forbid that Moses and all other prophets should write after Deuteronomy? Moses spoke only of his one Book. Who will afterward forbid John to write his Gospel, yet indeed he wrote it thirty years after his book of prophecy. He spoke only of adding or detracting to or from his first Book, even his Book of prophecy, Revelations. Each Book was a Scroll, and these warnings spoke only of each book's own contents. From early times through later times, the scrolls were subject to such tampering, and the prophets and Apostles knew this, and by these admonitions, you also know this.

Yes, there are many errors and omissions in the Books which remained and were chosen in the Old Testament, and of the New Testament. Yet these have many true histories within them, as you know from the evidences coming forth from the earth; and many true accounts, and stories useful to your instruction and learning of the workings of the Spirit, and of the follies of foolish choice, and of the laws of righteousness, and of the workings of your God among the children, and of the nature of prophets and prophecy, and of the nature of the children, and of the need for obedience, and of the need for repentance, and of the need of an Anointed One, and an Infinite Atonement, even of Emmanuel. You are Intelligence, and you can receive them even as they are; much of the Truth you need and want is readily before you still. I do not fear the criticisms of men, nor the errors of books. I AM THAT I AM. Fear not to insult me in seeing what is true. I am a God of Truth. Fear not to see error in your brothers and sisters. Fear not to forgive the errors, and them.

I forgive them. Cannot you?

Yes, I can, I typed.

Yet the Books of my Chosen and my Apostles as you have them gathered are only Part, as they were eventually gathered together from amid many more books.

Now you are finding a host of other ancient scripts which were cherished and worn with reading by the ancients of my Chosen, and by the First Generations of my Apostles and their followers, the Fathers who inherited their words. These Scrolls and Books are often found among other, and later works, filled with many contrary teachings, teachings contrary to all you find written correctly in the Scrolls and Books and Letters that were gathered and kept.

There are many books written by jealous and vain children who wished more to see their thoughts in writing and held as scripture than to know and teach truth; and they wrote many confused things. And there arose many who despised their flesh, and saw their bodies as contemptible, and though all I have caused to be written testifies of my joy in this earth and its beasts and fowls and fishes and herbs and gardens and you, and that I myself created the bodies of man and woman and said 'It is good,' still there have been those who have hated that which is good which I made and gave unto you as a gift, and such have devised fantasies written to support their anger against the body, and to deny the rising of the body in incorruption, even in the Resurrection.

Yet as they are branches from an original vine, search for the root of the vine within these books, and many treasures of knowledge you shall find. The vain who wrote to see their words as books mingled original truths among their writings to assure their palatability among their peers. And even those who fell away took with them many original parts they cherished, and though they built strange and false teachings upon them, still the fragments remain true, for they are from the true root of the vine. Thus these are of some value to you, above the fascination and study of their antiquity and strangeness. Among that which is contrary are remnants of that which is true; the contrary is often wrapped around the root of the true, which it tries to alter by philosophy unto the convincing of others that it says something different than it says. Many parts of the root lost from other books can still be found at the core of these.

So search the early writings, and the best writings, search them closely with the Spirit, for in them are remnants of many treasures of knowledge for you to find and learn. These things have been hidden from the children, and they are brought forth now in your time for you, and even these testify of me. The child who has shall receive even more; the child who has refused to receive shall have even that taken away. Always remember: that which follows in harmony with my Word as you already know it securely in purity, you may receive in faith as it testifies of me and my ordering of the universe.

If you could receive more of my Word, would you receive it?

Know that I have called many prophets whose names you know, but whose words you have never seen. Elijah of old and John the Baptist are only two. These were great prophets; John, one of the greatest ever born to woman. Where are their words? Many are the prophets' words which you do not have.

Know that I have called many prophets you do not know, whose writings did not survive even unto the end of First Temple, and who in that day of conflagration prophesied but were never recorded at all. These things are clear to all who read the Book of Exodus and know of the sojourn in Egypt after the days of the Patriarchs, and the Books of Kings and the Books of Chronicles, wherein many struggles and losses may be comprehended. By the time of Josiah, much was lost; and in the days of judgment under the hands of the Babylonians, only that which was saved was saved; it was not all.

These things you know. Believe what you know.

Know that of prophets familiar to you and prophets unfamiliar to you, and of Patriarchs, and of Apostles, many Scrolls and Books were written. Some became neglected as the beliefs of the children embraced false ideas; some were corrupted by scribes with diverse beliefs, who altered their teachings with biased redactions; all were set aside in sundry times by those who saw what they were and who wanted them not at all.

Among the many Books that were not wanted at all were those which contained the knowledges of the Earth, stars, and multitudes of worlds, for these did not confirm the system of astronomy of the children Aristotle, Hipparchus and Claudius Ptolemy, which became fully embraced by the time of the Fourth Century theologians, in what remained of the church. Their desire to weed out all scripture which disagreed with their new theological system of belief cunningly anticipated recourse to the Books for answers to natural questions; and so all evidence was omitted which would challenge their system, and only that which agreed with their false system of theology was allowed. The Books permitted to become part of the canon, the collection of Books which became the New Testament, were therefore theologically screened, and in so doing this, they devised a collection of Books which was bereft of many truths, including the truths which would have rejoiced at the coming of the children Copernicus, Bruno, Galileo and Kepler. And so the cunningly gathered Book was used as a weapon to suppress truth and murder the brightest children in my name.

Yet condemn not the Scrolls and Books of the Prophets and Apostles whose writings were retained, but see the evil of children who falsely use my name for their own maintenance of authority, and their system of vanity.

Know also that many writings were of very sacred things, and as wolves entered the fold and ravaged the faithful, and the faithful became caught up in eloquent speeches and fine words and prided themselves in the convincing of men and sought flattery for their learned ramblings, even then did I command that many Books and Scrolls be hidden up, for the children were no longer able to receive such Holy things, even the words of my Son who spoke to the Twelve after his resurrection, during forty days before his Ascension.

Those who believe not in my Son and who believe not in his Resurrection nor his Ascension believe not in such things, yet all those who accept Him and in truth declare His name know He taught many great things to the Apostles, for is it not so written in the Books and Letters they have and hold dear? How then shall they doubt there are other books?

Yes, many of these Books have become corrupt; yet study the best of them well, for they too testify of me. And still there is an almost perfect book.

Know that I have had prophets in all lands, among all peoples, in given times of old. What the people could receive and bear, was given. Not all children could receive and bear as much as the next; still, in the beginning, as much as was given was given the same, and it was given clearly.

Yet you may see that their words have become shrouded in many retellings; even so, you may pierce the veil and find within them the threads of truth once given. See what you know within them, and know that these, too, testify of me.

Know that I have commanded all children, in the east and in the west, and also those in the north and in the south, and in the islands of the seas, to write what words I have spoken to them. All who believe I AM their God will not tire of my Word nor become weary of my speaking; they will rejoice in all of my word as they can find it. And unto the ends of the Earth may they seek, and in diverse and unfamiliar places shall my Word come forth and comfort them.

After the many Scrolls and Books gathered together of the Jews for the Old Testament and of the Apostles for the New Testament, what are some of the other Scrolls and Books I should study?

A brief download appeared.

Know that you must read all things with the Spirit, and search for that which is true within them. All of these as have been preserved over the generations, or hidden up until your time and now discovered anew, are here within your Text Data

Base, as you directed your brother Kevin to have them installed. And so your computer equipment here contains all of them, but these are not all. You have the long known Apocryphal Books which were included in the Bible collection; and the Apocrypha and Pseudepigrapha, both of the Jews, and of the Apostles and others; and the First-, Second-, Third- and Fourth- Century Father's writings, well known and preserved from generation to generation, the ante-Nicene Fathers and apologists: there is much to be learned therein of the things I have just told you. And you also have the many new discoveries from out of the dust and caves and sand: the Dead Sea Scrolls of my children the Jews, and the Nag Hammadi library of a sectarian Christianity; and still you also had installed into this memory the host of additional scrolls and books only recently found, previous hitherto never seen by any in your generation, nor for many generations, for they were hidden up since early days.

In this your brothers and sisters in archaeology have done well. They have found in these last generations many precious writings of old, treasured and revered by those much closer to the beginning than they, books the early children knew and read and studied and from which were taught great truths, which have now spoken from out of the dust, and speak now again, to your generation. They speak abundantly of angels, and visions of the creation organized out of matter yet unorganized, and many worlds that I have created, and of my children also on many worlds, your brothers and sisters. These ancient scripts verify your science today, and from them all may know these things were known long ago, for I revealed them unto those who were prepared. The discovered books of ancient understanding are legion and growing. In these you will find many things which were not permitted to remain with the children of their days, for they fell into unfaithfulness, and rejecting these, preferred to propose their own wisdom.

And so what was given and learned, was lost and unlearned. Search the teachings in the Scrolls and Books gathered into the Bible, and search also the early Fathers of the Word, and you will with astonishment see how many of these things you have had all along, but you have ignored them. Many parts of the true root are to be gleaned elsewhere. Though much in these was modified by redactions of the generations who had them, to fit the teachings of diverse beliefs, just as much was retold in the teachings upon the Books to fit the party lines of Orthodoxy among both my Chosen and the children of The Word, do not fear to search them, for even the apostate children began with great truth in purity, and it is not entirely disguised or lost. You are Intelligence, and as you seek, you shall find all threads; see them. You will marvel at what you find.

Surely above all things you will marvel at the things in them which sound as the words of your most learned theoretical physicists of today, speaking of the expanding universe, of the formation of galaxies and planets, of the hydrogen fusions and elementary exchanges moving within stars, of numbers of other worlds and knowledge of life throughout the cosmos.

You will ask how, knowing the ancient pages you read came from the dust and sand only in most recent time, knowing the genuinity of their antiquity, how such ancient peoples of no learning and without telescopes and knowledge of photons and mesons and quarks and gravitational collapse and light spectrum analysis could know of great heats and accretions of matter unorganized in the clouds of dust of the void, and worlds even your generation cannot see, though they have mathematically calculated much of them. How could such a simple people, of no learning, speak so clearly of things you have wrested from nature only in this time, at great effort? Surely, they testify of my prophets, and of me. Surely they testify that in all ages and times, I AM.

The screen again remained blank. My turn.

A question had come to me as I had been reading, for truly I did not understand how that which was sacred and holy and given by God could be garbled and modified and added to and deleted from. What power did man have to do such things? So I typed

Why have men had power to corrupt the truth?

Another download. It was several pages. I began to read.

The Free Agency of my children is the most inviolate gift I have given them. It is the key to greatest good and worst evil. It is the least understood gift of all my gifts. Because of it, men do good from which they grow, and they commit evils from which cause many to suffer, but by this, all who will, learn why evil is evil. Yet because of Free Agency, the children are free to rebel.

And they do.

You understand that the muscle unexercised never develops. So it is with choice. You are eternal. You are children of great future and potential. Agency is the freedom to choose, good or evil. Yet to exercise it, you must have knowledge of good and evil, and opportunity confronted with choices. So, you must have knowledge, good and evil must exist in your midst, and you must be taught; yet your most vital learning comes from experience. For this, you are here. During your life, you observe many reasons for choosing good.

But not all wish to discipline themselves to choose good. You see their consequences, heaped upon others, and fallen upon them. You experience their consequences of evil upon your self. You experience and see, this is 'bad.' And when you choose badly, you experience your own consequences.

By experiencing these consequences, many more children awaken who otherwise would not, and go on to become all which is within them to become.

Though the Truth has been given repeatedly at sundry times and places, the vanity of the children is rebellious, and many prefer to rebel, and usurp. This is so in matters of territory, in matters of possessions, in matters of money, and in matters of thought. It is your Free Agency to think as you will, to accept what you will, to believe as you will on all things. Yet not all will abide sound doctrine.

And that all might be just, even they must have their Agency.

Thus, though prophets have declared great truths of Spirit and Redemption and Creation, the teachings of rebellious men and their obsessed ideas have been taught and learned by most children for religion. Their posterity learned not the words I spoke, nor of the visions of true prophets who spoke of me. As men suppressed knowledge of me, and then suppressed knowledge of nature as it had been revealed, all that remained was what they saw around them; and this, most of them misunderstood, almost entirely.

As it is not given to but a few to have visions, most must exercise Faith and walk by Faith. In this there is great purpose. As the children could not observe nor measure me, many became apostate and preferred the smooth words of eloquent philosophers, and followed diverse definitions of a god. They would not believe what they could not observe, and they believed not what I showed my prophets. They preferred to believe what they thought they saw.

So also they threw away visions of the cosmos, of myriad worlds and suns, of the organization of matter and of their own bodies. They could not bear the thought of siblings on other worlds; they could not see the particles of dust of which they heard they were made. And so they made up their own explanations of nature. They scoffed at what was revealed, declared it nonsense and discarded it, preferring what they thought they saw in the earth and sky. They believed what they contrived themselves to explain nature as they imagined it to be in their great ignorance and vanity.

There is great vanity under your sun.

Vanity is strong. Even when wise children unveiled these truths for themselves as sciences, yet their siblings would give them no peace, nor believe them. And this was not always condemnable, for not being prophets, their sight was only partial, and they proposed truths beside fantasies, and truths wrapped in fanciful imaginings. So the child Anaximander the Greek comprehended the myriad worlds, yet he falsely taught that the earth was the center of the universe. His truth of many worlds was rejected, because it offended vanity; his error of geocentricity was tenaciously embraced because it had always pleased vanity. When the Greek child Aristarchus shortly after affirmed the sun as a star, and stars as suns, and the earth's orbit around your sun, the children rejected his truth, preferring their vanity. They saw the displacement of the earth from the center of the universe as a demotion, as if the place where a child lives affects its preciousness. They chose instead Aristotle, who scientifically affirmed to them their geocentric universe. In many things the child Aristotle saw clearly, but in many, many things he was wrong.

He was allowed to be wrong by the law of Free Agency, and by Free Agency the children were free to choose his false scientific proposal over Aristarchus' truth. The children have the gift to follow what choices they choose. In their choices the children have repeatedly chosen their vanity and ego, not truth.

The child Hipparchus scientifically built upon this vanity, and the child Claudius Ptolemy finally canonized the geocentric universe with additional false scientific embellishment, which a new generation of philosopher theologians with an apostate theology chose and embraced for their church. Just as the children rejected the prophets, they rejected physical witnesses. Ultimately, the children prefer to see what they think they see, and tell themselves what they want to see, even when it is in opposition to all that is visible and to be seen. So it is that they enshrined Aristotle, Hipparchus and Ptolemy, for these told them what they wanted to hear, and then died.

And the dead scientists who were wrong were cherished, for the glorious ghosts of honored men's beliefs sway men far more than the things which can be seen, or measured. Thus these become indisputable, even by evidences.

So it was that even in Persia and other lands which paid no allegiance to that church or faith, the universe and heavens of Ptolemy were also held inviolate, and believed, and unchallenged even by what was seen.

As it was for the children who studied the heavens, so it was for the children who studied the body. Though animals had long been cut open in preparation for food, and the bodies of men had been savagely opened by beasts and accident, and slashed wide in vicious war, thus exposing the inner view of the organs to the eye, still fantasy and imagination prevailed over that which was observed. From the child Empedocles to Polybus to Plato to Aristotle, biased observation and absurd explanation danced their staggered dance ungainfully through recognition of truth and proposition of folly. Yet these were honored men, and thus their error was enshrined with truth. Though shortly after these, the brilliant children Herophilus and Erasistratus learned greater truth and tried to correct old beliefs, not all would listen. And so also the serious Roman child Celsus, who intimately knew the human body and recognized much more clearly what he saw, was overshadowed by the systematic eloquence of the child Claudius Galen, who had personally seen little inside the human body. Though the child Galen was accurate and clear in many things, by Free Agency he chose to follow his own whims from among the other childrens' studied knowledge. And he heaped upon his errors of anatomy his even more mistaken theories of the body's functions, especially the workings of heart and lungs and intestines. He looked back centuries to the old concept of pneuma, wrongly proposed by Empedocles. But he liked it. Thus he wrote: it is so.

And so eloquent were the child Galen's writings, and so convincing his bodily explanations, that after him, physicians stopped all medical research for over a thousand years. For, they believed that Galen had discovered all there was to know of the human body, and therefore all believed that any further work or study would be futile. Even as little more than four hundred years ago, your siblings, the learned children of medicine in England, still denounced and persecuted any who might dare to say that Galen's writings contained any error.

Thus the physicians of the body enshrined the books Galen and declared·his gross anatomical errors and utterly fanciful physiological theories of the body's workings to be 'inerrant' for fifteen hundred years, even when dissection repeatedly evidenced the contrary in truth; even as did the astronomers from Persia to the British Isles and the apostate theologians grip the false geocentric universe of the child Ptolemy as 'inerrant' for almost fifteen hundred years.

Thus see: the children had false truth chosen for them, by blind leaders in each generation, until the days of Copernicus and Bruno and Galileo. And even since then, the children have been giving up their false universe begrudgingly.

The child Kepler understood. He wrote his astronomical observations of the heavens without caring if a century might pass before a reader would be found, for he realized that I had awaited thousands of years for a physical witness to this universe, to finally prevail among the children, and what was a little more time?

The child Kepler knew, that his sibling Copernicus had been threatened by unholy Inquisition to recant truth he knew to be true, and wisely published his final and best work only at the moment of his death. And Kepler knew that only shortly after him, the child Giordano Bruno had reaffirmed that millions of worlds indeed exist, with life upon them, but the child Bruno had been burned at the stake by men of mere human authority; Galileo had died miserably in prison.

Though it had anciently been science that had energetically championed the flattery of men's vanity, until the theologians had accepted them as true; now the children of science had finally seen the errors of their earlier siblings. Now the theologians in fiery rage and power declared the sciences of the children Aristotle and Ptolemy to be 'inerrant,' and disputed and condemned. Though their own Primitive Fathers had taught truths otherwise, these they ignored.

The child Kepler knew me, and knew the Fathers, and knew the Prophets. In his studies he had been held back by Phythagorists, not Prophets. And in his flash of wisdom, he envisioned a distant future of celestial ships navigating space, carrying explorers who feared not the vastness of the universe. Yet as the prophet Ezekiel, to whom I showed your day and who dared to record what he saw: flying jets with great wings and roaring turbine engines which people entered and exited and flew here and there as they willed, able to land and roll on heavy double-tire assemblies, the child Kepler's future vision was also disbelieved, though his vision was merely a science.

The child Kepler always saw me in everything he studied, and thought it not folly; for this he was blessed.

So too, the child Isaac Newton was also brilliant among the children; and as

Copernicus, Kepler, the child Leonardo da Vinci, and Einstein, the child Newton knew that the truth had been given by revelation in the beginning, but it had been corrupted and distorted, fragmented and retold. He searched diligently for its traces, surviving in enigmatic forms in diverse literatures, and understood his goal as the discovery of truth through a dialogue between hard, disciplined inquiry and those threads in the ancient writings. Yet this child who was able to invent a new mathematics in one night, the calculus of variations, was ignored in his own day almost as the prophets of old; virtually no one of his generation attended his lectures, few cared to hear his thoughts. As he measured the observable universe, he also measured the Temple in Jerusalem. As he studied nature and learned the laws of inertia and measured gravity, he studied the prophet Daniel, and searched John's Book of Revelations, and in prophecy he found connections with his scientific work.

Behold five of your most brilliant siblings, all of whom knew and understood that truth leads to truth, who found me in what they discovered.

The child Christiaan Huygens lived in Holland, a land choice for its tolerance of ideas, well exercised in Free Agency. Huygens comprehended all of these truths: a heliocentric solar system; stars are suns; that there are billions of planets; that there should be life everywhere in the universe. With him, in Holland, was another beginning.

Yet vanity is strong. The children are slow to face the shock of having believed another child's fallacies as truth. They prefer the blissful comfort of ignorance, so they may live out their years without letting go of their paradigms. Even when they let go, they let go slowly, and not wholly, nor with joy.

Shortly after Huygens, the child John Michell comprehended enough of the cosmos to understand gravitational singularities as black holes, even two hundreds years ago. But none of his colleagues believed, nor for many generations thereafter, for they could not observe it. They still did not want to know the truth. The truth of the child Michell was all but forgotten. Then at the dawn of your century the brilliant child Chandrasekhar again correctly understood gravitational attraction within massive bodies in the universe and predicted again, as Michell; he went even further, using new tools and new words, explaining that the Exclusion Principle would prop them after their fuel was exhausted. Yet Chandrasekhar became the object of much scientific hostility; even the child Einstein wrote a calm but still disbelieving paper against his idea. And so, hounded by his colleagues, he abandoned all work in this area of physics. Only later, all came to believe and accept Black Holes.

Yet stubbornness against truth continued still: the child Stephen Hawking, who came to understand that black holes must emit radiation, was greeted by his scientific colleagues with ribald disbelief. The chairman of the conference called the child Hawking's work nonsense, and wrote a paper declaring the concept false.

Yet now he and all those present have had to reverse their unbelief in that which at first they all thought incompatible with their beliefs: they learned that they could not continue to believe in general relativity or quantum mechanics and disbelieve emissions from black holes. The child Hawking is right, for he comprehended a truth.

And so it is with beliefs based on incomplete observations and prejudices of those who think themselves learned. As you say of yourselves, man is a creature constantly given to premature decisions on inadequate grounds. Those who know only in part believe it indicates to them all; and as the children have ever been jealous of the gift of prophecy, they wish to predict as soon as they think they know some thing. So they do; and as they do, they delight in holding to their own imaginings as real, and all else as folly. By many false sciences thus have the children come to know some things; and yet in vanity many still mock the Prophets and say they never prophesied anything.

In truth, the children are still ill prepared to hear the truth.

Even now, the last generations of the children who have made the tools to finally disprove the follies of the ancient usurpers of truth, have not realized the triumph they have achieved. They have vindicated the words of the prophets who saw what I showed them, and they have become physical witnesses along side witnesses in Spirit, and shared the same truth with the children, using their tools and the new words in their mouths.

And so the circle is now complete.

Yet vanity is strong. Now the words of the ancient prophets are forgotten; and though found, they are again hidden. They are carefully silenced by the children of science, and ignored by the chroniclers and biographers of science. These children flee from the very thought that an unscientific child might receive knowledge of the universe revealed by a God, of stars and suns and the births of solar systems and planets and the step-by-step processes designed to bring about envisioned ends.

And yet, from where then, did they write these things?

Verily these things were given, even since the Beginning, and my children have written them, and in many forms the words survive. Some survive very clearly, so that the children of sciences must acknowledge them; yet they laugh, and say, 'this was merely coincidence; this was only by accident. They did not really know any real thing.'

They credit some children, only because they deduced the cosmos for themselves, yet completely deny another group, only because these declared they had received of God, who spoke first the same truths. The children of the sciences ignore these, though many references within the ancient prophets speak of the true concepts learned by the children Anaximander, and Democritus, and Aristarchus, and Copernicus, and Bruno, and Galileo, and Kepler, and Huygens, and Newton, and Einstein, and Hubble, and Hawking.

Yet the children may choose to silence and ignore truth. For, above all things they must have Free Agency to become what my children may become.

Search within the Scrolls and Books and writings I have noted to you, for they validate not only Genesis, but Democritus, and Aristarchus, and Galileo, and speak of these things long before any of these could prove that what they comprehended and knew could be demonstrated in observation. The prophets spoke clearly of these same things, and all should stand together as witnesses.

Yet why is the witness of the prophets ignored? I typed.

It is the Free Agency of the children to ignore the witness of prophets.

They are ignored, because they testify not only of the Cosmos, but of me.

I have always gloried in nature and shared the knowledge of its organization, and shown it to my children as my greatest joy. Those who suppressed the study of nature are not of me; they are the same as who suppressed and sequestered the knowledge of me and my ways from the children. They are the same as tried to usurp knowledge of the very access to me, which is in all of the children, which is their Birthright. Be assured that these were not my servants. They served only themselves. As I was obscured by these usurpers who wanted pre-eminent power over their siblings, and by priests who loved in vanity their own interpretations, who sought their own will rather than mine, so also their obsession of control brutally oppressed the children who only sought truth, and the knowledges which your generation is still obsessed in discovering.

Vanity is strong. There have always been children who have loved their own ego, idea, fame and might more than me, science, right or truth.

As yesterday, I was in overwhelm, but I was getting used to it.
This wasn't so hard.
I could follow.

I think I understand, I typed optimistically.

I know you do. You are my child. You are pure Intelligence.

Between yesterday and today, I have understood that we have learned a lot, but we are still very far from knowing all; we are very stubborn about receiving new things, but we have Free Agency, and can choose truth, even when it is not observable, even when the tools to observe and measure it have not yet been found; we are here to learn, we are here to learn the truth.

I thought of a question I had to ask.

How are we doing?

As you perceive: of all that is, your generation has learned but in part.

You still do not fully know how simple grass is turned into cows, and elephants; nor do you understand more than a fractional part of anything you have mapped in your own bodies, even for all of your study and learning of it, which is truly vast and admirable in every way.

Still you stand in the shadow of creation's vastness, knowing little, almost nothing. You have progressed in grace, by Free Agency. You grow amid truth and error, often from error to error. Some errors evolve in truth toward truth. Democritus imagined the atom, yet his atom was error: it is not indivisible. Dalton's atom was also error: it is not a solid. Rutherford's atom was still error, though he accurately understood the nucleus. And Bohr's atom was error, with dot-point electrons in orbital energy levels. Your charge-cloud model and string theories are coming closer; by Free Agency the truth will one day be known.

You have learned of suns and stars, Cosmos and worlds, the hard way, by refuting the ancient prophets, both in your sciences, and your religions and churches. While the prophets and Apostles and early Fathers taught you as Spiritual Witnesses of suns and worlds, you stoned them. Then you burned the children of sciences, who tried to be physical witnesses to you. In this way you have continued generations in absence of information which you always had; and still you ignore much new information speaking to you from out of the dust.

Absence of real information leads the children to myriad false theories. Behold the planet Venus. The children saw it was covered with clouds; they thought of water vapor. Thus some theorized that beneath these clouds it had a surface of swamps. Others said no, it is covered in oil fields. Still others said no, due to heat from the sun and high carbon dioxide in its air, such a water-vapor clouded planet is covered by an ocean of carbonated seltzer water. These are not ancient fantasies and myths. These are very recent theories, proposed by intelligent, serious, respected children of science. They were all proven wrong. How did they theorize then, so far from the truth? Because they had no idea of the truth. The truth has turned out to be something very different. The surface of the planet Venus is dry, and hot. Now that the children know the truth, they may ask: were any of these false theories less humorous than the strange declarations of the prophets to the children in their days?

And the prophets' words were not false; they are now known to be true.

There is much the children can learn from revealed truth. Believe it.

Much of what you believe as true scientific truth is not true.

Only recently some bright children discovered that it is the friction in a convection current that causes larger, heavier objects to rise above the smaller objects in a vibrating enclosure, such as a can of nuts, or gravel in a bin. There were previous physical notions everyone accepted, all carefully worked out and scientifically explained, but they were false. No scientist questioned them; then a few chose to test the theories. They found they were wrong. The explanations and models so long used, accepted, taught and believed were, simply, wrong.

Many other models and beliefs will fall away, as they are also wrong.

Some will be replaced by new false theories. Some will topple before truths revealed by your own tools, and inquiries, and observations, and findings. New books will be written, and many will forget that what they taught for truth from the old books was false, even as they will forget that not all in the new books is true only because the books are new. Yet they will teach it as truth anyway, until one day the new book also becomes old, and its false ideas are old. What is old and true, endures; what is new but still false, passes away.

All of this I see in progress going on, every day.

Even as the children declare themselves free of jealousies, closed-mindedness and hostility toward each other's ideas, they exercise Free Agency in both proposing the false as they propose the true; in rejecting the false just as they reject the true; and in believing the true, just as they believe the false.

In all things they must choose.

After yesterday's discussion, I thought we knew a lot, I typed.

Though you know much, you still know little. You can clone an animal, if you have an animal to start with. Except that you take my DNA to make a clone, you are clueless as to how you must begin from hydrogen atoms to make a one-cell organism. You cannot even make a single part of a cell. And there are so many parts, organized so precisely, in a single cell. You have discovered that when a good working cell is functioning in your body, it carries out some 6 trillion reactions every second of every minute of ever hour. It is time for the children to acknowledge Design. Even giving you the head start of having all ninety-two of the elements at hand, and the chemical compounds at hand in your laboratory, you know not how to fabricate with them, from scratch, a multi-celled plant or micro-animal, much less a fully functional, balanced and well-tuned human body into which an Intelligence may be born and move as a physical being with the increase of physical powers.

All of your work is based on the Design, which you have studied to obtain your detailed knowledge of the Design. All that you do will be no more than tinkering with the Design you have received and seen and identified within you and in all life forms.

Will you accept the challenge to start from scratch, and with no borrowed materials, but using only raw unorganized atoms of elements and raw unorganized molecules of compounds, structure the molecules you need and bond them into a perfectly ordered and functional helix of Human DNA, and still using no borrowed materials, make another; and then likewise make the diverse molecules needed and structure its correspondent RNAs; and then organize these and create the molecules and membranes needed and structure them into chromosomes, X and Y; and from scratch then structure cytoplasms and tissues with integrity and get them to hold form as sperm and egg; and then put all your perfectly ordered and structured microparts into these and then fuse them into a new body's beginning? Do you accept this challenge?

Without borrowing and deriving material from that which is already made, though you have the Design, will you try to make a human body from scratch?

Yet why bother, you will say, when you can borrow?

For DNA is free.

Though the children at one of your great university medical schools have taken out a registered patent for a genetically altered mouse, and many other children have taken out patents on a host of other genetic 'inventions' including altered bacteria, altered cells and altered molecules for which they charge money, yet my DNA and life forms are free for you to use and borrow and alter; they are my gift to you. And so you choose to borrow that which is given free and then deny the Giver and the Designer of the Design you copy and alter. And so you borrow in arrogance and vanity, without thanks, nor due.

You may choose to use your gift wisely, or hurt yourselves as you often do. Though ten thousand times ten thousand good choices may be made unto helping the children, you are on the threshold of learning the consequences of one bad choice, or one evil choice, which may end all further choices.

Yet it is given to you to choose for yourselves what you will do.

There is much you do not know. You are still children.

Though you have learned much of your earth, you still don't know what the mechanism is of the movement of the crustal tectonic plates, or what causes Ice Ages, or what structural quality causes water to expand as it freezes instead of contracting as everything else, or how hail is formed in the clouds, or the exact mechanics of something as simple as rust formation on iron which you see every day.

You still haven't even figured out how aspirin works.

Yet you now have words. You have the prophets, those who were always with you, and those who are coming forth now, if you will receive them. You have tools to observe the unobservable, and to measure, and you have great and myriad means to share. You are coming to understand the Design.

Some day you shall acknowledge that the Design declares its Designer.

I finished reading. A lot to absorb. A lot to process.
Time. I looked at the clock. Very late again. Time to close.

I think I'd better close for the night.
Thank you for your patience with me. I'm still getting used to this. I've got a lot to think about again.

Very good. I'll be with you. Talk to you tomorrow night. Goodnight.

Good night, I typed, and closed down.

I sat for a moment in silence, pondering the things I had seen this night. I looked at my paper with its questions and notes. At the bottom I saw my words written

God is. Angels are. Spirit is. Faith is. I AM.
and
Science is.

I sat and looked at those last words a long time. They meant a lot to me. God is. Science is. Now I was sure of a few more things.

Below these I now wrote

Prophets are. Prophecy is. Revelation is.

As I walked in the dark from the lab tent to my tent, I looked up above me at the narrow swath of sky and stars scintillating between the high canyon walls. They were beautiful. I stopped a moment, just gazing up at them, and at the softly blue-glowing walls of the towering canyon surrounding me.

Billions and billions of stars were out there. Billions of planets were out there. Their flickering light managed to reach us on our world, from so far away. What we didn't yet know filled unread volumes more numerous that all we had thus far written.

Yes, we still have a lot to learn.

Chapter 14

Day 33 in the Wilderness:
$\quad\quad$ The Creation of Matter and Spirits

My eyes fluttered and squinted against the light. I was awake. Again, it was late. Oh well, this was a new schedule, and that was OK.

Everything was again as I had left it just last night as I went to sleep. This was still not a dream.

Dressed and fully awake, I went to the artesian spring, drank from the cool water, filled my cup and walked over to the strings and stakes and half-excavated quadrants of my excavation. This did not look appealing today. A pleasant walk in the wadis would be nice. I hadn't done that since finding the Urim and Thummim. After a quick look at something in the computer, I would go for a walk. It would be good to get some exercise and see a change of scenery.

Breakfast was simple and good. As soon as I was finished I went to the lab tent and sat down at the computer. I turned on the power, and booted up the system.

I sat and stared at the desktop menus.

Before talking to God again, I wanted to check out some of the things we had discussed yesterday. They were the central focus of what I intended to ask today: *the creation of the universe.*

I had been told that all that we are learning today in science had been revealed through prophets in most ancient times.

Was this true?

My archaeological training had already acquainted me with most of the major creation stories of ancient civilizations. They were not scientific treatises of the universe explained by scientific minds, but religious knowledge of ancient peoples, clothed in intentional mystery. We could not go back historically very far by science, but in the religions' myths we could go back to the dawning of humanity.

Ancient people told their children that the accounts they handed down had been revealed by their gods in most early time. Was this perhaps what God had spoken of last night? Was even this myth not really a myth at all? Had one truth been given at sundry times by the same God, only to become garbled among most peoples?

I knew the tales were fabulous to us, set in allegorical story framework. Yet I also knew that our definition of *myth* in our time as 'something untrue' was arrogant, and blinding. The original understanding of *myth* was truth told through a story. The story was told in *symbolism*. Carl Jung and Joseph Campbell had already opened our eyes to see that myths embody profound truths of the human psyche, astonishing perspectives into the human emotions and mind, the archetypal awakening journeys of human experience, told magnificently in easy-to-remember stories, in symbolism.

Yet I knew there was more in myth than the human psyche.

The stories often contained great remnants of other truths. One had to know a truth to suddenly see it amid the myths. Yet soon, it became clear that the same foundational story was being told over and over again; only the names of the actors and the places of setting and situations were constantly changed, kaleidoscopically shifted. Once the first hidden truth was discovered, the pattern of masks became clearer; the cloaks obscuring identities and acts distilled into more familiar faces.

It did not take a genius to see in the green-faced, resurrected Egyptian god Osiris, the promise of the resurrected Jesus; just as it didn't take a genius to see in the Hindu Holy Family of Shankar-Parvati and baby Ganesh the familiar figures of Joseph, Mary and the baby *Yeshua*, Jesus. Jesus was born to die for the world and to be resurrected; Ganesh was killed but brought back to life by giving him an elephant head, after which he became the mediator between man and God: all Hindu prayers begin and end with Ganesh.

Yet in the Hindu religion, this Holy Family was portrayed at a higher level: Shankar, or Shiva, is God, and Parvati, his wife, is Goddess. This was the family of God the Father, Goddess the Mother, and God the Son, a pattern repeated countless times in mythologies. Yet any Christmas manger scene repeated the general appearance of father Shiva beside Parvati, with baby Ganesh in her lap.

It was just as easy to see that as the Hindu Rama is the incarnation of God, Lakshman his brother is as John the Beloved, always faithfully at his side; Hanuman the Monkey General easily finds counterpart in the Archangel Michael, even with his battle of righteous monkeys against the monkeys of evil.

Krishna, also easily perceived as a Hindu Christ figure, shared many thoughts with the faithful Arjuna, the man who as a baby had been put in a basket and set adrift in a river to escape death, just as we know Moses had been set adrift in the Nile in ancient Egypt.

The same discoveries could be made in countless cultures.

Then there was the curious name Adam, so phonetically close to the Egyptian god Atum, creator of the universe. And the name Atum, in the ancient Egyptian, so close to the ancient Greek word *atom*, chosen by Greeks who lived in that ancient world, the word for the unit of which all things are created. Was there a connection?

It was like deciphering messages written in code.

Scholars and academics liked to sigh at these similarities and parallels, saying the Hebrews were incorrigible borrowers. But was this the truth? Had the truths of cosmos and Messiah been given to humankind in ancient times by God in many places, by the same God, only to be shrouded in mystery and garbled by retellers?

I knew also that sacred truth was often cloaked in symbolism to be understood fully and known only to the initiated. John's Book of Revelation was a prime example. And as any scholar knew, the original knowledges and beliefs of almost all ancient religions had indeed become cluttered with generational embellishments and increases, added to by the chain of tellers, in which they labored to sort out from the redactions the seeds of the original beliefs.

But still, there was much reality beneath the ancient masks.

The creation myths especially were symbolic coded messages, highly symbolic tellings of things held as profoundest truth by their tellers, to which we in our day had lost almost all of the keys of decoding. But all of the stories, when unmasked, became clear blueprints of a common astronomical, cosmophysical understanding. This fact had come through loud and clear in school.

Clearly, someone had been very busy, seriously sharing these astrophysical visions.

The *Nihongi* and *Kojiki* of pre-Yamato Japan, transcribed from oldest oral tradition, were very clear in establishing that the Sun Goddess, Amaterasu, was not created first, nor was she the creator of the world. She was the offspring of two previously existing deities, or, should we understand, *suns*? This followed exactly the determinations of astrophysics: that our sun is a second- or perhaps even third- generation sun in an older cosmos. The account reveals that gods already existed before the formation of our sun; the concepts of planetary geological form and vegetation and water distribution already had been conceived, or implemented elsewhere; what was lacking here, at our point of the universe, was a body to govern or 'lord' the system: a sun. This understanding of the sun as governing body of the solar system - which clearly had to be gravitational even if not understood - though tacitly ignored by astrophysicists, could only have one meaning: the most ancient Japanese had a clear comprehension of heliocentricity. There could be no doubt of it. Also of great curiosity in the *Kojiki* was the creation of human beings from a joining of the sun and the storm god, Susa-no-o. The Japanese see themselves as *children of the sun*. In pure astrophysics, are they wrong? What more clear understanding could be had? Elements created in suns, combined with the elements of storms: air, oxygen, water and electricity; Amaterasu and Susa-no-o. Very biological. I also remembered the sacred Shinto understanding of the *kami*, best translated as *spirits*: *kami* included deities, human beings, and all other objects: birds, beasts, trees, plants, seas, mountains, and so forth. Everything was spiritual to the Shinto.

In oldest China, remnants of most ancient oral tradition in the *Huai-nan Tzu* summarized that before the Great Beginning, all was vague and amorphous; the Great Beginning produced emptiness, and emptiness produced the universe. This had always stupefied me: *'the Great Beginning produced emptiness, and emptiness produced the universe.'* Yet recently, as physics unfolded the reality of atomic empty space, I had come to glimpse that our atomic matter is virtual emptiness, and truly this 'atomic emptiness' - matter - had to exist for a universe to exist. Atomically structured emptiness did produce the universe. The *Huai-nan Tzu* went on to affirm that the universe then produced *ch'i*, the vital force, understood as spirit, and the ether filling the sky and universe, also denoting the basic substance of all creation. Remarkably, it said, *ch'i* 'had limits.' This too, had always eluded my understanding. Limits, to spirit, to space, to the substance of creation? Physics would certainly validate limits to the latter two. But limits to spirit? A confounding precept. I remembered that this primordial Chinese understanding clearly stated that the universe had taken form first; the earth was formed only long after, something about the difficulty of the heavy, turbid matter to solidify. This seemed to agree perfectly with astrophysics. Most striking to me now was my memory that the sun was not said to have begun as a light, but only after a long time did the hot force of the accumulated *yang* produce fire, and the essence of the fire force became the sun. What a shockingly precise description of ongoing accretion, gravitational condensation, heat build-up and final ignition - fusion - in the sun. This had been written down twenty-two centuries ago. How had they known these scientific facts of creation?

I knew that in the ancient Sanskrit creation epics of India - the *Vedas*, especially the *Rig Veda*, and the talmudic *Brahmanas* and *Upanishads* - they spoke of the beginning as *'darkness concealed in darkness;'* that only vast stretches of water existed. Among a host of deities a supreme god, Indra, slew the serpent demon Vritra who enclosed the waters of heaven and the sun. Was this the cosmic creation, wherein 'sun' had to be understood as the primordial singularity of matter? Or was this the memory of our own sun's moment of atomic ignition, the burst of fusion blasting forth its initial fires?

Splitting open the belly of Vritra, Indra released the essentials of creation - water, heat and light - and then later, by the laws of the god Varuna, cosmic order was eventually established. Then there was the story of the 'cosmic egg,' from which the universe had been 'born.' The story was tangibly preserved in Hindu worship through the oval *sivalingham* stone. There were in fact many myths of the 'cosmic egg,' throughout the cultures of the world. Whether the story of Vritra or the egg, it seemed to me the clear beginnings of an expanding universe: water, and atomic fusion and all of its benefits in producing matter and converted heat energy and light. This was as close to pure physics as one could get. Second to Indra was Agni, the god of fire; to Hindus, fire is still regarded as the liaison between gods and man. We now know our atoms were made in the fire of suns. Is this then, a strange concept to us? Not any more. The Vedas say that Varuna used Surya, the sun, as his calipers to make our local solar system. If the sun was his calipers - an instrument which makes circles, or orbits - what more clear indication can there be of the central function of the sun in organizing the solar system? Did this not point to an original, lost knowledge of heliocentricity?

What did it matter that this was lost later to philosophers, just as happened among the Greeks? The concept of geocentricity was so philosophically attractive, even the practical Greeks couldn't resist giving in to it. How often had philosophy overthrown knowledge?

The ancient Indian Buddhist doctrine of *Sunyata*, "Emptiness," clearly comprehended all things as instable, impermanent, fragile in essence, 'like something borrowed,' organized into their form, and then inevitably destroyed, only to be again re-gathered and reformed. Was this not pure astrophysics? Even seeing our own bodies this way, wasn't it truth? As the suns are gathered and burn and die and give their matter to new suns and planets, even to life forms such as we, we know our bodies came from dust and return to dust; we come from ashes and we return to ashes. And while we live, most of the space we occupy is atomic 'emptiness.' I remembered that by the *Vedas*, and the later *Mahabharata*, the ancient primordial god Rudra had become known in his name of power, Shiva, the One whose cosmic dance created, maintained, destroyed and re-created worlds and suns and galaxies in continuing cycles of stellar births, deaths and rebirths. This too, was pure astrophysics. Shiva's wife, in her name Shakti, is Energy. The cycle of a universe given by the ancients of India told of a process in Brahma extending back over 8 billion years; there were even more distant calculations. University classes disdainfully brushed aside these astonishing parallels to mathematical physics as fortuitous accidents. Yet was all this ancient comprehension of the stars and our solar system and the universe accidental? I also remembered that according to the *Vedas*, both deities and humans had their specific functions to perform in accordance to cosmic order. Most curious. Most curious indeed.

I knew that the Maya of the ancient Americas had calculated astronomical observations of the stars and movements of the stars to a phenomenal degree, even calculated the solar year to within only seconds of what we know it is by our computer technologies. We had only three of their books, now called the *Codex Dresdensis*, the Book of *Chilam Balam* and the *Popol Vuh*. Their creation myths, like so many others, told first of nothing but waters. Fire was the first thing created, very astrophysical; then an 'inchoate sun' was created, and then, time. The same story was told by the Inca, that the earth was roughly formed, and only after all of this did own sun burst forth in light. Like the Mixtec and Aztecs, who worshipped a fourth-generation sun, *Tonatiuh*, the Maya, the Toltec, and many other peoples of the Western Hemisphere catalogued a cosmological history of several previous sun's births, destructions, and re-births. This complies precisely with our own astrophysical understandings. Their stories also maintained that the earth went through a number of epochs, and had been destroyed and recreated several times. This was fully in harmony with our most recent discoveries of upheavals, erosions and new upheavals; of tectonic plate shufflings and re-arrangements of the land; of biospheric stasis, castrophic destructions and 'punctutated' bursts of new life upon the planet. It was good earth science. More curiously, could the myriad Mesoamerican pyramids built to sun deities from Mexico City to the world's largest pyramid, Pachacamac in Peru, all testifying of the ubiquitous worship of the sun, be a direct implication of an ancestral understanding of the heliocentric solar system amid the distant stars of space which these people charted, measured, calculated and understood so well?

Yet for all of their astronomical understanding, I remembered clearly that most of these Western Hemispheric myths told only briefly of the creation of the universe, as if it were but a fragmentary glimpse of an incomprehensible setting; they then quickly shifted to our microcosm: the bulk of the saga always centered on the formation of the earth, this earth, our planet. This earth-focus was strikingly repeated in the North American Tribal myths of creation: virtually all of them omitted any consciousness of a vast universe; virtually all began abruptly with the story of this planet's formation - often so parallel to the Bible's Genesis rendering that the stories almost appear tainted by their Christian recorders.

But ethnological evidences show they are not: the parallels to Genesis found among the many nations and tribes, including the Iroquois, the vast Algonquin, the Muskhogee in particular, the numerous Sioux, the Minnetarees and the Mandans, the Zuni, even the Tupi-Guarani of the great Amazon basin consistently have been found to be untainted, ancient oral traditions. The extensive nation of the Delaware tribes associated their creation story with the ceremonies of the Big House, definable only as a Temple which represents both God and Creation, with deeply important ordinances.

The most extensive telling is perhaps among the Hopi, one of the many tribes whose history claims it is the first human race born, yet which among the many has the most detailed account of that claim. Their 'First World,'

Tokpela, was indeed endless space; Taiowa, the Creator, created a 'Nephew,' Sotuknang, whom he commanded to create the universe in proper order so all things would work harmoniously with one another according to his plan. This, Sotuknang did: from endless space he gathered that which was made manifest as solid substance, molded it into forms, and arranged this solar system with its seven planets. This was just the beginning of the process, which for our earth became ever more detailed, until life forms were designed, placed upon the earth, finally introducing man.

It was curious to me, that in spite of man's eternal arrogance, all ancient myths consistently told tales of grasses, plants, trees, fishes, birds and beasts all being created first, before man. How could the ancients have guessed this order? It flew in the face of human imagination, in total defiance of man's vanity, always seeing himself first in everything. In the Creation story of the Hopi, the first human beings created could not speak, for many generations. A most curious detail in light of homonid fossil discoveries. The Hopi recount three subsequent phases of our earth's life development: *Tokpa*, *Kuskurza* and finally *Tuwaqachi*, the 'complete world' in which we now live.

This was the predominant pattern: stories with little of the creation of the universe as a whole, but much of just this planet, a microcosm among a vast and endless space.

Why?

All of these ancient religions spoke of spirits - good and evil - and of wars among the good and evil spirits, and of evil spirits acting against humankind. They all spoke of animals, too, as having spirits.

And then there was the great Babylonian Creation Epic, the *Enuma Elish* - 'When in the Heights' - inherited from the earliest Sumerians and imprinted on the clay tablets, now known from several different archaeological discoveries. The allegorical planetary saga is clearly understood in the severed head of the goddess Tiamat, said to finally be put in position - in space, where all the saga unfolds - whereupon the greatest god then raises the mountains, opens the springs, and through her eyes opens the rivers Tigris and Euphrates. Tiamat was Earth. Our planet. This epic telling of the origins of our solar system recounted great violence, shatterings and a passage of time during which all that came to be, settled to be. The sun, a god called Shamash, was a judge; justice resided in him. Shamash was thus the great governor of the solar system, ruling the planets. Though knowledge of heliocentricity is not academically conceded to Mesopotamia as a given awareness, was an ancient root of this understanding not clearly remaining? And we know, geocentricity is not *declared* in the texts; are we right to assume that the reciprocal *lack* of direct heliocentric definition in the fragmentary clay tablets thus far excavated is an affirmation of geocentric perspective?

I knew that the Sumerians had made intricate astronomical calculations, and measured distances to stars in millions of miles. Their numbers for vast astronomical distances and immense ages of the earth are still considered fabulous: too large for their time, and still far short of the true distances. Today they are smiled at and called 'fantasies.' But were they perhaps rudiments of understanding of time and space we are loath to assign to the ancients as actual scientific comprehensions? Why? Even the Greeks started way off, with absurd calculations. In the days of Herodotus, the Greeks calculated the sun was only about ten miles away from earth; fifty years later Anaxagoras calculated the distance was 1800 miles; a hundred and fifty years later it was nudged up to 5,300,000 miles. These were the esteemed Greeks; their figures today are considered the beginnings of scientific knowledge. Why, even Kepler's best shot at the distance of the sun was only 26,400,000 miles, about a quarter of the span. So, are we perhaps too harsh in our disdainful view of the clay tablets' vast numbers as mere fantasies? The numerous cuneiform astronomical clay tablets, did, in fact, give the coordinates of so many stars around the full sphere of the earth that it is not mathematically possible to accept a flat-world perception by their astronomers and mathematicians: they clearly knew the world is a sphere. And, their observations of planetary motions preclude all but a heliocentric interpretation, though we have no proof of it other than the astronomical calculations and mathematical conclusions.

I remembered that there was an ancient culture that had calculated the distance to the sun as an incredible 92 million miles, almost exactly its true mean distance from earth. Too close for coincidence? Perhaps it was not coincidence, nor accident.

These mathematical calculations were discovered by the father of archaeological science, William Flinders Petrie. The Egyptians, well known as a very cosmological people, who also believed wholly and passionately in the resurrection of the body, built pyramids as monuments imitating the primordial rock of creation which had emerged from the primordial waters of chaos in space.

The cycle of creation was ritually observed in the Great Temples at Thebes, wherein a great pool represented the waters of chaos to all initiates. The Pyramid form, like the obelisks of the Temples, pointed to the sun; the pyramid was the Rock of Creation. Structurally oriented to the sun with a precise exactitiude paralleled in but a few ancient solar edifices, the Great Pyramid of Cheops especially revealed an engineering which was difficult to accept as accidental. Not only is it a perfect geometric form, with the four sides of the base bearing the same proportion to its vertical height as the circumference of a circle to its radius, but no matter what system of unit measure is used, each of its base lines are mathematically an even ten-millionth part of the semi axis of the earth, repeated 365 times - once for every day of the year.

In other words - a decimal fraction representing the daily penetration of solar rays from the surface of this planet through to the center of its core.

That was not all. Its unit of length is the even five-hundredth-millionth part of the polar diameter of this planet.

Petrie's numbers were not vain, contrived math tricks; they yield the equivalents by whatever base unit of measure is used. Most striking of all to Petrie was his shocking discovery that the height of the Great Pyramid - 486.25 British feet - multiplied by the ninth power of ten - one million - gave 92,093,000 British miles. This number almost exactly corresponds to the mean distance of the earth from the sun, so closely that the 270 mile difference is meaningless. Some say that difference is only caused by the tip of the pyramid's limestone sheathing having been broken off.

As one affirms understanding of the pure cosmological creation symbol which the pyramid most certainly was built to be, these precise fractional measurements can hardly be dismissed as mere chance.

Yet how could people 2,400 years ago know such astronomical and geophysical data, and why incorporate it in precisely even decimal fractions in a monument to the creation of the universe?

Josephus cited an earlier historian, Berosus, who wrote that in very ancient times there was a man among the Chaldeans, righteous and great, skilled in the celestial science; Josephus claimed that man was Abraham. Josephus said that Hecataeus of old had written an entire book about Abraham; and that Nicolaus of Damascus had spoken of Abraham in the fourth book of his history, noting that the greatness of his knowledge was remembered even unto his day. Josephus recorded oral traditions preserving the story that it was Abraham who had gone from the land of Canaan down into Egypt and stayed there a while, where he communicated to the Egyptians mathematics, and delivered to them the science of astronomy, which he said had thereby come from the Chaldeans into Egypt, and from there, to the Greeks.

Was it true? Jews had been telling this for thousands of years. How could Abraham have learned so much about the universe?

At any rate, this was all quite a little panorama: the sun of the *Nihongi* created from two previous suns in an already existing cosmos as definite 'lord' of the planetary hosts; the creation of 'emptiness' in the Chinese of which the universe was created; the exploding belly of Vritra in the *Rig Veda*, releasing light, heat and water into a universe, and the long stories of eventual formation of stars and our sun and this world; the central place of the sun in the Mayan and Aztec astronomies of the pre-Columbians, with stars so well measured and calculated; the saga of the Hopi among a plethora of tribal creation stories; and the vast astronomical recordings of the Mesopotamians, and the creation mysteries of the Egyptian temples, and astronomy of the pyramids.

So much for the width and breadth of creation mythologies.

It was clearly a lot of good, solid physics.

How had these realities of physics been known so long ago?

Still, it was only a partial understanding of astrophysics.

Then, there was the Bible.

What did it add to this litany of the universe?

Curiously, the Bible had not been taught in school as a serious ancient creation epic, not as the other ancient creation stories. All I knew of it was what I remembered from Sunday School, nothing really scholarly at all. It had just not been academically considered. Yet according to its own pronouncements, its was the oldest and first source of all such knowledge of creation.

If one were to hear the Bible, the Hebrews had got this knowledge revealed from God, first.

This is exactly what God had said last night.

I suddenly thought it funny, that I knew the redactions of the Babylonian epics and the root Sumerian words for so many things in the *Enuma Elish*, but I had never gone into the Hebrew at all.

I could do that right now, using the linguistic and phonetic database tools I had requested installed into this computer system. They were right here, and a lot more.

And last night, God had said that there was a lot more.

He said that there were many ancient words right here in my computer, right at my fingertips - ancient words about creation, about many worlds existing, not just our one inhabited planet - all recorded and written on scrolls and papyrus, written long, long ago.

I had nearly six thousand hours of voice recordings in the original ancient tongues, readings by scholars and students, and everything with absolute interface, so the original ancient language script, and its English translation, could be accessed on the screen.

This was a first-class tool.

It was time to use it.

I slid down the menu to TEXT READOUT, opted it, and slid down to VERSION: English Translation, and opted again. In a few instants the screen came up for Document Search by English Translation, and I was ready to roll. The texts I wanted to search were the Biblical and Extra-Biblical literature. Selected. The languages were Hebrew, Aramaic, Greek, Latin, Syriac and Egyptian-Coptic. Selected.

I sub-selected Hebrew Bible. That was the place to start.

I typed in 'CREATION, and tapped Vocabulary Search.

The result was instructive.

CREATION: In the original Hebrew Bible there were two main Hebrew words- *bara'* and *'asa* - and two additional Hebrew words, all translated somewhat interchangeably into the English as either 'create' or 'made' or 'formed,' or 'begat.' Also, derivatives such as 'creature,' referring both to animals and human beings, came from the 'create' word. The range of application of these four words began in the very first verse of Genesis, and went from Genesis 1:1 on.

Selecting Lexicon-Dictionary I instantly had the English equivalents of the four Hebrew words. The Hebrew word *bara'* was the initial word used for 'create' in Genesis 1:1, and it meant: *cut out; pare; shape;* and also, in some places in the Bible it explicitly indicated a *'renewing'* of a thing that had become old, or weak, or that had been absent. In Genesis 1:27 *bara'* was used three times, all describing the creation of man out of explicitly pre-existing material: dust, or the smallest particles of matter. The Hebrew word *'asa* meant: *to do; to make.* The other two words meant *mold; fashion; form; fabricate;* and also *get,* and *acquire.*

The application of all of these words was to already existing material, an understanding of explicit denotation and connotation in the original Hebrew usage. There was no confusion about this in the original Hebrew. Thus all the words describing 'creation' dealt with giving shape or form to existing matter, doing something with it.

I suddenly felt a rush of anger, remembering all of the times I had been taught in Sunday School that the Hebrew words specifically meant 'out of nothing.' They didn't mean that at all. No *creatio ex nihilo* in the Hebrew, expressed or implied. This had been a dogma, not Bible. It was not, 'The Word.' I checked several Bible references footnoted in the Lexicon that were given as affirmations of *creatio ex nihilo;* I discovered that in the original, they did not mean non-existent or nothing, but 'invisible.' What is 'invisible?' Atoms are invisible. Sub atomic particles are invisible. Dark matter is invisible. I shook my head and scanned the main 'create' Hebrew word, *bara'.*

It came from the root: *'to organize.'*

Enough of paradigms and dogmas. It was time for me to see what was there, and not just believe what I had been told was there.

I entered the word CREATION and tapped the Search key.

Lots of hits.

I began to scroll, and read.

Genesis 1:1 *'As a beginning: God shaped the heavens'*.....plural in the original. Interesting. *'.....and the earth.'* It says *'As a beginning,'* a place to start, for telling a story, not 'in the beginning' of everything and the universe. It just says, 'as we start this story, know that God shaped the heavens out there, and he also shaped...... land.' This was really interesting. The word *'eres* does not mean 'earth' as we use the word for our globe; it means *'land,'* or in a more general sense, that which is solid, *matter*, as opposed to that which is not matter - water, sky, or space. *'Eres*, as in Eretz Israel, the Land of Israel.' Land, solid, as opposed to air and water. *Eres* is often understood as 'the earth' in later passages, but here, did it mean 'earth,' or the 'land,' the original formation of solid *matter in space?* At any rate, it then certainly went on to tell a little bit about the process of this planet's formation. OK.

Genesis 1:7 *'And God shaped the firmament.....divided the waters which were under....from the waters which were above the firmament......And God called the Firmament Heaven.'*

I never really noticed that before: This was a description of space, before the accretion of the planet. Water below the heavens divided from water above the heavens. Water above? In space? I scrolled back to verse 6 and saw *'in the midst of the waters, and let it divide the waters from the waters.'* That was as the planet itself was being formed. *Divide the waters from the waters.* In space, which is called 'Heaven.' I didn't understand.

The etymology of the Hebrew word 'Heavens' might yield some clues. This computer tool was a whiz: a few clicks and I had it.

Shamayim, from the root words *esh*: fire, and *mayim*: waters. Curious, *mayim*, waters, right in the Hebrew word for the 'heavens.' I still didn't understand.

Yet by this, then, a clearer, scientific reading of the first verse of Genesis could read that in the beginning *God shaped the fire, the water, and the solid matter, 'eres.* The word *'eres* meant 'land' - rocks, mountains, all kinds of ......well, planetary matter. Very curious. So many ancient philosophies spoke of making all of the elements from earth, fire and water. In school we had learned to chuckle smugly at the foolishness of the ancients who thought everything was made of earth, fire and water. The folly of the ancients, we said.

On the other hand, the 'hot big bang' theory certainly answers to *esh*, fire. We understood that matter - *'eres?* - was formed or took atomic shape in this hot process. The biggest discovery of physics clearly understands the nature of 'heavens' in a name beginning with *esh*, the fiery big bang, not to mention the fact that physics clearly affirms space is the expanding home of *esh*: burning suns by the billions, in burning galaxies by the billions as far as we can see. And then, I also remembered: physics has shown us that hydrogen was produced right at the beginning, the majority matter of water, and that almost every compound of matter in the cosmos contains water, which means water must have been produced very early in the universe, in great abundance. Just the water enveloping our own sun, the vast spherical cloud of ice crystals and ice planetesimals orbiting the extremities of our solar system, is an unimaginable amount of water, around just one star.

Physics certainly affirms 'heavens' defined as *esh* and *mayim*.

And whether *'eres* implied 'solid land-type matter as opposed to non-solid *esh, mayim* and space' or our planet 'earth,' this was very astrophysical.

Maybe the ancient Hebrew word *Shamayim* knows more than we think it does, and testifies of an ancient knowledge we're just catching up to. I would have to ask about this. I scrolled again:

Genesis 1:16 *'And God cut out two great lights'*.....The sun and moon. Physics says they were accreted out of a greater cloud of matter; physics also believes that all the bodies in our solar system were accreted at about the same time: sun, moon, earth. *'Cut out,'* of the vast matter there. The earth, being smaller than the sun, probably was fully accreted long before the sun had accreted enough mass to ignite hydrogen fusion: the sun would have still been a huge, cold, non-luminous ball for some time after the earth had reached its primordial size. The moon was accreted the same way.

More than accurate by all standards of physics.

I scrolled on:

Genesis 1:21 *'And God fabricated great whales, and every other living creature'*..... fishes and birds. This was after the planet had already developed an ocean, after land had been pushed up, or whatever happened that raised primordial land masses. Creatures were placed into the developing habitat: life forms were organized. They skipped over the micro organisms in telling this story; so what? Nobody could see them anyway, yet; why get into a lot of tedious explanations no one would understand for thousands of years?

Genesis 1:25 *'And God fashioned the beasts of the earth'*........ all of the land animals.

Genesis 1:27 *'So God fabricated man in his own image, in the image of God fabricated he him; male and female fabricated he them.'*

Yes, that was very clear. We must look pretty much like God, from what it said. And fabricate is a good translation here: DNA is being 'fabricated' in laboratories. We can fabricate with DNA, because God first fabricated us. The word 'created' here was the same used for 'creature,' meaning animal, only here it means us. I remembered singing from my childhood, *'All creatures here below......'* We were part of those creatures. All God's creatures were creatures, creations of eternal matter cut out and pared and molded and shaped and fashioned with form, by fabrication into a design. We creatures, we were all fabrication designs. It had been a lot of work. It took some time. He rested afterwards. It was right there, in the next entry:

Genesis 2:3 ....*'for in that day he had rested from his work which God cut out and fabricated.'*

Genesis 2:7 and 8 *'And the Lord God formed man out of the dust of the ground, and breathed into his nostrils the breath of life; and man became a living soul........and there he put the man whom he had formed.'*

Dust. Was it interstellar dust? Atoms? Subatomic particles, the really little dust? What did it matter? To Hebrews back then, I knew: they didn't have a word for anything smaller than dust. The fact that we can look at this word now and understand it down to elementary strings is only slightly less astonishing than the fact that ancient Hebrews knew that's what we're made of in the first place, even if they didn't have words to describe it any better than that or tools to demonstrate its elementary truth. So, dust.

Genesis 5:12 *'And Cainan lived seventy years, and begat Mahalaleel.'*

Now this was interesting. All the 'begats.' 'Begetting' was from the same root word, 'create.' The same Hebrew root used for God's creation of man out of the dust was used for 'creating' human life in the womb in a mortal woman, through the union of man and wife. We created life too. I scrolled on.

Jeremiah 1:5 *'Before I formed thee in the belly I knew thee; and before thou camest forth out of the womb I sanctified thee, and I ordained thee a prophet unto the nations.'*

There was something else we had talked about yesterday. What is a prophet? I had asked. God knew Jeremiah not just before he was born, but before he was even conceived! Before Jeremiah was conceived he had been ordained to be a prophet 'unto the nations.' I remembered what I often heard at funerals: the body returned to the earth from which it was made, 'and the Spirit returns to God, who gave it,' usually something like that. That pretty much implied a knowledge that our spirits came from where God is. But when had our spirits been created? When had we had our beginning?

Within a few scrolls here was another direct Creation reference:

Job 38:1-7 *'Who is this that darkeneth counsel by words without knowledge? Gird up thy loins like a man; for I will demand of thee, and answer thou me. 'Where wast thou when I laid the foundations of the earth? declare, if thou hast understanding. Who laid the measure thereof, if thou knowest? or hath stretched the line upon it? Whereupon are the foundations thereof fastened? 'Or who laid the cornerstone thereof; when the morning stars sang together, and all the sons of God shouted for joy?'*

Stars, singing? I remembered something, and quickly selected New Testament, Revelation and typed Search for: STARS.

There it was. John was talking about Lucifer as the Dragon: *'And his tail drew the third part of the stars of heaven, and did cast them to the earth'*...... and it went on a few verses later .... *'And there was war in heaven: Michael and his angels fought against the dragon; and the dragon fought and his angels, and prevailed not; neither was there place found any more in heaven. And the great dragon was cast out, that old serpent, called the Devil, and Satan, which deceiveth the whole world: he was cast out into the earth, and his angels were cast out with him.'*

This was the war in heaven, but the *'third part of the stars'* were not stars as in 'stars,' or 'suns.' These were the angels who had lost Paradise, and been cast out. These *stars* were the children of God spoken of right there in Job. In the scope of time, this all happened before the first human flesh came upon the earth. This was the inspiration of Milton's famous epic poem *Paradise Lost*, the war among the angels. There was a reference. I selected it, and had Isaiah 14:12-13 *'How art thou fallen from heaven, O Lucifer, son of the morning! how art thou cut down to the ground, which didst weaken the nations! For thou hast said in thine heart, I will ascend into heaven, I will exalt my throne above the stars of God'....*

The stars of God were not the literal stars, here, either. They were the angels, and the word *'stars'* referred to rebellious as well as obedient angels. The Bible called angels *'stars,'* whether good or bad.

Funny, I thought: we use the word *'stars'* ourselves, for people: - *star* athletes, *star* performers, movie *stars*.

Do we use that word because of a memory, I wondered?

And, Lucifer wanted to exalt his throne above all of the children of God.

Are we *the morning stars?*

Here I was trying to understand time, and God was asking Job where he was at the time just before the Creation of the earth. Was God implying to him that he was one of the *'stars,'* the morning angels, the children of God who had shouted for joy when they saw the foundations of the earth laid in the heavens for them to come to, as we are most certainly here?

The thought suddenly struck me.

Had I been there, too?

Was I a star?

The answers were everywhere, all pointing to it.

I am a child of God.

Where had I been, when He laid the foundations of the earth in space? Could I have been in the same place with Jeremiah, even though I had not been ordained there to be a prophet unto nations? Could I have been one of those children of God, singing, who *shouted for joy* when this Earth began to accrete into a planet?

And what of the 'stars,' the angels, both good and bad?

I would have to ask about this.

I scrolled more, over a multitude of passages all using the words translated 'create,' but referring to people making things, especially potters working with clay, and crafts people making things out of raw materials. Always out of already-existing matter.

I stopped scrolling at Psalm 95, where the lesser Hebrew word meaning 'to form, fashion or mold' out of already existing matter was used in direct reference to the Genesis creation: *'The sea is his, and he made it: and his hands formed the dry land.'* Yet something else suddenly caught my eye. Verse 1 said *'O come, let us sing unto the Lord: let us make a joyful noise to the rock of our salvation.'* I knew this verse; I knew it also ending in *'a joyful noise unto the Lord,'* the Rock of our Salvation. Rock. Oh my gosh! Here was the Egyptian thing, the first rock they worshipped with the creation gods in the temples at Thebes; the primordial rock which the mighty pyramids proclaimed to the world for over two hundred generations. I clicked on the Reference key over the word ROCK and in an instant Psalm 18 was before me on my screen. Verse 2 spoke clearly:

The Lord is my rock and my fortress, and my deliverer;
My God, my strength in whom I will trust;
my buckler, and the horn of my salvation
and my high tower.

I was stunned. These were the words Yehoniah had written on the underside of the amphora shell! The pottery shield he had placed over the sword of Goliath, sealed with the dedicatory prayer of the Temple of YHWH at Yeb in Egypt, which Dr. Brannon had found. I clicked Reference again, and it took me to 2 Samuel 22: 2 and 3: *'The Lord is my rock, and my fortress, and my deliverer; The God of my rock; in him will I trust: he is my shield, and the horn of my salvation, my high tower, and my refuge, my savior.....'* I clicked Reference again, and had Deuteronomy 32:4 before me: *'He is the Rock, his work is perfect: for all his ways are judgement.'* *'The Lord is my rock.......'* The Rock. The Rock.

There was more to all of this than I was getting!

I scrolled on anxiously now, finding something else, fascinating.

Isaiah 45:18 *'For thus saith the Lord that shaped the heavens; God himself that formed the earth and made it; he hath established it, he molded it not in vain, he formed it to be inhabited: I AM the Lord; and there is none else. I have not spoken in secret, in a dark place of the earth: I said not unto the seed of Jacob, Seek ye me in vain: I the Lord speak righteousness, I declare things that are right.'*

There it was. He formed the earth *to be inhabited.* He had revealed what he did, and had not spoken in secret. *'I declare things that are right,'* he said. Some of it was here in what I was reading.

But he had said that there was more.

I finished scrolling the Hebrew Bible, and quickly accessed and opened the New Testament, and entered the word CREATION.

Many hits. Important ones referring to Genesis: Matthew 19:4 and Mark 10:6 and John 1:1-3 and 10.

But then I saw an excerpt in Romans:

Romans 1:20 *'For the invisible things of him from the creation of the world are clearly seen, being understood by the things that are made, even his eternal power and Godhead; so that they are without excuse: because that, when they knew God, they glorified him not as God, neither were they thankful; but became vain in their imaginations, and their foolish heart was darkened.'*

There it was. It's all here to see: the cosmos; the solar system; this planet; the wellspring of life. All we ever had to do was see it. We're finally doing that. We're learning all of these things: the stars, the universe, the earth, its ecology, our own bodies, DNA. Yet what was written nineteen centuries ago on papyrus was so true in our new day: the more science reveals to us of the universe and our DNA, the less thankful we are to God. We truly have become vain in our imaginations. Just because we can understand it, and see how it works, and how it was done, we think it can't be of God, because we have been taught that God is 'incomprehensible.' Well, that's not what he was saying here.

Hebrews 11:3 *'By faith we understand that the worlds were framed at God's command, so that things which are seen were not made out of what was visible.'* It didn't say out of what wasn't there; it just said it wasn't visible. Even we can't see atoms, or dark matter, physical dark matter or exotic dark matter. Much less the ancients. And *'worlds.'* Whether 'worlds' or 'universe,' dark matter we still can't see even with all of our technology, or an original singularity, it wasn't visible, at least to ancient people. Perfectly good physics.

Titus 1:2 *'In hope of eternal life, which God, who does not lie, promised before the world began.'* Here was this again - something happening before our world. God promised eternal life before the world began. To whom did he promise it? Us? That's certainly what's implied here, to us. Before the world began! Here we go back to the Book of Job: we obviously existed before this world began. Where were we? What were we? We were certainly conscious enough to be given a promise. In Job it says we shouted for joy as we watched the process for making this earth begin. But the big implication here is that the universe had to already exist and be expanding before this specific planet was formed in it. This is very good physics.

Ephesians 1:4 *'According as he hath chosen us in him before the foundation of the world, that we should be holy and without blame before him in love'* ...... It's all saying the same thing. How could we be chosen before the foundation of the world, this planet - a place to live and have a mortal probation, a testing place - except that we existed also, before the foundation of this earth? It says we were chosen *'before the foundation of the world.'*

The conclusion is unavoidable: the 'heavens' must have already been initiated and expanding for us to be in space, to be given a promise, to be chosen, to watch and shout for joy as the matter for this world and its sun and companion planets all began to swirl together and accrete in space to form this remarkable solar system.

The biblical records clearly distinguished time between the initial shaping of the universe as an expanding whole and the formation of this little solar system and planet in the midst of it all.

Yet where were we? What were we?

I scrolled down past more and more.

Romans 8:19-22 also spoke of creation...... yet suddenly verses 15, 16 and 17 caught my eye, just before it:

'...But ye have received the Spirit of adoption, whereby we cry, Abba, Father. The Spirit itself beareth witness with our spirit, that we are the children of God: and if children, then heirs; heirs of God, and joint heirs with Christ; if so be that we suffer with him, that we may be also glorified together.'

That was profound. It was so clear. The many scrolls of the Bible spoke harmoniously, unanimously and clearly.

Time for another word-search.

I exited that search, re-selected the Hebrew Bible, and entered my next word: UNIVERSE.

The Hebrew Bible hits were few. I went to Dictionary.

That's why. Apparently, they hadn't been too interested in the vastness of space: no words, really. They hadn't made the words. They had expressions like 'the all, and 'heavens,' shamayim. That was all. Interesting. Was it because they knew enough to know that a greater understanding was beyond their ability to reach, and so they preferred to concentrate on the 'here?'

I next checked the New Testament, which we still think was originally written in Greek, negative evidence aside.

I discovered that the word for 'universe' used in the New Testament was COSMOS. Fascinating. The very word. I brought up the search function, entered COSMOS and tapped the search key. The computer searched. The finds downloaded.

I about fell out of my chair.

The hit was startling.

The word COSMOS, in the New Testament, had 180 entries.

That was the actual word in the New Testament Greek.

COSMOS. A hundred and eighty times.

I began to scroll, and stopped at the most remarkable phrases.

The parade just kept going and going and going, on and on.

The Bible talked about the cosmos, a lot!

OK. It was time to go to the scrolls, archaeological parchments and papyri, the new discoveries, the extra-biblical ancient books and papyrus texts. I sucked in my breath.

Program menu.

With a few quick moves of the mouse I was out of the Bible Documents program and selecting the Extra-Biblical texts.

DEAD SEA SCROLLS.

NAG HAMADI PAPYRI.

Etcetera.

I went down the menu.......and opted, All.

I selected the languages again: Hebrew, Aramaic, Greek, Latin, Syriac and Egyptian-Coptic.

Now, Find. Type: WORLDS, CREATION, COSMOS, MATTER.

Enter.

The computer went through its electronic ritual. I felt a certain sense of marvel as its inner circuitry and electromagnetic sensors scanned through the documents. This was the most advanced technology system in the world, and it was my tool for looking at some of the oldest surviving ancient scrolls and papyrus relics found in the dust and dirt of time. These ancient, decaying, fragmented texts came from the caves of Egypt, from the caves of the Dead Sea in Israel not far from my own camp, from tombs where some had been buried as cherished possessions of their original owners, from desert sands and excavations. They had been discovered by goatherds, by guano-fertilizer diggers, by Bedouin nomads, and even by archaeologists who carefully removed dirt from atop dirt and exposed them to first light in almost two thousand years.

In little more than an instant, a massive download distilled upon the screen. The numbers were remarkable: hundreds and hundreds of appearances of these four words in the texts.

I shook my head as I scrolled and then clicked page after page. There was a lot here. This was a lot.

Scrolling back up to the top, I began to slowly scroll and scan, and where I saw phrases of particular interest, I stopped to read. In the first ancient text, from the DEAD SEA SCROLLS:

The Morning Hymn: *'Blessed is He who by His power made the earth, by His wisdom founded the world, by His understanding spread out the skies.'......* Power, wisdom, understanding. Not an act of caprice, not a process without forethought and calculated knowledge, knowledge of things known and perceived, and then, understood. *Spread out the skies....* an understanding of expanding cosmos? OK.

Dead Sea Scrolls, Hymns: *'You have stretched out the heavens...... Everything which it contains you have established according to your approval...... And in the wisdom of your knowledge you have determined their course before they came to exist.'* That seems pretty clear. Expanding universe of fire, water, space; the cosmos is as it is because this was perceived to be the best alternative; the total motion of the cosmos and its burning spheres was calculated, chosen and designed in a fully completed concept before setting anything in motion. This was well thought out and planned.

Dead Sea Scrolls again, Rule of the Community: *'From the God of Knowledge comes all that is and shall be. Before ever they existed He established their whole design'*........ Again: forethought, in calculated design, before initiating the first thing. A fully pondered sequence based on knowledge of what would happen in the result of every procedure and consequence to the furthest extension of unfolding.

From c. 320 A.D., Nag Hamadi Papyri: On The Origin Of The World: *'Seeing that everybody.....says that nothing existed prior to chaos, I in distinction shall demonstrate that they are all mistaken, for they are not acquainted with the origin of chaos, nor with its root. How well it suits all men, on the subject of chaos, to say that it is a kind of darkness! But in fact it comes from a shadow, which has been called by the name darkness. And the shadow comes from a product that has existed since the beginning. It is, moreover, clear that it existed before chaos came into being'*........ What was this talking about, 'a shadow' that 'comes from a product that has existed since the beginning?' Dark matter? *'Now the eternal realm of truth has no shadow outside it, for the limitless light is everywhere within it. But its exterior is shadow, which has .been called by .the name darkness. From it there appeared a force, presiding over the darkness.'* Was this talking about a primordial singularity, like a 'black hole,' containing all of the matter, the *'light,'* which could not escape? Then it said *'It became pregnant of its own accord; suddenly it engendered jealousy. Since that day, the principle of jealousy amongst all the eternal realms and their worlds has been apparent.'* Pregnancy implies....what? A process that would end in a birth, something coming forth out of it. Was this *jealousy*, or *envy* as it said before that - an ancient understanding of *gravity*? Envy, jealousy and gravity all pull toward themselves, and want to hold, to keep. I read further *'Now as for that jealousy (gravity?), it was found to be an abortion without any spirit in it.'* This was hard for me to interpret by what I knew. When gravity came into existence, was it as if it were dead, and useless? Why would gravity in just dark matter be useless? *'Like a shadow it came into existence in a vast watery substance.'* Here's the water thing again. Obviously, vast quantities of water are in the universe - ice planetesimals, vapor molecules and ice molecules, but what's the point here? I didn't understand this. But the next part seemed clear: *'as with a woman giving birth to a child - all her superfluities flow out; just so, matter came into being out of shadow and was projected apart.'* 'Projected apart' - an explosion? A big bang? Matter was 'projected apart,' from that initial point. This was amazing. It was written in Roman times. It went on for pages talking about the ordering of matter in the chaos; *'matter....matter......worlds.....matter'*.... I could see this began, it seems, at the same place where physicists begin today, long before the formation of our sun and planet. This was long, and would take some studying. I would read it at another time. I clicked and scrolled.

The Codex Brucianus Manuscript 96: It says *first, there is matter.* An easy next question should be, what do you do with it? You organize it to create things. *Creation is organization,* it says. OK. Same as Hebrew.

The Stromata 2 of Clement of Alexandria, teacher of Origen: *...matter..* amid *'background material'...* What is 'background material?' I wondered. It's there during the ordering of *matter.* Dark matter? OK, it says the whole creation is to be understood as the imposing of an inner order on outer material, a progressive of organizing material from the center out. *You build the inner structure; outside is more material which you progressively take into the structure as you build.* Is this talking about accretion by gravitational attraction?

The Berlin Papyrus. *'At the same time, the great thought came to the elements in united wisdom, spirit joining with matter.'* I'm not sure what it means. Something to ask.

The writings of fourth century Bishop Synesius: *'The cosmos is not simply a oneness of self, of nothing and nothing else, but rather a multiplicity comprised in a oneness.'* There. Was this a description of myriad local accreted galaxies and star systems, separated by vast expanses of interstellar space? Was this saying that they each feel the combined overall influence of the whole, *'oneness,'* gravity playing its role in matter as a huge, expanding organism, the cosmos?

In The Gospel of Truth, here was another one.......*'Unity engulfs matter within itself like a flame.'* That sounded like accretion into great density, gravitational density resulting in fusion, suddenly igniting and engulfing the accretion into a flame, a sun. There was more: *'When the flame engulfs substance to form a new unity, then obscurity becomes light.'* Wow! Very simple language, but it sounded like heat in the unity, and fusion into a new substance - hydrogen fusing into helium? - and this process produces new unity of substance, a compound, like helium or even heavier compounds? And the process produces energy which escapes in the form of light! It certainly sounded like the ignition of fusion in a sun. There was more....... as the mass in the number of worlds increases the cosmos is expanding, and...... *'All spaces come forth from the Father, but at first, they have neither form nor name'*........ and, *'Only the Lord has penetrated the terrors of empty space.'*

The First Book of Enoch: .... *the ultimate horror is being in a place without a firmament, without a foundation beneath.......*

In Forty Day Literature: The Apostles ask about the Creation. Jesus cautions them, *'Don't ask for that.'* ......they plead to know......He says *'No, it is better for you not to, because it is more frightening than anything else if you do not know what is going on'.....* He tells them, the disciples of his time two thousand years ago, in a time when there was no technology, no telescopes, no way to comprehend any of these things, no way to convince anyone else of these things, that people can't remain in their right minds after seeing it! OK. Next.

In the Clementine Recognitions: Peter the Apostle....... is explaining the heavens to Clement.......matter is at first inert.....it's sterile......you have to do something to make it live.......it has to be energized.....old matter has to be re-energized. He actually uses the word *'energia!'* This was written almost two thousand years ago! This is from an archaeological artifact, written eighteen centuries ago! I went on.

In the Pistis Sophia: it talks of 'light' and 'spark' put into matter. *'When we say Light, we think of our kind of light,'.......* but that is wrong, obviously. What were these people talking about then, when they spoke of *'Light,' 'Spark,'* and other energy related words?

The Pistis Sophia continued: This is long.......lots of stuff here....OK, here's something: *'Let matter rejoice in the light, for the light will leave no matter unpurified.'* Not sure what that means, but must be relevant in some way. It goes on.......old matter that has been used and is to be renewed passes through a process where it it melts down, it's purified.....the action of the light always has a purifying effect, whether it's the first time or whether it's being reused........by the action of the 'spark' it no longer matters if it's old matter or unused matter, since by the action of the spark or the light upon it, the matter always becomes renewed.

Then here was something else interesting in the Psalm of Thomas: *'My Father, the joyful glorious light, summoned all of the Angels of Peace.......all his sons and all the angels ......and established them that they might rejoice in his greatness........ All bowed the knee before him and..... sang his praises together...... hailing him as the Illuminator of Worlds.'* This was like Job, the foundation of our world, our earth.

And in the recently discovered Creation Apocryphon papyrus: *'On that day began the discussion in which gods, angels and men participated. And then*

375

decisions of the discussions were then carried out by the gods, angels, and men. But the Prince Jaldanaoth did not understand the power of faith'...... and so was denied ...*'the authority over matter...'* which the others shared. This was the time John spoke of in the Apocalypse, before our coming to the earth: the war. Lucifer - Prince Jaldanaoth here - was denied power over matter because he did not comprehend Faith. He was denied..... a physical body - in which he would have gained power over this matter! Yet I was confused: Faith is the power by which the worlds were framed?

The ancient Syriac papyrus Ginza: Talking about the creation of this world.......Jesus is in the place where the Father is..... He's being instructed by the Father........He says *'Go down to that place where there are no skenas'....* OK - *skenas* from the Greek *skene* 'tent', used the same as for *topos*, 'place', a place set apart for the carrying out of a particular place or activity..... a dwelling place, then......a place in space where there is no dwelling yet.....create there....... a world. Then he says *Adam, this is the place in which you are going to live..... Your wife, Eve, will come and join you here.........here your progeny will thrive.......* Adam sees it before they come. He already exists as a Spirit. He marvels.... *'No words could describe thy power over all thy worlds'.....* there it was again: plural, *worlds.........* Then Adam speaks to us...... *'The Father taught me about the worlds of the Lord and the glory that abides therein. The Adam of light treads upon the earth's trembling foundation that is laid in the midst of the worlds.'*

I couldn't believe what I was reading. This was an ancient papyrus text*!* *'The Adam of light treads upon the earth's trembling foundation'.......* Adam was a Being of Light before the Fall. It was so clear. This was ancient! It was pure physics! And there was more: *'worlds'.....* And down here again, further ..... *'For the creation of endless worlds follows a single pattern laid down by the creator.'* I knew astronomers and physicists had determined that the elements - our 92 atomic elements like hydrogen, oxygen, carbon, magnesium, sodium, chloride, nitrogen, iron, copper, silver, gold, uranium - were all across the cosmos, and that many planets in other solar systems should be made of essentially the same materials, in about the same way. Was this an ancient expression of that physical truth?

The Apocalypse of Abraham, very old Hebrew text: He's praying; he's already seen a panoramic vision of creation in the universe and has understood it very well; now he's wanting to know how stars are made....... an Angel appears......the Angel takes him. He says his spirit left his body....he didn't actually go there physically, but he saw it all.........he's totally blown away by it all.....he doesn't understand what's going on, what he's seeing..........OK, he sees an indescribably mighty light, and within the light is a tremendous fire, and within that is a host of mighty forms that are constantly seething and exchanging with each other........they constantly change shape as they move, altering themselves, one exchanging with another......he can't stand it any more: *'Why have you brought me here? I can't see a thing. I've become weak. I think I'm out of my mind.'* ......he is terrified of not having anything under his feet.....he wants to lay down and hide his face, but there's no place to lay down......Whew! As they reach the innermost part of the star, they hear deep, immense and terrible rumblings he can't describe, they are so loud........even the Angel is getting nervous and anxious........they leave; he's very glad to get back home again.

This was truly......unimaginable. What ancient person before the Industrial Revolution could imagine such a thing? What was he describing? Obviously, great plasmas of heat and fire, and no place to stand, no place to lay down. He was in the midst of a surrounding light and heat. There was direct implication of comprehended vast size of the star. What did he mean by their moving in and out of each other, transforming, exchanging one with another? Hydrogen atoms fusing into helium? Heat and unimaginable gravitational density fusing simple atoms into each other and into even more complex atomic structures, new elements? Or the 'faces' of churning heat cells on the sun's face that we now see with our telescopes – that look like a fire-ball honeycomb covering the entire surface of the sun, churning billows of fire that billow up and then are sucked back into themselves. Is that what he saw? Whether heat cells or fusions of elements, this would be a good description of what we know is happening, for someone not having a vocabulary.

This was awesome. I could not help but think of the times.

What a truly terrifying journey for an ancient person. Even at the height of the Roman Empire, what did the ancients know of real power, or energy? I thought about Abraham, about all ancient people, suddenly confronted with powers we know today, and take for granted. What would ancient people think, if they were suddenly standing on the ground next to a roaring 747 jet on the runway testing its engines at full thrust blast; or if they suddenly found themselves free falling out of a small plane at high altitude, plummeting in the air without even knowing that the thing on their backs was a parachute, or what a parachute is, or that it works, and it stops your fall - and that sky-diving is something we do for fun? Or what if they were suddenly set on the ground in the White Sands desert at the moment of the first atomic bomb explosion - there, personally, standing in spirit, even a mile away from Ground Zero? What would they think of the light of atomic fission, of the searing heat, the body shaking sound, the vibrations, the shock waves? Even we, who knew all of these things and daily talk about them over coffee and toast as we turn pages of the morning newspaper would shake in terror, if we were standing right THERE!

Even the simplest of these experiences was something which exceeded all of their life references. Though I could imagine them, they were frightening to me. I *had* stood on the ground next to a 747 jet engine just idling - it was deafening! I *had* been high up over the earth, in a jet, within its metal body enveloping me and shielding me from the wind blast, a floor beneath my feet, and still the first time was a bit intense until I got used to it. But I had never been sky diving. I didn't know the feeling of falling, and falling, with nothing below. And as for atomic light and heat and blast thunder, I didn't even want to THINK about being close to Ground Zero at White Sands.

Yes, an ancient person without any preparation for these things, with no way to relate to them afterwards, no words to even express them........ This was Abraham's best attempt at describing something even I was at a loss to imagine. This was the inside of a star. Who, being there, unconsumed, wouldn't think she or he was going crazy? What a terrifying, shocking experience.

Is this how Abraham had gained his legendary knowledge of the cosmos, of the creation of the universe, of stars, of the earth?

Suddenly I remembered the Holy Kaaba , with the black iron meteorite in Mecca, the most Holy object in all Islam, which five times a day every good Moslem turned to and bowed toward in prayer to God. This black meteorite was said to have been a gift to Abraham by the Angel Gabriel. Westerners privately laughed at this story. But my goodness, what if it were true? A 'souvenir' from a remarkable journey through space? Was this all just fable?

The meteorite in the Kaaba, absolutely, was real. It was from space.

I scrolled again.

Here was something in I Clement; he's writing about Abraham: Abraham's experience must have been more comprehensive and instructive than we imagined..... *'Abraham has been greatly witnessed of; having been called the friend of God. And yet he steadfastly beholding the glory of God, says with all humility, 'I am dust and ashes.' '* While being shown the creation, and suns, and stars, Abraham must have been told of the physics of what he was seeing, and how these things ultimately made the materials by which even he was physically made. Knowing now what I know of his experiences, he must have known: we are made of dust, subatomic particles, infinitesimal particles, and the elements of our bodies are indeed the ashes of great stars. He spoke it so clearly for us to know, the true learning of his enquiries: *'I am dust and ashes,'* yet probably no one, not even Clement, understood what he was really talking about. How could they know? We're just barely grasping the idea now.

I scrolled on.

The Dead Sea Scrolls, the Jubilees fragment: God is talking about Enoch, with whom He walked and whom He took up, alive, into the heavens...... *'Enoch, after we instructed him.......wrote down all the mysteries of the heavens, and all the paths of their hosts'.......* At a very ancient time, a written description of the solar system, possibly more than that, from observation. The orbits of the heavenly bodies.

The Askew Manuscript: OK... *There are many mansions, many regions, degrees, worlds, spaces and heavens, but all have but one law.'* It goes on and says 'The worlds exist so that intelligent spirits may come and inhabit them'......

This was curious: I understood many mansions, and regions, but what were degrees? I understood worlds in plural, but what was I supposed to understand from 'spaces,' and 'heavens?' These came from the plural 'cosmoses' - plural universes? What did this imply?

Josephus, speaking of the Essenes: *'Their doctrine is this....that the souls are immortal and continue for ever: and that they came out of the most subtle air, and are united to their bodies'.....* Spirit described as being made of matter finer than dust....out of the most subtle air... that's finer than dust. A finer matter than we know?

The Berlin Papyrus again: *'The living spirit clothes itself in a body of elements through which it is able to carry out its works in the world.'*

The Dead Sea Scrolls, Hymns: *Yea, over mere dust hast Thou wafted Thy Holy Spirit, and hast so molded that clay that it can converse with angels and be in communion with Beings Celestial.* Clearly, though physical bodies are made of this matter, we are still given the capacity to hear and speak to angels, and *Beings Celestial*, whatever they are.

Again, Dead Sea Scrolls, The Zadokite Document: *By 'Sons of Zadok' is meant those elect of Israel that have been designated by name and that shall go on functioning in the Last Days. Behold, their names have been specified, the families into which they are to be born, the epochs in which they are to function......* This sounds as if the spirits created in the beginning wait their turns, and only become clothed in a body of elements in chosen times and chosen generations. Odd.

The Book of Second Jeu, very early Christian book held in the highest spiritual esteem by early Christians: OK. This is really interesting. ...... *A person, spirit, who is sent to take charge of a new world, as Adam was sent to take charge of this world as First, is called a Jeu...... Jeus become fathers......* Among the several things this was telling me, it clearly defined the use of the term 'world' as meaning a planet inhabited by life, especially human life. Most remarkably, it was telling me that Adam's spirit being placed into his body of flesh in this earth was neither the first time God did this in this universe, nor was it the last; and, it was a process for bringing the birth of a generation on a world, to being the mortal parenting of children.

The Gospel of Philip: *Only progeny is eternal, only children go on forever. That's talking about us. We are eternal. .....the worlds are countless...... they have been going on forever......*

Was the expression 'they have been going on forever' just a phrase, or did it imply a universe before this one? Physicists for some time have calculated back to a Big Bang, but few have dared to guess what went on before that. Did time begin at the beginning of this universe, or had there been universes before this one, before the Big Bang? Was our universe just another in a cycle, of a series? Yet it was clear about one thing: we, the children, we are eternal. Suns may form and burn and perish and end, galaxies may form and swirl and dissipate, but we, we the children, we are eternal.

The Dead Sea Scrolls, Psalms of Thanksgiving 1: *'When Thou dist stretch out the heavens.........Thou dist also make potent spirits.........spirits immortal took on the form of holy angels........When, too, in Thy power Thou dist create earth and seas and deeps, in thy wisdom didst Thou set within them spirits immortal........So hast Thou made his flesh a promtuary in this world for that spirit of man which Thou didst create to last throughout all time and for ages infinite'.......* More of the same; all quite clear.

The Apochryphon of James, the Brother of the Lord: *......in all the worlds there is a common pattern of rule....... there is one rule everywhere...... the same rule exists throughout all the worlds.* Was this talking about physical laws, or some form of spiritual rule? I guess it made no difference: it says these things are the same all over the cosmos. This is about what physicists assume; it should be true about God's laws as well.

Here was something else in the Dead Sea Scrolls, the scroll called The War Between the Sons of Light and the Sons of Darkness: *'Thou art He who created the earth and the rules whereby parts thereof are assigned to desert and wasteland; likewise all that issues from it and all the fruits of its yield; the bounds of the seas also and the reservoirs of the rivers; the cleavage of the deeps; all manner of beasts and fowl; the fabric of man and his offspring'......* They understood that there are rules, consequences of choices in design which govern the way the earth became! These were definitely 'natural rules,' governing ecologies; here is a rudimentary understanding of ecologies, whereby parts of the earth become lush while others would become deserts, governed by the measure of the sea and the *'reservoirs of the rivers'* and *'cleavages of the deep.'* OK.... very few rivers begin as lakes, so 'reservoirs' has to be springs.... groundwater 'reservoirs.' What could *'cleavage of the deep'* mean? *'Cleavage'* is the word used to describe the lines along which rocks break. *'Cleavage of the deep'*.... tectonic plate cleavage lines? Could this be a primitive, simple understanding of subsurface plate movements *'of the deep,'* an essential part of the *'rules whereby parts thereof are assigned to desert and wasteland'* while other parts thrive with *'all the fruits of its yield'?* This phrase *'fabric of man'* is curious enough. Recognition of chemistry, compounds and matter of tissue design? Overall complexity of biological organism design? DNA program conceptualization? With virtually no vocabulary, the vestige here is still pretty clear. Where did they get this stuff?

More from the Dead Sea Scrolls, Psalms of Thanksgiving 1: It is speaking of the creation, and the purposes of various geophysical realities on this earth as consciously designed by God, and here it says God made *'meteors and lightnings, to make them discharge their tasks'*........ I don't get it. The Dead Sea Scrolls indicate that meteors and lightning have a purpose to discharge? Meteors and lightning?

OK, scrolling, scrolling.... OK, in the writings of Jerome, 400 A.D. He translated the Septuagint into Latin and gathered the early Christian books selected for the Bible and translated them into Latin for the Vulgate Latin Bible........ OK, he says here that Origen, the early-generation Father after the Apostles..... *believed that there were countless worlds*....... that he did not believe as did Epicurus the Greek that they all existed at once......that rather they were constantly coming into existence and passing away. *'This was the old Christian teaching of the Primitive Church.'* So I'm seeing.

OK. Origen. Let's see....... Yes. Here's one of them. *'This is not my opinion; this is what the elders used to teach. There will be another world after this one. And in the same way, there were other worlds before this one. We thus share a common nature with other worlds.'* That was pretty straight-forward and plain.

Here was something else: *'All cosmoses follow the pattern of a single world, which is called the type, the archetype. Ever since the beginning this has been so, keeping the entire physis in the state of joy and rejoicing.'*

Here it was again: *'cosmoses,'* in the plural. Universes. Did this refer to a cycle of universes before ours, that is, a previous universe before ours began sometime eight, twelve, fifteen or twenty billion years ago, depending on who you were reading? Or did this refer to more than one universe - 'cosmoses' - existing beside each other in a vastness of space beyond our 'bubble' of expanding universe? In other words, other 'bubbles' of expanding cosmoses in an immensity exceeding our ability to comprehend?

Either way, here were ancient people, writing about *worlds* and *cosmoses* in ways which only recent physics dared to propose.

I scrolled through the Epistle of the Apostles, and immediately noticed: *'Where my Father is, is entirely different from this world. There you will see lights that are nobler than your kind of light. In the millions of worlds that God made for his son, every world is different from the others and wonderful in its own radiance.'*

I was reminded of the words of the Bible of the Apostle Paul after he had been lifted up 'into the third heaven,' that *'Eye has not seen, nor ear heard, neither has entered into the heart'* what he has seen and heard. Nobody else has seen it. Nobody else has heard anything like it. Nobody has any frame of reference with which to relate, to even imagine it. No words. No images. No idea.

In the Odes of Solomon: *'The worlds were made by His word and by the thought of His heart, so they are all as one. There is no rivalry among them, but they are glorious in their firmaments and agree among themselves, fitting together like the lashes of an eye. All rejoice in each other, each being more glorious and bright than the other.'*

How could each be more glorious than the other?

Maybe here was an answer: in the Pistis Sophia: *'Other worlds cannot possibly be described in terms of this world. Not only is there less in common between other worlds and this world, they differ as widely among themselves as any of them does from us.'*

What did this mean? If the 92 atomic elements are essentially found the same over most of the cosmos, then the rocks and minerals and compounds should be about the same.

But what about land masses, and mountains, and beaches, and waterfalls, and geological arrangements? They would all be different, even if the balance was kept about the same. Just on our own planet we have such geological and ecological variety, and each vista is spectacular in its own right. How would we see an exact Everest, or Matterhorn, or Niagara Falls, or Grand Canyon? Mountains, waters and canyons might be similar, but each would be its own marvel.

But moreso, what about DNA patterns? What about plant and bird and fish and animal shapes and colors and sizes and forms? Just look at our own Earth! In just the living species, from the sea to the forests to the animals and the birds, the insects - life microscopic and huge - what life species living today is not a wonder to see and understand? And as we look at the past of our planet - the fishes and animals and 'dinosaurs' and mammals now extinct - what a stunning panorama of spectacular life forms! Is this all that can be structured and designed with DNA? Can God design other shapes of plants, leaves, trees, insects, reptiles, amphibians, fishes, planktons and invertebrates? Can God make other shapes and designs and colors of mammals and birds? Is the 'zoo' of life only this? What perfectly wondrous creatures might he have thoughtfully designed and placed on other worlds, in just as superb array as on ours?

How about the configurations of stars as seen from other worlds? What would a night sky be filled with if we were to gaze out into this same cosmos, only from another *skena*, another *topos*, another dwelling place, another habitation, another world?

Next, recently discovered writing of James: *In the limited confines of the flesh, which condition all our thinking, we can't possibly grasp the nature of other existences or even begin to count the number of other worlds.* This was written in ancient times!

In the Dead Sea Scrolls, the Testament of Kohath: ....'*and God of Gods for all Eternity. And He will shine as a light upon you and He will make known to you His great Name, and you will know Him, that He is the Eternal God and Lord of all creation, and sovereign over all things, governing them according to His will.*'

Here was another: Clement again, in First Clement: '*God is the Father of all the worlds.*'..... and then again...... '*He knows them; they keep their courses and covenants with Him; He calls them by name, and they answer him from eternity to eternity. As the Father of greatness is in the glorious world, so his Son rules among those cosmoses as first chief lord of all the powers.*'

In the Dead Sea Scrolls, The Genesis Apochryphon, the words of Lamech to his wife upon the birth of Noah: .....'*Take an oath by the Most High, the Lord Supreme, the Sovereign of all worlds, the Ruler of all the heavenly beings*'........ worlds, clear and unambiguous.

More, in the Hebrew Talmud: ....the Minaean Jews had taught in error that this was the only world, so, '*To correct this we say in our prayers today, Mi-'olamim l-olamim, worlds without end, using the plural.*' Who could dispute this? It is written.

Here was something else in Hebrew, but.... How did this get in here? This is late, very late: 11th century A.D. I guess Kevin was trying to cover all the bases he could. OK. Maimonides, the great Jewish intellectual: '*This world is but a speck among the worlds and man is as nothing. Man is nothing in the midst of the worlds.*'

If Maimonides knew it, he must have known it from Hebrew literature. If he could understand it in the eleventh century, where was everybody else at that time? Why didn't everybody know?

Here was something else, in Josephus, speaking of Patriarch Jacob's understanding of his son Joseph's dream about 1800 B.C.; Josephus explains it by the most ancient oral traditions: Antiquities of the Jews 2:16 *'as guessing that the moon and sun were like his mother and father; the former (moon), as she that gave increase and nourishment to all things, and the latter (sun), he that gave form and other powers to them; and that the stars were like his brethren, since they were eleven in number, as were the stars that receive their power from the sun and moon.'* The moon giving increase perhaps recalls the tides, I don't know...... I knew of a plethora of feminine allusions to the moon all centrally dealing with birth cycles - increase - which we probably don't even understand yet. We think the moon has nothing to do with plant growth or any other 'increase,' - what do we really know? A seed buried under the soil is stimulated by infinitesimal cosmic changes to suddenly sprout, we know that much. Equally significant here, though, is the glaring phrase about the sun, *'that gave form and powers to them,'* i.e. the planets, earth among them. There could be no doubt here that this ancient oral tradition was about the planets, for it specifically recognized *'since they were eleven in number, as were the eleven stars that receive their power from the sun,'* which 'stars' were the planets. This was remarkable. Eleven planets were known; and, Jacob of old understood that they receive their power - light? orbital velocity? - from the sun. This would seem to place the sun in a central understanding.

Was this a latent, remnant knowledge of heliocentricity?

I came to the last thing, from the Gospel of Truth:

'All the other worlds look to the same God as to a common sun.'

That was profound. In one phrase, it told me that the ancients understood: there are many worlds; and all worlds have each their own suns; stars are suns; worlds look to suns as the center; and, all the worlds look to the same God.

As to a common sun. That meant that they understood planets normally look each to its own sun.

Each to its own sun.

Was this too, a garbled remnant memory of heliocentricity?

I had seen enough. I was prepared for tonight's discussions, but all of this raised new questions. Where could I begin?

The beginning of Genesis did not really say in Hebrew 'In the Beginning,' but *'As a beginning,'* and gave an account of the formation of *this earth* as a beginning to a history of *this earth*. The Bible clearly declared that before *this earth* was formed, Hosts of Heaven and Angels existed; children of God already lived with God and shouted and sang at the beginning formation of *this earth*. There had been war in Heaven, in Heaven *before* this earth was completed, and a third of the Host was cast out for rebellion. Clearly, even without all of the additional extra-scriptural readings, something extensive had been going on and existed in the universe before *this earth*.

My questions, as I had written them, began in the wrong place.

The Bible was clear: this earth was not THE beginning.

So what was? What existed before this earth?

A whole new set of questions began to form in my mind.

I exited the programs and shut down the power. The temperature in the *skene*, the tent, was already 89 degrees.

Walking outside the tent, I squinted in the bright Judaean sun. What a morning! I went over to the spring again, took a long drink, filled my canteen, and headed up the wadi. I needed a good hike.

I was amazed, as I walked, how changed everything looked. It was different, not really looking for anything. It was hard to describe, but now that I had found what I had come to find, the rocks and cliffs looked less foreboding, less threatening. I had a feeling of security, completeness, and a comfort as I walked among these silent mountains of stone. Now the hills and rocks and cliffs seemed friendly, unconcerned with my presence and passing, no longer menacing or sinister as they had always seemed when they were trying to keep me from discovering their secret treasure, when I was desperately reading their every hollow and line. I was no longer probing them, neither with my eyes or my hands, and they were no longer evading me or trying to conceal. I found myself smiling as I walked along and gazed up all around me. These hills and cliffs were magnificent, beautiful. We communed. It was good.

After a while I stopped at a good place and ate my lunch, munching and looking up at the tops of the ridges and the blue sky above. When I was finished, I hiked a bit more, and then turned back toward camp. It was a good walk. When I got to camp, I went to my tent, lay down on the cot, and fell asleep. I had a good nap.

When I awoke it was twilight, and already getting cool.

I quickly prepared a dinner and ate it. Tonight was going to be good. There were lots of important questions to ask.

I went to the lab tent, sat down, turned on the power, booted up, went straight to the Internet program, and typed in

WWW. URIM AND THUMMIM .GOD

With the tap of a finger, it whirred into action, and the page appeared on the screen, cursor waiting. I enthusiastically typed:

Good evening! I had a very good day. How are you today?

I felt very good about tonight's greeting. I felt this way.

Hello. I'm doing fine. Today was a very good day, thank you. Lots of good things and positive learning all over the world.

I reached into my pocket and pulled out the list of questions. It was quite scribbled with additions and rearrangements.

I think I know what I would like to talk about tonight, I typed.

Good. Where do we begin?

I have a number of questions about the Creation. I have finally seen how clearly the Bible speaks of time before the formation of this earth, and, I guess, this solar system. Our sun and planets, including this earth, are all that Genesis is describing, right?

Yes.

Then I need to learn about Angels, Fallen Angels, and Children of God who saw this earth's beginnings from..... someplace. I think I need to begin with... us. We are your children, but what are we?

You are Intelligences, Spirit Children, Beings of Truth and Light, with a physical body made of Energenes.

I don't understand, I typed. *What are our bodies made of?*

Energenes. There is no solid matter as you experience it; nothing is physical as you perceive it. Yet the universe is physical, as it is spiritual. Your physical estate and the estate of all matter in the universe is not an illusion: it is the physical state achieved by use of the true laws of this physics. Yet it is truth for you to comprehend: You are pure Light, a perfection of harnessed energy, trapped momentarily for your use both as a physical matter and in power to function, to move it and use it as you choose and direct, by your command.

How is it done?

The secret of the creation is the organization of 'solid' matter out of non-solid energy. It is to be understood in the First Law: that there must be Opposition in all things. This was revealed anciently.

I thought the law of opposites was first formulated as a theory by Anaximander and Pythagoras, and canonized in Aristotle.

Among my children in some places of the world, not all knowledge has been equally appreciated; some have set much of it aside. In the part you speak of, though this was given, yet it was set aside anciently, for it was little understood by the generations, and so, unwanted. However, later children wisely perceived this truth; these children you know, for they wrote of it.

Yet see among my children who settled in India: since ancient time they press their hands together in greeting and prayer, palms pressed with elbows out. In this see the ancient symbol of the secret of the universe: 'opposition in all things.' The Hindu children greet each other with this knowledge, and recall it in in prayer, as do still other children in your world. They received this truth with great awe even in ancient time, and comprehended its fundamental basis. Yet what was given to them has been greatly retold, and though it is retold in allegories and stories of much beauty, it must be searched diligently to be found and understood. Yet there is great wisdom and benefit: these too testify of me.

See today this most visible vestige of ancient truth revealed to you. Even you know some in your land who when praying, clasp their hands together, opposite against opposite, though the memory of why they do this is forgotten.

Why is Opposition in all things the First Law?

This is the great secret, of this physics, of the body, of the creation, of the Spirit, and of all the universe. It is the principle which makes everything possible. There are ospposites within opposites, and within these opposites are opposites. These all may be used to great advantage, and marvelous effect.

You have learned that matter is energy, and energy is matter, and that neither one nor the other form can be destroyed, only converted. In this, they are opposites, yet in every exchange, freed energy may be used. There are many forms, and many purposes of beneficial use. This was foreseen in the Design.

What you call subatomic particles, having opposite charges, which both attract and repel, thus can attract unto organized atoms, and molecules, and compounds, and react as 'solid,' for they usefully repel. All masses of this physical matter become possible even because of 'opposition in all things.'

Only now have you come to understand Opposition as a law of this physics, yet you still little understand its total significance in your being.

You have developed mathematics and comprehended physics enough today to comprehend this. I AM the one who revealed it millenniae ago. Only now can you come to understand what was recorded so clearly in Genesis: your physical bodies are made from the dust of the earth - subatomic energies trapped in unities of elements and compounds of those of the earth - and to this same elementary dust will these physical bodies return.

Yet you are more than just this physical, and you are eternal. Neither matter nor energy can be destroyed; therefore you cannot be destroyed, for energy is eternal, and Intelligence energy organized into Spirit Bodies retains form eternally, by the same law, in the physics of Spirit Matter: this you are.

Then it is by the Law of Opposites that suns and planets and worlds are made. You spoke yesterday of many worlds. This morning I have read about many worlds. I have read about Hosts of Heaven and your children. I saw in the Book of Job that before this world was formed, it is written that the children of God shouted for joy.

Yes?

Was I there?

Yes, you were there.

Were we all there?

Yes, even as it is written. You are the Hosts of Heaven, and you existed before the earth was. You understood what was coming; this next world was for you, and you sang, and shouted for joy.

We were there, in space, and saw the beginning of this Earth begin to accrete and draw together into an attracting ball of gravitational impact, into a world?

Yes.

Did we help?

Yes. You were part of it all. Each of you has done his and her part, and earned your right to be here. Never forget this. All whom you see in this world have earned their right to be here, by their valiance.

We earned the right to come here?

Does this surprise you? Each and every one who is here, who has ever been here, who will ever be here, earned this right by obedience: not just a vote of support, but by following the command and lending energy and the power of Faith into all that has become what is in this local dwelling ecology.

Know this and remember it well, for in this knowledge you may comprehend much that you see in your world. This was known from the beginning; and that the reward would be great. Though not all will return in the highest status, yet all those who kept their First Estate and earned this Estate will have immortality amid the Glory that each can sustain, save those who willfully throw away their gift in contempt.

This was known since the beginning: that some will not fully succeed. All accepted this, for you also knew: where there is a greater Glory, so there is a lesser Glory; in the House of my Father are many mansions, all of Glory. Those who desire and follow me shall be known, and in no wise lose their reward. All of you born into this world accepted this. And you chose by your Free Agency.

Why would so many Spirits have wanted to work and come here, knowing that some of us will suffer here, be hurt, feel pain, be lonely, have heartbreaks, be poor, hungry, cold, sick, and die so wastefully and so miserably? Why would we choose to do this?

The difference between cold, silent, unenclosed endless space, and the enclosed, warm, musically divided space on a planet with boundaries and controllable limits - a physical place, as you saw in the ancient texts: a skena, a topos - is so greatly to be desired by Intelligences long isolated in space that even a modest stature in a 'physical' world is ever more desirable over the highest possible existence in an inert, incorporeal, cold, boundaryless void.

The gift of this kind of energene-matter existence, with boundaries and locality, is reward sufficient to make the least Intelligence happy for eternity.

But there is more. Much more. You cannot imagine it, so there is no point in trying to describe it. You understand this, that you cannot imagine all things just now. But much awaits you, all of you who keep your Second Estate.

Why are there many worlds? Why have you made so many Spirit Children?

There are many more Intelligences than you can imagine; there are many more than all those you see and know on your world that I have helped even in this generation. You do not remember the longing of the Intelligences.

Why must there be many worlds? To comprehend this you must comprehend the equilibrium of all things since the beginning, and comprehend the equilibrium of large scale local regions of a vast universe and how it is balanced. Many worlds form, and many may be positioned and groomed into ideal skenas and dwelling places for those who long. Many may be groomed.

Yet you are still children, and children are not sensible. How often do you break that which is given to you? Even a few of you can destroy an entire world. Look at how few of you have already polluted an entire earth, though from the beginning you have been entrusted to dress it and care for it. Yet as you leave its garden, you cease to be one with it, and to understand your stewardship over it. See the remaining stewards: tribes of the Amazon, tribes of the Andes, tribes of the islands, tribes of the bush; see how they live in the garden in harmony with it. See the Kalahari Bushchildren, how they receive every part of their environment and ecology with gratefulness and humility. They do not kill an animal lest they first carefully put it to sleep, and when they kill for food they ask forgiveness of the creature whose gift they take, and they give it thanks, and assure it that its gift will be received with rejoicing. This oneness you forget.

As you leave the garden, you forget this, and see yourselves as warlords of power, and you become puffed up, and ravage, and destroy wantonly, with no regard for tomorrow. As children you are selfish, and messy, and you fight. It is better to keep you separated into reasonable groups; it spares your many worlds. And there is no shortage of worlds; yet to you is given only this one.

Those Intelligences for whom I have created spirit bodies become my children, out of all those Intelligences which are. Know this: They are many Intelligences. They are more than just those on your earth.

So, there are many earths, even before ours. Where are they?

Across the expanse of this galaxy, and across the expanses of the many galaxies, throughout all this universe. There are myriad suns as yours, which is a useful type for worlds; and earths, just as this one, which is a useful size and composition and distance from a sun. On these live your brothers and sisters.

How many worlds exist?

My creations are without number to you, but I have numbered them all.

Are we the same, on all these worlds?

You are the same, and yet what is the same? See yourselves even here on your world: though you are the same, yet you are the most individual of all creatures. Look to your individual minds and selves and see your diversities; look to your nations and tongues and cultures and traditions and see yet more of your diversity. Look to your generations and times and periods and Ages, and see even greater diversity. When are you the same in your own world?

And yet if you ask about your bodies, are you all made in this likeness, yes: so are all of my children made in this likeness, in the likeness of God are you all made.

Are there different plants and animals on the other worlds, different species and forms than we know here?

I AM a God who loves infinite variety, and as many beauties as I can imagine which can function well, it pleases me to make, and see, and enjoy.

Shall the children who tinker with the DNA of the design be any different? If they can imagine something beautiful and useful, will they not create it? You are my children: shall you take any less joy in a new life form you design? As you learn to mold a new species of plant with a new and never seen shape and leaf and flower, will you not hold it up for all to see; and as you have adequately endowed it with balanced metabolic function, and its is healthy, and survives well and reproduces well, will you not joyfully exclaim to your siblings, 'It is good!'? When you learn to create, will you ever tire of creation?

Just as you, the children, create from a few notes and tones an infinity of new beauties in music; and with a few colors, infinite beauties of painting, and of a finite number of forms, infinite beauties of sculpture and art of all kinds, remember: Lifeform is Artform. You will delight in its endless variations, as each form is given its perfect functioning, balance, health, and ability to survive both within its balanced organism and its fully balanced ecological environment.

If we were there with you and watched the beginnings of this earth and sang and shouted for joy, then it follows that the Angels and the Spirits who rebelled and were cast out were there too.
I would like to know about the Angels, and Fallen Angels.

You have so much about this now to read and study, and you have your own personal experience; but many of you do not accept what is written, because it is from so long ago, and as few have seen either, many jealously say nothing is so, and deny any truth to those who have seen, and know.

It is as the new things which the children have invented and accomplished, even setting foot on the moon: many children in far remote simple places refuse to believe, for these things are too new, and as they have not themselves seen it, they say nothing is so, and deny any truth to those who have seen, and know.

My children are very humorous in this regard: half of you do not believe truths because you have believed the whispers saying "It is old, so do not believe it, for the old ones knew nothing;" the other half of you will not believe truths because you have believed the whispers saying "It is a new tale; do not believe it: it is told to impress and deceive us; it is not possible, nor true."

In most of my children I see a little of both of these halves, and all of you believe some of both deceptions. Yet I will teach you again.

You know: there are hosts of Angels all over this world, and they are exceedingly busy. And yes, there are many fallen angels, you call demons, and they too are exceedingly busy. There are many entities who do not have the interests of the children in mind, and wish only to confuse and control the children of your generation. It has been so, since the beginning.

Tell me more about them, please.

You know Spirits can be seen and unseen. Many in every generation have seen them, and for seeing, they have believed. Wise are those who have not seen, and still believed. This is a gift not all may use. Of those who have not seen, many do not believe, and they spend wondrous time foolishly explaining away that which is, and is in spite of all their unlearned denials.

You yourself have been a humorous child in this learning curve. I watched you in your younger years. You died and had your Near Death Experience, and your spirit left your body, and you experienced marvelous things which you as a twelve-year-old saw in rightful awe. Though in those days few people knew of these things, and you found you could not speak of them even to your own parents for fear of them thinking you had become unbalanced or brain damaged in your accident, you knew that you had left your body; you learned the great secret: you are a Spirit inside a body of flesh and blood. You thereafter found it easy to believe in Angels, yes, even though you had not seen them, for you had shared an identical experience in Spirit.

Yet, in spite of this, as you grew and went to school and then to university, you listened to the lecturers in the Psychology classes who disdainfully spoke of spiritual things, entire lectures on 'voodoo' and 'possessions' of evil spirits, which they said were imaginings. They exposed, they thought, the foolishness of belief in 'devils,' and said that there are no 'devils,' and you affirmed this total disbelief. What they mocked, you mocked.

For you, to believe in what the professors belittled was nonsense. The power of mockery is great, and many who see clearly are put to shame among their peers by it; even as the wish to be seen as wise among the learned doctors is great, and many deny what they would believe, for fear of being mocked.

And so you believed Angels because you read of them in your Bible; yet you disbelieved the devils because of shame, even though they were in your same Bible. Yet it was not your fault: the sophistry and arrogance of the learned puffed up in their imagined learning taught you the pride of imagined superior perspective over the 'ignorant' who so believed, and the shame to be so silly as to believe in devils. The professors spoke of power of suggestion, and, being innocent, you believed. You believed in the rightness of disbelief, in spite of your Near Death Experience, and your knowledge that not all souls are good.

Then you went to live in Brazil, where there is great activity of those who worship in the religions of Macumba, and Xango, and other Espirita rituals where they worship the Father of Devils, and evil spirits, and offer them their bodies to come into, wherein the spirits give them power in return for the gift of flesh. You soon heard many things, and firmly disbelieved; and you disdained those from your country who believed in these things as real, whom you thought should have known better in this scientific day and age. I watched you chuckle as you listened to them, disbelieving their seriously shared experiences of what they had seen. You believed none of it. You had been to school. You knew.

Yet then came the first time you saw an evil spirit, and it grasped your arm and you felt instantly your whole body cold, and ill. You saw it and you felt it, and yet you still disbelieved, until you could disbelieve no longer, for you could not deny what was happening to you, and you finally cried out for help.

I did not type anything back. I just sat, thinking. My mind was already back then, back there. It had been in the *nordeste* of Brazil, in the late 1960's in a little house on a side street in a little town where I was staying, and it was true: I had been a total skeptic, no - a firm disbeliever in all those things.

As soon as I got to Brazil I heard of spirit possessions - spirits entering into people's bodies at *espirita* and *macumba* rituals - and of objects moving without being touched, of strange lights, of voices of the dead speaking through mediums. It was all black magic to me. I heard of Allen Kardecke, who officialized the *espirita* religions and their sacrifices and offerings so often found at crossroads in clay pots in the morning after midnight rites: yellow-colored meal, and black chickens with their necks bitten through, the blood dripped into the meal, often surrounded by cigarettes, cigars, aguardente drink bottles, condoms, perfumes, ladies' garters, and cryptic prayers. And I heard of Ze Origoh, the unschooled man who supposedly received the spirit of a dead surgeon, and performed miraculous operations on cataracts and cancers, supposedly witnessed by doctors who remained baffled by cures done with kitchen knifes and without blood; of many other strange and often miraculous things - curings of diseases, and more. Talk of these things was everywhere, both from the Brazilians whom I could forgive, and from other Americans whom I scoffed for their gullibility: they should have known better.

I believed none of it. I had been scientifically raised. This was the twentieth century. I was college educated. I had been told. I knew. It was just hocus pocus, tricks and 'power of suggestion.'

Yet that night, my American friends and I had been sitting in our little narrow house when it happened. The house was really just a long hall from front to back, with two tiny bedrooms on the left side, one just inside the front door and another toward the back, leaving a small open room between them and another at the back as a kitchen-dinette. You could look from the front door straight through the 'hall' to the back door, and through the top of the double door which usually had the bottom closed. The small back yard had walls about ten feet high, stuccoed brick with big jagged broken glass bottles cemented in all along the top so no one could climb over, and at the far end was a big stand of tall sugar cane, which looked like bamboo.

As we sat that night chatting in the open room in the middle of this hall-house, my chair stood in the hall passage, and I could look down the hall to the kitchen area and the double door, which was open at the top, and closed at the bottom, as usually.

Suddenly the lights went out. We were not alarmed: it was the weekly rolling blackout. They happened regularly, for the population had outstripped the region's ability to produce adequate electrical supply. So, each sector of town took its turn being shut off while the rest of the city had power. You got used to it: the power would just cut off, and you'd be in the dark. In a few hours, it would come back on, as another sector of town would black out.

We didn't care. We just kept talking in the dark.

From my chair I had a clear view back to the back door. The scene looked different now, a negative in black and white, with the whole inside of the house black and only the upper open half of the door left bright: outside there was a bright full moon. As I sat listening to my friends talk, adding a few words and laughing, I gazed out the open upper door, into the moon-bathed back yard.

I could see the walls and the sugar cane almost as clear as day. But suddenly, I saw what looked like a man, but he was transparent, a shadow, standing at the back of the yard, right in front of the sugar cane. It was strange, because he was a man, but I could see the sugar cane through him: he was just a shadow.

What was this?

I didn't really quite understand what it was, and I dropped out of the conversation, focussing on this shadow man in the back yard.

Almost immediately, he began to get bigger, and bigger. That's what it seemed to do: he got taller, and wider, as if he were growing. The back yard, so brightly bathed in moonlight, was becoming dark.

The man-shadow just got bigger and bigger, and the square of moonlight and back yard I could see through the open upper back door kept getting smaller and smaller around the shadow, until the bright moon-lit open door was eclipsed by the shadow, and everything was as dark as a night with no moon at all.

Yet even when the light was entirely shadowed, I could still see the sugar cane and the back wall!

I was about to say something to my friends when suddenly I felt a feeling like I had never felt before, horrible! Uggggh! I felt a sickening, ill sensation, and a cold chill poured into my body as if I had suddenly been filled with ice water. What was happening to me?

The sudden rush of sickness and chill was so intense that for a few seconds I couldn't speak. Finally I croaked out 'I feel sick.'

My oldest friend, who had lived in Brazil a long time, heard the sound of my voice and hesitantly asked, 'you don't mean sick-sick, do you? You mean something else, right?'

'Yes,' I shuddered. The feeling was deepening. This friend had told me a lot of things about evil spirits, which neither I nor the other two of us had believed, but as I sat there in the dark, listening to him stand up out of his chair and step toward me, I suddenly knew: the shadow in the shape of a man, transparent, see-through, was an evil spirit. I was in the clutches of something that wasn't supposed to exist, and which I could not see, except for a shadow!

When my friend reached me he put his hand on my shoulder: it jerked as if he had gotten an electrical shock. He left it there only a few seconds, and then removed it.

'There's an evil spirit holding onto you,' he said. 'When I touched your shoulder the feeling you're feeling ran up my arm and into me. As soon as I took away my hand, it was gone. It's got a hold on you.'

By this time, I was becoming terrified. This was real. I felt horrible, a feeling I cannot put into words, for I know no words to describe it. Only cold, and terrified, and sick, ill - horrible.

My mind was awhirl. I was a scientifically raised intellect and we were all Americans; we had knowledge of technology and science, all the world could offer. This couldn't be happening.

But it was.

My friend sent our other two friends out, immediately, and told them to go for a long walk and not come back for at least an hour, because it could let go of me and grab one of them. They left, fast.

He turned and told me that I had to pray, to command it to depart in the name of Jesus Christ. He stayed to help me until the spirit left. We both got down on our knees. I was terrified beyond my wildest dreams by now. I felt as if I were going to die.

I began to pray out loud, and my prayer was very loud and very desperate. I rebuked the spirit forcefully, commanded it to let go of me, to go away, to depart, and as nothing was happening, I then prayed to God for more strength, and prayed for faith; then I rebuked it again, more, and again. My friend knelt beside me in prayer, and he also was rebuking it and commanding it to go.

And then, all of a sudden, it was gone.

I felt warm again, and the terrible, sick feeling was gone.

That fast. It was just......gone.

I instinctively brought my hands up and felt my face, and patted my chest and sides and legs: I was perfectly OK, and wasn't afraid any more, and it was gone.

It was the wierdest thing I ever experienced. It was just gone.

My friend quickly stood up, grabbed for me in the dark, and pulled me to my feet, saying that we had better get out of the house and go for a long walk away from there before the spirit decided to take hold on one of us again.

That had been quite a night. I no longer disbelieved evil spirits.

When you look through a transparent human being and see it walking through the bottom of a closed double door toward you, it changes your life. And this was only the first time, of many.

A few days later I came to better understand exactly what I had seen and why the spirit seemed to get bigger and bigger as I sat there, looking at the double door at the back of our little house, and I figured out the scientific, physical reality of what I had seen.

I realized that if a person walked toward me from the back yard, the closer the person came, the bigger the person would look.

As this had been a transparent being, a being of shadow, which apparently could walk right through the closed lower half of a door, I had watched it walk toward me from the sugar cane in the back yard all the way up to my chair, a straight line of vision and walking.

In the dark, seeing only its transparent shadow, the increase in relative apparent size was nothing more than the normal apparent increase in size of anyone's body as they walked from farther away towards a viewer. Because it was just a transparent shadow, I was focusing more on the stand of sugar cane at the far end of the yard, and I didn't perceive any shortening of distance between us; I didn't realize something was coming closer. As it got closer, it just looked bigger, because I had no depth perception of it or distance reference.

I also realized that if a solid person walked toward me from the back door, I would see a only silhouette around them of the light and yard outside and of the door frame, which as they walked closer to me would diminish as they appeared bigger and bigger, until the person's body got so close to me that I could no longer see any of the yard or door behind them, just the oncoming mass of the person walking toward me until he or she stood in front of me, completely blocking my view. It was, in fact, simple physics of optical geometry.

That is what had happened in the moonlight: the spirit had walked to the back door, then through the closed bottom half, walked toward me in the hall, and more and more overshadowing the door behind by the closeness of it's spirit body, until everything was just dark, except for the dimly lit square of the door which I could see through its body - the back yard wall and the sugar cane.

It had been real.

I had many other very real experiences of a similar nature over the next couple of years. I heard and saw numerous other spirits, some in broad daylight. Transparent beings. Unbelievable, even when seeing them. The Brazilian spirit religions abounded in such experiences among its adepts, yet the spirits were so bold in this part of the world that many uninvolved people, just as I had been, suddenly became confronted by these myriad spirits.

I met a family which had been visited at night by spirits of bright blue light, even appearing through the walls of their third-floor apartment, terrifying the entire family. They all saw it, together. I visited the apartment. I looked out the windows at the straight drop below. I saw the wide-eyed terror on the faces of the children as their parents told of these repeated intrusions, and saw the children nod, validating everything their parents told. The family had easily confirmed that these were not spirits from God.

I found that experiences of this nature were not uncommon.

I talked with people who saw spirits regularly; some who had even made friends with them. As I had now seen spirits myself, I no longer doubted what I heard. I listened intently. I learned to recognize the hallmarks of these real spirit experiences. As those who shared them with me knew and understood what they had seen, I knew perfectly well why they believed what they saw. It was real.

The smug and learned university teachers back home in the schools were mistaken. Though certainly in many places of the world many crackpots and charlatans made up stories, just as likewise many false illusions were created by tricksters to exploit the curious and the desperate, it was not all tricks. And, though in many things the power of suggestion most certainly was a great and real power, nonetheless, there are spirits; they do have power; they are real.

From real experience comes real knowledge.

I had not believed in these things. I had not expected this. I had not looked for this. I had not wanted this.

I just experienced it.

After I returned to the United States, to a country where no one believes in these things, I almost never talked about my experiences, because no one believed, and these were serious things. The first few people I dared to tell, even though they were my friends and knew me, and respected me, they looked at me hesitantly, and smiled, and looked away a bit embarrassed for me, and they sheepishly admitted that they didn't believe me. They thought I was telling tall tales, the homecoming stories of bravado.

Yet I did not resent their disbelief; nor were my feelings hurt.

I felt reconciled in accepting other's disbelief: for, if I had not experienced these things myself - no matter how many people might tell me such things, nor who they might be - I don't think I would have ever overcome my academic and intellectual disbelief. So, I overcame my expectations of anyone believing my accounts, for, if I had not experienced them, I would not believe them myself. Thus, except in moments when these things needed to be told, I was silent.

Yet I had experienced them, and my life was changed by it all.

And so I typed:

What have I learned?

These are the spirits who are denied flesh, those who rebelled of your generation, before the first of you came to inhabit bodies on this world. They have been cast out for their disobedience, and they shall never have bodies. Even the evil ones among you who are born in this world will have dominion over these, for all who kept their First Estate shall be resurrected, even the evil, and those with resurrected bodies will have power greater than those without them, and thus have dominion over them. They are the spirits who rebelled.

There are those among you who think they are the spirits of your dead, for so they declare themselves. They are not. There are those among you who think they are entities from other worlds, for so they declare themselves. They are not. They present themselves in many ways, to deceive, and gain power.

You have power over them. Only you can give power to them. Those who give themselves over to these fall under their power, and great evil is done, to themselves, and those whom they harm.

Who are they, these Spirits who rebelled?

As you know that you were there before, so they were with you also in the beginning, and they are your siblings in Spirit.

It is not fable: there was war in Heaven, and among all of your generation, those who rebelled were cast out.

Mourn for them in sadness. They are your siblings who wished not to risk Free Agency, and chose another path: the easy way to passing a probation, but without exercising or learning, and thus without acquiring the qualities required to become co-heirs and be endowed with such power, which cannot be.

There are no shortcuts to receive as co-heirs that which you may receive.

You, my child, and all of you who are born into this world, are those who held steadfast; you were valiant, and you chose in Faith that which was right, and fought valiantly.

For this, you, and all born into this world earned your right to come.

Since I returned home I have never heard of the kinds of things I heard of there. Why are these spirits there, in one part of the world, and not in the United States, in North America?

They are where you are, yet they move about you in silence and stealth, for as the children here do not believe, even so they reduce certain power of the spirits; yet because they disbelieve, they open themselves to other influences and whisperings, and the children here being unprotected by knowledge of the truth, they fall vulnerable to other deceptions, equally harmful. You are easily influenced. You are so quick to believe that you are above influence, yet in this is your greatest weakness to fall.

They were cast here before your coming; they remain here. Unlike you, they have no veil over their memory; they know all that you knew before your birth here in your flesh, even great things, and knowledge of many things yet to come, of the future. This knowledge they use to appear wise. They are not. Their wish is to bring the children down, to divide them by jealousies, distrusts, using wealth, power, political, racial and religious hatreds to render the children of each place and era more vulnerable, to make the children miserable even as they are, without light. In ages past they have whispered, and been heard, and thus they have distorted and hidden spiritual truths. These things you see.

As they have been here on your earth, they have seen each generation as it has been born, and as it has lived. From this experience, too, they know great things. They use this knowledge to deceive many in the flesh: they share their knowledge with cunning and thus gain strong followings; they share words and visions and knowledge of lives of those who have been born and lived and died which they saw and knew in their days, and thereby deceive many by their knowledge of past lives, leading them astray. These things you see.

Their work is ever more simple. You pride yourselves in believing in no nonsense, and yet you have set your faith mostly upon power, rich possessions and prestige, and technologies, and so your vanity is easily influenced. Thus among your technosocieties, they do their work silently, and invisibly.

Look and you will see their great success, for everywhere, as you know, amid the good done every day by the multitudes of good and hard working children, evil does abound, and more every day. The more your generation denies the existence of evil as a real power, the more it spreads out and clutches your societies. Never has a generation so firmly exclaimed that 'there is no Evil,' and never has a generation seen such rampant evil among itself.

That is the greatest deception of Evil and the Evil Ones, the Children of the Lie: their whisper is that there is no evil, and that they do not exist. Many believe, and so they fall into diverse follies and swiftly go down the path of destruction. Their love of their human family has grown cold, and instead they love things and power and fantasies. Their hearts fail them, and can no longer guide them, for they have so shouted down the still small voice within their hearts which once reminded them of what is wrong, that they can no longer hear, nor feel.

Look across your land and ask: how safe are you from acts of violence and evil? How much do you fear the stranger? How much do you fear the dark street, the isolated alley and parking lot, the shadow wherein you cannot see, the unlocked door of your homes? How safe are your small children from evil and harm and capture and terrible death, and your older children from secret combinations and secret societies whispering to them to join, pressuring them to enter in dark covenants, wherein they give up their Free Agency, and become slaves of evil divisions in which they hurt others to prove themselves, are blinded to the needs of all others save their own, and to the pain of any but themselves and those whom they think are their own? For these, their love is killed within them, and their hearts leave their families. Ask yourselves: what evil whisperings have you heeded in your families, that your families have fallen so far into evil that your children have no models upon which to cherish Faith?

Even so, the spirits you speak of still congregate in greater numbers where they are given power and are invited to enter bodies, which in some places of the world, even where you were, many people give them, following religions of deception, and inviting them to have flesh, which they are denied.

Yet wherever there is evil, they congregate; therefore: flee from all evil.

The Angels are here also. Tell me then about Angels. Certainly they must be stronger.

Angels are around you at all times, and yes, they are much stronger. Yet they will not always strive with you in the stubbornness of your flesh, and as you resist them, they must leave you to your own devices.

Seek to live worthily that the Angels may dwell with you. For, they will not dwell in unclean houses. Though they may seek to whisper, as they are filled with love and compassion, they will not dwell in unclean houses.

Comprehend that they are present and around you.

Live with them consciously, being aware that they are with you, and you will come to feel their presence and see how often you are aided by them.

Express gratitude to them frequently, remember they are around you, and you will feel their joy, and have an increase of blessing.

Though you may be injured and killed by those who choose in their Free Agency to harm you, you will not be left unattended, and comfort shall surround you, even in death. Those who have died innocently in horror have been met instantly by my Angels, and comforted, and guided back to me.

Live in disbelief and rejection of the Angels and you still will be helped. For they, even as I, love even those who deny them in ignorance. By love and love's guiding they take great joy in all they do for the children.

Yet for those who refute these Celestial Spirits, know that less can be done, and most sadly, those who refute them cannot feel the ecstasy of joining in the resonance which surrounds them.

And indeed, the resonance surrounds them less. And those who continually choose evil surround themselves with so much evil that few are the Angels who endure it, and such are left unto themselves. And there are those who choose such evil that they are left unto their own destruction, for they will not abide comfort, nor guiding, nor whisperings, nor sound choices.

Where the Angels are honored, they congregate in greater joy.

You have honored that which is good and sought good in your life, and you among many have also received great gifts, through the veil.

You have a physical experience with Angels.

Do you remember the Voice in the High Sierra which saved your life?

The High Sierra.

The Voice.

Yes.

I certainly did remember.

I was only about thirteen years old. My family had gone to Whitney Portals the first day school was out, in early June, and the heavy snow of winter still lay deep at the 8,000 foot elevation.

I had decided to climb up the trail toward Mt. Whitney. I knew the trail well, having climbed the trail to the summit already three times before, and hiking the lower trails many more times. This would be a golden opportunity: I could hike up the slopes without trails, without switchbacks, and make incredible time.

I did. I was up to Mirror Lake in no time. I was far past it well before noon. I was reaching timberline elevation, over 10,000 feet, by lunchtime. I had not seen another living human soul.

Soon I was up past the last trees and into the barren rocky amphitheaters of the mountain just below the sheer cliffs rising up to Keeler's Needles and Whitney itself. Lake Constellation was up to my side over the rise in its own corner scooped out of the mountain.

' I had climbed the whole way in snow, still never seeing another person, or even any tracks in the snow. It appeared that I was the first person to go this far up the mountain.

Being a city boy from the flatlands near the beach, snow was virtually unknown to me. I was reveling in it. As I reached this mesa of granite and sand flats, I was surprised to see that the flat tops of the granite stone were bare; the snow had melted in the all-day sun. Yet where I knew the sand flats to be, the snow remained.

I walked along the flat granite mesa and enjoyed jumping off onto the snow a few feet below. It crunched and splattered out from my eager feet.

I then noticed that the river which flowed out of the lake through the rocks at the base of the higher mesa of the lake was completely snow covered, and I could walk across it and up the snow-covered hill to the upper mesa, to see the lake.

Never having been able to do this before, I was thrilled at the prospect of finally getting to the this high altitude mountain lake.

Up on the mesa by the lake, I found the same kind of bare granite flats and snow-filled sand flats. Here, up on this higher mesa by the lake, the sand-filled cracks and seams between the solid rock were like snow sidewalks or snow paths obliquely stretched across my line of hiking toward the pass. I walked along the flat granite and jumped onto the snow, along granite, and poom! Jumped on the snow.

The day was beautiful: the lake was deep crystal blue, reflecting steep snow slopes and brute jumbles of granite rock at the bases of a hemicycle of towering rock cliffs. I turned to take it all in. The view was spectacular. I gazed around at the high grey granite walls circling the lake, and on around to Keeler's Needles like thousand-foot-tall knife blades of massive granite stone jutting up into points in the pure blue sky. And there, farther on beyond them, was the majesty of Mt. Whitney, its austere sheer face looking out over the Owens Valley ten thousand feet below. I turned further around, completing my circle-panorama of the mountains and this bare granite mesa far above timberline, and gazed out at the valley so far below, and the White Mountains beyond.

It was breathtaking.

I was all by myself. I looked down the way I had come. There were no trees here. I could see all around me and more than a mile distant down the slopes, all white. There was no one else there at all.

Yet as I reached the next snow sidewalk, just as I was about to jump, I clearly heard a very human voice right behind me yell out

"DON'T JUMP!"

I stopped in my tracks. I turned.

No one was there.

I looked all around the treeless slopes.

No one was there, anywhere.

This hadn't been an echo. It hadn't been a voice carried from afar which reached me. This was right behind me, just a few feet. I wasn't dumb. I knew what a voice right behind me sounded like.

I looked down at the strip of snow going off to my left and my right. It was just another strip of snow between the rocks.

'You're just scaring yourself,' I thought in my mind, and I turned and poised myself once again to jump on the strip of snow before me. Yet just as I began to throw my arms and body weight forward into the jump, again I heard, in urgent tone, yelling right behind me

"DON'T JUMP!"

This time I turned more quickly. There was nothing there. Nobody. I looked all around. Just me and the snow covered mountain.

'Come on, you're just scaring yourself,' I said out loud.

Again I swung my body forward to jump onto the snow.

"DON'T JUMP!" I heard a third time, clear and right behind me.

This was getting ridiculous. But now, as I stood silently, I suddenly

402

noticed a faint trickling sound of water coming from beneath the snow I was about to jump on. Just a faint, soft trickle.

'Maybe there is a puddle of melt-off water under this snow here, and if I were to jump on it, I'd get my feet wet. It's a long hike back down the mountain in the snow. Maybe my feet or toes would get frostbite....maybe that's what something's trying to tell me,' I thought to myself in my mind.

I started to jump again, but by this time, I was spooked, and I swung back and stood looking at the snow, listening to the little trickling sound.

'OK, I'll throw a rock on it and see if there's any danger,' I thought, and looking around, I found a medium sized rock, picked it up, and hefted it up over my head.

After all, if I was going to throw a rock on the snow and there was a puddle underneath, I might as well make a good splash!

I threw the rock, expecting to see some snow fly up and some splashing water.

But that's not what happened. That's not what happened at all.

The rock just disappeared down through the snow.

And the long strip of snow stretching off to my left and to my right suddenly cracked and split where the rock had gone through, and started to fall down into a crevasse; it cracked fifteen feet to my left and fifteen feet to my right and then farther left and farther right it cracked, and the whole strip just fell down away into the abyss which was opening before my shocked eyes.

Down and down the long strips of snow fell, all along the crevasse, until I saw the huge chunks which had been right in front of my feet crash into a violently churning, swirling rage of icy water a hundred feet below me. I watched it all as if in slow motion, as all of the whole strip of snow fell into the raging water, chunks to the left, chunks to the right, farther left, farther right, until all of them had fallen into the churning water and been twisted and broken and smashed into pieces and washed on to my right, on and down into the rocks which I could see swallowing the water in the dark of the abyss.

This was the main outlet of the lake.

This was the fissure which the water from the lake had cut into a deep channel over time, which had been covered by a fragile roof of snow, looking for all the world just like all the other strips of snow unmelted on the sand flats between the granite rock.

Had I jumped, I would have fallen to my death.

My body would have been wedged into the rocks.

I probably would never have been found.

I would have just disappeared on the mountain.

But I had been saved, because an unseen personage had yelled in my ear from just a few feet behind me, and commanded me not to jump. Tears came to my eyes as I remembered that moment.

I had told very few people about this experience.

I had never fully understood it myself.

All I knew was the Voice had startled me, stopped me against my wishes, frustrated me, and annoyed me. Yet it had saved me.

And it was real, just as real as any other time someone has yelled behind me. It was not in my mind, but loud, and clear, and only a few feet behind me on a bare mountain with no place to hide.

What was that? I asked.

An Angel, watching you.

I remembered more. There were several other times in my life in which I could have died, but something had intervened. One had been only a few years ago. I had been very depressed, and alone, and as I lay in bed at 4:30 in the morning all alone in my house, I had begun to think thoughts of ending my life. I began to want to do what I was imagining, and was feeling very close to having the resolve to get up and do it, but suddenly, in the dark, I was startled out of my wits and jolted upright in my bed by a shout only a few feet from my bed in the dark:

"DAVID!" a Voice shouted in the silence of my room. I looked all around me in the dim light of night, but I was alone.

I thought of my Near Death Experience, when I had died, yet my Spirit lived, lived by itself, and only after a while went back into my body, and I lived again, a physical being; and I thought of these and the other times I could have died, should have died, but didn't.

Am I not supposed to die? I asked.

Not yet.

Why me? I asked. For I had wept bitterly in anguish at the untimely deaths and senseless loss of many dear friends. Why was I still alive?

You have work still to do.

Was that an Angel, too, that morning in my room?

Yes. That was an Angel, too.

There are Angels, and Fallen Angels - and disembodied spirits?

Yes. Your experiences have not deceived you. These are real. There are Just

Spirits not yet born into flesh, and Fallen Spirits forever after denied flesh; and there are Spirits already born into flesh that have lived their day and left the body as it has ceased to live, death of the body. Of the Spirits that have already been born into flesh in this Second Estate, and died the First Death of the body, there are Just and Evil among them. The Evil Disembodied often find alliance with the Spirits of the Fallen Ones, and join them. Yet the Disembodied Spirits of the Good, the Just, often choose to serve, and still serve here in Spirit.

Who are the Angels who watch us and help us?

They are Spirits still awaiting their time to be born, and Spirits of the Just Children who have already lived and received their bodies and died, who have been worthy and choose to still serve; and there are many Just Children who have already received of the Resurrection; these too, serve as Angels, and they have Resurrected Bodies of flesh and bone. All of these watch, and record, and they help from time to time in many ways as it is needed. Your helps have not been unusual. Yet there are more unusual needs, and many there are who have spoken to Angels and sat with them at table, without knowing.

Can we call upon them?

Yes, you may; and you may speak to them if you feel they are there, and they will rejoice; but it is not given to you to call them for selfish reasons. Even your own life may by its losing serve a purpose you know not of, and if you are so called to give, so shall you be rewarded for your suffering, that you gave so all may be given full chance to witness and learn and repent and desire righteousness. Know: the Angels are my servants, not yours; they perform the ministering of my bidding, not yours. They obey Eternal wisdom, not yours.

Yet know that they are there; believe, and your blessings will increase.

What about people who call upon the Spirits of those who have lived and are now dead? Some people do that.

What comes to them comes in deception.

It is not given to you to seek or follow such practice; you cannot summons, nor is it given to the Just Spirits to go at will without being given Holy Errand. You are here for specific reason, to learn by experiencing good and evil, and to get used to the powers you receive already in your physical bodies which are eternal gifts unto you. As you are here to learn and obey by Faith, it is not good that you know or see all things; were it so, it would have been given you. You are Agents unto yourselves, and it is yours to obey, not summons.

What comes to those who summons in darkness comes in deception.

The Deceivers feign many identities and forge many deceptions. They abide here since the Beginning, and have seen all things. They know of lives, and many details of lives which they have accompanied and watched greedily in jealousy over thousands of years in many lands, wishing they had flesh, following the bodies of those who were Obedient and obtained. When they find children who list to hear them, through which they find momentary power and share in flesh, these things they gleefully whisper and share, adopting shadowy guises, so many believe it is their own past lives they glimpse. Count the souls who have lived, divide by two, and you behold One Third of a whole. Before the foundation of this world, these billions rebelled; this One Third is so numerous that few have been the lives unobserved and unwatched by a jealous multitude. They know much, things past and prophesied, of lives and places and events witnessed and thus easily retold of memory; even some future things they know.

Yet beware those who receive a familiar spirit; avoid those who pretend to reach through the veil, for those whom they reach will usually be of the Deceivers, and by this you give them power over you, for you have invited them. Most often those children who call upon the Spirits of the dead hope to avoid Faith and choosing in Free Agency, hoping for occult wisdom. If they have faith enough to receive any Spirit at all, they are visited by the Disembodied Spirits in rebellion, who are great deceivers, who use their unveiled primordial knowledge to appear wise and to deceive, and to lead many astray.

For this reason all generations have been counseled and commanded to not go unto necromancers, nor seek to know fortunes or futures by inquiring of the dead. For you are children, and thus you are easily deceived; after giving many tempting morsels do the spirits of deception lead you from the Great Truth which you must grasp and hold to for your redemption and exaltation.

Beware of all such things.

Thank you. I'll ponder this and study more about it.

That is good.

I'm ready for a new question, still about the early universe.

That's fine. What is your next question, then?

This has to do with matter, physical creation in the universe. The words all say 'shaped,' 'fabricated,' 'organized,' words like that.
I've read that galaxies and suns and black holes and planets are 'irregularities' in the evenness of the cosmos. Physicists don't understand what causes 'irregularities,' or the gravitational gathering and accretion of matter in the universe into uneven, concentrated formations, which are the

galaxies and suns and planets and moons. How is it done? Why did all this happen like this?

It happened as the solution to the Need, and the solution chosen became chosen as it provided the most useful potential of all.

According to your partial knowledge of your physics, a uniform, 'even' universe is thought to be 'orderly.' According to such physics, you believe that nature should want things to be even, and orderly. This is true.

Yet it is only one perspective, that evenness is order. When one advantage can be perceived over another, the provision of increase is order.

Physics is a reverse perspective of mathematics and probabilities, with no allowance for conscious intervention at any point or time. It is a perspective which does not allow for Consciousness within a cosmos, nor which recognizes Design as Order. To see order as Design is to admit a Consciousness and a Design, as well as a purpose. Knowing the purpose would greatly assist in prediction within the Cosmos, yet it is a bold step. If a universe has no purpose and is accidental, then evenness is a safe and correct concept of order. Yet if there is Consciousness, and there is design and purpose, and the organization of that Design and purpose tends toward greater order in organization, then to avoid seeing it only leads to confusing conclusions which fail to predict well.

The question between the two is consciousness, or unconsciousness.

Know that: processes intentionally set in motion delightfully create the 'irregularities' or unevennesses in space observed, with purpose. There is great randomness and unpredictability within these large scale actions, yet they yield much predictability on small scales, and among many resulting suns and planets and moons and planetoids and matter, equilibrium obtains and useful localities are achieved in abundance, sufficient for the Needs. These obtain concentrations of gravitational forces, produce heat, light and radiation from atomic reactions, and mature into formations of energy sources and habitable spheres of planets, upon which organic life forms may grow, and when the whole is seasoned adequately, the bodies of the full Design may be introduced and Intelligences may enter into them and extend their capabilities as you see yourselves doing. From among the many which result, the best may be chosen.

As I have told you, the observable universe is the algorithm of a Design with the purpose of experiencing the exact experiences which you call 'Life.'

Once Forethought is allowed, Organization following ideal function and performance is 'Order.' The highest ideal achieved is the highest level of order and perfection. Though you do not understand all of the reasons why galaxies exist in clusters as they do, nor why vast areas are void and without galaxies, nor why the speeds of galaxies in the expansion of space are set as they are, nor why the speeds of the suns whirling in rotation around their galactic axes are set as they are, nor why the speeds of their planets around their suns are all as they are, yet you are able to look at your planet, and see you live comfortably upon it, as do your brothers and sisters upon countless other worlds that have obtained similar equilibrium and been chosen, and thus you see: it works. Continue to see the Whole, and you will come to comprehend how and why it works. As you calculate the consequences of altering anything that is as it is, you begin to see how perfectly each part plays its role in maintaining the equilibrium of this organization, and ultimately thus to alter what is as it is requires great compensations to maintain this organization for life at the planetary level as it eventually obtains as Designed.

Though some children may amuse themselves in this exercise, and calculate alternate proposals which might work, are their calculated results desirable to your conscious Intelligence as a choice of selection?

Again, think of your Free Agency: would you trade any of those severely limiting potentials over what you experience with your Intelligence in these bodies, in this environment? Thus all must be as it is; and so it is.

I think I grasp what you mean. Maybe we can come back to this thought a little down the road here. My thoughts at this moment continue on the origins of matter and material organization. What can you tell me that I can understand?

First, at the elementary level, your physics of this form of matter speaks of only Four Fundamental Forces. Three of these - the electromagnetic force which obtains between particles with electric charge; and the weak force, which has very short range affecting all matter particles except those which carry force; and the strong force, which has the shortest range of all and holds neutrons and protons together to make atoms, and holds quarks together within neutrons and protons - the children have fit somewhat well into a loose Grand Unification Theory, which they abbreviate and call the GUT. Of course they have the problems reconciling certain aspects of gravitational attraction over the whole. That's the fourth force, gravity. It still causes them problems. They do not understand how to combine it all together. There are reasons for this.

While the children already understand things such as the Exclusion Principle, and many other forces, still they have not yet admitted to nor measured other forces equally important in the physics you can observe.

Love. Faith. Intelligence. Spirit. Prayer. Priesthood. Good.

Still there are opposite forces to these, and the opposites as well have their powers and force. Hate. Doubt. Wrong. Curse. Priestcraft. Evil. Those who use the force of hate exercise a faith in it; they use their intelligence with it; and their spirits; and, in the powers of cursing, there is prayer directed in evil, and priestcrafts do they use. They are opposite forces at work in the universe, yet they have only very short range influence, while the greater powers are as great as even Gravity, reaching unto the ends of the universe. The opposites are poorly understood by all who have chosen to use them, even from the beginning, and they ultimately frustrate more their users than those upon whom they are used. This too is in obedience to a law, which they disbelieve.

In disbelief is much marvel of misery.

Surely the children of numbers will laugh at this proposal. Yet what is, is, and what is beyond predictability because of consciousness will frustrate them.

Put with the Four Forces to which your physics admits, these make many more than ten forces you must take into accounts of your observable universe. Yet there are more, which you do not yet know. Still, until at least these you know are studied mathematically, those who wish to render these things into mathematics or a GUT shall be frustrated in their efforts. As the children use mathematics in the effort to predict everything that has happened as mathematically consequential, unconscious, and therefore a predictable universe as it is now and has developed since its beginning, so they shall be further frustrated: intervention has existed and exists, and will ever exist, so they may mathematically predict only to certain thresholds, upon which they will always fall back into the confusion of not understanding why they cannot either predict nor calculate all things as unconscious, without the nudge of direction.

Their desire is admirable: to understand all that has taken place, and to find ways to mathematically predict how it should have happened, by observing how it is now. And their work is not without benefit even as they persist in avoiding the consideration of consciousness.

Nonetheless, even consciousness and Design have followed that which nature has had to offer in potentials, and it is the mind of God which has comprehended what to do with it all, for all of you and your siblings who otherwise would still be, shall we say, lost in space.

Does this surprise you?

Many there are who look at the universe and see that it is the same in every direction they look, and at this they marvel. Why is it so, they ask?

They are here for but a fraction of an infinitesimal instant of the time of this universe, and have seen nothing of what has been before, and even as they behold the observable universe as it is now, yet they do not behold it well, but only in part, and dimly. You in your day are as Copernicus in his, for there is much you can imagine, but not all, and much you can see, but not all, and of all you can imagine and see, yet you know little, and still you fail in much, and imagine fantasy amid truth, and as Copernicus, you as yet cannot show even yourselves all things in which you are right, nor those things in which you err.

Nor can you see now as would be required to prove to yourselves what has been happening in the universe, and yet within many hearts, you deny the possibility that I may behold an unused expanse of space, filled with Dark Matter, and by choice and will ignite it into charged condensation and therein begin anew the process of adding a new local system to the whole. They so quickly forget that even the children Copernicus and Galileo and Bruno were unable to convince, for lack of tools to demonstrate, show, and prove.

Yet even so, all they had comprehended was so.

Except that I show it unto a prophet again, how shall you see it yet as you still cannot peer adequately beyond your limits, nor see into the past of time and behold the spark and ignition of a region out of Dark Matter into clouds which will take the lengths of time you now comprehend it takes for such a process to begin, be set to swirling, accrete, gather, ignite into suns, and follow through the processes as you understand they must, until habitable worlds obtain?

Even as much of this is going on around you and you see it, you attribute no purpose nor plan to it, nor any conscious process, nor any Design.

You would see it all done before you at once, and hear my voice from the Heavens declaring it unto you, and then, you say, you would believe.

Yet you are here to learn Faith, for it is by this power of Faith that even suns and galaxies and worlds are nudged into being that the Great Purpose may continue to unfold, as it has from universe to universe, always.

Though a prophet would see it and speak it to you even now, would you believe a living prophet, or would you mock him, even as your fathers?

The profoundness of this question hit me with deep impact. I did not even know who might believe me, were I to tell these things.

These powers you mention - Love, Faith, and all that. They have real effect in molding the universe?

The Power of Love is real. It can be reduced mathematically. It is not anecdotal; it is empirical, and predictable. Its affect on all life forms, spirit and Intelligence, even of the most insignificant lichen or viroid, is real. It can be measured, but who has dared to appear a lunatic among scientific children and search this field, so fruitful yet so scoffed? As Love is a variable, laws of variability must be applied in its study; the force and power increase logarithmically. When the children learn how to recognize the orders of Love, and thereby dare to measure them, they shall find that all that is power, is power.

The power and force of Faith is not anecdotal and this force can be observed, measured and rendered mathematically. Many ask why you cannot prove it on a given morning by moving a mountain. Yet with Faith as little as a mustard seed mountains are moved, though not usually by those in your Estate. First, there is no need; second, small as is a mustard seed, who among you believes, and has need? Yet again, its variables require a Turing Machine to calculate, so few have perfect Faith, and few know overall what is best in the long term for many; therefore they do not know what to ask, nor towards what they should direct their faith. As they ask for that which is not in their best eternal interest, but only their momentary selfish interest, they exercise faith in vain. Faith misdirected is still effective, and many a child is granted that which is not good for them, so that they may receive, and learn that their wisdom is not my wisdom, and to not choose by whim. Yet when one becomes in tune more and more with the Spirit, then one knows more how to exercise faith, and to accept that which is not understood beyond the veil, but which is for your long-term good. Accepting that which is disappointing is also Faith; it is power unto you.

The power of Intelligence is unimaginable to you in this Estate. Yet know this: the vast portion of your brains which you do not use is held in reserve for your future use when you can control yourselves in its use. The power of your Intelligence coupled with your resurrected bodies, coupled with Faith and Love and higher powers, is a wonder which those who obtain shall know.

Spirit houses the Intelligences, and the force of Spirit is formidable. You understand powers within powers in the Four Forces and atoms; you have yet to fathom powers within powers in the physics of Spirit matter. Spirit is matter, yet it is organized by another physics, related to this one you know and compatible with it.

The effects of Prayer observed on the ill is not anecdotal, but empirical, and observations are of measurable power and force. It can be observed and rendered mathematically. It is not as predictable as mesons and bosons, or as carbon monoxide reducing iron atoms into ferrous oxide, or any other of a trillion predictable processes and reactions of chemistry. Yet it is unpredictable because of variables you can see, including the faith of the one praying, as well as the nature of what is requested, which is not always best nor possible within the reality of other's Free Agency, and, also due to variables which you cannot see, nor easily calculate, and these are the long-term needs of many souls. You are not here just for entertainment and recreation, but also to learn, and denial often teaches you more of what you and others need to learn than granting every wish, no matter how noble it may seem.

Priesthood is the power to act in my name for the good of all children. It can only be used in accordance with the laws of righteousness, and few who have it attend its use seriously, and many who have it use it in unjust dominion. This power is greater than most presume, amid many who falsely believe that because One came who became the Eternal High Priest that in this all celestial authority is withdrawn from the children. The evil of men has removed this authority for many generations, yet it remains an Eternal Order, and the ordinances thereof are powerful blessings.

The power of Good is the power of Life, a replenishing observed in babies neglected and uncared for and in the elderly whose energies wane as they are ignored. Yet young and old find renewed energy and life as they live with and share

411

Life with each other, in the spirit of goodness. The observations of babies and caring thoughts and touching in goodness and Love, and of children of all ages, and of old children, who thrive more with the shared goodness of living creatures, even cats and dogs and other animals given to affection, is real and not anecdotal; it is a force which can be observed, and expressed mathematically in its activity.

When the vanity and prejudice of the sciences humbles itself to recognize the now-called anecdotal observances, and devotes the same effort and concentration to their study as is done to understanding the process and effects of AIDS and astrophysics, then new laws and forces will be charted and their uses and predictabilities will be discovered, and mapped, to the satisfaction of many.

Yet it will not be learned by your hard mathematics of physics, which is useful for determining the exact physical needs of a universe as this and worlds as these and of bodies as these you have been given, but not for comprehending choice, Wisdom, or any act of a brain that can think.

Has it never struck you, that the mathematics of your greatest intelligence thus far has no place in it itself for the factor of Intelligence? It is a tool to describe everything around you except intelligence, and yet only those of great intelligence can devise it, and explore with it. Why then pretend that Intelligence affects nothing? Intelligence is all around you to observe, and yet until now, you have mathematically denied it, as if it does not exist, and you exclude it.

This has been the great unspoken Exclusion ·Principle: the exclusion of all recognition attributable to intelligence from your observations.

As you have called The Mind accidental, and Intelligence a mere local freak evolved of hydrogen atoms, you have excluded it rigorously from everything you calculate. Only now do you begin to awaken to the error of the child Descartes whom you have so enshrined, to finally admit that all is not packaged as he and so many others have wished.

Opposites always exist: as there is logic, so there is Intelligence to see opportunity, best and worst, degrees, and Choice. As there is knowledge, so there is ignorance, wherein Wisdom is hidden. There is joy, and pain. It is your nature to in vanity believe you know all of a thing, and unaware, you calculate without all factors. Thus your conclusions are often faulted. Among yourselves, being children, you do much without reason. You see pain, and a universe in progress, and conclude there is no God, though you see all but in part. You see not the fullness, and you conclude in error. You know not what I know.

You have many great mathematical surprises before you.

When you have progressed to envision a soft mathematics that goes beyond the unpredictable, and is able to account for that which is Intelligence and therefore able to use Free Agency and exercise choice, with Intelligence, then you will begin to chart new discoveries into powers you have long known, admitted, and observed, but still denied.

You do not consider these powers in the initiating of gravitational masses, of accelerating accretions by these forces, of changing the directions of large scale motions in the universe and even small scale motions in the universe, yet many questions you raise and have left unanswered because they fail to respond to your considerations are evidences of your need to consider more than all you have thus far acquiesced to include in your calculations.

Which are the greatest powers in creation?

Love as power, and Faith as power. It is by power of Love that all things are as they are, for without love, though there would be a universe, it would not be as you behold it, and you would not be here to observe it at all. With the power of Faith you can move more than mountains: you can create them from the Energenes out of what you call Dark Matter, charging and organizing the units of energy so that they become charged opposites and charged neutrals, to form with each other each kind of stone and mineral for a planet, which though made of no more than void space and infinitesimal units of energy, do act as if they are 'solid as a rock,' to use your phrase. I AM Love, and the power of Love is the driving force which motivates the doing. The power of Faith is the force which moves that which otherwise will not move, or would follow its own course. Faith is an intervening power, and in your brief moment of life, in your distant perception of things too far away, you merely see and wonder about things which should resolve according to formula, but do not.

As I hear all you say about all these things, I feel like nothing, and I can't help but remember people talking about 'Nothingness.' Before I existed as a Spirit with you, was I 'Nothing?' Am I truly 'Nothingness?' Am I going to return to a state of 'Nothingness?'

Nothingness is almost always misunderstood, for you have until now had no reference to relate to in your ponderings. Yet it is your true state of being on many levels. The religions which speak of 'Nothingness' preserve ancient revelations about Intelligences in the void, and of your physics of the void. They remember Opposition in all things, and its symbol, and atoms, and great spans of time, even better than my Chosen children, who little concerned themselves with matter or time. My Chosen kept infinitely better records, which serve the world infinitely better, yet these things also testify of revelation, and of me.

You ask; I will tell you: As 'Nothingness,' an inert Intelligence, you existed unimaginable time; in 'Nothingness' you were lost; from 'Nothingness' you were lifted up; in the face of all, you are small beyond your imagining. Until you are proven and obtain, without your earth you shrivel before your sun, explode and freeze in the vacuum of space, and cease to exist: you are infinitesimal 'nothing' amid the realities of the cosmos, and your state is still 'Nothingness.'

413

Yet as co-heir you may become master over the elements, and all things.

Yet know this: as a 'physical' being, you do not exist. You are not solid, but are made of Energenes charged and organized to act as solid, though you are nothing but energy, and empty space. You comprehend this today. Grasp what you comprehend. This, too, is your 'Nothingness.' Your perception of yourself will be altered as you internalize this truth. When you are able to fully grasp the significance of your state as a being of Light and Energy, you will begin to function as a Child of Light instead of a being of solid matter as you believe yourself to be. Here Faith unfolds, which you so little understand. It is real, the greatest of powers. And because you perceive yourself as only physical, you do not seek the best gifts, which are of the Spirit.

To comprehend the Energenes in your body is to begin to become master of the energies which are gathered and organized to make your 'physical' body, which is inhabited by your Intelligence within your Spirit body. When you understand the vast space of nothingness which truly makes up the space you think you solidly occupy, and when you understand the vast nothingness of the Energenes themselves when they are yet unorganized, then you will understand and have reached the knowledge of 'Nothingness,' and you will comprehend what mastery over it may imply to you over this matter.

It is not that you will have reached 'Nothingness.'

You have been since the beginning: Nothingness.

Rely upon that which is greater than you, in your nothingness.

All that you have earned and received in this Estate will rise with you.

In the beginning, this was given. It is important for you to recognize in the confusions of ancient knowledge that great things were given, if but partially understood. See within these truths the revelations of Creation. You have the evidence in those places where this misunderstood knowledge is preserved.

If you doubt your nothingness, think of this: A neutrino shot through two miles of lead or ten miles of lead touches no other energene in any energene group, or atom. Think then: how vast a void of space are you, my Child of Light?

Thank you for this. It is a lot to think about. May I go on? I had Dark Matter on my list, and you spoke of it. What role does it play?

Dark Matter is nothing more than - to use an expression you can understand - a type of matter not yet organized.

Opposites exist in all things: as there was and is uncharged matter, there is and has been charged matter. Dark Matter is Primordial Matter, yet unorganized, yet uncharged. You have heard that if the electricity were turned off in atoms - if the electrons, neutrons and protons were turned "off," that all atoms and matter would fly apart and none of it would hold together.

This is what Dark Matter is: matter with the charge turned "off;" more correctly you may say, it was never yet turned "on."

Dark Matter, yet unorganized, is remarkably uniform and even; it is also useless to manipulate for function, for it neither reacts nor can be reacted upon as matter which has been charged and organized; it is inert. Being not yet charged in its primal or first phase of organization, it is uncharged and unable to be organized as you know 'charged matter' on Earth and in your visible universe of already organized matter: the matter of which you and everything else you can detect is made - which is why you can detect this matter, measure and analyze this matter. It is useful only as a raw material, and for gravitational equilibrium of large scale mass distributions in the universe.

How is it used as a raw material?

Charge is what begins to organize it: charge gives it the essential polarization and neutral which brings into existence opposition - that which attracts and repels and allows for the behavior you call 'physical' or 'solid' or 'matter.'

I'm confused. You speak of 'polarization' - that would be positive and negative - but you also speak of 'neutral.' I thought 'neutral' meant no charge.

'Particles' *without elementary charge* are not the same as 'charged' particles which also have 'neutral charge:' neither positive nor negative charge. 'Neutral charge' *is still an elementary charge.*

Dark Matter is *uncharged matter:* neither positive, nor negative, nor neutral.

You speak of etectr-ons, prot-ons, neutr-ons, and meso-ons, bary-ons, lept-ons, all the typical "-on" suffixes for charged particles. Dark Matter will not be any kind of an "-on" when you find it, because yet unorganized Dark Matter is by your physics "-off" particles: they are 'uncharged' and thus they are not "-ons," for they are not yet "turned -on."

How can something be 'neutral' and still have charge?

The children will discover that the term charge has been defined only within your current perspective of electromagnetic behaviors as you have identified them: positive, negative and neutral; and within which you believe all things are 'charged.' 'Uncharged' particles are 'uncharged' as pertaining to your current standards and definitions of 'charge' as you use them within the charged, organized atomic matter you know. Yet you do not know all things.

So how is it used? What does it do?

When Dark Matter is 'charged' it converts, and becomes 'solid matter' subatomic particles as you know them and can detect them with tools made of like matter. Charged Dark Matter then may begin to become 'organized' through interaction with its own 'particles' which now have more than gravitational attraction, simply due to the new possession of 'charge' which then causes them to attract, bond and therefore also, to repel.

As you see, Dark Matter is 'particle' matter yet uncharged and thus it does not organize itself according to your narrow laws of limited Physics, which laws you have thus far discovered only are concerned with 'particles' that are charged and thus behave as 'solid' matter having the typical, observable properties of attraction, bonding and repulsion, or opposition.

You will discover that Dark Matter is the stuff of 'uncharged strings;' it lacks the properties of 'spin,' 'resonance,' 'vibration,' 'color' and 'flavor' peculiar to 'charged' subatomic particles. It is the multi-fold lacking of 'charge' - the positive, negative and neutral - and the effects of 'spin' and so forth that in combination makes these particles undetectable to your tools, which are all made of and all based on the expected presence of these properties in the matter you observe.

Yet there is Opposition in all things. As there is uncharged matter yet unorganized, so is there also charged matter yet unorganized, and both have their useful roles.

And what happens as soon as Dark Matter becomes charged?

You can make 'solid' things of it. It becomes what you call units of the kind of energy you know: yet disorganized units of energy. These can become organized into bonded units, by aligning opposites as they attract and bond to each other, creating larger units: atoms. The energy thus charged and organized creates what ultimately can be called 'matter' and its conversions. It is opposite-balanced and opposite-centered, thus presenting outward likes which repel each other and act as solids when there are none.

Energy is in constant flux between being organized and coming apart. It takes energy to bond energy; energy is released when units are broken free. The simple food you eat and digest is designed to do nothing more than create a way for you to ingest energy, break its components down, receive some of that energy in the process, assimilate it into your own energy unit, use it, and pass out as waste the parts which were not fully broken down.

Space is about -460 degrees below Fahrenheit zero, very cold. Your bodies need to be about +98 degrees above that zero to function optimally.

How is this done? Very simply, by creating bodies which take energy units provided as food, processing them, using the energy to replenish the energy you are constantly releasing and returning to the cosmos, and replenishing your tissue units.

The energy units now charged and organized by opposites into likes or repelling substance or 'matter' are but a fraction of the matter units in the cosmos. They are found in every part of space.

Being as these energy units are not yet organized, they are available for endless creations, destructions and re-creations.

What purpose does Dark Matter serve in its uncharged form?

Its only property you can currently measure is that detectability which is only indirectly observable - gravitational. Your understanding of its nature and role in general, of gravitational force and gravitons, may enlarge your understanding of the atomic physical matter as you know it. The eventual understanding of this factor - that though Dark Matter 'particles' are uncharged and thus do not interact with any of the four forces of 'organized' or 'charged' physical matter directly as you know and observe, except that they do exert a gravitational force within the expanding universe as an integral whole - may prove useful in your final formation of a GUT.

I don't understand.

As the current regeneration of this universe began, the matter was orderly and even. However, the manner of its expansion allowed chain reactions of ignitions charging some of the matter; as it expanded, 'charge' was triggered in Dark Matter, and obtained sporadically within the expansion. Where Dark Matter became 'charged' a local chain-reaction of 'charging' quickly obtained and resulted in the localized condensation of newly formed subatomic particles, as you know them, into the clouds of gasses which, now with the interaction of the four forces, began to condense inwardly into galaxies and individual suns. As mass density produces heat, a point is reached when fusion ignites, a sun is born, and new elements and compounds are formed, from which may be accreted and formed at a later phase, planets, the small local 'disorders' you observe in the universe today.

You notice that the localized condensations caused by 'charged clouds' of Dark Matter are somewhat evenly spaced; the cause of this will be answered as you learn what triggers the initial 'charge' phenomenon itself. You do not know what 'triggers' the 'charging' and thus the conversion of Dark Matter to subatomic 'particle' matter as you know it and typically observe it throughout the universe; nor do you know what phenomenon causes such localized conversion condensations to fizzle out and remain localized rather than spread and consume the entire universe.

All you know is that the condensations have virtually no Dark Matter within them, and that they exist as if within a bubble of Dark Matter around them. What has happened to the Dark Matter which is missing within the bubble? It is accreted into the giant masses which collapse into the densities in which heat rises and rises until it ignites suns, and from this new conversion and radiation of energies, many things may be accomplished. Yet the cause of the void of Dark Matter within the bubbles is the observable energene matter observed within which has become charged, condensed, and accreted into the forms you see and know. From this you should know that all of these forms are condensed from a conversion caused by the spark of charging.

The combined new effects of charging - the weak, strong and electromagnetic forces produced in the newly converted matter - cause a central contraction of the matter, pulling it inward and away from the outer edges of the localized area of condensation; a critical mass is reached in which the inward speed of condensation exceeds the speed of outward charge, thus reaching a breaking of contact with the Dark Matter cloud and the charging force, ending the conversion reaction, resulting in a local 'irregularity.'

Know this: that the universe did not have at any time a 'naked singularity,' and that indeed there has never needed to be a 'naked singularity' at any time.

We haven't yet even proven that there is Dark Matter, but I believe you that there is. How will we encounter it?

You will eventually discover how to isolate and 'charge' Dark Matter 'particles,' which cannot be called *energenes* for they are yet uncharged; and though they are inherently energy also, they are without charge as you know it and thus are not energy as you currently define energy.

You have guessed that Dark Matter is abundant, perhaps 90% of the mass of the universe; as you discover the way to isolate, 'charge' and convert it into its various normal *energene* conversion potentials, you will find that they will behave just as you observe all presently charged subatomic 'particles' in the universe. They will form elementary substances through attraction and heat bonding. However, you will not observe this interaction easily at first, as their immediate behavior is as radiation, heat and light, which may displace them rather quickly far from you before they interact and bond with other *energenes* into atoms. You will want to conduct such a 'charging experiment' in a new accelerator for similar conditions which trap and hold the newly formed 'particles,' or *energenes*, for observation.

As you experiment with this concept and attempt to invent instruments which can detect Dark Matter 'particles' not yet charged, without the key atomic nature of opposition and thus without attraction, you will discover the ability to detect and measure quantities of Dark Matter, and a new learning process will begin.

Know this: you must proceed with caution in the area of experimentation in attempts to 'charge' such Dark Matter, and you should confine the process to controlled quantities of very small proportion, to avoid setting off a chain reaction in your local vicinity of space which could have inconvenient results.

If it's dangerous, why don't you tell us not to do it?

When has this been effective? You persist in many directions which are not good for you, nor for your planet, only because you see you can, and some perceive economic reward. Fortunately, you are in no immediate danger of capturing and working with any but the smallest quantities of such uncharged matter; you are safe.

I have seen you use a word a number of times - Energenes. I don't know this word, though I'm beginning to understand its use. What is an Energene?

It is a good word for you. You need a new word, for 'particle' is utterly wrong, and it has been used too long in much confusion. Energene is ideal. The units of primal energy are best called Energenes in all of your languages.

Why? Please explain.

"Energene" brings to mind energy, engines, genes, generation, genetics, and genesis, or Creation. Creation is order, following an order, being formed according to an order. Everything in the cosmos is made of Energenes. These are what the children of your generation call particles. Atomic particles, subatomic particles. They behave in particular manners, and due to this natural behavior, they naturally seek to form that which is desirable to form. Due to this behavior, they keep the forms which they gather together to create. They tend to act on the micro level much as you observe gene formation on a macro level.

Are all particles, energenes, ultimately all one kind?

No. They exist in many forms. Their character aligns with the resonances, and as they change from form to form they adopt transient forms, each which serves a purpose.

How many forms of energenes are there?

More than one hundred. More than half you have found. Yet some are not detectable by tools of this physics of energene matter. All those which are of your matter you can detect, and over time you will find them.

You will eventually find that Energenes act together in predictable ways; these behaviors were foreseen, and as they are good, this matter was best above all others. Its most useful property and behavior is that of building up from order to order. Its behavior on the smallest scale is carried forward and continues on the larger scale. You see this in ideal forms: the structure of atoms build into the structure of molecules which build into the large scale structure of a matter, such as a crystal. In some pure crystals you see in the macro what exists in the micro. You just have not comprehended how far into the micro the pattern is repeated.

What advantage is there to this behavior?

You have proposed to say that Ontogeny Recapitulates Philogeny. This is not correct as you apply it, for you do not yet comprehend the wisdom in the Design of DNA, and you imagine processes which are not required, for you are unable to understand what can be done in Design. But you are learning. DNA is a Design which begins at the smallest level, and is added upon, with increase. The whole continually equals more than the sum of its parts, as it builds upon its bases enhancing the capability of all functions. DNA is the logical extension of Energene potential: upon its bases can be built infinite varieties all following its predictable bonds; and as the organism function works, upon it may be built an increase, until the ultimate Design is made perfect: you.

This is the great secret you have yet to comprehend.

DNA Recapitulates Energene Behavior.

The building process evolves from the smallest unit: as the micro energenes attract and bond together, so the unities of energenes bond together; as the unities attract and bond together in forms ultimately as parts of atoms and as atoms, so atoms ultimately bond together in forms of molecules, and compounds, and matter, and tissues, all because of the initial structural attractions at the smallest order. So it is at every level of every order. From the original building pieces come the patterns of inherent behavior exploitable for the fashioning of elements, of compounds, of rocks, of water, of simple organic molecules, of complex organic molecules, and eventually of the most complex DNA. That is why this physics was chosen for matter: much combines and will exist by itself only because of the inherent properties of this physics; but utilizing it and building upon it and fabricating the Design of the ultimate DNA for Intelligence to inhabit for mobility and power as you see it, requires Intelligence.

So what we could be and are, was determined from the beginning?

Yes, from the beginning.

Our body was the original vision, the original goal of all of this?

You speak of the Exalted Body, which those who obtain will receive in its fullness of Exaltation in the Resurrection. Yes, that is the end goal perceived, which directed in simplicity all choices, from the beginning. The rest has been following through on the promise of the perceived physical Design and its eternal rewards, as provisioned in this physics, and providing a proving experience to you in all things wherein you may see your willingness to learn, and obey rules.

Most of what your generation has discovered in these truths they have discovered though they have not yet seen. Nor can they see any of it, but still they believe in their tools for they can see the measurements. That which children can measure they can accept as if they have seen. You still have no tools to detect and measure those things which since the beginning have been made known in part and reminded to you.

But know this again now:

You are children of Light, almost as I AM, and you are children of Spirit before matter; you are Spirit within matter; and after this matter, eventually you will be perfected in a tabernacle of yet finer matter, the Finest Matter.

As you have known these things but not yet made the tools to measure them, you have rejected them, even as all children of previous generations rejected the truths some discovered and knew were true, for none had yet the tools you have made. The time is advancing that you behold, and believe again.

You have faith in the children of your generation, and their tools, and thus you believe them who speak to you these truths even though you cannot see any of the things they speak of, nor know for yourselves that anything they say to you is true. You trust in them. You place faith in them. You believe in all that they say though you cannot see it and they cannot see it. You believe in the measurements of their tools, even though you do not understand how the tools work, nor the nature of what is detected and measured. Nor do they who tell you these things understand their tools nor the nature of what they detect and discover. Yet what they do not understand they have accepted. It is a faith in that which is not seen, and not understood, and which by their own understanding defies understanding, and defies logic as they perceive their logic. Yet they believe. And rightly so, for it is truth.

The day must come in which they recognize their faith, and understand it for its power and direction. Only when they awaken that mind and with an eye fixed to the obvious truth that I AM and pursue the unfolding discoveries to understand the mind which brought all of this into possibility of being will they begin to explore the possibility of tools which will measure that which they now think cannot be, and does not exist.

When their every understanding aligns in truth that they are discovering the mind of their God, as children will desire to know the mind of the parent, and to know the order by which any thing is made to be and how what is made works, then they will unfold a consciousness which shall unfold, for it shall not be in opposition to that which they seek, but in awareness of all that they seek. When they accept that I AM as they accept all else they cannot see and which defies their sense of logic, which they do not understand but accept must be accepted though it defies understanding, for it works as it is true without need of understanding, only because it is true, then they shall extend their reach and find that which is yet to be found, for they shall know what they discover in its fullness.

Thank you. A new question, please. When I first connected the Urim and Thummim to the equipment, I began to pick up tones. What was I hearing?

The Resonance of the Cosmos.

What is this, and what is its origin?

The origin of the resonance is energy. The resonance originates in the energy of Love, and Faith. There are those who will still scoff at this, and smirk as children, yet discoveries await you which will sober them.

You do not think of these as resonating forms of energy. You speak of various forms of energy: kinetic, heat, chemical, mechanical, atomic, to which are added others. The most far reaching of all, in terms of the elements of this Creation and their handling and use, are Love and Faith.

In this resonance, you and all beings of Spirit communicate, even so.

You know the power of Love and Faith, and experience it; you feel what it does within you; you see what it triggers in emotions: will, determination, anger, compassion, jealousy, hatred, and more. You know and feel this resonance.

These are a great power, visible, and detectable. This power can be measured, though not yet with meters and gauges; no one of you has yet discovered how to measure it. And until a child of science believes enough to dare the mockery of colleagues, who will attempt this reward, this process leading to discovery? Imagine the mockery, as serious science. Yet they will.

To exert Love is to project an energy. You know this energy at least as it feels within your physical body. You know it is real. What you do not know, nor guess at all, is the effect it has upon all forms of energenes. Likewise Faith. You see the energy of faith, you feel it, you see the effects within a life and action directed by faith, or non-action by non-faith. Faith capitulates action. You understand this in terms of mental resolve and bodily response guided by mental resolve. But you do not understand the actual energy itself which Faith is and causes. Both Love and Faith are Cause and Effect. The energy of Love and Faith are greater in scope and application than any of you children have ever yet imagined. For this reason you fail to mature in them yet. But that full awakening will come in a future time and place.

All energy resonates according to its nature.

Love is an energy and a resonance. Faith is an energy and a resonance. These are the resonances which brought about all you see as it is and began order from amidst chaos. Learn this, and learn.

What is the source of the resonances?

I AM.

What do the resonances do?

Among many things, they affect Energenes, the atomic particles. They are reflected in mass, charge, and spin.

I have heard of 'spin' in atomic physics, but I do not understand it. What can I understand?

The rate of 'spin' of an energene is constant. They do not really spin, as is known, yet today the children of the sciences find themselves as the prophets of old: they have no better word. The same who mock the word 'dust' must say 'spin,' even with all of this. For lack of ability to visualize more than a globe on its axis and for not having words to describe this character, they speak of 'spin.'
There is a reason for this.
All energenes of a type are the same; they resonate at the same periodic. Velocity and spin create different mass. As the resonance is altered and vibrates to the cycle of the next resonance, the 'spin' effect changes. It is the effect of resonance. This is a helpful knowledge in fully utilizing the energene.

Are energenes only different because of velocity and spin?

Yes. Resonance decelerates and accelerates in increments up and down, to levels, which must be maintained or all reverts to chaos. This is part of 'charge.' The sympathetic character is controlled each by its tone, a resonance of energy, even as a violin string resonates to a harmonic in the atmosphere. Energenes resonate to the tones established in the cosmos. The tone is received and maintained by the masses of the energenes throughout the cosmos: the character of the many regulates the one, and the one regulates the many. There are many tones of resonance, which order and control the various states and characters of the energenes resonating in their needed harmonies. And so all act as one throughout the cosmos.
This will one day be discovered through measurement.
These energene resonances are "the music of the universe."
The Urim and Thummim receive them, and the resonance of Spirits, and Angels, communicating across the cosmos, and your technologies here in these units have converted them into the resonances you have heard.

The tones?

Yes. The resonances you were reassembling as sound are not sound. But through the Urim and Thummim and your programs you have reassembled them as sound. You understand them better in this form, but know: they are not sound. The heart of the cosmos is ordered by these tones, vibrations, energy pulses, which each at its rate allows order to prevail, and this creation of energene matter to exist. This was revealed anciently, but it was misunderstood.

When and where, and how was it misunderstood?

The children who still sing the song of the Om, they remember this knowledge of the Tone, without remembering. They who meditate upon its tone, do so only in memory, memory and attempt to recall this truth of their creation which they have lost, which they no longer can recall. They no longer remember it as the symbol of the circle, of the eternal round, of the gathering of matter, nor do they remember it represents the resonance of the cosmos, yet they have remembered it is important in all. Search these things, for they too, testify of me.

What was an original energy, after Love and Faith?

Superconductivity in the cold of space.

I do not understand.

Superconductivity. It presents no resistance to the free flow of electrons; it is the continuous flow of current with no applied voltage; it exists at or near absolute zero. This condition is found in space. Space is the perfect place for original creation. There are many things which can be done differently in absolute cold. Those who have an ear to hear, hear.

Where did the energy come from? Initially, at zero temperature, current could flow indefinitely in an existing mass density without applied voltage.

The potential was there.

Once the best use of the potential was foreseen, it was arranged and ordered in materials which would superconduct, and there was a beginning.

Then how was, the beginning?

Void of space. You know this. Darkness. You do not remember this, but it was. Until there was light, there was only darkness. There were Intelligences in the darkness. Inert. Hopeless. Helpless. It was not good.

There was Dark Matter in its form of uncharged energy. You do not comprehend this, but it was. Its potentials were envisioned, and they were many. Of

424

the many alternatives, one physics was seen to yield a continuing increase of potential, dust built upon dust upon dust which could be organized into a long line of creations, from the very small to the very great, the vision of which stretched out infinitely. The system of energy conversion and distribution this physics afforded was the best of all, and as it would yield a matter which acted as 'solid,' and places upon which to stand, and light within which to see, and solvents with which to mix the electrolytes of life, and cells and tissues with which to fashion wondrous vehicles for Intelligences to rise from their darkness and inert sadness, it was seen that it could be good.

And so it was imagined, and the means to do it was imagined, even in the mind of God was it imagined, and so it was done.

And it was good.

You see it and yourself, and you know: it is good.

Yet at first there was only light and heat, and darkness.

As the expansion became right for condensation, great clouds of light and accretion by gravity began, and suns were formed, many kinds of suns, and as I saw them I knew they were good.

Many great galaxies of suns were formed, and the large scale motions were set and each balanced the other until all was balanced, and from these came elements for making worlds, and new suns.

All of this was done, and many worlds were gathered from the dust of the cosmos and formed, and generations before yours passed through their probations and to their Kingdoms before you. Many are the Kingdoms which have already been provisioned for the Intelligences.

This is the scene which existed when your world was begun in its space.

Some may tell you that this is a demotion, but believe it not. Many of the first shall be last, and many of the last shall be first. Do you believe? Know then that it is true, and neither time nor place in the cosmos is of consequence to you as you are loved; only your love and obedience will show what crown you may receive and bear. And when it is yours, is your own life not sufficient unto itself?

And all of this was done, and existed, before your generation began, before your Intelligences were made Spirit Children, and your journeys began.

You are on a great journey, with your brothers and sisters of all generations, of all times and all places. Do you doubt that there is Love enough to go around? Will you not rejoice in all lives, even as you rejoice in your own? Will you be a jealous child, and resent what is yours only because it is shared?

You began long before this world began. You are co-eternal with all of the Intelligences, and you were, as were they, eternal from the beginning.

The record you have thus far received has always been given as a knowledge of your world, its beginnings, the beginnings of your world among the Fullness of Creation, and it has been in progress since before your world. Yet once the children

425

began to come, their excitement was great, and their joy abounded in the wonders of this earth, and they wandered, and forgot this.

Now that you are fully awakening in knowledge, see what you see, and see.

Genesis is only a description of this solar system and world?

Yes.

I receive it. This is actually a relief to learn, for it answers all of the questions which our discoveries have asked us of this world.

You speak prematurely, but so is your nature.

You have asked how it is done. Let me suggest to you more.

Think about the elements. A single proton, electron and neutron: Hydrogen: a gas. Two: Helium: a gas. After joining into more gasses, finally Oxygen: a gas. Mix Hydrogen and Oxygen: they bond: a liquid.

And what a liquid! The basis of all life in this type of energene-matter creation. You are born of the water and of the Spirit, and yet you still connect almost none of what you know and see, nor the symbols of your origins.

Water you should come to comprehend. It exceeds virtually all else of the physics of this matter in this Creation of universes and worlds you see and know. It is a perfection of art and design in art, and within its cycles the potential of life became perceived in its fullness, line upon line and precept upon precept.

Water - two parts hydrogen and one part oxygen - should explode. At first imagining, it should be the ideal liquid fuel. Hydrogen is the most explosive flamable as a gas, put in direct contact with the one element which makes it burn: oxygen. The two as gasses must be kept carefully separated.

Yet it neither explodes nor burns when bonded, and two gasses become a liquid: they become the ideal biosolvent among all chemical combinations.

Water is miraculous.

Behold its behavior. Boiled it expands 42 times its volume, rising and quickly cooling to re-condense into water. Freeze it and it appears to confound nature: it does not contract, but expands slightly, so as ice it floats, being less dense than its liquid form. If not so, a planet's ocean floors would pile up with ice and it oceans would freeze. Also unlike almost everything else, it will not compress. Pressurize it and it can be superheated without boiling; in the tiniest droplets it may be supercooled far below freezing, and rain condenses on it.

Water is the solution to the big problem: to identify the ideal structure of an ideal solvent, the most flexible of elements to do a miraculous job. How does water defy natural laws as it appears to do? This is wisdom in me. It is simple, yet effective above all solvents.

A major problem resolved: Life in its optimum form, in this solvent matter.

All life can exist because of the solvent, water.

Much water was therefore made in the beginning, and the cosmos is literally filled with it. Around your solar system is a great orbiting bubble of frozen water masses: you call them ice planetesimals. When these are dislodged from orbit and fall toward your sun, you know them as comets, and you marvel at the bright tails formed by the solar winds, blowing away water molecules and dust. You know the size of some; you know not the size of all, nor their numbers. Yet they continue to play an essential role in your system, and in the ecology of your world as you live upon it.

This water was formed in very early stages of the universe.

It is an essential part of the success of the Design.

Are these the waters in the Heavens which we read of in Genesis, which were divided, some of them being separated to earth?

Yes.

One last question. "As a beginning," Genesis outlines the formation of this earth. Why? Why give knowledge to people who would never understand until now? Is this knowledge really that important to know, even if we have no way of comprehending?

You are my beloved children. For you to understand who you are, and who I AM, and what you may become, the creation is key. For this reason you are instructed in it, again and again, and for this reason the knowledge of it has been obstructed by Evil, by those who were disobedient and cannot inherit who burn in jealousy, who would rob you of your Glory.

It is the key to who I AM, from where you come, why you are here, what you are, what you may become, and what you will do when you become what you may become.

To understand the creation is to understand my mind.

To understand my mind is to come to know who you are.

Yet so many generations before you have feared this knowledge.

Is it frightening for you to remove the veil and peek into the mechanism of your own creation?

Is your faith only strong in ignorance?

Can you withstand the revealing of the truth of all things?

Or are you so afraid that you still cling to your ignorance as your savior and your god?

Will you always wish to worship a God without his true Physics, and pursue a Physics without Design or God?

When will you open your understanding that one leads to the other in an eternal round?

Can you enjoy a house that you have seen built from the very foundations, with every mix of concrete, every cut of every board, every forming and firing of every brick, every hammered nail, every tightened bolt, every connection of every wire, every sheet of drywall set up in its place, every bit of paint in every hue, every rock and soil of flooring, every piece of every material?

Can you only buy a ready-finished house to live in to feel safe? Or can you see its skeleton in the forming, and see how each step is done, and when it is finished, look back knowing everything there is framed by a blueprint intelligently ordered, and know all of it, and respect it the same, and love it the same?

Can you only buy a palace and see it a palace if you have not known its architect? Or can you see its Designer, and comprehend that you are a Being almost as He is, and know him without hiding your face in fear for you see yourself in His Being?

Can you know me, and behold me as Designer, and as you come to know how you were made as my children, still retain your sense of security?

If unveiling the truth frightens you, if discovering the answers to "How?" frightens you, then touch that fear, touch and touch it until you know it well, and you will at least begin to understand the feeling of non-physical existence out in space. This is all that there was before all of this that you see.

To see all of space around you, yet to be unprotected and marooned in the vastness of space, is too much for most Intelligences. It is too vast.

Is it too great for you?

Know that the more your ability is to understand, accept and still enjoy, the greater the mansion you can abide.

The less one can know without fear, the smaller the divided and enclosed space and mansion you must be in to feel safe.

This brings me full circle. I am beginning to see the picture as it forms, yet as it forms, I see that I, that is, all of us, we were there before this world was. We have been your spirit children for a long time. We have many brothers and sisters on worlds across the universe, on worlds which were formed before ours. I am part of a generation, and I was there with you when this earth began to gather together and form in space, and I too lifted my voice and shouted for joy. I was there. All of us born here, we were there.

Yes, you were there.

That means none of this is actually new to me.

My child, you are beginning to awaken.

So right you are. None of this is new to you.

There is an infinite truth and absolute truth about the atom, the body, and the universes, and so is there an infinite, absolute truth about me, and about the role of intelligence in the Creation of successive universes, and worlds, by the organizing of matter and the Design of life.

They are what they are.

I AM THAT I AM.

When all truths are known, they shall be seen for what they are.

Then all shall know.

I think this is enough for tonight. I'm saturated again, I typed. I was exhausteded. Looking at the clock, I blinked in astonishment. It couldn't be that late. But it was. We had talked most of the night. No wonder I was tired.

That's fine. You've done very well.

Thank you. I need to sleep. This is a lot to sleep on. I'll think about all this tomorrow. I already have some new questions that I will be asking you about some of this, before I go on to the other questions I already wrote down to ask you.

Very good. I'll be with you. Until tomorrow night. Goodnight.

Good Night, I typed, and looked at the screen. It did not seem like enough to say after such a night of discussion. It was not enough.

Thank You I typed.

I sat and stared at those two small words, and then finally exited the program and shut off the power.

Yes, I thought.

Yes, most sincerely.

Thank you.

Chapter 15

Day 34 in the Wilderness:
        The Creation of this Universe and this World

I couldn't believe how late it was when I awoke. Yet I hadn't gone to bed until very late, or should I say early - early in the morning. Not too long before sunrise, in fact. Thus it was no surprise that the clock showed it was already after twelve noon.

I got up, and discovered I didn't need to get dressed: I needed to change clothes. I was still wearing my clothes. That was another thing I seldom did. Yet I felt myself very much in a forgiving mood, and smiled. Nothing was quite the same; a few accommodations to a new schedule were very acceptable. After all: there was nothing routine about anything I was doing.

I prepared and ate some food without regard to which meal it should be. I was already halfway to dinner and hadn't eaten breakfast or lunch. That would have to be a consideration tonight: if I was exchanging time here, I would need to prepare a couple of easy to eat meals and have them on hand in the tent by the computer to eat as I was reading God's responses.

I had to laugh again. In fact I chuckled. I felt like a little child, giggling about how casually my mind thought about it - food by the computer to eat while I was reading God's responses. I obviously was getting used to it, but I wasn't yet used to it.

As soon as I finished eating I picked up my canteen and went out to the spring. It was still flowing water, cool and clear. I pressed the canteen down into the pool, feeling the upward pressure of its buoyancy until the mouth dipped below the surface and water began to flow into it, and heavier and heavier, it began to sink, until it was full and I lifted it up out of the water.

Water.

It certainly was a miraculous thing. If it didn't exist, would our chemists and physicists have been clever enough to invent it? It certainly was a most wonderful structuring of chemistry and physics. It made possible the bonding of rocks and minerals into a true crust on the planet, among other things.

I looked up around me at the rocky canyon walls. A lot of people didn't know that, I mused. Yet a massive percentage of rock weight was water, bonded at the molecular level, and I well knew that a rock subjected to dehydration virtually crumbled to dust. We would have no planetary crust or mountains or rocks without water, which was built into the driest of dry rocks. Water literally held our rocks together, and the world.

It was not just in the oceans. It was in everything. You almost couldn't make a compound without water somewhere in the formula, no matter how dry the resulting matter might appear. It was the almost universal solvent providing the ideal liquid environment for most of the life species on the planet. Because of it soil bonded into dirt instead of blowing away as dust, and because of it soil was soft and friable for roots to dig into and digest rock and organic fragments, and worms and micro-organic life forms could thrive. Soil without moisture was hard, as a rock.

Water dissolved almost every mineral and trace element and delivered them to aquatic life forms from single cells to the largest, in ocean, sea, river and lake, as well as provided oxygen delivery for respiration within itself to all things living in it.

I knew that if my lungs dried out inside, and were not coated with moist water, I would instantly suffocate and die. It was the thinnest film of water which allowed the life-giving oxygen in the air to reach my blood, and the deadly carbon dioxide and other waste gasses to escape back into the air from my body processes.

As an archaeologist, I had seen dried human bodies. I had seen enough mummies to know what a dry human body is like: beef jerky; not much to be done with it even if you were alive inside.

Feather light, and every muscle and sinew hard as a rock.

Totally immovable.

Well the Egyptians had spoken of *The Water of Life*, and depicted it as baptizing the candidate clothed in white preparing to live forever. Without water, no life form would be able to experience movement of any kind, especially bodies as complex as these.

Water was the ideal vehicle for all multi-cellular bodily activities, from cell fuel delivery to waste extraction, oxygen distribution through the water-based blood, chemical deliveries of all kinds throughout the body, to the miracle of raising an arm, moving a finger, taking a single step.

What a miracle, just imagining a movement in a limb, and seeing it rise to one's imagined command. Motion. The simple ability to reach out and grasp something, anything, and carry it back to the body. The simple ability to put foot before foot and move from one physical spot to another, by choice. All possible, because of water.

And here it was flowing up from within the earth, to quench my thirsty body. I took a long drink.

It was good.

I hiked the whole afternoon, strolling, actually. I gazed around me at the Wilderness of Judah in wonder and awe.

As I stepped over rocks and sand and beheld the austere, jagged stones and dry river, I again found myself imaging the prophets and tattered refugees who had walked among these same rocks and sand, gazing up at the same cliffs and sky.

It became late, and the sun began to dip behind the mountains on the far side of the Dead Sea, which though I could not see it, I knew it was happening, for the light was gone from even the uppermost ridges of the canyons above, and the sky was quickly darkening. I was already heading back to camp, and the coolness was welcomed.

When I reached camp, I cooked a good meal, and put together a hand-food meal for later in the night.

As soon as all was set carefully on the table beside the computer, I switched on the power, booted up the system, and typed

WWW. URIM AND THUMMIM .GOD

The page appeared on the screen. Without hesitation I typed

Good evening again. How are you tonight?

Hello. I'm fine, thank you. How was your day?

Just fine. I slept late, and walked the wadis again. I thought a lot about the ancient prophets who walked in these canyons, pondering what they were learning, just like I'm doing.
You know what I'm really glad for?

No, what?

432

Good hiking boots. I was thinking today about covering this kind of terrain in sandals. I've seen the ancient sandals from Judaean times they found in the Cave of Letters and at Masada. I like boots.

A lot easier on the feet, aren't they? How was your hike?

I really enjoyed it. The wadis are beautiful. The little plants and bushes are beautiful. The sky is beautiful. The birds I see soaring way up there are beautiful. Their cries are beautiful. Everything is so beautiful. The spring is beautiful. Water is beautiful. Thank you.

For what?

For all of it. For life. For water. For rocks. For the way all this is put together. For all the animals and plants. It's a beautiful world.

Thank you. You're welcome. I'm glad it pleases you.

How was your day today? I guess that means how was our day today? And I just realized, 'we' are more than just this earth. How are all of us, on all the other worlds?

Oh, you're doing well, overall. You had a good day here on your Earth, all things considered. Your brothers and sisters had a good day on their worlds, too.

It's sort of different, thinking about them, I mean.

Yes.

Are they as difficult as we are? Or do they get along better?

Most of them get along a bit better than you do. Your family here is a bit more selfish than most.

Sorry.

It's not your fault. But your images of alien life forms so brutally wrecking death across your planet - it's not like that. What you see there is merely a reflection of yourselves, your fears, and your own aggressions and fascination with killing. Your brothers and sisters would be delighted to meet you, and would bring you gifts. They are not warring people. The best in you is in them and more. They are not conquerors. They are builders, and helpers. They love each other. They care about each other's problems. They love you.

They love us? They know of us?

Because this world is more difficult than the others, for this reason, the One Anointed to bear the burden came here, to live, to teach, to suffer, to die, to bring to pass the Atonement through which all Children on all worlds receive Grace, Resurrection and Forgiveness as they look to him and repent. The Expiation and Atonement are known to all of the Children, and as it has been proportioned from this world to all, all worlds know of this world, as they know of Messiah. Just as the worlds and your siblings were repeatedly revealed to your ancestors, your world and the great Atonement are known to all. Yes, they all, all know of you. But as with so many things here on your world among your family, you have suppressed your knowledge, even of them, completely, though it was given, and you have it written before you. It is part of your selfish and jealous nature. You have always wanted to be the only child. Yet they know you, and know of your troubles, and they pray for you.

We have people on other worlds praying for us?

Yes. They know of you, and love you. They know life in the Second Estate is a difficult trial, and they grieve for each other's hardships. They pray for those whom they cannot see just as they pray for those whom they know well.

Why don't we pray for them in our prayers?

You can.

What is it like to live on a better world, where people don't hurt each other so often, and instead of wasting so much time and money on war, they help feed each other, and clothe each other, and shelter each other?

Imagine it, and as more of you begin to imagine what it can be like, expending your energies in making each other's lives more comfortable and cared for, the more of you may look at those whom you call 'them,' and see instead 'us' and 'we.'

Just like my lectures to the kids at the university.

Just like your lectures to the kids at the university.

I thought about our human family, and our past, all of the generations we had lived, all of the things we had done, mostly thinking we were alone in the universe. I thought of the smoothly polished stone axe which so often passed from one child's hand to the next child, touched with such awe and reverence and wonder, handled by so many children, made smooth and

434

beautiful by the fingers and labor of a woman I never knew, but whom I taught the children at the university to remember with all the women of our past generations as 'Grandma,' and I realized, as I thought of the parade of generations and cultures learning what is here on this planet, learning what can be done with it, and hopefully learning how to treat each other better, she had not been alone. We are a family, and we have a Father.

We are all in the universe, learning.

Before I begin our discussion tonight, I would like to say Thank You for all of the things you have been sharing with me.

You're very welcome. You ask good things. You sincerely wish to know. You receive wholly what is given.

Thank you. They are mostly things I have thought about for a long time.

Where do you wish to begin tonight?

I pulled the paper out of my pocket, which was getting more and more wrinkled and smudged from being pulled out of my pocket again and again during the day as I walked and thought and thought of new questions, and scribbled and wrote so I wouldn't forget what had come into my mind to ask God.

OK. Here we go.
I've heard those who say the universe is, in so many observable ways, self-sufficient. They say that there is nothing for a Designer to do: it seems to take care of itself.

Yes?

I guess I'm asking: Why does it take care of itself?

Why wouldn't it?

Well, you're God. I thought.... it needs you, you hold it together.

And so it does, and I AM, in ways you know not of; however, what's wrong with taking advantage of the behavior of this matter to set in motion a process which can be used beneficially as it unfolds? Because a process was envisioned that works, I can't be God?

I certainly wouldn't want to imply that.

435

Yet there are those who would. They do not understand: It is not needful that a Designer should incessantly meddle in things properly unfolding as they were ordered to unfold, especially the matter in the universe. That would be quite a poor design, wouldn't it? The purpose was to create topos and skenas, and for them to exist and endure long enough to be worthwhile to the development of Intelligences. It has all worked out rather well, don't you think?

While there are forces which continually work to undo that which is done, the scope of the Design is such that both in space and time there is immense ability to accomplish much as that which was set in motion follows the course in which all was directed. The whole was watched until it was seen that it would follow an intended and initiated course, and then, as was foreseen and planned, it became largely self-regulating, as designed. This is the design.

As the processes of many phases are slow in your time - the mortal Second Estate is but the blink of an eye in time - you do not see the unfolding or the intervention which shapes that which is unfolding. You observe that all seems to be unfolding according to natural laws of the physics you have thus far identified. Why should this surprise you? I am not Father because I defy nature, but because I have mastered nature, and know how to use it for good purpose.

My work is to bring to pass the immortality and eternal life of the Children, and my purpose was to enable Intelligences to focus on that development. Thus the first need was a balanced, self sustaining environment, an order, a Cosmos.

I would like to sort of take a tour tonight through the Cosmos, the universe, and our own small solar system in our galaxy, and our earth. You've already laid the groundwork for me to understand a lot of things I hadn't ever even thought of before, but I'm still very confused, and I would like to get a clear, concise picture, all in one sweep, very focused.

I think what I'm wanting to ask is: How do you make a universe that works so perfectly, and galaxies and solar systems that work so perfectly, and an Earth with life on it that works so perfectly, with so much of everything being autonomous? I mean, in other words, how do you make such a self-sustaining, self-renewing, self regulating, self sufficient world? Can you give me such a picture?

Is that possible in one night?

Yes.

OK. I have some specific questions, and some general ones. Let's begin where I can imagine. There's a lot of talk about the first seconds and minutes and days of the universe, from what we believe must have been its physical origins as matter. I now understand that this must have been eons before our world was made as described clearly in Genesis and elsewhere.

We believe that it was incredibly hot in the beginning. Why was the original universe so hot?

The concentrated density which obtains in a condensed gravitational singularity containing a mass of 10^{105} charged and uncharged energenes possesses a potential of vast energy and propulsion. Ignition of such a density creates immense heat by the rubbing of energenes against energenes as they move in disassembly and spread out. You would call it energene friction, in classical terms. Within this expansion-friction, enormous heat erupts, radiation is produced, and spontaneous, simultaneous charging of energenes not yet charged begins to take place, initiating unevenness. Hydrogen and helium are formed as the charged energenes are very close and heat overcomes their independence, bonding them into atoms; the desired process begins.

Wholesale quantities of hydrogen and helium were formed, as foreseen.

Be optimistic about your studies. At certain points of your calculations, you believe that all you know of physics breaks down. This is not true. Your growing understanding of physics is very good, and it improves; yet your understanding is limited, and thus you know not how to comprehend what you have no tools to calculate. You believe your mathematics only serves you when it can predict. This is too rigid a perspective for you, and you must know: not all is predictable by mathematics alone. Mathematics is only a language you have invented to speak to yourselves, and it is an incomplete tool; accept its limitations to speak to you what its vocabulary allows. You are learning well.

The child Einstein believed that I do not play dice with the universe. In his comprehension he was perfectly and exactly right: I do not. Chance is not permissible: the consequences are too absolute.

Yet the flaw in an absolute law of total predictability is that it fails to comprehend that all does not have to be predictable to be good. All does not have to fulfill the same purpose to be purpose, and to be good. The Design is fulfilled within the fullness which obtains as it is foreseen and expected, which is thus predictable. The random results foreseen all serve a purpose; they can be utilized. Yet nothing would have successfully unfolded except for the observance of a series of specifically demanding conditions, which were met.

A specific condition was prepared, with a random predictability of specific unfolding, yet a general predictability of gravitational accretions suitable for energy sources around which habitable worlds would obtain. Because of Consciousness and Intelligence, random predictability was and is wholly within successful fulfillment of plan, choice and expectation, adequate for optimum utilization of the results, as you see around you.

Before the beginning of the universe was evenness, but almost from the instant of beginning of this universe, it was not perfectly smooth and uniform. Control of the unevenness is the key to exploiting mass and creating localities which serve as habitations.

The unevennesses which accreted by gravity and other forces applied have become the visible universe, yet not all localities are needed for habitations; in fact, individual planets such as your earth and other similar worlds could not exist if all suns were as yours, and if all planets were as yours. There is great variety within what can and does serve overall purpose, and these may and do develop randomly, which frustrates nothing, and enhances all. Many localities serve diverse needed functions within the purposes of gravitational and other needed balances. Those localities which obtain ideal conditions for habitation are available to be chosen and are further prepared, until they are ready for the introduction of the life process, and children. The wisdom of the overall plan is that it provides time, space and quantities of worlds sufficient for the unfolding of the Design, and this is all that was needed.

Why is the universe the same in every direction we look, and so uniform on a large scale? As we look in any direction, groups and clusters of galaxies exist in about the same manner, rather evenly spaced. Why is this?

Balance is desirable. It is not the nature of charged energene matter to so distribute itself; gravitational concentrations have a tendency to attract more and more to themselves: they are greedy, you could say. Yet there are large scale forces of repulsion, just as there are large scale forces of gravity, and these are part of the design. You have not yet discovered them, but you will.

Another thing which you have yet to realize is that as you scan the universe, and comprehend that not all galaxies and suns are the same age, you must comprehend that this simple realization of new galaxies coming into being is not without conscious initiation, and planning. Where balance is needed, precisely placed processes are initiated.

After the initial random ignitions and chargings and accretions, as space between organizations obtained and became sufficient for new organizations, new processes were initiated. As are all process and organizations within Creation, they serve myriad purposes. Most importantly, as matter yet unorganized is set in motion, it becomes organized for Intelligences to inhabit.

This brings me to the question of expansion, you have mentioned several times. I have heard from astronomers at the university that the rate of expansion is phenomenally perfect since its initiation, inasmuch as it appears to be expanding just fast enough to barely overcome gravity and not re-collapse back into its own center, yet it is not too fast, and in fact if it were just a little faster they say its speed would be too fast for matter to gather together into galaxies and suns. In other words, its rate of expansion is perfectly balanced. They say that computer models have shown virtually

438

every alternate rate fails, and the universe would not exist except that it has this perfect expansion.

How did the universe start with so nearly the critical rate of expansion that separates models that re-collapse from those that go on expanding forever?

When the concept of creating matter of this physics obtained, within it all eventualities were perceivable, and all were perceived. You, as children, so often initiate processes and begin before you have thought out to the end how you shall proceed, and what will happen if you follow your initial course. For this reason you so often find yourselves caught in a terrible lurch, as you did not think things through, and suddenly an unanticipated consequence confronts you. Yet see that you are indeed capable of thinking things out to extensive eventualities, and by seeing what you see, opting to proceed because things will work out acceptably; or halting, and reconsidering new alternatives, because you have foreseen an eventual problem evolves. You can do this, for you are Intelligences, and you are my children. You share this gift. You are here to exercise this gift in a frame wherein you can do less damage than is possible to initiate in larger scale environments.

Simply, for the Design to accomplish its resolved purpose, the universe had to provide maximum duration of continuity; the rate of expansion problem was perceived, comprehended, and its precisely balanced rate was calculated and the conditions required to produce it were arranged at every step of preparation. There are many steps of preparation. Yet always with the desired yield in mind, consideration obtains the wisest counsel, and as circumstances must become to maintain all balance and provide the homeostasis and continuity for that yield, so all is done. As it was perceived it needed to be, so it was planned and ordered. Wherein there is Intelligence to perceive, all is perceived; wherein there is power to order, all is ordered. You perceive the realization; you observe the result.

Thank you. Still on expansion and time within the universe before the formation of our world: I have also heard from astronomers at the university that organic molecules are found in asteroids, comets, meteorites, and in interstellar space. These include amino acids and other complex molecules, even complex hydrocarbons. Less than 200 have been identified in extra-terrestrial matter, though tens of billions of different organic molecules exist. How did these organic molecules get into space?

The children who theorize that given the age of the observable universe and its stars, and the younger age of your sun and planet, that life has existed previously on other planets before yours was ready, even planets in your own galaxy, are right. Life has existed before you and gone on to the next phase - Resurrected and Glorified states. Worlds that have long served their purposes whose suns have aged are not spared from natural destruction, yet all is an economy within my wisdom, and matter which has been used is still very useful, and its presence in the universe serves purposes which are wisdom in me. This has been revealed to prophets: that galaxies, stars and planetary systems are being created and destroyed all the time. Your sun is a third-generation star.

What makes a sun burn?

A sun gathers cold matter gravitationally; eventual attraction impacts and the density accreted compresses space between energenes, and the combined accumulation of energies thus converted into heat increases until it reaches critical mass density heat; nuclear fusion of hydrogen ignites at about twenty million degrees, yet it does not reach maximum output immediately. It can take up to 2 billion years for a sun's heat output to reach full efficiency. The most probable candidates for ultimate use are helped and watched until it is seen they will obey, and mature properly, so all the cells are balanced, sunspot activity reaches its ideal eleven-year cycles, solar winds of charged protons and electrons radiate evenly, and everything else works as it must before life can be sustained on a skena, an orbiting dwelling planet.

A last question of things I remember from lunch room discussions at the university: What is the origin of the density fluctuations in large scale space, that is, the gatherings of matter, the accretions of matter, which form into galaxies, suns, planets and moons? I guess my real question is: How are galaxies formed?

Where there is space and matter yet unorganized, it is gathered; from a large area of space matter is drawn into ever decreasing area, ever smaller and more condensed. The Spark of Light changes all, beginning from the center; when all of the chosen area is converted, those who are Obedient and Faithful join together for The Gathering. It is a process of taking the vast and dispersed, and gathering and refining it into the ever smaller yet greater, step by step. This knowledge was given in days of old. Some there were who built unto its many layers of memory. You have this creation symbol among you from ancient times, as it has stood for thousands of years, yet you have lost its many meanings unto you, as it rises from vast numbers below to its perfect point in the heavens.

How is this gathering of matter into galaxies and suns done?

When you have imagined the One of Light in the midst of the Heavens giving Light into that wherein was only darkness, and then imagined the whirling Dance of the Children of Lights, the Dance of the Intelligences in Spirit amid a void of space to set it in circular motion, all in unison speed, holding hands in Spirit and gently pulling inward along spiral chains toward a center wherein they finally hold hands in perfect circles, reeling in matter until it is set in motion to continue gathering unto itself, then you will begin to comprehend the One, and then the beauty and the force of the Intelligences and Spirits and the power even of Faith as it acts upon matter yet unorganized.

It is the Dance of the Children of Lights joined hand in hand from the first to the last in Faith, and into Eternal Circles. It is a Dance of Joy. For, it initiates the gathering of matter inward toward circular motion to become galaxies, ever inward gathering matter in a circle; and then the Dance divides into families, and the Light purifies, and ever smaller circles gather matter for suns and worlds on which they may finally find dwelling.

Depending on the number of Intelligences, and the original volume of area set in motion, and the density of matter yet unorganized contained therein, single galaxies thus accrete from one million to one trillion suns.

On your planet, count how many billions of souls have already been born, and consider that this is just the number of Intelligences born into your world, one of only tens of millions of worlds in your galaxy alone.

Count then with numbers, and you begin to understand the numbers of Intelligences, and the beauty of the motion set swirling into a space.

Your Local Group contains a total of twenty-seven individual galaxies in an area, to your measure, three million light-years in diameter. Your Milky Way Galaxy whirls near thirteen other galaxies, and your nearby Andromeda Galaxy turns amid nine other galaxies; still there are others which revolve at close distance. Know this: not all suns attract matter and accrete and hold planets. Many suns exist with only asteroids, planetesimals and dust around them.

Your own galaxy has formed within it over four hundred billion suns. Of these, almost a quarter of them are as yours, the ideal sun for Life Worlds. Though over twenty billion of these ideal suns have planets, or planetary solar systems, less than twenty million planets in your galaxy have the ideal mixed composition with substantial iron core, high silicon content, and are within the tolerances of ideal size and therefore ideal gravitational force to be molded and adjusted in their orbits into habitable skenas, dwelling places for Intelligences.

The dance of your Milky Way has set it to rotate one full cycle every 250 million of your years, and the speed of your sun is five hundred thousand of your miles in every hour as it orbits around the core of your galaxy. At the end of each of your days you have journeyed twelve million miles through space following the original whirling dance of Spirit Intelligences.

Was I one of them?

All of you who are born herein were among them, and many more, as you can now see, both from your siblings in science, and from the scrolls.

For so long, people have declared that the scrolls say that the universe was created just for us, and for us alone.
You never said that, ever, did you?

No. I never have said this thing. Nowhere do you find this written in any collected scriptures or even remnants of revelations among any people, only among the private interpretations of children. All children jealously want to be the only child. Many in their jealousy and vanity have said it, and it has pleased the vanity of generations upon generations, to imagine they are the only ones.

Yet you see that I have told you that your sun and your earth were created for you, and this by your being here you know is true.

Yet also know, that as you are eternal, and were among the Intelligences all for whom this universe was made, it is not untrue to say to yourself: all of this was made for you. For you are many across the universe, and among many, are you not one for whom all was made? And, is my Love not sufficient unto all?

This planet was watched and ordered until it obeyed and became suitable for all organic life forms, and it was prepared to receive you, my precious children of this generation. It was selected and chosen for you of your generation who would come here. This planet was perfected for your family of this generation, and it only is yours, by inheritance.

There is enough for all.

Grasp the reality of your being, that you are Children of Light, My children, children of Deity, able to grow up and inherit all that I have, all that I AM, all which as children you are endowed to be able to become.

You fear to share your substance one with another, and in this fear that you will not have enough you prefer to see each other starve while you build weapons of war, and play with them as toys, killing each other, wasting the very substance you think to hoard. Even as you afterwards rebuild that which you have leveled in destructions, you continue to build machines and devices of war to take new portions of this planet to call your own. Watching your weapons kill in taking and holding your small pieces of Earth is not enough: to secure your supposed conquests and hold your imagined lands and barrier borders, you seed the earth with death-keepers which kill so you may go away. In your greed to possess lands, you render the very lands you hold dead, even unto yourselves. In your greed to gain wealth from the land, you name your death-keepers mines, for to you they yield up imagined gain. Yet you have blighted your planet with so many millions of land mines that monthly I see over 2,000 innocent children - many of them in their most tender years as even you call children – mutilated and killed. You have gone away, and you do not see it happen. But I must see their legs blown off and bodies

442

shredded, as they are mutilated and killed! All so you may keep imagined holdings of lands, your supposed portion of this Earth, and keep out those who do as you do, who come to take, and take back. All because as a generation, you hate to share what you have imagined is yours.

The selfishness I see every day on this planet is an outrage to your royal birthright.

This I see, while you in your smallness argue hotly over whether or not you are the only children of your God in the entire and vast universe.

So great and important you think you are!

Get over this.

It is time to grow up.

How do you fashion and form a world?

Large scale organization of matter forms many kinds of worlds; all are beautiful and serve purposes; among many formed, some serve greater purpose than others. I may choose of the best for you. After an accreted world is seen to be capable of becoming ideal, I again send the most Obedient One to administer to its preparation and seasoning for children to eventually come. Even as there are many children, so over long time there are many new worlds continually arriving to a state of preparedness, and those who will go to them are chosen, and elect their choice to go.

As you see the universe is so evenly ordered in every direction you look, thus you can see that it is evenly appointed; each part of it is as good as any other; thus you can see that it is of no importance or consequence or preference to most Intelligences in Spirit as to which world becomes their home. Bonds of Love between Intelligences in Spirit are of greater importance than skenas, and as you have formed bonds and friendships and loyalties unto one another over time, so you follow each other often in large groups unto the skenas as they mature and are chosen.

Herein you still have not comprehended your eternal Free Agency, and mine, of choice.

There are more thousands of trillions of suns than you are able to imagine, and more planets than you are able to imagine. Of these, many are not suitable for the best forms of life design. As many worlds are formed, all serve their purposes of balance within this whole, yet so too are there thus many worlds from which to choose.

Does it matter where a world and its sun are found within the whole? There is vanity and more vanity under your sun, but you may look outward into the universe and see for yourselves: it matters little. Does it matter where in the cosmos I choose a planet upon which to plant life? I tell you again, it matters not, and many worlds there are which are perfect and suitable for optimum life in its forms as I have found it best survives and lives within its portion. Within the space you see, I have the choice of worlds, and as there are many, I choose those which have become obedient unto the greatest end, even that of life.

Those which have fallen short still have their glory, and they are worthy, all. Yet of the best I have chosen, and do choose, and shall choose to bring to pass my designs and purposes.

So I may understand more clearly, what makes a planet ideal?

It needs to be in orbit around at least a G2 class sun which provides appropriate energy with extended duration, without excessive radiation; it must be a planet of about your Earth's mass, which provides ideal gravitational attraction to hold an atmosphere of about the same thickness, density and pressure weight as your Earth's, and provides adequate weight to objects at the surface without being gravitationally excessive - a problem which quickly runs into complications requiring skeletal and muscle increases which then require increased fuel consumption and adjustments ad infinitum which ultimately alter the Design beyond its optimum functional ideal. Trust me: you wouldn't like to be stuck in such an inferior model. The gravitational mass is critical to lightweight, sporty body articulation; thus, planetary size must meet the archetypal standard; it can be easily adjusted and refined through collisional paring or accretion. Very importantly, it must have a substantial iron core, and proportional silicon content must be very high: of this the silicas are beneficially formed for ideal rock and thus soil purposes. Thus local sun class, and planetary size, iron core and silica content are primary considerations.

Having good size and good content of matter, orbit is easily adjusted from any pattern and distance to just the right distance from the sun source. Re-adjusting planetary orbit is very fun, and it is spectacular. Spin is adjusted in this same process, and whether it must be slowed or accelerated, the day as you know it is ultimately of great importance to all life forms. Weeding the patch of excess planetary orbitals is very great fun, and serves multiple purposes: clearing orbital pathways, spacing orbits to proper gravitational influence ranges, and creating the vast quantities of small orbitals, grit and dust which are needed constantly on a Life World over the long-term to sustain climactic processes and water cycles: you've got to have them in the solar system. Your love of fireworks and your game of shooting marbles in a circle derive from these memories; now you know why some have enjoyed the game for millenniae, and you all thrill to aerial displays. Orbital distance must be adjusted to critical tolerances: it dictates gross energy received and mean velocity yield which results in calibrated annual cycles. The AU distance from your sun is according to archetype, and it yields the best terrestrial environment for carbon-water based organisms. A Life World must have an orbiting moon. Distance from central sun and ideal moon mass, size, orbit distance and mensal cycles all affect solar and lunar gravitational influences on oceans, land, crust, plants, you, single-cell organisms, as well as total energy delivery per square foot of surface, mean temperature, water cycle equilibrium, and very importantly, month and year length, which is not arbitrary and directly affects your organism functioning. You have circadian cycles of days, circamensal cycles of months, and circannual cycles of years, and these must be optimally provisioned or you will not thrive. They are not incidental to this life on this world, but follow what yields an optimum in an organic design: regeneration cycles of tissues, hormonal cycles, energy storage cycles, rest cycles, electromagnetic cycles, and myriad other systemic cycles of organism which yield optimum health.

Planetary water will derive from heat release from within stone where it was bonded from planetoids during the initial accretion phase; from ongoing molecular bonding; and from the heavens, sent from the abundant supply of frozen planetoid water masses.

The precise tilt of the planetary axis can be adjusted for proper seasons much later, as it becomes critical only when organic and topographical preparation approximate requirements for your arrival and thriving.

When proper orbital balance is achieved for a planet of proportioned and adequate content, the planet will receive adequate but not excessive heat and energy; have adequate but not excessive self-gravity, lunar and solar gravitational influence; attract, develop and hold an appropriately layered and weighted atmosphere; hold and sustain appropriate water supplies as oceans; experience perfect circadian and circannual cycles; be malleable into appropriate topographical configurations of land mass distribution amid surface waters for temperature moderation and climactic homeostasis, and mass elevations for condensation irrigation cycles; and experience seasonal cycles needed to stimulate circannual rhythms optimal for regeneration and health.

When this is accomplished, then over time you must further refine and adjust the surface to prepare it to sustain ecosystems for a successful planetary environment. Water, wind, temperature and electricity do most of this work. The need is to conclude with well distributed land masses straddling the equator to promote ideal distribution of water, oxygen and nitrogen cycles, and moderate weather patterns which will obtain due to geographical topography; you need an adequate distribution of flatlands for plant and animal growth and proliferation; and tall mountains in mountain range masses for temperature buffering, wind current modifications and local generation, of condensation precipitation action, resulting subsoil water storages, etc.

Of course the vast oceans will continue to provide planetary homeostasis in the atmosphere and water cycles, to buffer organic processes on land and limit them in size to an adequately diminutive magnitude so that their negative products

445

do not overwhelm the balance, and most critically to assure adequate water constants on land which will never accrue more than .03% of what is contained in the main bodies over the entire aggregate land masses. Ideal water supplies are determined by the required water needs of the surface land you have above water line: calculate water to fill oceans accordingly - the three-to-one surface ratio is ideal - and you will need to assure the formation of adequate lakes and rivers for water cycle and land organism availability and usage. Swamps are very efficient oxygen and nitrogen systems contained in relatively small space, and they must be proportioned and well distributed. Lastly, as part of the water cycles and oxygen cycles, land mass needs must accommodate tropical forests, grasslands, savannahs, coniferous forests, temperate woodlands, deserts, taigas, tundras, glaciers and ice caps.

Within these, you need to think about how to provide for food-fuel energy provisions to sustain these bodies. The design of food organisms is endless and fascinating. They follow simple, archetypal patterns: food pyramids are the path by which energy flows into the system from its sun, through plants, to the animals that eat them; food chains are the descending sources of energy to plants through a series of larger animals eating smaller and smaller animals and finally plants, which store energy from the sun. Food webs are the woven tapestry of food chains. There is an infinite flexibility of variety in plant and animal design potentials for these through DNA design, and what is practical and functional can be made also beautiful, curious, unusual, inspirational, friendly and fascinating as imagination can envision, always remaining within the perimeter circle of thriving functionality within each design.

It sounds like a lot to put into order.

Nothing complicated beyond your means: you are my children. Yet most important for you to learn is Humility, Faith, Obedience and Perfect Love. There is no use for planets without these. Yet on planets, Intelligences learn these.

Tell me of Intelligences, please.

Intelligences have existed eternally; they are co-eternal. They are not all equal; there are some great and noble, and others that are lesser to those. You, the Children, are Intelligence of the First Order; even these are many.

Yet Intelligence alone is able to do little more than think, and this not as you know thinking in this Estate. You are Intelligence in Spirit Body as my child; and as you were obedient and valiant, you have earned the right to come unto a world, and receive a body, even the optimum mortal vehicle of Spirit Intelligence: thus you are also flesh.

Could you show me about Spirit Matter Bodies, here, please.

Spirit bodies were fashioned for you, being Intelligences. As I AM the creator of your Spirit, I am your Father, and you are my children in truth.

Spirit is matter, but it is a finer matter than you are used to seeing, touching and measuring. You know Near Death Experience, you have been out of your body in Spirit when you died, and you have seen the shadows of spirits, and beheld many Spirits; I do not need to speak to you of Spirit, for you know.

Know this: Spirit is matter organized according to a physics other than that which you know and therefore measure.

Your tools, instruments and technologies are not made of Spirit Matter; thus they can only detect and measure energene matter that is organized in the exact opposite and like structural patterns you understand as 'solid' or 'physical' or 'matter.' For this reason, those who only trust in this generation of tools foolishly forget how much you have just begun to detect and measure that before you could not detect or measure, things which before you knew not of, and thus would not have believed even if told. In the vanity and pride of these new tools, many think they thus can detect all things, and they vainly forget how much does exist that you have not yet devised tools to detect and measure.

You have not yet found the way to detect or measure the several other combinations of energy units which make up other kinds of 'matter' in bonded energy units which repel. You have not yet imagined to search for the physics of Spirit Matter.

But I tell you that Spirit Bodies seem as physical to each other as you do to each other. Yet without will and Faith, they are impalpable to you. Spirit matter is a finer organization than is this physical matter you know, yet whereas this matter is transitory and disintegrates easily, Spirit Matter, once organized in Spirit Bodies, retains its integrity and organized form forever.

The one type of bonded energy matter - yours that you know - does indeed pass through the other. For this reason Spirit Bodies may inhabit bodies of flesh and blood, and you do. As you are formed in the womb and your Spirit enters - when your mother feels you begin to move - then your Spirit Body is bonded within your physical body, and they become virtually inseparable, except in death. Spirit and body together become a living Soul.

The organization of spirit matter, as I told you, is not the same: not the same atomic structure or use of energenes. It is an entirely different structure. It is, by comparison, infinitely fine and therefore light in weight, yet it is subject to Intelligence as the physical body is subject to Intelligence. Knowing as you do that the densest of physical energene matters is virtually all vast open space, for this reason marvel not at the fact that your Spirit body inhabits within your physical body without interference, and the two move as one.

All of the vast space between protons and neutrons, and the immense space between nucleus and electrons in the atoms making up your physical body, is indeed vast space for such small units as the energenes. and if they are charged in different types of organization, they obtain a different form of opposite, and they do not repel physical matter from the micro distance you understand as a surface: they pass between each other as if they were not there at all, and by principles of attraction between the two physics, they may be bonded as long as the organism lives. In this you will comprehend that life itself exerts a force, utilized and interactive as a real force between the two physics.

Those who have an ear to hear, hear.

When your physical body dies, your spirit continues, as a palimpsest. It is easier for you to think of it this way. You can still see the spirit, but not with your physical eyes, just as the faintest palimpsest on a scroll is still visible, but not with your physical eyes. You need different eyes to see a scroll palimpsest. So it is with the spirit. It is there, though you cannot see it with your physical eyes.

But I have seen spirits, and I know a number of others who I believe have actually seen spirits. I'm not talking about attention-getters. I'm talking about people who have seen as I have seen. How do we see spirits with our physical eyes?

You do not.

I don't understand. I have seen them, with my own eyes.

You forget: you are also Spirit. Through your eyes of flesh, you see with your Spirit eyes. Spirit may behold Spirit. Yet most Incorporeals will not.

I understand. Please, show me: how is our Spirit a palimpsest?

It imprints all you see, experience, think, and process. Your thoughts, memories, experiences, feelings, all that is you, all that is your individual reason, intellect and consciousness - all of this is imprinted on your Spirit just as it is in your physical neuro system. You are this palimpsest of all you have known. The Spirit Matter is more enduring than the physical body of this estate, this creation; and while your brain neuro imprint dies and vanishes in only minutes after it is cut off from oxygen and electro-chemical charge, you keep all sensations and thought processing which imprints to your spirit; it is yours forever, for all eternity. To the children of this generation, you may comprehend that Spirit is to physical as is the value of ROM to RAM.

As your spirit is a palimpsest of your body, so it is also a palimpsest of your mind, your entire consciousness, all of your memories, learning, experiences, wisdom, feelings, everything that makes you distinct from your closest brother, and your closest sister. The children who study the science of the brain do not fully comprehend why the brain functions of identical twins are not identical; they must comprehend that identical DNA division is separate from a reality that each physical body receives a distinct and eternal Intelligence in Spirit Body, and the brain is but a shadow of its Intelligence in Spirit.

You know that you have come to understand many things which only a few generations ago would be impossible to understand even if explained. Accept that this too will evolve in your understanding until you have the means to understand it, and it will seem as simple and commonplace an idea as any other concept of discovery your scientists and consumers accept today.

In the meantime, as you still do not understand how aspirin works, nor how memory in your brain works, yet they serve you; so this serves you as well.

Spirit beings cannot do as much as you can. I know you think the spirits can do more than you, because there are certain things they can do interactively with your type of matter which you cannot do, such as pass through your matter. Yet do not over-rate this. It is the nature of interaction between the two types of matter, that one can pass through the other's vast inter-energene space. Yet you have never thought about the fact that you can pass through spirit matter just as readily. You need not be jealous. In fact, you pass through spirit matter regularly in the course of every day. As you come to understand spirit matter as real, as it is in reality, you will suddenly see yourselves as truly magical and super-powered beings of light, which, my child, you are.

You, as children with physical bodies, are beings of much more light, a greater concentration of Energenes. You, by the nature of that increased energene weight which you talk of as atomic weight, have advantages over and above those of a Spirit Body. The spirits are very much jealous of this. Thus, the spirits which shall never have bodies as yours are very jealous, and they often try to enter your bodies, so much they crave the feel of this kind of energene-matter, and this kind of body. These are they which rejected the concept of Free Agency, and as they refused to be a part of such a creation, they cannot inherit it. Only after it was made did they finally see what a wonder it is.

Remember always: there are several types of matter, yet none of them are matter at all, only different organizations of energenes, which react differently toward themselves, and among themselves.

I understand now there is a physics of Spirit, and as you said, I don't need any explanation for there being Spirit. I know Spirit. Please, however, could you tell me more about Intelligence? It is hard for me to grasp that I am co-eternal, even as Intelligence.

There is little I can tell you of at this time that you can reference, and your memory of your existence in Spirit with me before this world was formed has been veiled from you, for a wise and good purpose.

Thus hear and understand this: an infinitesimal sphere of light is within you: it is you, the you that is you. It is Intelligence. Without Love, it is virtually inert, but it can nonetheless grow in consciousness; as consciousness of Love increases, so does its capability. Yet it can act only to a point.

It is, however, of immense capability, and when given a vehicle to drive, it thrives. The finer physics of Spirit gives it a body, a Spirit Body, and within this you become, that you may become. Yet the increase experienced within a physical body is of many multiple orders.

If your physical body is ill, your Intelligence may examine its vehicle; there are those who have awakened to see it hovering over them. As if startled at being discovered, it has been seen to instantly dive back into the physical body. Hear and believe: you are capable of great healing within yourself, if you will believe, have faith, and receive the blessing to which you have birthright.

Intelligence is the essence of being; it is the glory of God. It needs a vehicle, a body to drive, to become an entity and exercise its potentials and capabilities to become matured in all potential. It needs a mortal physical body to drive and utilize for all that can add to its capabilities in the probation of a Second Estate. It will need an immortal physical body, organized on yet another subtly different physics, to obtain and receive eternal joy.

Intelligence without articulation knows no joy, but only sadness and anguished longing amid the dark of eternal night, the immensity of that night. As the distant points of starlight began to first shine, there was joy. Since the beginning of the Plan and the Design, all Intelligences have received Hope and Joy. That is your reason for existence: in Spirit, now, and as a Resurrected Being. Joy.

The child Beethoven, deaf to all sound for many years, remembered, in the isolated silence of his mind, his own being as a little child, floating in the night amid the stars, floating in the waters of night and stars, and he remembered the good news, and the Hope; he remembered seeing the moment of fulfillment, and the Joy. He remembered being there, in silence.

From this joyous memory, even deaf, he wrote his Ode To Joy.

In his music, Angels now raise their voices and sing.

Thank you. I understand much better now. I have been wondering, however, as I have been receiving these words, what is the purpose of worlds? If we already existed in space, and our Spirit Bodies can exist in space, and I'm assuming that Resurrected Bodies can live in space, why confine ourselves to such a little world?

A vastness of space is not a joy. Having nothing near you to see, or observe moving, is not a joy. Unending openness and nothingness is not joy.

Enclosure of space, with things close, privacy, protection, is a joy.

A small space which encloses you, and protects and shields you from what is all around you, which contains you, this is a joy.

A skena, a tent, in the midst of a desert ocean of space, is a joy.

That was a prime need: to make in this limitless, boundaryless expanse a specific place, a spot, a limited and enclosed place, divided from other space.

The purpose was to divide the heavens, as I have said before.

Dividing the heavens is so desirable.

You have forgotten what it is like, existing out in the expanses of wide open vastness in open space. It is good. It is nice. It is beautiful. But it is also depressing.

Does this surprise you, to relearn?

As your Intelligences occupy a particular place in space, so they yearn for a place on which to stand, a place in which to find shelter, a place in which to find privacy. Privacy is wonderful. You know this.

The creation of a planet with a place to stand on and an atmosphere which divides it from outer space is divine. The night opens the heavens to the home you all have known, always. You see your first home at night just as you saw it from space without the physical matter. Except that on a world, you see only a part of it at one time.

You now know, by your movies and special effects, how to imagine space all around you, in every direction you turn. But this is still only an illusion of understanding, for you have not done it in this mortality: you only see the screen image, which like the night sky, is limited to a very partial view, less than 2% of the spherorama you can see in what you call deep space.

Nonetheless, night is comforting. It is your view of your home as you have known it for eons. But during the day you are able to forget about all that vast space out there, and enjoy your own divided and provided place of space, with its wonderful limits of sheltering closeness.

On the open sea you feel secure when you have a ship around you. In the air you feel secure when you have a plane around you. On land as you travel at high speeds you feel safe and secure when you have a car, or a truck, or a bus, or a RV or train around you.

When you relax to read, or see images on a screen, or cook, or eat, or speak among yourselves, you like the feel of a building, or a house, around you.

When you sleep, especially, you feel secure when you are enclosed, separated from the rest of all that is around you. You want to sleep in a house, in a room in a house, a place you know is protected.

When you leave your houses, you take houses with you.

You love skenas.

You love a tent when you are in the wilderness.

Look within yourself, and behold a memory.

451

No matter how much you love the open spaces, the out of doors, you know that you still crave the closeness of a tent, of walls, of a cabin or a house or building after only a short number of hours.

After how long do you long for the feeling of safety and relaxation in an enclosure, a tent, a house? Usually, every eighteen hours is a maximum time in the open for you. After forty-eight hours of exposure all day and exposure all night, the comfort of an enclosure is an enormous longing. Even those who are separated from any kind of man-made shelter or divided, enclosed space, seek the natural enclosed space of a cave, or a hollow between boulders, or the overhang of a large rock, or the enclosure of a group of trees, or a low bush with overhanging branches.

It is not just for warmth, not just for imagined protection. It is for the craving of an enclosure.

You have not asked of Hell, but I will tell you: Hell is to be forever exiled in the vastness and coldness of open space without light: eternal darkness, far from radiated energy, cold, and non-physical. A place where there is no creation of organized opposites. A place where there are no opposites. Such a place cannot be 'physical;' it is only empty space, with nothing tangible. In the outer realms of the cosmoses, such places exist: without light, without warmth, without opposites, without physical tangibility for lack of opposites to create likes and repelling physical bodies.

This is Outer Darkness.

This is the ultimate hell of eternal existence. You can only imagine it from your very limited and finite understanding. Unless you go there, and face it knowing it is your eternity, you cannot understand it at all. Only those who go there will ever understand what it is.

Vastness of space is depressing. After eons of loneliness, and vastness, the comfort of closeness is delightful. There is nothing worse than outer darkness, where the opposites are not organized, and energy is not concentrated, making it empty and cold. It is desolate.

The concept of planets allows for the creation of self-contained spaces: spaces which have limits. Boundaries and limits give Intelligences comfort and security. The lack of limits is depressing, when refuge from it does not exist, when that is all there is.

Just as you love flying in a hot air balloon but also love to come back and put your feet on the ground, to see mountains and trees nearby or buildings around you and above you, to be inside your house and rooms which limit the space you occupy - so it is in space.

Just as you love to travel all over the world, and see Grand Canyon, and Kilimanjaro, and the Gobi, and the Amazon, and so many other wonders vast to your earthly measurements, you ultimately long for your own little enclosed space, and seek and find relief back in your created environment, within its walls, within its space-limiting barriers which provide you with a defined unit of space you feel comfortable to manage.

It's hard for me to imagine living in dark, open, endless space.

Limitless space is difficult to imagine; it is more difficult to live in.

You have promoted a film, saying *"No on can hear you scream in space."* This phrase is an archetype; it is a symbol of one of your deepest horrors.

Think of it. Imagine it. It is true. There is no sound, in space.

Without an atmosphere, made of organized energenes, utilizing the law of Opposites attracting and likes repelling to create a blanket of air held in place around a planet by gravitational pull exerted by that same law, no one can hear you scream in space.

Without suns, and planets in orbit around suns, there is no air.

Without air, you cannot hear any scream. Nor can you hear music. Nor can you sing. Nor can you talk as you delight in talking among yourselves.

You are thinking: but aren't there other ways of communicating? Yes: I hear your thoughts even now.

Yet: isn't the sound of speech more beautiful?

Isn't the sound of music more beautiful?

Isn't the sound of laughter more beautiful?

And what of color? What of all things which are not, without the physical?

Without this physical, there is no interaction with photons nor any light spectrum. There is no color.

Without this physical, there is no shape. Think of every shape that pleases, that brings you joy just to see its form, that soothes, that inspires, that strikes awe and wonder into you.

Without the physical, there is no touch. Think of every texture you touch, smooth and warm, cool and soft, rough and primordial, solid, soft and yielding, every touch which contacts your skin and your fingertips.

Without this physical, there is no taste. Think of every taste you know, in every combination, every savored mouth-watering delicious taste that your tongue and mouth can know.

Without this physical there is no smell. Think of every flower, every perfume, every aroma of food cooking, bread baking, forest garden, seaside, all that you can remember, the smell of your baby in your arms, the smell of your child's hair, the clothes of someone you love.

No one can hear you scream, nor can you hear, or see, or touch, or taste, or smell anything in a void of space.

The child Beethoven, deaf for so long, deprived of the gift he most treasured -

453

sound and hearing - remembered himself floating in silence amid the expanse of space looking at the distant stars, deaf, and remembered the Hope of this Creation; suddenly, he remembered, and he re-discovered his Joy.

Think of every art within nature, and then think of every art of your own hands - all of the shapes, colors, sounds, of grace within dances, even motions of machines. You delight in your fast and colorful cars, your soft and shimmering clothes in all of their colors and patterns, your architectures, your paintings, your sculptures, your sleek housings of your machines of technologies. Your lives are splashed with colors and shapes and textures and touch and taste and sound, and none of this could you experience save be it for the creation of suns, and planets, and galaxies, and a cosmos wherein all of this may obtain.

Space with boundaries and physics is most comforting to an Intelligence.

Thank you. I will ponder all of this.

I have a number of questions about this earth. I guess I will begin with something you mentioned as necessary for a planet to be ideal. I believe I'm assuming that this, our world, is an 'ideal' planet. You said that to be ideal as a Life World that a planet must have a substantial iron core. I know our planet has a massive central iron core. Let's begin there. Why?

There are a multiplicity of reasons why a Life World must have an iron core, and not a small one, but a very substantial iron core. This is so important, and yet few of you have even begun to think about its full scope of importance in the whole of a planetary formation that is to be chosen as a Life World, to sustain the DNA Design.

There are many questions to be asked: Why is it still so hot? Why hasn't it cooled? What keeps it hot? What keeps it from heating just that slight bit more which would melt up through your crust under your feet, over-heating that thin skin of cooled matter upon which you live your fragile lives?

You have asked and answered a few questions: How does its radiated heat affect the temperature of the crust and thus the atmosphere which, where they meet and you stand in just a few feet of space, forms your thin living layer, your "life zone" as you have come to call it?

A very visible need has been understood in surface and atmospheric temperature. Your Earth's core is indeed still molten and hot after all this time. Indeed you have noticed that the layer within which you can survive is quite minimal: a few thousand feet of atmosphere upon the thin skin of a cooled solid matter. You cannot live except upon it. You cannot go up very far above it even on a mountain, or you rapidly feel the loss of strength and poisoning from carbon dioxide buildup due to lack of atmospheric pressure in your lungs to complete the transfer of gases in your blood. You call it 'altitude sickness.' It is illness to your organism resulting from insufficient atmospheric pressure to maintain the optimum intake of oxygen and exhaust the waste from your cellular activity as you live every second. If you rise up too far into the thinner and thinner atmosphere, you die, suffocated from this inadequate pressure for osmotic transfer of elements to keep you fueled and carry off buildup of gaseous waste elements from your blood.

Yet before you become too seriously threatened with suffocation, you find the air temperature drops suddenly, quickly below that which you can endure. You are constrained to stay very much close to sea level, not too far up the small mountain slopes, or you cannot live well. Your organism cannot thrive.

Those who have an ear to hear, hear.

Yet as you cannot go straight up, neither can you go straight down very far before you run into life-threatening troubles. Go very deep into the crust, and you reach the heat, and the heat kills your organism, your physical bodies. In your deepest gold mines in South Africa, which penetrate only two short miles and a bit more, temperatures already reach 120 degrees Fahrenheit, enough to kill you in just a few hours, without special precautions. Your deepest geologic borehole is 9 miles, which is deep; you know even higher temperatures there.

Yet your crust is fragile; it is filled with cracks; it is thin: on the average, only about twenty miles. It is very thin in some places. Under the oceans, for example, where it is mainly composed of basalt, it is a mere three to seven miles thick, while beneath the upper continents, which are mostly just light rocks such as granite, though it may be forty miles thick in many places, in some, it is a mere twelve miles thick. From crust down through to opposite crust is almost eight thousand miles of molten liquid heat, and you walk upon an eggshell. Your whole crust is but a floating collage of pieces of paper, a wafer-thin flotilla of tectonic plates overlapping one another, with an almost four-thousand-mile drop into the liquid molten matter just to reach its center. The tectonic plates of your crust overlap and move under each other in subduction because they float on the liquid mass, and move; some overlap on only one or two sides, and are moving away from each other over long, eggshell thin lines under your oceans. You know your crust is thin enough and cracked enough and overlaps loosely enough that the red liquid stone inside your earth can and does push up through it, to remind you of just how fragile your thin layer of life is between a mass of burning liquid rock and an endless space of freezing vacuum and void.

Yet all of this serves a purpose. Without the ability to arrange land masses, a perfect equilibrium for weather and climactic control would be impossible. As matter gathers gravitationally in space, impact converts energy into heat, and molten magma spheres form by hydrostatic gravitational force and angular momentum. The planet quickly grows by intense bombardment of accreted material, and the surface of the sphere remains as an ocean of magma until the heavens thin out and accretion declines. As an ideal planet for life must have oxygen and volatile material at its surface for later processing, the economy and timing of accretion material available is best when a good smattering of this type passes over and accretes near the end of the process. As the surface of the magma ocean begins to cool and form a crust, continuing impacts cause irregular surface masses; broken crustal plates then move and ram each other, piling up mountains of cooled crustal matter. All the while this is happening, impact upon impact thinning out the heavens and gathering together into a world continues, and continual heat keeps the growing sphere heated; just as an enormous smelting vat, iron and nickel and other heavy elementary metals impacting it from space melt down from the astro rock ore and iron meteoritic materials and gravitationally trickle in a constant flow through the mass into its gravitational center, forming an all-metal core. While the smelting process is going on in the heat just below the crusting surface, the jumble of lighter-weight higher masses which eventually remain above waterlines when oceans form tend to slip and slide onto the imbalanced side of the wobble, as a group.

This is sometimes capitulated by catastrophic processes required for the ultimate purpose and need. Earths intended for Life Worlds cannot be alone. There are Opposites which need to be provided, and can only exist through completion of the archetypal design. The key Opposite of a Life World is achieved in the capture of another, smaller planet, pulled in and held in orbit around the Life World, all for great and wise purpose, which is in me.

Your earth was forming ideally, and thus it was ideal that one of the smaller accretions, even a small planet, should be nudged until its path could merge and join the orbital path of your earth. A smaller accretion, following the ideal pattern yet too small for habitation, was therefore utilized as such smaller smelting spheres are utilized in all sun systems of earths: it was nudged and pulled until it swung into trajectory for eventual joining with your world.

If the trajectory of the smaller planet and the relative speeds of the two are perfectly adjusted, they need but meet closely enough and the gravitational pull of the larger will capture the smaller and swing it into orbit. Yet this is not necessary at the early phase of planetary accretion and smelting. Often direct impact better provides the slowing and capturing impetus; this was the process used in the case of your world.

The moment of union was spectacular. Both your earth and the small planet had accreted adequately to smelt iron cores, and as the smaller planet approached yours in space and was pulled the last fractional into collision course, in its last minutes both molten planetary surfaces literally rose up and reached out to meet each other. The relative speed of the smaller planet was precise and slow, and it collided slowly upon a calculated tangent line. It took over two hours for the collision to conclude from first touch to separation. The gentle and slow-motion impact gouged deep into your earth, peeling back its pasty mantel almost all the way to the molten iron core, and it also tore and sloughed back its own mantel. The forward momentum was so great that as the mantel was torn back from the smaller planet exposing its molten core, part of its heavy molten iron core poured into your earth's core as it caromed off reeling. The glancing impact sheered a huge mass of pasty mantel from off your earth, and pushed it before itself as it slid off into space; but the slowing effect of the impact on the smaller planet, and the glancing drag across your surface sufficiently altered its trajectory such that it was pulled reeling around into tight trajectory around your planet, where it has remained captured and in orbit. The feat was accomplished, and well.

The huge mass of hot molten mantel scooped and carried away on the new companion quickly spread and bathed its entire surface. The wound on your earth filled in and healed over time, and your planet continued to season and settle as all earths do. Over time, due to the continued plasticity of the inner sphere of your earth which it maintains by virtue of the massive iron core, the resulting planetary tidal bulging pushed the secondary companion further and further away as it needed to be. Such a close proximity initially created gigantic ocean tides during the primordial periods, excellent for accelerating erosion in grooming, but far too severe for safe shore lines where children will play.

By this method of secondary planet capture, which gouged a huge hole into your earth, an increased rotational wobble added to the continental merger already progressing on the opposite side of the sphere.

While continental formation is random, and random land mass form is quite OK, even without procedural impact capture to secure the required secondary companion, the normal random surface land mass formation is seldom balanced. In fact, wobble in angular momentum, the rotational spin of imbalanced hot magma spheres, usually tends to slide such crustal masses to one side of the planet during the initial hottest phase. This frustrates every eventual purpose. If a planet's core is not of prepared iron, the planet eventually cools and solidifies, and it will be either very flat if little surface mounting occurred, or, its land masses will remain all congregated on one side. Neither configuration satisfies the needs of Life Worlds; they are many, and demanding.

Yet by plate tectonics entire continents may be moved, slowly, or more rapidly. Even after formation is near complete, and water oceans cover the planet, some ocean floors will continue to spread, with newly raised and cooled basalts filling in along widening gaps. Other plates impact along colliding plate boundaries. Where the top ridges rise and buckle with pressure, beautiful and practical formations are created: on your earth, these have become your Himalayas, thrust up by collision of the Indo-Australian plate, and along others, the Alps, the Rockies, the Andes, all useful and needed weather and water cycle tools.

As your planet originally accreted and solidified the crust over which its waters boiled and steamed until it cooled enough for them to condense into the oceans, most of the high masses were lumped up on one side, along the equatorial line and southward. This would not yield a suitable climate and weather to sustain complex life forms, for a variety of critical reasons.

Yet it was not a problem, as it is no problem on any of the worlds which accrete into this type of world. Being hot and molten inside, the crust floats on a slippery layer of discontinuity, and it can therefore be easily manipulated.

Over the Preparation Time, the original land masses which had risen enough to remain above the waters were moved. They had a long way to go before this planet could become suitable. They were persuaded into two masses which you have now noticed and even named: Gondwanaland and Laurasia; these were further rotated into a single mass which you have also identified and named Pangaea. This by rotation was able to be broken into convenient land mass pieces and moved as was needed to further balance wobbles in the rotation and provide better climate distribution. The placement of land masses and oceans has a direct effect on water cycles, heat distributions, winds, and thus on all plant and animal and especially mammalian life. Still there was need of additional relocation of land masses to create the optimum conditions for the children. These were accomplished even while the seasoning process was reaching its final phases, until it is as you are upon it now.

The crust you live upon makes up less than 1% of the volume and mass of your earth, and you walk upon less than one-quarter of it. The molten liquid mantle which is between your crust and the hot iron core of your planet makes up 84% of your Earth by volume yet only 67% of its mass, or weight. Herein you begin to see the significant presence of the iron core of this kind of planet.

The layer of your life is so thin, so thin a film upon this world. You live on a skin of matter that is the right temperature for you - a thin skin which just barely covers the molten sphere which is 99% of the mass of this living place, and under a thin blanket of atmospheric pressure which provides your needed external body pressure of fourteen pounds per square inch to offset your internal body pressure of fourteen pounds per square inch - in perfect balance of opposition - allowing your essential dissolved gas transfers to maintain your continual burnings and promote optimum physiochemical metabolic functions while it keeps you from exploding outward.

Yet you never fear even a second of all your born days that you will suddenly be burned to carbon, or frozen by the almost absolute zero of space only a sort distance above, or that you will burst in its vacuum, the vacuum of space so close above your fragile heads.

The iron core, however, is the secret to all of this.

While the iron core is only about 15% by volume of a planet such as this, it is 32% or about one-third of an Earth's mass.

This central weight of the core plays important roles in many continuities.

It is actually made of iron with some nickle, and minor trace elements, in particular uranium, it own heat source. That is the beauty of the whole concept. Due to pressure, in spite of the heat, it maintains two 'layers' as a core - the inner core, solid, a ball about 800 miles in diameter, and an outer 'layer,' a molten mass of liquid metal, 1,400 miles thick. Thus the whole ball becomes an inner spherical core about 3,600 miles thick in diameter. The pressure which obtains inside it by the weight of rock upon molten mass is equal to three million atmospheres of pressure, over forty million pounds per square inch. And its temperature? It ranges from 7,000 to 9,000 of your degrees Fahrenheit.

But what is the source of this essential and required heat so long after formation? This is the beauty of the whole design. While the original heat is introduced through the accretion impact process and through many additional impacts of large masses at high speed - enormous transfers of kinetic energy into heat impact energy which at the same time are used to adjust orbit, spin and axis orientation, among other refining needs - much of this heat is lost over the time required to grind and condition a planet into proper surface soils, grow abundant amounts of organic matter for healthy ecologies, produce enough free oxygen to supply sufficiently all inorganic and organic chemical bonding attractions until adequate free oxygen remains in the air for large organism respiration. Though not all accretion heat is lost - there still is some residual cooling - it was quickly perceived that heat retention alone would be far below requirement and utterly fail by the time the planet could be seasoned and prepared for your receiving your bodies. Something else was needed.

The solution was resolved in atomic engineering.

The answer was found within the structuring of the energenes into the atomic structures of the elements.

There are certain combinations which naturally 'like' being together: nucleons bonding in groups of 2, 8, 20, 50 and 82 have a great bonding stability. Yet there must be Opposites in all things: where there is stability, there may be instability. This was quickly seen: other unities are slightly less stable. Some are very unstable. An advantage was perceived in the potential of instability. It was foreseen that it would be possible within this physics organization to make atomic unities that do not 'like' being together: they would be increasingly unstable, heavy elements with very large nuclei of more than 82 protons. These would be more than unstable - they would be radioactive, and in their actual atomic decay, they would produce slow and controllable heat.

However, obtaining this structure posed its own engineering problem.

Under normal heat and fusion conditions in suns of ideal size as were comprehended and envisioned ideally for fueling and sustaining Life Worlds, the tendency to expand due to the heat of hydrogen fusion is balanced by an Opposite: the contraction and force of gravitational collapse into itself. This is the ideal condition, which produces a long-lived light and energy source for worlds. However, in such ideal stars where the Opposites are well balanced, and fusion, heat and gravitational density fuse atomic nuclei into heavier and heavier elements through repeated completion of fusion of the majority of species nuclei present, the process of gravitational collapse and new nucleosynthetic fusion continues only to the final endothermic formation of a nucleus of 56 protons - iron - the very useful and precisely needed product for the Design of the ideal life organism vehicle for Intelligences, a precise purpose of Design of ideal suns as they are designed.

Such suns serve multiple purposes, as do virtually all things in the Design: they provide light, heat, radiation and myriad useful elements including silicon and iron. Iron is a most remarkable element, the most stable nucleus of all, and it is essentially the nucleosynthetic marriage of two silicon atoms. You are just now beginning to comprehend the usefulness of silicon crystals for their remarkable and highly useful atomic structural properties. Yet the energy required for the endothermic fusion process to synthesize iron in a sun becomes its last triumph, after which it shrinks into what you now have named a White Dwarf. The solution to the long-term inner heat needs of planets destined to become life bearing worlds is not accomplished in ideal suns, of perfect size and balance.

If one is to force the fusion process to its limits, to obtain the element potential of the heaviest possible nucleus which, in its oversize imbalanced instability, will by that instability decay and thereby produce the needed heat source, one must provide conditions for the fusion cooking and bonding of atomic elementary units into nuclei of more than 56 protons.

This problem was also envisioned in algorithm and solved.

The answer was to do the illogical and form immense suns far too gravitationally powerful and far too hot for Life Worlds, which live only a short time and then explode. Thus in the opposite of the ideal, purpose and response to need was obtained.

The solution then was to accrete and build giant suns which would burn fiercely for a short life and then, due to immense gravitational density and successively heavier nucleosynthesis, reach the limits of stable instability in nucleic increase. Having reached the highest eventual nucleosynthetic species exhaustion, when the last atoms had been fused and heat expansion could no longer sustain the weight, total gravitational implosive collapse would occur. This collapse would take only seconds, in which instants an unimaginable amount of gravitational energy would be released, and substantial energene friction would obtain, triggering an explosion.

Such a sun would explode in what you call a Supernova Explosion.

This explosion is of immense violence, and disrupts a wide area of space. Vast quantities of radiation are also expelled and oceans of charged particles, both helpful to the overall purpose yet harmful to the Design of life, become captured by the large scale magnetic fields within their galaxies, for which a compensatory shielding mechanism was devised for the worlds. This would be resolved by the iron core under design through its magnetosphere, and by other engineered properties of the gasses of the ideal atmosphere.

However, the giant sun would have to be called a failure of design in engineering: it did not endure, and it ended in devastation.

Yet in it, great purpose is accomplished.

By their immense size such suns obtain unimaginable gravitational density by collapse pressure and unimaginable high heat. Within them, under these specially designed conditions, nucleosynthesis can produce heavier nuclei until the sun explodes - a moment which creates even greater pressure and heat. In the heat and pressure of such an explosion, medium-mass nuclei are fused into the heavier elements and light nuclei capture neutrons which begin to produce beta-particles. Additional elements of great use are formed.

Copper, silver and gold are among the heavier products of these explosive failures, and many other heavy elements which were perceived as possible within atomic structuring; all are abundantly produced. Among them is of course a vast supply of elementary iron, needed for the cores of earths. These elements are all blown out into surrounding space in the expanding explosion envelope, and become the elements for making worlds.

In the beginning, these were therefore the suns of preference in the galaxies. I organized vast, widespread multitudes of such immense suns, and the universe was literally ablaze with rapid successive blasts of Supernovae everywhere you looked as it expanded. To you, observing it all, it appeared as an infinity of strings of firecrackers and fireworks, on a cosmic scale. Each galaxy became a cosmic popcorn popper, by design. Using Opposition, the majority of the material could be contained by initiating mass cycles of clustered explosions. Explosions were set against explosions, and the opposing forces of material impacted against each other largely cancelled outward loss, bouncing the material and energy back and forth amid chaotic clouds of flying matter which remained largely trapped for the next step by the physical interference of its own impacting, and, by the mass gravity of the infant galaxy.

This time period, during which the rough, gross preparation of matter in the universe was effected for its eventual refinement and usefulness in worlds, was a period of violence on a magnitude you cannot imagine. Tremendous ongoing explosions threw matter in every direction simultaneously, resulting in a continual impact and violent interactivity of matter on large scales. To accomplish the ultimate needs of the plan and the design, successive formations of supernova suns needed to progress through their generations, by which eventually matter was organized out of matter previously unorganized.

Obviously this was a needed process to produce the required materials for Life Worlds, the skenas for Intelligences to come to and inhabit. Yet just as obviously, it was a process so violent and destructive that it had to be accomplished early in the process, quickly, on a grand scale - and then be curtailed only to levels needed for continuing synthesis of new worlds in the ongoing expanding universe.

You may imagine clouds of asteroids, meteors, rocks, gravel, sand, grit and dust flying every which way and colliding, again and again, collision after collision, until clumps of matter were nurtured and persuaded to begin gathering, which then by gravitational attraction drew matter upon matter unto themselves, colliding against the growing mass with immense energy and force.

Intelligences and Spirits can endure these processes, for they are not affected by this physical matter charged and organized as it is.

The process continues as larger and larger spheres of accreted matter form, and over time more and more of the loose matter flying about is attracted and flies smack into the path of a large body - sun, planet or moon - and accretes into its mass, thus clearing the air, as it were. Your solar system accreted a number of planets, as well as moons, following the somewhat predictable process; each body became, in the early system phases, a sweeper, a vacuum collecting debris and clearing the general spatial region more and more. Your planet Jupiter has been a successful regional sweeper, and it still acts as a buffer to your planetary orbit more than you might imagine.

I thought that Jupiter was just a giant gas planet, with nothing but a metallic hydrogen center mass. The prevailing theory is that it is a sun that didn't accrete enough mass to ignite fusion.

This is what you have been told by the children who theorize. They err and have erred in many things; the frequency of discoveries of errors in their theories will continue to increase as they explore with their newly made tools, on their path to discovering Truth.

Yet know this: though Jupiter has accreted from the initial unorganized local cloud matter a solid mass much smaller than its visible giant diameter of accreted gas. It has been accreting supernova debris for several billions of your years, debris of the same composition as your planet and others. Beneath its thick cloud layer and liquid hydrogen sea is indeed a central mass of solid planetary matter.

The proof of this you see without understanding: the Great Red Spot as you have called it is more than a storm that has lasted centuries in the same place; it is the swirling movement of the cloud layer around a massive planetoid almost the same size as your world which finally succumbed to the gravitational attraction and fell to the surface. The seas of liquid hydrogen swirl around it fiercely due to the high velocity of the planet's daily rotation. It still stands above the sea as a massive eroding mountain many thousands of miles high, causing the colossal disruption pattern in the chemical-stained cloud layer which you observe as the impacted mass plows through the opaque gas. Density variations due to chemical composition and temperature bands cause the colors, but you know this.

The central solid planetary mass of Jupiter residing within its sea within the vast and heavy cloud cover revolves on its axis every ten of your planet's hours, a ten-hour day. Due to Jupiter's giant circumference, the surface speed is enormous. As you remember its composition is quite different than your planet's water and air — gravitationally formed liquid hydrogen and heavy chemical gases — this surface velocity creates different effects than your Earth's seas and atmosphere. The reality of Jupiter's surface is the reverse of water flowing down a rocky riverbed. With Jupiter, it is the planetary mass surface which moves faster than the sea and dense gas atmosphere cover: the mountain thus cut its way through the slower-moving density of the sea and thick opaque atmosphere. This results in the myriad ripples and bands you observe in the colored, opaque gasses, caused by the numerous salient features of the solid planetary surface rushing below. It is not the only such salient surface protrusion.

You do not believe this, but you are soon to learn of its truth. Know then that this giant regional space-sweeper has been very busy in your solar system, gravitationally and physically clearing a wide orbit swath, as have been in times past all of the orbiting bodies of your solar system, even your own earth, and your sun itself. You see the heavens filled with debris still; in the beginning, this local region was vastly more cluttered and dangerous.

Only when these quantities of loose, flying matter are significantly reduced, and the frequencies of impacts are reduced to only the clouds of small bits and pieces which are actually needed for healthy planetary function and climactic homeostasis, can life be initiated on appropriate planets. Until the loose cannon balls, as you might call them, have all found homes, safe orbits or been accreted, no skena is safe for the children.

In the final stages of this sorting out process, while some large pieces are still flying about in useful trajectories as may be exploited for refinements to orbit, rotational speed, axial inclination, etc., the initial organic phases may begin on moist land and in the oceans. Microscopic life in soil and water produces the needed components of atmosphere and the organic molecules for eventual increase of ecological demand. Even extensive organic seasoning may be accomplished while ultimate refinement of astro-planetary and surface planetary conditions are undergoing final adjustment. However, the heavens have to weed themselves out and become calm before the children may physically inhabit an earth.

Once the process of incorporeal life was begun in any galaxy, the nucleosynthesis process had to be locally confined. Initially, it was a wholesale process; now it is always planned at great distance from any inhabited skenas. Clearly, in any region where a supernova is to be accreted and processed, no existing uninhabited worlds can be processed or prepared - even if they are virtually ideal; they would be of no use. They are ignored, or knocked out of orbit by collision and moved to more suitable areas for later benefit. Thus you see, only worlds capable of being refined into ideal worlds, located in ideal neighborhoods of the cosmos, are chosen and prepared.

It is by the engineered instability of supernovas that the heaviest and most discontent nuclei can be formed, all over 82 protons, the pinnacle of which is the element of most critical need: the most radioactive of enduring elements.

Though instability is, in the perspective of engineering, a failure, yet the utilization of all things possible can often yield surprising opportunity.

The ultimate success of the solution resided in the last heavy atom which could be practically fabricated with long-term instability: uranium, which you call uranium-238. In all normal aspects, it is a truly poor bit of work: it has an instability and alpha radioactivity which makes it lethal to life organisms - the opposite of the primary purpose of the Design. Its slightly lighter cousin, uranium-235, has a much shorter life, and produces even greater radioactivity. Yet in their curious instability and radioactivity, they provide the required planetary core heat through their slow, controlled nuclear decay.

Why are there such unstable elements in the universe, you have asked?

Because they were needed. They were created to fulfill a very specific and critical need in problem-solving the formation of a Life World model that could maintain static temperature within a very critical, non-negotiable range.

Uranium-238 has a half life of fourteen billion years - long enough to satisfy the long-term need required over time. It decays slowly into a succession of unstable elements: thorium-234, protactinium-234, and so on until the atom is reduced to the much lighter lead-206, very stable, very useful for many practical things, especially in electronics, but cold. Neither lead 206, 207 or 208 will produce heat. Stability serves its purpose, but its opposite also serves.

In all, three such nuclear disintegration series were perceived, and all three were organized to serve in the heat production process. And so I caused there to be an unstable, even dangerously radioactive elementary chain.

Yet it keeps Life Worlds alive.

That is its purpose.

Melted in the iron-nickel core of Life Worlds in exact calibrated quantities, kept from critical mass by specific mix, uranium decay delivers the precise heat to the surface through the crust to maintain the required surface/atmospheric equilibrium temperature of the thin Life Zone required for the optimum Design.

Its heat also keeps the inner planet molten as liquid for tectonic plate movement and land mass arrangement critical to weather and climate regulation; for critically needed volcanic activity seeding atmospheric particles for the water-condensation rain cycles and many other soil and ecological processes fed by volcanism; and other useful ecological purposes. All of this can only exist by the presence of an iron planetary core.

And yet the quantities of unstable heavy elements are such that it keeps the whole inner earth liquid and hot, without overheating the last few miles of surface, or melting it. The planning is exact; preparation proportion is precise.

You know these things, for you have discovered them, but you have little comprehended how this engineering and Design has been an essential and incompensatible design in the maintenance of a constant mean temperature under your blanket of warming atmosphere.

Yet it does more; much, much more.

I finished reading this, realizing that I had just seen for the first time the creation of the universe as it was, and how it evolved, and why. This had brought me only to the threshold of the beginnings of an earth such as this one, such as ours. And still there was much I knew nothing of yet at all, about the formation of life, and the purpose of this iron core in the realization of the whole.

I believe I understand the process up to this point. Please continue now and show me how it all works together.

Very well.

The children have not yet imagined nor explored the role this metal core plays in the total charge of a planet such as this. This role is great, and essential. There is effect upon all of the energenes in the planetary sphere of its field; they are collectively affected by it: both non-living and living matter. You have yet to fully wonder how this core's charge and presence affects all life upon the planet. You have yet to fully wonder how this core affects the exchange of charges in the inorganic structures, as well as the organic structures.

Remember, your physical creation is of structure within structure within structure within structure. All interact to form a whole: you. You have not yet fully understood either the nature of or the reasoning for even one level of your structure. Neither have you comprehended the full complexity of any organism as you begin to reproduce DNA; nor do you know why you might be able to reproduce it; only that because of energene behaviors which exist without your understanding, it can be done. That is all you know.

Yet the role a planetary iron core plays in the exchange of charges in these interconnected organic bodily structures, from interactive systems to tissues to cells to molecules to atoms down to the smallest energene, you have not yet begun to fully question. This much it is you still take the core for granted.

Aside from specific density and its affect upon the axial rotation which orders your days and nights exactly and gives you your ideal time of work and rest, it serves an even greater purpose.

An ideal Earth's core of iron-nickel provisions, by its charge and presence, not only heat retention and generation as you have just seen, essential to land mass topographical management, temperature stability and homeostatic weather cycles of the planet, but it also creates a major electromagnetic field.

The extensive effect of this magnetic field overall in virtually every aspect of inorganic and organic structure and function in existence on such planets is an inquiry you have only begun to contemplate.

It creates conditions of electromagnetic alignment: a curiosity which leads to exponential unfolding of uses and benefits; it promotes and enhances many kinds of essential ion formations and exchanges, electrostatic accumulations and discharges; it helps protect you from the solar wind, residual radiation and charged particles from ancient supernova explosions, as it creates a magnetosphere and magnetotail above the atmosphere, which also influences the formation and maintenance of an ideal atmospheric layering essential to life below it. Because of it you see the aurora borealis, which is the visible effect of a critical planetary function essential to your life here, not just a pretty phenomenon; it is the diverting and funneling of electrons and other particles away from you into harmless trajectories. It exerts major effects upon your bodies - semi-static field and electrochemical functions in your neurological mobility- and thought- function systems; even in the hemoglobin in your blood. It is as essential to you as it is to migrations of birds, insects and whales; you sense it no less and are affected by it no less; it plays no less a role in the constant orientation of every cell in your body.

Like you, it is free to move, and while you know your current magnetic north, it switches polarity, which it has done many times over the past to useful advantage; and it moves miles a day, shifting its center.

You have yet to question how such an iron core and its resulting electromagnetic field assist in such essential planetary preparation processes as the formation of the great masses of sedimentary rock. The grinding of the infant surface of an earth again and again with heat, cold, wind, rain, electricity and water to create appropriate quantities and grades of particles for soils and needed continental sedimentary rock you understand, yet you will some day marvel at the role this core plays in accelerating the process and enhancing it. The mineralization of sediments by exchanges of ionic charges can occur rapidly, given the right conditions. Conditions are more readily flexible than you believe, and you have not comprehended them, for your tools of measurement do not tell all you of the possibilities, only of what they can detect.

The iron core plays its role in all of this.

Yet there can be too much of a good thing. The stellar mix is too rich in iron for a crust chemistry; it must be depleted. It is a critical necessity to smelt the iron from the upper and surface portions of an earth intended for life of this Design. The problems of organizing worlds are many, and every solution must and does serve multiple purposes. As it is necessary to have an iron core, so it is necessary to reduce the crustal iron content natural to stellar material mixes. You have seen a large piece of iron buried in the sand at the beach, from a cable or some other machine, and you have seen the sand and rock quickly bond around it, concreted and cemented as if new stone. It forms this in only a few years. Such concretions are small examples of what would happen to all loose soil particles if there were any more loose iron in the soils than is present. The silicate-rich and iron-poor mantel and planetary crust are ordered so by design, for otherwise, with the electrolyte salts dissolved in the waters, not only would the sedimentary rocks formed at the bottom of oceans be useless, all land would be in a real sense petrified and the Design of life could not thrive.

The whole earth was a sea of water surrounding a mass with a center of iron, and yet you marvel and think only of time, and not your planet, nor creation, nor its physical nature. You have so many answers before your eyes which yet you ignore, because you refute Design.

Though among systems which all play their critical roles it is difficult to signal a most important key role, yet the formulation of your blood is a most triumphant achievement in answer to the need of the Design, the solution to over a thousand bodily functional problems in this mortal physics, all requiring remedy in order to fabricate mortal physical life in this form of matter. Its base is pure element, even pure water, traces of many of the atomic elements, and its primary element, iron.

The iron in your blood was made in stars before your world; within your body courses the matter of suns. You are celestial children in all ways.

Know that the core of all Life Worlds and your earth are not iron-nickel by chance; nor is it by random chance that your blood is a solvent mix as seawater, with special iron cells. The possibilities and potentials were seen, from the beginning, and the proportions and requirements were met, all by Design.

Too many children still think only of coincidence that your blood and the core of the earth are both based on the principles of iron and the essential elements and salts dissolved in water as the sea. From the beginning, the characteristics which were exploitable for the continual introduction and distribution of oxygen into the system, and the removal and expulsion of carbon dioxide from the system, were perceived as only the beginning of the wonders which could be designed into a blood based on iron, salts and trace elements in the ideal solvent, water. There are so many other roles it plays that only some are known to the children who study them.

And the electromagnetic field around you, aligning the atoms of iron in the hemoglobin cells of your blood as they form and as they function, helps you at every moment in every day of your lives.

Thus for all of these things and more, Earths must have iron cores.

I see the truth of it. Please go on to show me the rest of the connection between the elements in the earth and in blood.

There are about ten million compounds known to you, which can only be broken down into their constituent elements chemically, not by physical means. All of these are made by the atomic building blocks of the ninety-two elements, in diverse combinations and proportions. All of them serve purposes, and all purposes serve.

As your Earth has smelted and percolated its metal into its essential core, built upon it is the pasty mantel which it keeps molten by uranium decay. Between the spheres over spheres in layers are transitional discontinuity layers which are slippery, and allow for movement: the Gutenberg and Mohorovicic discontinuities as you have named them after the children who discovered them. These slippery layers and the ability of layers to slide over each other at disproportionate speeds and directions without excess drag minimizes the number of earthquakes you experience on the surface, and provide critical cushioning of shocks of various kinds. You would not want to design an earth without them.

Below your eggshell crust, from the center above the 1,800 mile thick metal planetary core, is the bulk of your earth: you have named it the mantel. Well it is named, for it is worn as a cloak, and as a cloak it both protects and warms. At the uppermost level of it is the asthenosphere, 186 miles thick, which carries the crustal plates just below the Mohorovicic discontinuity. The lithosphere, or sphere of stone, are the crustal, tectonic plates themselves.

Essentially, the mantle is made of silica, iron, magnesium, and metal-rich minerals. These are brought to the surface for valuable enrichment of atmosphere and soil by the function of volcanism. This is in itself a complex and fascinating diversity of processes, and by them all, you see into that which you cannot see, and receive that which is cut off from you can you therefore cannot receive, but yet you do; for it is required; so was all designed, to fulfill all foreseen requirements.

The crust of ideal worlds must also be composed of the appropriate proportions of minerals. The content is easily manipulated in the impact accretion process: excesses can be smelted down into the lower spheres out of harm's way, and shortages can be remedied by nurturing and nudging flying chunks containing the needed materials, minerals and compounds into collision trajectory. This is much easier than you might imagine, when you fully comprehend the frenzy of flying matter speeding in all directions at the beginning of such organization cycles. And, the tranquility of time. The purpose is to achieve ideal suns and solar systems with good orbitals, and, if everything lends itself to that end, only one ideal world per. Even this is not of any great importance: enough quasi-ideal worlds obtain overall that suns which never catch and hold orbitals or solar systems which never accrete even one planet capable of being groomed and cultivated present no shortage; they still serve their essential purpose in the large scale balance of motion and equilibrium.

As I would like for you to comprehend the composition of the ideal crust, allow me to show it to you here charted for your eyes to scan it easily:

oxygen 45%
silicon 27%
aluminum 8%
iron 5.8%
calcium 5.1 %
magnesium 2.8%
sodium 2.3%
potassium 1.7%
hydrogen 1.5%
titanium .86%
phosphorus .1%
manganese .1%

and there are also diminishing traces of:

fluorine
strontium
barium
sulfur
chlorine
vanadium
zirconium

Note these elements and their proportions, and I will show them to you again at a future time and place where they will become more significant to you. Yet for now, know that as they leech into water over time in an infant planet, by myriad repeated circulations of evaporation and rains and re-evaporations and again as rains, and mighty winds blasting torrential raindrops, and storms you cannot imagine which can rage harmlessly on an infant planet before life has been introduced, with spectacular electrical discharges, full heat of steam, full blast of wind currents beyond powers you can fathom, gigantic wave action and ocean current powers mightier and more violent than anything you can envision, all dissolving, dissolving and dissolving elements and minerals as the waters are beaten and pounded and blasted upon the rocks, and as the rocks grind and are pounded and ground and smashed and crushed into ever smaller pieces with ever greater total fragmented surface area, and from deep waters descending into cracks and fissures into the heated depths of the crust and the mantel over time, leeching under heat and pressure more minerals and elements and compounds until they are saturated and superheated and burst up into the moving seas and mix

469

with the raging currents - they dissolve to form sea water in its essentially formulated proportions, and these elements, and their proportions, find their parallel in your own blood.

The essence of your mother earth courses through your body, a harmony of this physics, a unity of nature within nature, all providing the success of the Design of life, each by contributing its best characteristics, its best gifts, to you.

In the beginning, all of the rocks on your earth began as rocks of fire - fire from the suns wherein they formed their atoms, and fire from exploding giant suns, and fire in the molten crucible of the accretion smelting vat as your earth gathered matter unorganized and processed it into compounds of wonder.

Of the fire-born rocks, which you have well called igneous, most abundantly formed are granite, diorite, gabbro, peridotite, diabase, rhyolite, andesite, basalt, obsidian, and pumice. Each has shown your ancestors its purpose. Temples and obelisks, houses and statues, grindstones and paving stones, fine sharp tools and jewelry, and light abrasive stones to smooth the calluses of your skin.

As these are ground down and pulverized and smashed and crushed, and the waters wash them down to where they may settle in slowly running or still waters, they form layers, and in time, they too, become new rock. Of these sedimentary rocks you have made much use, of shales, sandstone, siltstone, breccia, chert and flint - the wonderful tool making and fire making stones, conglomerate, and from the salinity of the oceans - precipitated gypsum, and from later organic origin in your oceans and swamps - limestone, and coal.

As all earths season and mature under grooming over their preparation phases, pressure and heat work upon both igneous and sedimentary rocks to alter them, and they form metamorphic rocks, most abundantly slate, schist, gneiss, quartzite and marble from organic limestone and dolostone.

Upon this crust of lithoshperic plates is your bedrock, and your loose rubble regolith layer.

Upon this is the most critical part of your planet's preparation, also a mere skin of gossamer thinness, you soil. This soil, the organic loam, is part of what takes its time to accumulate. This soil is the organ of the earth which can support rooted plants. It is in most places only one to six feet deep: immature and mature soils; dark topsoil, rich in humus. Also because of this, you live. And yet you have treated this thin layer as if it would replenish itself overnight.

From out of this soil your ancestors have gathered the stones which they have napped and chipped into tools, to hunt; and from out of this soil your ancestors have gathered the fruit which can be grown in it by the design of plant DNAs which produce roots that produce enzymes that digest the very dust of the earth they touch, and then soak it in to produce fruits and vegetables and every goodly herb for you to eat and for medicine and for cattle and for all manners of animals which feed upon the herb and convert its stored solar energy into their bodies, wherein you have them for meat, and by eating herb and meat, your ancestors have received each day their daily replenishment of energy from your sun, and they have so thrived until your day.

From out of this soil your ancestors have taken clay and shaped it and formed it with their hands and their fingers, and with it they have fashioned curious and beautiful figures of women and men, of animals and birds; also they have formed bowls and pots in which to cook, bowls and cups and plates with which to eat, and fine potteries and exquisite painted vases with which to serve their needs and beautify their lives. The fragments of these, broken and whole, you have found buried in the earth and often still upon the surface of the soil, and you have touched them with trembling hands and fingers, touched your ancestor's lives, and you have felt their closeness, and you have felt joy.

From out of this soil and rock your ancestors have taken clay and made brick, and they have hewn stone from out of the hills and mountains, and with these they have built houses, palaces and cities in which they have lived and learned the things which this probation must teach them, even how to choose right from wrong, good from evil, and to feel compassion and love for each other in all things. In their many places they have seen their brothers and sisters who have not chosen the better part, who have chosen evil and harm, and the sorrows and anguish which they have witnessed has imprinted the souls of most to understand why evil must not be chosen, and why good is desirable above all things. These are they of your ancestors who have obtained for themselves a rich inheritance, and all they have learned shall serve them.

From out of this soil and rock your ancestors have smelted copper and tin, and with this copper and bronze they have made their bronze age, which has flourished before you as the children have learned how to shape and fashion tools in fine and curious workmanship. Wondrous vessels have they made, and also vessels and ornaments of fine gold, and silver, and also of precious stones. These, too, you have seen as they have been found, left by your family of past generations, a testimony to you and witness of the goodness of this earth and its gifts.

And iron also have they learned to smelt and work, hard in its sturdy nucleus, requiring greater heat than the heavier metals, yet resistant and resilient and useful for building upon that which had been learned could be built. And so your family had its iron age, and learned how to fashion things of iron, and they grew strong, and powerful, and flourished as they harvested the fruit of the land, and traded among each other, even with gold, and silver, and copper and bronze. These too, they eventually struck in coins, and you find them in the sand and soil of your earth, and hold them in your hands, and turn them in the light to catch images worn smooth from the handling of generations of hands, images of kings and queens and princes and princesses, and you marvel and wonder at their day as you hold their coins in your hand.

As you look at all of these things, the rocks and metals and soils and stones, and the things made of them, see all that is living around you, and understand that this is the design: for you and they are all made of these same elements and unities of elements; of the self-same substances are you designed. For it is in this physics and these elementary fruits that the finest chemistry was perceived, and of its best potentials and qualities the ultimate organism vehicle could be perceived to articulate, empower and endow Intelligences in Spirit, and so all was set in motion and ordered and organized and refined to furnish the right atoms and molecules for these bodies to be, that you, the children, might be lifted up.

Look about you, and see the wonder of these elements and their unities, and look within your body, and see: from this same dust were you envisioned as you could be made, and so it was done as wise counsel comprehended, and planned, and ordered, and designed, even a cosmos and suns and worlds.

Father, I am in awe of this all, and the words that I hear within me are only two: Thank You. Excuse me as I'm a bit on overwhelm. Not from the information; it's easy to understand. I'm feeling so humbled as I see the lives of my ancestral family on this earth, and see so fully how all you have made in it has been here for us to find, and learn to use, and discover how to use in greater and greater ways. I feel like nothing in the face of it all, and yet I hear you in my mind now every time I say this to myself: I am not nothing.

I hear you telling me: I am your child.
I must learn to treat myself accordingly.
I must learn to treat my sisters and brothers accordingly.

This is why you are here. This is what each generation in its turn learns.

I am certainly learning. You have led me to my next question.
For life to exist upon a planet, this type of life - as you have told me, the optimum design of life form for an Intelligence to inhabit - there obviously must be water, and there is. I love the oceans. Please show me the origins of the seas and oceans.

Oceans give life to Life Worlds in many ways. Water is the solvent of life. Oceans are the reservoir of life solvent. You think they are the first environment in which initial micro life forms are introduced when only inorganic food sources exist. Yet the entire process of accumulating an adequate biomass and organic matter supply begins on the rocks, in the wet soils. Globally, oceans produce much of the positive supply of oxygen, needed to maintain equilibrium in all things for life. If an oceans dies, this source fails. Oceans are key to life.

Yet there are other challenges even more critical which oceans resolve.

As the ideal biological system is carbon based in structure, abundant carbon must be produced and provided. Much of this will chemically bond to oxygen, which

472

it just likes to do. Myriad processes required to provision a new world incidentally produce carbon dioxide, such as volcanism, an essential earth-grooming process. Yet just as carbon is needed, and carbon dioxide can be used to practical application in a variety of biochemical and biometabolic functional designs, there are opposites. Too little creates shortage and certain processes suffer; too much capitulates high ratios of CO_2 in the atmosphere, and for several reasons, this can kill a planet. Again, oceans are the key. If an ocean on an earth dies, carbon dioxide will quickly triple in the atmosphere. This will cause most oxygen-breathing organisms to die. Further, there is the temperature regulating problem in which CO_2 levels play such a vital role. The greenhouse effect will kill most life even if the gas ratio would not.

Living oceans resolve a primary need. Marine plants use CO_2 for cellular functions, and they capture and hold vast quantities of it. Yet this mechanism is not enough. The algorithm found an answer in the potentials of precipitation, of dissolved carbon dropping as solids. CO_2 dissolves in water, and by chemical bonding, it is precipitated to ocean floors; it forms limestone, which has captured and removed vast quantities of carbon dioxide from circulation in the atmosphere, maintaining a global balance. A living ocean is required for life.

There are so many such equilibrium problems to solve in reaching and maintaining a balance on a world for the optimum life organism designable to survive and thrive. The refining process is as a mighty pendulum which swings in exaggerated rhythms far to one side of the need, and then back and far to the opposite side of the need.

When there is an optimum perceived, it and only it is acceptable as a final yield, for anything less is inadequate to what can be; and the bodies of the Design have very narrow tolerances limiting the range in which they can flourish, and also great and precise demands which must be met and maintained, thereby setting the limits and range of conditions and substances in which they must be, in order to thrive.

To thrive is the only purpose; thus there are many problems to solve before the ideal environment may be established, prepared, conditioned and balanced so that purpose may be accomplished, and unfold. As the algorithm of the Design was perceived, so the procedures of its fulfilling were ordered.

To thrive, energy must be made available to the vehicle, to the body, in constant supply, and in controllable release: a balance.

The source of physical life's energy is the solar body.

Energy from an ideal sun - yours is an ideal magnitude sun as are all chosen earth's suns - reaches the planet surface, by your earth's systems of measuring energy, at about five million horsepower per square mile of surface per minute. That is per minute. The total solar energy falling in every one-hour period on an ideal earth such as yours, which you now know is of archetypal size and archetypal distance from an archetypal sun, is enough energy to meet all current global needs for an entire year. A year in an hour. This is then the daily equivalent to burning seven hundred billion tons of coal every day.

Much of that energy is used to balance the required surface temperature on your ball of rock in space. If all surface heat came from magma through the crust, ground temperatures would shoot high above the limit of survival just to keep the atmospheric temperature warmed to the proper range. It is the same problem of the cold earth: without the heat radiating from within, external heat from the sun adequate to warm and maintain the surface would overheat the atmosphere and the Life Zone. Either way, a unilateral heat source cooks one side of the Life Zone in the process of reaching an optimum of the other. Only a balanced bilateral heating design will work. This was foreseen; it was provided.

Yet how is an individual portion of this energy to be harnessed?

How is this energy to be packaged and distributed in increments small enough for a single organism body of optimum Design to utilize, without consuming it? It needs energy; an energy source is designed and provided. Yet a human body's energy need for one day is substantial: if delivered all at once, it would burn up the body instantly. How shall the energy be meted out? And once it is meted out, how shall it be regulated within the organism?

The problems were perceived; an algorithm of solutions were designed.

The solution to the problems begins with water, and the cycles of water.

Within the cycles of water are three additional cycles.

Thus there must be and are four major cycles on all Earths.

First is a global water cycle, in which evaporation from oceans, lakes, rivers and soils, and transpiration from vegetation and animal organisms is re-distributed and perpetually made available as needed through condensation in wind blown clouds, and precipitation back onto land and waters through a continual water irrigation. This accomplishes solvent distribution and solvent availability, and also greatly moderates surface temperature heat. All other parts of the planetary design being optimal, the water cycle assures a perfect climatic homeostasis as it assures adequate supplies of solvent for all life forms required in the world wide energy organism delivery web. Your bodies are approximately seventy per cent water, and endure little temperature range.

Second is an organic carbon cycle. It cannot operate without water. Thirty to forty per cent of volcanic emission gasses are carbon dioxide, which become part of the atmosphere. Once carbon is distributed through such volcanic action and fabricated by organic processes, much of it comes out of the air into the water-photosynthesis process where it is trapped in plant tissues and fibers as long as they are living, and in humus and coal when they are dead. Here you recognize carbon as the great solar energy engine that it is to all life; without it you would not exist as a biological body, and without it there would be no plants to receive solar energy, capture it, and store it for you to use. Carbon is also removed out of the air and from plant matter and metabolized into animal organisms, by respiration and ingestion, where it is converted with solvent water into diverse compounds as parts of cell tissues. Carbon is also drawn out of the air into water and aquatic organisms, and compounded into solid limestone where it is trapped, as you know. It is returned to the air by respiration, burning wood and grass, decomposition of humus and animal matter, and combustion of fossil fuels. Provisions had to be carefully ordered for its balance, for as much as it is needed, it can quickly obtain in excess, and in excess it destroys the entire equilibrium required. Your bodies are largely made of carbon, and water.

Third is a nitrogen cycle, a gas in the atmosphere, yet moving with water in chemical processes in oceans and on land, it works the metabolic processes in virtually all organisms, always returning to air. You know of the nitrogen cycle need in plant growth: without nitrogen, there would be no plants of the type required for the fullness of this design's potentials. It is by the catalyst of nitrogen that the main engine of energy capture and storage for your bodies grows: the biomass of plants. Yet only a few of you are fully aware that aside from your constant need of plants, you too, are in absolute need of nitrogen within the design of your bodies: it was identified as an ideal element bonded in proteins, an essential part of amino acids. Your very DNA design is dependent on nitrogen. Without it, the Design would be immensely inferior. You would not like to be in it. Also, the phosphatides are nitrogenous protein bodies, and in your blood, they are part of your food in transit. Again, the cycle of solar energy captured, converted and transported to each and every cell depends upon this cycle. Nitrogen is also part of your metabolic non-protein systemic processing as constituents within your body plasma, where it contributes to waste collection and disposal management through your blood: urea, uric acid, creatinine and ammonium salts. You are also built of nitrogen, in DNA design. Though nitrogen is used in your Design but in minimal amounts, yet without it, for myriad and diverse reasons, you could not be as you are. As you are is good.

The fourth need is an oxygen cycle. This is the most marvelous wonder of potential in this physics, captured in design. It is the most precarious and demanding of all cycles. An ideal atmosphere must be within a range of about twenty-one per cent by volume, which is, you will note, unusually high compared to other planets and satellites which are left essentially as they form. Much less than this, and the optimum organisms designable cannot function. Too little, and there is not enough to drive the energy processes in cells. Much more than this, and precipitated combustion becomes a problem of rapidly escalating severity as availability rises. Too much, and you burn up the organisms, and you eventually burn up the planet.

These are the most basic cycles a life world must eventually sustain.

The oxygen cycle is ideally initiated about half way through a planet's seasoning and preparation cycle. Before there are oceans for the water cycle, and prepared, eroded and ground rock granules to provide a surface upon which micro life may live and feed, there is no point. Until the oceans are adequately saturated with dissolved minerals and salts and trace elements, even single-celled life organisms will not survive, unless they are inorganic feeders and chlorophyll producers, and even these do not thrive in the oceans until there is inorganic matter adequately dissolved in them.

How is life established upon a new planet?

As all other conditions begin to take shape for sustaining larger organisms in the necessary chains and pyramids, the anticipatory step begins in the wet primordial gravel and sand soils. The new erosion soil surfaces provide ready inorganic food sources, protected secure environments for mass reproduction, and they are always ready before the oceans. You do not believe this, but wet surface sand is the first ready eco habitat, ideal for seeding first life.

Life is first introduced into wet erosion sand soils for two reasons. First, at such early stages of preparation, grooming and seasoning, the oceanic environment on a young planet still cannot support even single-cell life forms. There is no food, except dilute inorganic food. It is insufficient. Yet massive tides saturate young soils with mineral-laden electrolyte life-solutions, and in such saturated erosion soils, the first organisms can feed. Micro plant photosynthesis begins to release free oxygen into the atmosphere, and the multiplying cells begin to form a biomass and eventual source of organic food and organic matter. These first organisms continually wash into the seas in the water cycles, and as soon as the seas are ready, they too, begin to sustain life. In this manner a biomass is produced as needed to establish the larger, more complex multi-cellular life organisms, and the process is set in motion for all life.

Most of the initial oxygen this first life produces is of course bound at once in the water itself. As much as one-third of this original oxygen is usually bound in water. In water and air where it touches, it begins to oxidize the many solid rock compounds.

The exponential increase in the biomass, as the initial life forms exist in large enough quantities to introduce larger life forms and then larger life forms which each in turn rely upon the smaller as food and fuel energy transmitters, is more rapid than you have imagined, and more prolific than you have imagined. The opportunity to introduce new species of practical use in the process which at the same time are fascinating and delightful to behold and bring joy to observe, is immense. It is a time of great exhilaration, and satisfaction.

As the process is long and the needs for organic matter and a vast biomass is monumental for a successful introduction of children, the organic seasoning process is often accomplished in punctuated phases, as residual chunks of supernovas, stellar matter, planetesimals, asteroids, meteors and other matter in trajectory still smash into the incomplete earth and extinguish much of the life which is accomplishing the seasoning process. As these events are anticipated, and often such collisions are in fact nudged or drawn into collision to further adjust orbital distance, rotational speed and axis orientation, they pose no problem. There is a temporary decrease in biomass growth, but that proliferates more quickly afterwards than you might imagine. Soon the process is again growing along very well. As there are many wonderful species to enjoy, these periodic disturbances are opportunities to introduce new life forms, which is part of the biomass growth and world wide food web process regardless of disturbances. In this manner, the day all will become prepared and the earth will reach optimum conditions comes ever closer.

Usually it is after about ninety per cent of the preparatory seasoning processes and time have been accomplished that oxygen levels finally reach their proper and needed levels, as you observe on this earth now. At this point, large complex organisms may be introduced in oceans and upon land to complete the global preparation for introducing the children. Full oxygen levels are required to sustain the complex life forms which pave the way, and much additional accumulation of biomass and organic matter is needed before the optimum balance is reached.

Achieving these high oxygen levels after devoting all needed free oxygen to every oxidizing process required inorganically and organically is one thing. Afterwards maintaining the balance and limits of this range is another.

Balance upward is of course maintained by plant photosynthesis. Photosynthesis on land and in the sea produces most of the oxygen you require on a world. Water evaporation puts compound oxygen into the air, some of which eventually becomes available for certain uses. With good oceans and good forests and a healthy microbiomass, product usually meets need.

Balance downward is largely by continual organic and inorganic oxidation. Oxidation of everything traps oxygen. You have noted that silicates are the most abundant rock forms in your crust. Formation of silicates and other compounds capture and bind excess oxygen so the free oxygen content does not exceed the combustion threshold and ignite your planet and all of its life forms. If content begins to rise, volcanic emissions trap oxygen particularly well in huge quantities, yet in Opposition, volcanoes cannot be used indiscriminately to resolve upward oxygen trends because they also produce enormous amounts of carbon dioxide. Forest fires produce less carbon dioxide and substantially reduce the production base, and they have been very beneficial since most early time. Yet today, with your generation's current destruction of rain forests and wetlands, upward rise is not a problem your planet faces. Carbon dioxide increase, however, is a critical problem.

Oxygen balance is minimally regulated downward by another process: animal respiration. Yet this is where it finds its primary application: the central, originally perceived design of ultimate use; its true, original purpose.

Respiration completes the control of fuel harvesting and the calibrated release of converted solar energy in a living organism designed for the express needs of Intelligences to possess those maximum capabilities of articulation and mobility which this physics can allow a physical body of this required size.

This is the physical side of the Breath of Life.

The goal was envisioned; the solutions to its achieving were provisioned and ordered. Within the complex interrelated web of all purposes, all of the cycles initiated to provide adequate available free oxygen to serve the children were set in motion that this purpose might be fulfilled.

However, you see thus we have come full circle in all of these cycles to the first: water, and the oceans.

How did the oceans come to be?

After the archetypal creation was conceived, all has followed the same pattern.

In the initial formations of matter in the cosmos, among much heat and energene fusion, it was foreseen that much water would be formed. Much water is also formed in certain suns, and in early stages of all suns. This is of course superheated gas; it is eventually blown out into far distant orbit by solar wind, far out into the enveloping space where it condenses, becomes ice, and accretes.

Ice planetesimals and frozen water molecules are abundant in the universe. There is an exchange of waters between the heavens and the spheres, and it is perpetual.

When an accreting infant planet is forming, and incessant impact heat is keeping it plastic and hot, it grows into a sphere red hot and pasty, with a surface of magma seas. As the quantities of free-flying matter diminishes in the given locality, and collision impacts decline, the inner residual heat of the planet is inadequate to endure against the cold of space, and by radiated heat loss, the surface begins to cool. During this process, which is not as long as you have imagined, still great gaseous productivity erupts from the sphere, as it is repeatedly penetrated by incoming high speed matter. As the accreted matter reacts to the heat and shock vibrations and the matter settles and mixes within it, much water vapor is produced, but due to heat and low gravity, it is blown away by the solar wind. It flows out into the far distant void where it joins and accretes with the host of planetesimals. A planet receives; it gives.

An atmosphere begins to obtain as gravitational attraction overcomes the volatility of the heated gasses. When this occurs, the rate of giving declines, and more and more is retained, and kept.

By various mechanisms, frozen water masses, ice planetesimals, are struck or pulled from their far outer orbits around the young sun. Some of these strike nothing, and when they reach the far side they are pulled back; they become what you have named comets. As they near the sun, the heat and radiation cause them to evaporate; the solar wind blows the loosened particles outward, and this tail catches photons and glows brightly. The released frozen water is blown back out to the far distant orbiting comet cloud, where it accretes back into the planetesimals. In time, after myriad returns and passes by the sun in elongated elliptical orbit, a comet breaks up, and totally dissipates. The solar wind blows it all back out.

Some of the comets are pulled so directly toward the sun that they are entirely evaporated as they approach it, and thus in a single fall they are vaporized and blown back out by the solar wind.

Yet some strike planets, and moons. Many have struck your earth, as they strike all earths.

In the beginning, as an earth is cooling, due to more chaotic gravitational activities moving in the locality, many ice planetesimals are pulled out of their orbits, and some impact the magma oceans. The first of these merely explode, and no lasting effect occurs other than the small accretion of the dust and stone and iron contained in the comet. The water boils away and is quickly lost into space, blown back out to the orbiting cloud by the solar wind.

Yet as cooling proceeds, ice planetesimals help in the process, and their waters become the first thin oceans over the thin, cooling crust.

They boil in sporadic localities where undercrust turbulence slowly churns and heats and melts the thin crust. Yet for a period of time, the sea is boiling hot, just a few degrees below boiling, and the atmosphere is continually filled with steam clouds. These rise and cool, and condense upon the abundant volcanic and meteoric dust, and global rainstorms rage for a long time, cooler water raining down, boiling water steaming up into the atmosphere. It is a time of unceasing cloud cover, darkness, rain, lightning and violent storm.

Most of this original ice planetesimal water eventually boils away, and the solar wind blows it back out into its primordial orbit cloud where it rejoins itself again in the heavens. Yet some remains.

Continuing volcanism replenishes the oceans until the planet cools enough that the seas cool, sufficiently to begin the process of land sculpting and continental reformation. Vapors spewed out by volcanoes are sixty to seventy per cent water vapor; the rest is usually carbon dioxide. The water vapor continues to condense, and for a long time, a young planet is a hot tub.

When the planet and the oceans are cool enough that the skies finally clear for the first time, the first dawn of the first true day, it is still not a very clear nor cool day. Ultra-tropical conditions persist for some time.

Eventually, the sphere cools to the point that an inhabitable earth begins to be possible. The mineralization process of the waters continues, with myriad submarine vents circulating cooled water down and superheated waters up again, saturated with minerals and dissolved compounds. These still exist today at the deep bottoms of your oceans. You call them black smokers and white smokers, depending on the color of the thick, muddy water which blows up out of them. As they served a purpose then to help saturate the water with the required minerals and compounds, so they do now: equilibrium is always the difficulty when a homeostasis is required. Deep water fissure smokers are the answer to replenishing trace elements and minerals lost through sedimenting burial at ocean bottoms, and biodegradation and chemical bondings over time. The oceans are like a blood to an earth, and their content must essentially remain constant, for diverse reasons. Yet this problem is solved.

Behold the results, and recall these elements and quantities and proportions, for I will remind you of them in a future time and place wherein they will become of greater significance to you by what you see.

These are the mineral proportions which saturate the waters of an ideally seasoned and prepared ocean:

> chlorine 55%
> sodium 30.6%
>   as sodium chloride, salt
> sulfate 7.6%
> magnesium 3.6%
> calcium 1.1%
> potassium 1.1%
> bicarbonate .4%
> bromine .2%

with which there are myriad descending trace elements and compounds in very minute but still important and useful quantities. Behold now, within the fuller envisioning of the amounts of free oxygen in the oceans, the total elements of water in the oceans: the electrolyte solvent of hydrogen-two plus oxygen-one:

> oxygen 85.4%
> hydrogen 10.7%
> chlorine 1.85%
> sodium 1.03%
>   as sodium chloride, salt
> magnesium .12%
> sulfur .08%
> calcium .04%
> potassium .038%
> bromine .006%

carbon .002%
nitrogen .0016%
strontium .00079%
boron .00043%
silicon .00028%
fluorine .00013%

Almost all of the ninety-two elements are found dissolved and in suspension in sea water, including gold. So, the oceans are realized.

In ancient times, from the records we still have, most of my ancient ancestors didn't know that the earth had so many continents. They thought it was mostly water, seas. Both the Atlantic Ocean and the Pacific Ocean formed barriers to most round-trip traffic, thus most spent their lives thinking that beyond those waters was nothing. Even those who calculated the circumference of the earth and knew it was round - like Eratosthenes, and others - thought that passage around the earth was unobstructed by land until you reached the other side - the Orient, China. It seems the Asians, who knew of the people of India and Mesopotamia and the Egyptians, Greeks and Romans through trade, also thought that sailing East would only take them over great waters, with no land until they reached the far end of the Silk Route lands. Only a few Japanese from early times, and apparently the Phoenicians and the Egyptians knew of and maintained trade routes with the Hidden Continents - the mid-oceanic Western Hemisphere. The Egyptians kept these gold routes very secret; it was their great mystery, the land of gold. I have also studied that the people in the Western Hemisphere, what we today call the Americas, didn't know much about the existence of the Eurasian continent, even though again, archaeological evidence definitely shows visitors arrived from both sides - the Mediterranean cultures of the Assyrians, Phoenicians, Israelites and the Egyptians, even the Romans; and from China, Japan, and other Asian countries also. The people of the Americas, too, it appears, mostly thought the great oceans were all there was, and only had vague legends about distant lands by the time the Conquistadores arrived. I've read extensively about this in books by the great archaeological historian Cyrus Gordon and a number of other archaeologists. My ancestral people thought this was a water world.
I guess I want to ask: why is our Earth so covered with water?

Very well. There was a problem to solve. This was the solution.

The problem to solve was critical: how can an adequate supply of available water be provided to land masses for terrestrial life?

The ideal terrestrial life form is essentially three-quarters water. It must be three-quarters water to obtain optimum operational potential of all systems.

The quantity of water delivered to the land must be adequate to irrigate soils and provide ready drinking sources for larger life forms incapable of traveling very far in any given short time; availability must therefore be virtually ubiquitous. Yet the supply must be delivered gently enough to not wash away land surfaces, and infrequently enough for sunlight energy to adequately penetrate to the land surface most of the time. This limits the delivery of supply.

The algorithm of this problem discovers that after fabricating the best possible terrestrial porosity to act as a sponge for water retention, and the most efficient atmospheric evaporation/condensation-recycling systems through elevated land masses and mountain ranges, even with extensive lush tropical forestation, daily safe water availability over the required great land masses will still only obtain in fractions of a percentile of the main water source. No matter what configuration is used, the same minimums of water surface and maximums of land surface always obtain.

Though there are many mathematical equations which can be used to determine and demonstrate the reasons for the required water-surface to land-surface ratio, as the body Design of life is approximately three-quarters water, so it obtains that a planetary surface must be the same: three-quarters water.

The problem is ultimately resolved and expressed in the formula:

Water Evaporation Surface to Design Body-Water Volume= 3-to-1.

Thus ideal planets are water planets.

They must be so, to provision life.

Ninety-six percent of most earth's water stays locked in their oceans. The water can only be distributed to land via surface evaporation; the best and most efficient water circulation cycles cannot operate but a fraction of the time and must be gentle or the land will be constantly washed clean.

Ultimately, water surface to land surface must be 3-to-1.

This is not a random design: the oceans must have depth to thrive, and though vast quantities of water are thus globally in reserve, they are systemic ocean supplies, unavailable. Only surface yields evaporation; less than one per cent of this water will be available by evaporation to surface land for daily use.

In other words: if a world obtains much more than one-quarter surface of land above water, its life-water needs will never be adequately met.

If such an infant world can be re-adjusted by collision impacts, volcanic explosion or internal plate mechanisms, and a close to ideal world may be molded into functional proportions, it will be chosen. If not, it will be passed by, and not be chosen. Only worlds which can provide a water surface base of at least three-to-one water-to-land are worth preparing for the Design of life.

Ideally, by the time the children are introduced, after the last stages when the planet is cultivated and the harsh climactic swings have been stabilized, about three per cent of the water or slightly less is locked in ice caps at the poles, for a wise purpose.

The rest, less than two per cent, is in transitional holding patterns as stored groundwater or hovering in the air awaiting rainfall.

Groundwater is an essential part of the design. This is one of a plethora of reasons why it takes so long to prepare and season an earth: the original surface rocks must be ground down and ground down repeatedly, and sediments must pile up and become petrified repeatedly, and low places must be made high, and high places must be made low, repeatedly, until the required type of porous sedimentary sub-surface layers and surface soils are created.

Molten magma is absolutely useless for creating a subterranean water table reserve system; it is solid and impervious. Pulverized soils and sedimentary rock sub-layers are required for this purpose, and so an earth must undergo extensive reshaping and grinding and layering and lifting to finally achieve a proper base upon which the Design of life may ultimately thrive.

Yet see and behold: only a single per cent of total global water enters the planetary ground water system, the sub soil reserves from which spring artesian fountains, river headwaters and tributaries, and wells. This water table is critical to maintenance of soil humidity in grasslands and forests, and when it drops below required levels, plants die; when accompanied by extended adverse weather cycles, crops fail, animals die and famine occurs.

Thus with ninety-six per cent tied up in oceans, two to three percent tied up in ice caps, and a percent working in subterranean water tables, there is never even one per cent available for the actual primary purpose: life on land.

Less than one per cent of the total global water supply can be made available to all life on an earth - plants and animals - for all uses. Most of this one per cent, each day, is in the atmosphere waiting to precipitate. Only three hundredths of a percent of the total water will actually be immediately available as surface rainwater in the cycle at any given time. Only slightly less than one per cent of the total global water is all that such a vast water supply can deliver and provide, even with the most optimally functional weather and water cycles in operation.

Thus, see the challenge, the dilemma, and perceive the design which resolves it: as the land surface increases, the water surface for evaporation decreases; the volume of evaporated, wind-carried moisture for condensation and precipitation decreases proportionately, yielding an inadequate supply. You can see that your earth geologically obtained at the threshold limits of its maintenance. There are numerous great deserts; these too serve their purpose.

Yet earths which are to shelter life must be water planets.

Your world is about optimum in this regard; it is typical of what can be expected. About 284 thousand billion gallons evaporate from your oceans every day. Most of this falls back into the oceans as rain, for it forms clouds and condenses and precipitates over the three-fourths of the planet that is water. Thus the water you receive, even when it is too much at one time in one place, is precious.

We understand that life began in the oceans. Tell me of that.

You understand as you perceive, and you only perceive what comes before your eyes to perceive. What lives in water and dies there is often preserved; what lives upon the land and dies upon the land is rarely preserved, save by much water in the soil. In dryness there is disintegration. You believe life sprang from the waters. Yet what happened upon the primordial land surface, crumbling and grainy, wet with primordial waters, lashed by primordial electrical storms, bathed in primordial sunlight?

You have seen nothing, and so you conclude, nothing.

Ask: what grew first upon the earliest land, wet and warm, amid the grains of grit and sand, rich in nutrients, ready for life? You do not know, for it is all washed away. Where was it washed away? Into the oceans where all was settled onto the ocean floors. These you see.

All of your fossil records of earliest life come only from the sea. What do you know of the land in these times? Where are your surface samples? All eroded and gone. Where are your primordial fossil soils? You have yet found none. What life forms washed down from the land into the primordial sea that you have found, and called aquatic, for you are only children, knowing little?

You know nothing about the land; thus you speculate only on the waters.

Look to your best speculations of the nature of the land surfaces of your own Moon, of Jupiter, Saturn, and Uranus, especially your humorous speculations about Venus and Mars. How scientifically postulated, and almost always, how wrong? What then, of your own early, primordial earth, which you have never seen as well as you now see these others, even though afar? Times have come, and the children now finally begin to see the Moon and Mars and Venus as they are. Yet they soon forget: they had been wrong. The children like to shrug their shoulders, smile at each other, and with a grin, forget how science had championed the old theories, brandished in so much passion as certain.

Until the evidence of these was seen, though the truth might have been declared to them, it would have been denied, for the theories were cherished.

These distant land surfaces and cloud covers, though distant, you can now see well. As you speculate of life forming on other planets, you have many developed theories of how life could begin on an almost dry world, in moist soil, in humid cracks, in solid rock. Thus upon dry planets, you will search for life formed upon land, even dry land, with only the most minimal water. You will search for life on Venus, and in many other environments, for you believe in life.

But you apply no such potentials, excitedly calculated for other planets, to your own earth; here you think life must begin in oceans. Still, you are resilient. I do not worry about you in this, but in other things. There is much for you to learn.

Know that what you have yet to discover will continue to alter your fondest theories and beliefs. You will grin, and re-write many books, many times.

And you know this for now: the oceans are also a cradle of life.

As the oceans are a cradle of life, they are also the continuing showcases of wonderful life. The ocean has always been a wonderful aquarium of delights, and I have delighted in it immensely. All of the creatures which you have called sea monsters have been my delight, and to see them move and fulfill their measure of creation has been thrilling beyond your imaginations. Even those creatures which can abide to live with you, the children, the great whales, and small whales, and porpoises, and giant squid, and killer whales, and sharks of many kinds, and tunas, and sword fishes, and all life in the seas, all are a delight, and my pleasure as I visit them and behold them is unending. The vast majority of all life species on the planet have been creatures of the sea, from single-celled organisms to great species that lived before your time, to whales in your day. As you live, coral reefs house one third of all fish species, which are many, and all are a beauty to behold.

Yet the engine which drives life in the oceans is small: it is the plankton. All that dies in the ocean eventually returns its elements and matter to the water; this becomes a continual supply cycle of organic food matter, dissolved as nutrients and carried as micro particles. Upwellings of currents, storms and winds circulate the water and stir the recycled nutrients which have been unlocked from the dead bodies of animals, fish and plants by bacteria, and make them available to the swarms of plankton. Upon these nutrients, the small animal and plant forms which collectively you have named plankton thrive, and keep the ocean's waters alive. They clean the waters; they return the energy to the larger and larger species which eat them, and thereby thrive. The greatest of whales lives because of the tiny plankton.

From small things come great miracles.

And so there is another small miracle: the winds. The oceans would serve no purpose at all and be dead waters if it were not for the winds. Global wind currents create the ocean currents, and winds create the surface waves. Wind and water form a unique harmony. Even though there are oceans, winds are required for life, on land, and in the seas.

Here we come full circle again to the need of an iron core for an earth.

Winds can only arise because of the topography of the land, and the topography of the land can become appropriately diverse and mountainous only if you can design land masses which are well distributed around the globe, and which can ram against each other and thrust up tall mountain ranges. Continents can only be moved by having an iron core which keeps the interior of the earth molten enough for tectonic plates to relocate, spacing the continents appropriately as is needed for the water cycles to service them. And, by the time an earth has gone through its preparation phases, it is essentially ground down flat; in order to have the right kinds of mountain ranges or mountain ranges at all, there must be an iron core to maintain a molten interior as all original high places have been made low, and after the lands have been ground down and pulverized and deposited in sedimentary layers, they must again be thrust up and made high by the sliding movement and impact of plates ramming one another, thrusting them up into high mountains.

There must be winds, and to have winds, there must be uneven elevations; there must be great and mighty mountains of upthrust stone.

And there are gentle winds, because Life Worlds have an iron core.

Though it is in opposition of nature to be uneven, and all of nature works to scrub planets flat, except there are varied land types, vegetation, water and topography, there will be no uneven surface heating, and thus there will be no winds. If a planet is flat and even and there are no winds, the tropic zones of a planet around the equator will be dry deserts with temperatures of 130 degrees Fahrenheit, and the nearby northern latitudes will be as cold as Antarctica. The most inhabited latitudes of the planet will be uninhabitable, and ice bound.

Yet after all of this is comprehended, still for the ocean to live there must be a secondary planet in orbit around a Life World, as its moon. You will see that your moon is not an ordinary satellite; it is not a moon. See in your solar system: moons are very small in comparison to their mother planets, and even the moons of the giant planets are not as large as your secondary planet, your moon. Your moon is yet larger than two bodies you have called planets.

By your secondary planet's influence, the ocean tides rise and fall twice a day, causing a band of unique exposure along every shore line where land meets sea, creating the zone for all tidal shore life forms. You have partially comprehended how useful these have been in the seasoning and preparing of the earth for your coming, but you are still learning how essential they are to the continued health of the seas and thus to the planet.

Still your moon serves you more.

As the ocean tides are pulled by a secondary planet moon in orbit, so too, the land masses and tectonic plates are pulled, and the land actually rises up more than four inches to even fourteen inches, twice a day. As the surface thus rises, so the molten matter below rises, and thus there is motion provided. This is wisdom in me.

By this also the crust is lifted and distorted and set upon by great pressures, and the soft molten mantel beneath is pulled and reshaped, twice every day, all of which assist in the true mechanism which drives tectonic plate movement, relocates continents, thrusts up high mountain ranges, and adapts a planet to become a livable earth.

For the secondary planet's gravitational influence to work its rhythmic effect on oceans for life and on crust and inner mantle for slow movement, again, you see, there must be an iron core.

I understand now. It must have been very satisfying to see the finished state of this creation, with earth and moon in place, lands distributed around the planet and oceans filled with water.

Yes, it was, and it is. The placement of the land mass you call Antarctica under the southern ice cap took care of the problem of excessive land surface produced during continental formation, and balanced the planetary mass to its currently almost perfect equilibrium, compensating for the favorable continental distributions more heavily in the northern hemisphere where you will note there is no continental land mass over the north pole. Most of your earth's population has lived above the equator on these lands; they have been made favorable by their placement at these latitudes, a positioning made feasible by the counterbalancing antarctic relocation of the superfluous continental land mass.

However, the process of this creation, affecting this planet, your earth, is not over, and this too is by design.

I do not understand. What do you mean?

Your planet home was formed by accretion, the gathering and gathering of more and more material to a central mass, eventually becoming a gravitational magnet drawing to itself matter passing close by, and accreting anything which lay in its orbital path, and accreting anything which struck it.

This process is still going on, as it must.

I still do not understand. Please explain.

Much of the small matter pulverized in your local space, in size from rocks to nuggets to gravel to sand to grit to dust to micro dust, still orbits around your sun, as it does in all ideal systems. This is by design; it is not accidental, though it is mostly the product of other organizational and formatory processes: supernovas, nebula accretions, planetesimal collisions in accretion phases, asteroidal collisions in orbit, that sort of thing. Though these chips and fragments and bits and dust are produced, every part of the cosmos has been utilized in the design, and nothing is wasted: no energy, no matter. For every product of every ultimately determined process required in the algorithm, a use was perceived which would enhance and improve the whole, and as the advantage was comprehended, measures were established to assure its conscious inclusion in the process overall. The Design has been perfected by contemplating the consequence and result of every phase and process to its last potential, and as a contemplated course was seen to eventually yield the best possible result, every aspect of the process was contemplated for its potentials of use and application to the improvement of the whole. In this manner the algorithm of the perfect process leading to the fulfillment of the Design was perceived, and set in motion.

There is much residual orbiting fragmentary matter in your solar system, and so there must be. These are the meteors. They are debris from early periods of this solar system's formation, and yes, they are pieces from many sources - suns, asteroids, planetesimals, even pieces of some of the other planets in your system, blown off during major impact collisions and flung into eventual orbit around your sun, finally intercepting your orbit and plummeting to your surface. Yet these fragments, pieces, dust and nuggets are not debris in the sense you classify debris: wasted, shattered matter of no use or purpose.

There must be meteoric matter, and in vast abundance in sun systems which are to become the home systems of earths. Meteors are essential, and if they do not obtain in adequate quantities, orbital distribution and size for the ongoing purpose, then trajectories are pulled and nudged to provide pulverizing collisions to shatter and form what is needed. Your several asteroid orbital belts were precisely fabricated as they were to service this need; yet there are other residual sources of micrometeoritic material from the early cutting out and accreting processes from your original nebular cloud. These are captured and harnessed to the gravity of your sun, and they silently follow their orbits in perpetual reserve.

The frequent movement of comets in long elliptical orbits which cross back and forth over almost all of the debris orbits serve by design to continually pull and alter the orbits of much of this micro matter in the system, so that a continual supply is provided to your planet's orbital path.

What is the purpose? Why are meteors so necessary?

You see meteors in the night sky, and find some of them as they have landed upon your earth. The children who have studied these things know that each day millions enter the blanket of the atmosphere I created for you. In this it also serves its purpose; you breathe it, and it protects you. Yet how many have contemplated the additional tons of fine energene matter as ash which enters your habitat each day? Why was this all designed so? Why are these needed?

There are a multitude of essential and critical problems which these are brought to solve; and conditions they are brought to create.

You perhaps have no idea how much of this matter is intercepted by and intercepts your earth every day, just as you have little idea how dependent you are upon the heavens and their bounty for your literal daily existence.

Sixty thousand tons per year of this matter falls into your atmosphere. Most of it enters at high speed, and it burns into the essentially needed ash dust which fuels much of your weather systems and the water cycle over land.

The total number of individual projectiles or meteorites which would be bright enough to see every day, all over entire earth, is about twenty five million.

That is twenty five million shooting stars a day, as you have called them.

Most of these fall where their fire cannot be seen: in daylight skies, and over vast expanses of oceans and deserts and mountains. Dust and smoke, and lights from streets, buildings and cars obscure most of those you otherwise could see; clouds and fogs obscure yet more.

Most of these streaks of light are caused by grains only about a quarter of a gram in weight.

Micrometeoric dust is even more numerous, and of course, lighter. The micrometeorites are ubiquitous: in the air you breathe, the water you drink, and the food you eat. They fall as dust, and anyone who spends much time outdoors receives them on their skin several times a week. They are harmless, and in fact, help your earth.

Yet in all, sixty thousand tons a year is one hundred fifty tons per day. That is three hundred thousand pounds of matter, daily.

Your earth is still accreting.

And so it must.

It was seen in the algorithm that though water is a marvelous solvent and versatile in wondrous ways, the formation of clouds and raindrop formation in the clouds would not occur without a seed.

It was seen that over the oceans, salt dust evaporated from ocean spray whipped in the wind would seed the clouds and precipitate rain.

However, over land, there would be no salt spray. How then to trigger the rain, and water the thirsty land and all creatures?

It was seen that surface dust eddies and dust blown high into the sky could satisfy part of the need. Dust storms in hot dry desert lands would also serve a purpose, and in this deserts serve one of their many purposes. Also it was seen that volcanism anywhere in the world would, by global wind currents, would spread ever widening and thinning clouds of ash dust into the atmosphere from high elevations, thereby seeding clouds and rain globally.

Yet all of this was not enough. Those who love mathematics will perceive and tell you - volcanism alone is still not enough.

From meteorites, the three hundred thousand pounds of ash which falls rather evenly over your world every day completes and satisfies this need.

You have rain. It has been so, even since the beginning.

But there is more, so much more.

As you know, much of this bounty is iron. It has all of its atomic energene charge, yet also its electromagnetic charge.

Who has yet pondered the daily incoming of charged energenes, and the affect of these upon your atmospheric charge as it reacts against the charge of your earth's core? Who has yet explored and learned the wonder of how this daily entry of charged energenes affects the atmospheric charge and how this maintains the delicate balance of your atmosphere and the charges of your earth's core?

Why is the need of lightning?

You receive it with your rain, and you ask, How does it occur, and why does it exist, but you only ask in the sense of how does it exist and come to be.

Yet is lightning necessary?

Do you ask what would be the result if there were no meteors to burn in the atmosphere and sprinkle the atmosphere with charged energenes?

I see we are now talking about the weather.

I hadn't formulated any questions about the weather, but I can see that this is a very essential part of the ordering within the Design, and this is something I never really thought about. I've always taken the weather for granted.

Let's talk about the weather.

What do I need to understand?

It takes most of the physical existence of a planet to prepare the atmosphere and other systems and cycles to be just right.

The entire purpose of the algorithm of this Design is to give Intelligences in Spirit the ideal bodies made of matter of this physics, to experience the joy of being; whereby they may obtain exaltation, through Faith, in bodies of a higher physics which has mastery of all things in this physics. In this is great joy. The bodies of the Design are strong, adaptable, resilient and successful beyond even your comprehension as you thus far have understood them, but they are likewise very demanding in regards to requirements of unrestricted respiration, of narrow high and low temperature ranges, of exterior pressure, of systemic water levels and food intake maintenance, of exposure to substances which act as toxins to any number of their myriad tissues and systems, and to physical injuries such as battering, crushing, puncture and electroshock. While these bodies can and do take unimaginable trauma, sustaining and withstanding multiple punctures through tissues and organs, multiple bone breakages and circulatory interruptions and blockages, kinetic blows of immense magnitude and more, nonetheless, at times the slightest thing can terminate them: a single small hole in a blood vessel, a slight blow to a precise place in the head, an insignificant circulatory blockage at a key passage of the system, a substance harmless to others but which triggers an allergic reaction within their organism. Though remarkably sturdy, yet they are fragile.

The weather on an earth affects virtually all of the positive needs and negative threats to the survival of these bodies, and thus to the lives of the children when they come to experience Life.

Excessive cold will freeze them; excessive heat will cook and kill them; excessive dryness will shrivel and kill them; excessive water will drown them. Excessive winds will break their houses, shatter trees and building materials and fly into them and cut them to pieces, spilling their precious blood. And winds can pound them and stun or smash their nervous systems, their skeletal frames, breaking their bones, severing nerves and opening the circulatory systems which quickly fall below sustainable levels and they die.

The formation of an earth that will obtain optimum climactic and weather conditions and cycles is paramount. If after all else is done, the composite mixture of the air is not precisely within tolerated ranges and limits; if humidities and moisture distributions are not adequately provided within tolerable ranges; if temperatures are not moderate and closely within the prescribed tolerances of these bodies - all other astropreparations, geopreparations, chemopreparations, biopreparations and ecopreparations will be for naught. The organism will not survive. It will die.

Atmospheric preparations are co-equal needs, mandatory criteriae.

So, know that there are usually four generations of atmosphere in planetary preparation, but sometimes there are more. It depends on how much work needs to be done to prepare the planet, and how many significant collisions may be involved before the local solar system sorts itself out and activity dies down. By the time the process is over, most molecules of original atmosphere will be gone. Usually, ninety-nine per cent of the final atmosphere of a Life World is the result of biological processes. It takes a lot of life and a long time to season and prepare this to the right balance for the children.

As the accretion process begins, the sun of a system is also very young. A sun does not reach its peak performance for a long time; but that is OK; there is a lot to do in preparation of the solar system and the planet. During this early time many critically important processes are carried out successfully. A solar system is an ecosystem, and the space ecology must be balanced.

The first planetary atmosphere is hydrogen and helium, which quickly, and largely, blows off in the initial solar wind. The infant planet is usually incomplete, and thus has yet a weak gravitational field, insufficient to hold such light gasses. Yet this is good.

The second atmosphere usually forms after the planet has accreted most of what it will gather unto itself, a process which in time is rather short. By this point the sphere is already very hot, its secondary planet is formed, and it is often spinning up to five times as fast as it will eventually rotate - its day is only five to six hours. The planet's heat initiates volcanic action from within.

Volcanoes create atmospheric materials much as Venus' air. It is heavily weighted with water vapor, and surface pressure therefore can be from five times up

491

to seventy times the surface atmospheric pressure of an ideal world. The children would be crushed in such weighty air. Storms rage as they do on Venus, with catastrophic non-stop erosions yielding highly efficient grooming effects: powerful tides; strong ocean currents; gale winds; severe rains, and lightning. This process can go on for long periods of time as you measure it. The process is highly necessary for the erosion it achieves; for the rock dust formed which becomes the basis of early sedimentary rock, and the basis of the first primordial soil. Mineral content begins to accumulate in ocean water.

Eighty-five per cent of an earth's second atmosphere is produced by volcanism, within a relatively short span of time. This would not occur, except that a substantial hot iron core with balanced radioactivity is engineered into a planet. Planets which were not formed in this manner can never be earths; they are beautiful and useful in their own ways, but they will not be chosen. Except for the right composition, a second atmosphere either does not develop at all, or some other kind of atmospheric mix obtains.

In this second atmosphere there is no oxygen; it is carbon dioxide, nitrogen and trace elements of methane, ammonia, sulfur dioxide and hydrochloric acid. With the high water vapor content and immense pressure, this caustic atmosphere ravages the surface quite well.

Carbon dioxide content produces an intense greenhouse effect of trapped heat, both solar and geothermal, further aiding erosion.

The third atmosphere is an atmosphere in long growth transition. It evolves as microbiotic life begins on the planet, especially in the oceans. By this time things have cooled down considerably, but the climate is still very warm. Due to the warm temperatures, continual rain and chemically active atmosphere, the same elements and chemicals obtain on the land masses in the waters saturating surface gravels and primordial soils; contrary to your beliefs, living mirco organisms thrive on the saturated land as well as the oceans. The initial life forms are unique and special organisms for their role and purpose; they are introduced into the soils and the oceans. You have found some of their fossils in flint and other stones and marveled. They are wondrous. They begin the seasoning process. They served to produce needed oxygen and other compounds until they were periodically extinguished and replaced with other intriguing forms. There are so many possibilities, and as it is impossible for them all to co-exist, it is good to use the evolving stages of the planet's preparation for enjoying the diversity of infinite variety. These species are by design, temporary; they will die off when their job is completed.

The atmospheric ingredient these organisms begin to produce is of course oxygen. Oxygen is the key to slow-burning fuel usage. It reacts with almost all molecules, breaking them down and altering them dramatically. Yet this was seen to be the key to the most successful biophysics: oxygen bonds with many atoms and oxidizes them, from which much good can be harnessed.

492

It took a long time to reach an atmosphere with just one per cent oxygen.

Periodic asteroids, comets, and planetesimals slam into earths and vaporize their oceans, which then over short periods of time in intense storms rain back onto the surface, flooding and refilling the seas. The successive evaporation and re-condensing process is required to fully pulverize vast amounts of rock into suitable soil components in adequate quantities for the eventual needs of life-support systems of a water-land planet for the time of the children; and, to reach the required levels of minerals and salts in the oceans to a near blood-content level, for aquatic animals.

Finally, enough carbon dioxide dissolves in the sea water; blue green algae is introduced and creates a massive bloom, and this begins the wholesale formation of vast masses of carbon-based organic molecules, needed for larger and larger life forms.

Excess carbon dioxide accumulates, yet this problem is solved by bonding it in limestone and other compounds.

On your planet, for example, about ninety atmospheres are trapped in the crust as limestone and other carbonates, formed during these primordial times of seasoning and planetary preparation.

Life progresses, and oxygen levels rise. It takes a long time. During this time, a planet usually experiences myriad condition swings, a pendulum effect of extremes of heat and cold as well as other effects until its climate is stabilized in the needed way. In peak heat, ice seldom forms at all on earths, even at their poles. Tropical gardens erupt and thrive, adding to the organic stores. During cold phases, glaciers form and cover the land masses, further improving the erosion-soil formation process and further enriching the sea water by literally scrubbing minerals into the ice which then melt back into the oceans. Life forms on land and in the seas proliferate; a large biomass obtains. Yet this large biomass is composed of only smaller species of fishes, animals and plants still, and the ubiquitous bacteriomass, which was, is and always will be the most critical engine of an earth.

Eventually, after a long period of time, the oxygen content balances upwards to the ideal: twenty-one per cent by volume.

Usually about five-sixths of the preparation time needed to groom and cultivate a planet are needed to produce this ideal atmosphere.

This is the Final Atmosphere: it is your current atmosphere. I will give it to you as a chart so you can read it easily. Note it well, and remember where it is, for I will refer to it at a future time and place where you want to compare it:

nitrogen 76%
oxygen 21%
argon .9%
carbon dioxide .032%

neon .001%
helium .0005%
methane .00015%
krypton .00011%
hydrogen .00005%
nitrous oxide .00003%
carbon monoxide .00001
ozone .00004%
xenon .000009%
water up to 1-4% (in the tropics)
traces other gases less than .000001%

After this atmosphere and oxygen level is reached, the large, spectacular and mighty life forms may be introduced. It is a time the continents are moved strategically into more efficient positions; the tilt of the Earth's axis is adjusted into a desired inclination for seasons and other needs. On your world, another great Ice Age occurred, the longest and coldest winter of the planet. It resulted from additional adjustments which needed to be made in the planet's orbit and the continental tectonic plates; these processes disrupted the oceanic current flows and air current flows, and coincident volcanism obscured the sun.

The last stage is the final preparation. It is rather rapid, as time is measured, and during this time the ideal continental distribution is achieved to within optimum functional margins. In your world this saw the final thrusts which began to form the mountain ranges which would moderate and promote the type of weather cycles your body organisms, and those which can co-exist with you - need to thrive. The blossom of needed carboniferous molecules and full systemic balances suitable for the children's needs were also obtained.

However, your planet suffered a momentary setback during this phase. An anticipated collision was utilized for axial alignment and rotational refinement, and a large part of your atmosphere was coincidentally blown away, out of the gravitational field of your earth. The biomass was cut back, and when the adjustment effects cleared, whole new lines of species were introduced. Many old friends were lost. Yet in what is a short passage of time, a thriving new biomass restored the atmospheric loss, and though there is no real schedule as such, preparation progressed excellently. But, you may say that with this, and several lesser blow-offs, your planet has had seven major atmospheric phases.

This final phase is a time of wonderful fun, during which I am able to enjoy some of the most fascinating of my bio-engineering visions. With twenty-one percent oxygen, much can be done. On your planet, the biomass had to be readjusted several times as swings from cold to hot rapidly raised temperatures and necessitated punctuated introductions of new species better adapted to the new climate. Specialized life forms were required which could thrive in the heat and continue the organic seasoning. This gave me an opportunity to again enjoy some of my favorite life forms. Many of my favorite pets were ideally designed for that kind of hot, humid, lush vegetation climate, and tropical seas. Many of them are gentle giants, placid and docile. Wonderful creatures. Others, the predators, are precision aggressors, as fascinating as any lion, crocodile or angler fish. These always must be removed before the children come.

You have found many of their fossils, reconstructed them, and marveled at their size and form. I have watched your fascination with them.

It pleases me that you marvel at them as much as I do.

Not all planets go through this many swings of natural catastrophes, and in those that do not, such delightful temporary highlights cannot be introduced; yet there are other forms of animals, plants, birds, fishes, insects, in all classes and orders of life, many this earth has not known. They too, are wonderful.

However, shifts in dominant life forms co-habitational with the children are limited to those which will be able to co-exist. Though the children, you, were envisioned and known first, so you were last upon the planet.

Even the first have become last, as many of the last shall become first.

I now understand that there is a lengthy process required to produce the kind of atmosphere we need, and a planet that will produce weather conditions and moisture cycles as required.

What are the requirements of an ideal global weather system?

A world patterned after the archetypal model, therefore ideal and optimum for the survival of the children, has an atmosphere of the mix I have shown you, which lets through visible light and heat from the sun - all the planet's energy - holds and maintains that heat as well as interior planetary heat, conducts water vapor all over the planet, provides opposing pressure against your entire body surface counterbalancing your systemic outward pressure, promotes gaseous transfers in your lungs, supplies you with oxygen for energy harvesting processes, and provides protection against impact from most meteors, harmful solar radiations: x-rays, ultraviolet rays, etc., and very importantly, protection against the zero pressure of the very close and virtually total vacuum of adjacent surrounding space.

It is a shield you can breathe.

It is a shield organized in distinct layers.

You live in what you have called the Troposphere; this is air from the ground up, to seven miles at mid latitudes. It is but five miles high at the poles, and is ten miles high at the equator.

In this lowest layer is most of the free planetary oxygen, most of the clouds, and most of the weather. All of the clouds you see from space hold only one one-thousandth of a per cent of the worlds water; this is what keeps everything going.

495

Also within this sphere is the all-important jet stream current, which flows between 25,000 to 45,000 feet elevation. This is where your jet aircraft fly.

Above this begins the Stratosphere, which reaches up to 30 miles above your earth. In it, at about 20 miles above the surface, the color of the sky is relatively black.

The Ozonosphere is contained within the Stratosphere, from about 10 to 30 miles up. As you know, this protects all organisms from deadly ultraviolet rays.

The next layer is the Mesosphere, 30 to 55 miles above you. The temperature in this sphere drops dramatically to very cold levels.

The Thermosphere begins just above this, at about 55 miles up, and continues up to 435 miles into space. You will be surprised to know that the temperature rises again in this inversion layer.

Yet as many systems in the Design, there are systems within systems. The atmosphere is no different.

There is a sphere you have recognized between the altitudes of about 30 to 250 miles, which is beneficial in many ways. You have named it Ionosphere, and it is ionized by your sun's ultraviolet radiation. It possesses amazing characteristics as it provides you protection: it reflects radio waves. By this phenomenon of this atmospheric layer, you communicate by radio over large distances of a curved earth. You have discovered that it is divided: you have called its divisions the D layer at 35-52 miles, the E layer 52-95 miles - which is almost pure nitrogen gas, and the F layer from 95-250 miles. This last layer, though thinly filled with molecules, is, from 125-250 miles, almost pure oxygen.

You have also identified as Exosphere the actual atmospheric fringe which is the thinnest air, decreasing from 25-435 miles above you, mostly vacuum.

Far beyond these air spheres, there is the critically important magnetosphere, which extends out from 40,000 to 80,000 miles at the equator, curving back down and in at the poles.

The formation of the series of layered gaseous spheres is influenced by the magnetosphere produced by the iron core. There are two special exterior fields of it you have named after their discoverer, the Van Allen belts, one at 1,800 and at 9,300 miles, which hold and dispose of trapped charged particles.

You would not have this air or this atmospheric system this way without the iron core of your earth. The fruits of this Design are myriad.

One of the gifts of your atmosphere which you seldom consciously think of is its pressure: it stacks up to provide the ideal required amount of pressure on the organism to keep the water in the system from boiling; for gas transfers to take place at optimum levels for the tissue needs; for chemical processes to take place in cells; to hold the body together against the pressure which has to be created within the containment of your skin for the system to drive itself: the pumping of the blood, the pressure in each cell required to accelerate osmosis and gas transfers and respiration.

At sea level this is 14.7 pounds per square inch; in this close range live the majority of the children of the world. At 20,000 feet there is roughly only 7 pounds per square inch. At 100,000 feet, your blood boils, for lack of pressure.

In pressure and many other things, yet this atmosphere serves you more.

By use of air and the law of Opposition, earths are able to have rain.

Due to the nature of water and the nature of a designed atmosphere, water vapor is carried away as it evaporates from water surfaces. The evaporated molecules gather into microdroplets; then a curious thing occurs.

The microscopic cloud droplets which are naturally formed should touch and merge with each other in larger and larger droplets, yet this does not happen. But for engineered design, this would always happen prematurely, and clouds as you see them would never exist. In truth, clouds and precipitation as you know it should be impossible. It cannot happen as it does. But it does.

Simply, the microdroplets repel each other.

Cloud microdroplets are only about only 1/2,500th of an inch in diameter. They repel each other; for this reason clouds form, and water may travel afar.

The microdroplets can also become supercooled, down to as low as 20 degrees below zero, without freezing. Think of it: water, at 20 below zero, still not freezing. By this phenomenon, another mechanism of the most versatile and wondrous solvent, water, the microdroplets repel and keep their distance from one another until mighty clouds are allowed to build up and become saturated with moisture. These move upon the winds to far places, as they are needed.

Microdroplets continue to repel each other, even when they freeze.

At a precise point, they indeed freeze, and ice crystals form. Micro ice crystals also repel each other.

Yet it is they which will and do attract and accrete supercooled microdroplets, and gather them.

By the law of Opposites, supercooled water microdroplets are attracted to and attach themselves to micro ice crystals, and they begin to form what will become rain drops.

All rain drops begin as micro ice crystals.

Yet they do not yet become rain drops.

As microdroplets begin to attach to micro ice crystals, they too, freeze.

They touch and freeze, touch upon touch, and as they touch, each microdroplet sticks, and freezes to the growing crystal. Here you may learn a remarkable nature of energenes, and atomic resonance.

Due to the patterns of energenes, the micro crystals form exquisite large crystals, which you call snow. By the resonance vibrations of the energenes at varying temperatures, they form different patterns, dependant on the temperature and the molecular attraction tendency each level of temperature produces. From

497

32° to 25° Fahrenheit the resonance forms thin hexagonal plates; between 25° and 21° double-pointed needles form; at 21° to 14° hollow hex columns are formed; and between 14° and 10° hex-star sector plates form. At 10° to 3° the dendrites, multi-formed snowflakes are produced - it is the moment of free choice. Between 3° to -8° the temperature has dropped a level to a harmonic resonance, and thus again, hex-star sector plates form; by the same harmonic resonance, below

-8° hollow hex columns are again formed.

You little understand temperature and its effects upon resonant harmonics in subatomic matters, yet this school lesson has always awaited your discovery, and its teaching will lead you upon new paths of understanding. Temperature Resonance can be used in crystal synthesis to curious advantage.

Below a certain temperature, snow will not form.

This too, is instructive. Those who have an ear to hear, hear.

A million, to fifteen million microdroplets of water accrete to form a single snowflake, which will melt within its cloud at a certain point and become a raindrop, which then, laden with its precious water, falls to earth.

This potential was foreseen within this physics, and its was one of the myriad reasons this physics was chosen over others.

In the tropics, where clouds never get cold enough for ice to form, salt in the air from ocean spray condenses rain over the oceans.

One of the most wondrous properties of microdroplets is that they are all but weightless; they virtually float in air. They have a terminal velocity of only two feet per second which makes clouds rise on but a breath of wind. In this way, mighty clouds can and do form.

Part of the problem of engineering life on worlds is excess heat: as it obtains and increases, it withers and kills plants and animals in increasingly wider circles as each species reaches its own limited tolerance threshold.

As all parts of the plan serve, and all serve multiple purposes, clouds too serve many, many purposes and functions. They gather and condense water microdroplets; they cool and supercool microdroplets; they transport water moisture across great expanses of land to irrigate it for life; they cool microdroplets finally to the freezing point; they incubate accreting snowflakes, which melt into raindrops, and replenish the earth.

Clouds serve in yet other ways.

Most importantly they reflect the intense heat of sun, and thereby moderate global temperature. This is a necessity and value equal to rain.

And, they are beautiful.

Beginning at an earth's surface, in the names you have devised and given them, microdroplets become stratus, stratocumulus, and nimbostratus clouds, the main rain producer of the planet. They also form cumulus, and cumulonimbus

498

clouds, which can pile up to 30,000 feet and more in height, and from which heavy rain, hail, lightning and thunder come. Some of the children call them Thunderheads, for this reason.

High above, other types of clouds gather and form also. Altocumulus bases begin above ten thousand feet, as do altostratus, cirrocumulus, cirrostratus, and high cirrus.

The noctilucent clouds, which are rare and form at 45-54 miles are composed of ice crystals which enter your atmosphere from the cosmos. The atmospheres of planets act as sweepers as they fly through their orbital space: whatever is in the way, is absorbed. When your earth passes through thin clouds of frozen water molecules, whether from comets or other processes, the molecules are scooped and gathered, and compressed as they ram into the atmosphere; they slow and stop, and form thin, wispy clouds you observe without understanding. These dissipate in the wind currents, and then disappear. They are heavenly waters, which eventually mix with yours.

In all, the mechanisms and processes of weather, which keep earths cool, irrigate them and beautify them, have ranges and limits which push their thresholds at both ends. At times, even though conditions are organized to moderate them as gently as possible in a homeostatic world system, they cause harm and destruction. Even these form a great beauty of fascination within many systems of beauty and fascination in the organization and utilization of energene matter in this physics.

It is a remarkable system.

There are many systems within systems: from atoms, to molecules, to rocks, to water, to organisms, to ecologies, to weather, to planets, to suns, to galaxies, to cosmos. Systems within systems within systems. All are fascinating. This too, is the gift of this creation and all it provides, to Intelligences.

Without a substantial iron core in a planet to allow tectonic continental relocation and the upthrust of mountains, there could be no weather as is required, as you have on your world.

Yet all is an interwoven web, and over the world, all systems become one system, the geosystem of a successful world. The world wide web of systems interwoven, interrelating, interdependent and interbalancing must exist in this way, with little variation, or overall systemic failure begins, and the whole eventually collapses.

The number of contributing factors to global weather are many; look around you and see them. They are worth seeing, and learning.

Uneven heating of the earth's surface, an essential of design, causes pressure differentials; these produce the planetary winds, pulling and pushing air masses over great distances. You speak of planetary winds as trades and westerlies; these move across the oceans and move the mists over the waters and the land. And there are circulation cells, great wheels of rising and falling air, three in the north and three in the south around the whole world, the cycles of rising and sinking heated and cooled air: the tropical cells, the polar cells, and the intermediate cells between the equatorial and the polar. The intermediate wheels cause heavy precipitation between the latitudes of 40 and 60 degrees, making these some of the best latitudes for dwelling.

If it were not for these world wide winds, no earth would be able to sustain this life design. These are the winds which move the air, cool the planet, and distribute the water cycle. The water itself creates its own localized conditions, and these are what you usually speak of as weather. The greatest systems are cyclones, simple regional major air mass circulations traveling usually no more than fifty miles an hour, covering areas from five hundred miles to a thousand miles in size, taking a week and more to travel. Local system thunderstorms, which usually only last a few hours and seldom exceed 20-30 mph, are what deliver much of the needed rain in many lands.

Yet even on a well balanced earth, with finely tuned land masses and mountains, storms are generated which unleash immense energy. A hurricane, which is a local storm, may have winds 74-200 mph, and be 300-600 miles in diameter; it can last a week. A tornado, local and short lived, generates winds up to 200-250 mph, touching a path usually an eighth to a quarter mile wide, and it lasts only minutes. You see in these winds great power of destruction, yet they serve their purpose within the whole. Energy can not be created or destroyed, but only converted, and relocated. There are myriad processes on earths which create charge imbalances; there are others which conduct charge equilibrium. Much more than water is distributed and regulated in storms.

The wind energy in this weather you seldom contemplate. A cyclone wind velocity is 10^{14} joules, the same energy as that of an atomic bomb. A hurricane wind velocity is 10^{15} joules a minute, equal to ten atomic bomb releases every minute. Just one per cent of the energy from a hurricane would meet all the energy needs of the United States of America for one year.

Within the Design, energy redistribution is an essential need. Where there is a massive iron core, there are massive electromagnetic fields; where there are such fields and mass traveling through them, energies are in motion. Where there are streaking meteors and energenes released by atmospheric friction in burning, and iron atoms are among them, opposites of charge obtain. These may used to effect great advantage.

Why is there lightning? Because it is needed to drive life on Life Worlds. Each year lightning breaks down nitrogen and oxygen in the air and precipitates 100 million tons of nitrogen compounds onto the soils of the earth, fertilizing plant growth for food cycles and water cycles, a major factor of the homeostasis of an earth. Yet it does more.

The electrical current of a lightning bolt is 300,000 volts per foot. Some bolts exceed 15 million volts pressure. A truly powerful bolt may carry 345,000 amperes, enough to service 200,000 homes for 24 hours. An average storm releases one million kilowatts of energy; some release almost 2 billion kilowatts. There are 1,500 to 2,000 thunderstorms on earth at all times; 16 million thunderstorms a year. There are 6,000 lightning flashes every minute of every day on the globe. Where does all of this energy go? What does it do?

Lightning is perhaps one of the most dramatic exhibitions of the law of Opposites at work. Yet for your several theories, though you know opposites are at work, you do not know the true generation of lightning. Friction, falling electrons, negative charges, rising electrons, positive charges, you speculate on many things, some of which are at work; you have still to look at the role of the planetary core, the magnetosphere, the charged rain of meteoric dust gathered within rain clouds, and the realities of the process. All you yet know is that opposites obtain, there are energy imbalances, and lightning bridges the charges and neutralizes them.

This it does, and much more as well.

It is all part of Design.

As you have contemplated scientific explanations for the thunder that lightening produces, you have imagined the sudden heating of the long column of air, heated to ultra-high temperatures. This indeed occurs, and the electrical bolt truly displaces your planetary air, forming a lengthy vacuum tube quite thick along the main bolt trunks. Yet you have forgotten this long column of vacuum which the sudden expansion creates, and the force per square inch of your atmosphere along that vacuum as it abruptly collapses. While small children know the crack of air produced in the tiny flick of a whip, you have yet to imagine the clap of your air along the long column of this vacuum's collapse. And if the only service produced in this is wonder, may you therein learn the worth of awe in this organ of planetary air?

So, earths have a shield you can breathe, layered for myriad purposes, protecting you from many lethal dangers, providing containment of your inner body pressure as required to run your biomechanisms and life systems, receiving, processing and distributing extra-terrestrial meteoric dust as required, moving water for you and distributing it for myriad needs, and helping balance planetary electromagnetic energy 600 times a second.

Which brings you again full circle: such an atmosphere and weather process will only obtain on planets with hot iron cores.

I believe I've absorbed the panorama. I see it's getting late. Though I'm tired, I have just a few key questions which directly apply to all these things. May I ask them?

Of course.

Thank you.

In the Book of Genesis it appears to record that first life on the planet was placed on the land. The bringing forth of life in the waters appears to be afterwards. Other than that reversal of how we seem to see things happened, how we believe things happened by the words of those who tell us so, the whole Genesis account as it is recorded seems to follow exactly what current scientific understanding is of the coming of life upon the planet: life in water and then land; more complex animal life organisms in water; trees and large vegetation forms on land; large animal life organisms proliferating in the water; finally more complex animal life forms proliferating on land; and we - humans, that is - don't appear on the scene until the very last moment in both descriptions.

However, I've gotten confused as I read in chapter 2, verses 4 and 5 and 6. They say:

"These are the generations of the heavens and of the earth when they were created, in the day that the Lord God made the earth and the heavens, And every plant of the field before it was in the earth, and every herb of the field before it grew: for the Lord God had not caused it to rain upon the earth, and there was not a man to till the ground. But there went up a mist from the earth, and watered the whole face of the ground."

This last sentence sounds exactly like what you've been telling me, about the hot dry magma ocean, and the steam from the volcanoes. That's certainly a mist that went up from the earth. From everything I've read and heard at the university, it rained all over the earth for a long time during this period, right?

Yes, it did.

But I'm confused about the previous verses. I understand that there were no humans yet, but I don't understand what it means as it says 'every plant of the field before it was in the earth, and every herb of the field before it grew: for the Lord God had not caused it to rain upon the earth.' The whole previous chapter describes the Genesis, everything, as if it were happening, but then in chapter 2 this comes along and implies that it was somehow created, but it wasn't; it hadn't really happened yet. How was everything created 'before it was in the earth,' and 'before it grew?'

What does this mean?

Exactly what I have been telling you, it tells you.

What is that?

That this was all a plan, a design. A potential was comprehended, and of many physics the most advantageous was chosen: it would provision the structuring and organization of a marvelous physical body which Intelligences in Spirit could be born into, having life, and more abundantly. Opportunity to live, experience a probationary estate, and receive the inheritance which each could endure in a kingdom of many mansions was possible. The Good News was proclaimed, and the Hosts of Heaven rejoiced in thanksgiving, as you have read, and as you know. You and all of your brothers and sisters were there.

The algorithm of creation was envisioned in Spirit first.

What you read in this simple retelling in Genesis is that all of this, every part of it, was considered in algorithm from beginning to end, and a wonderful Design was perceived, and as it was first perceived, it was so designed, and in design it came into existence as a Spiritual creation of life, of the Design, of DNA, even before the first life upon this planet was formed.

The verses you read are an end, and a beginning.

It is an end of the account of the algorithm of the Design; it is a place of beginning the story of the physical creation of this one world in its solar system, which is not even told to you in the Book of Genesis, excepting for the last and final part, which you also see is absent from the previous account up through chapter 2 verse 6, which is the introduction of the first children, you.

Between this beginning of the physical preparation of the earth from the time that the great mists of steam went up into the atmosphere and waters came to first cover the earth, the entire process of seasoning the earth, and physically bringing forth life upon this earth, on land and in the waters, and of bringing forth larger life forms as enough smaller life forms proliferated for food chains to become extended, is a great and unrecorded story. Yet as it is implied, you have had it all along, and you have known it, though it has been perverted and distorted by many in their lack of understanding and infancy.

Among the first generations of your siblings were many very spiritual souls, and unto these I revealed what they most wished to know: they chose to know spiritual things. And truly, the Spiritual things are the most important.

To me, all things are Spiritual. Only children divide between the physics of Spirit and the physis they see, touch and know in this Estate.

Your generation in time is also made mighty with great and noble souls, many reserved for this time; yet among them, many have less interest in things they see as spiritual, and more in things seen as physical. In all things there is opposition, and many of the first shall be last, and many of the last shall be first.

Your generation is the first to know this much of the physical.

It is what you love.

You are doing well in your learning, and in this you are pleased.

Yet all was perceived and comprehended, and the algorithm was completed, and the Design organized and affirmed before the first single-celled life form was formed on the first earth, long before this earth which is yours.

So it was all designed in Spirit.

So it was fulfilled, even as you see and observe the universe around you.

Am I understanding correctly, that life can only exist on a planet about like this one?

No. Life can exist under entirely different conditions. Organisms are designed which live in extreme heat, extreme cold, extreme pressure, extremely little pressure, with different organic bases, with inorganic bases, at both extremes of the ph scale of acidity and alkalinity. Life is possible under other chemistries and other conditions and other elementary bases, with other solvents. But it cannot exist in complexity above a certain level of capability. Mobility is sacrificed. Articulation is sacrificed. Longevity is sacrificed. Consciousness is sacrificed. Creative and artistic expression is sacrificed.

The question is not 'can there be life?'

The question is quality of life.

You are Intelligence. You have capability. Virtually unending life forms can be designed and introduced onto earths such as these you live upon; hundreds of millions of species have in fact been formed and put here for wise purpose. Yet look at them all. Though some offer flight, and others speed, and others great strength, and others almost indestructible species endurance, do you want to have your consciousness, your Intelligence, transferred into one of these other bodies? Is the body of a cockroach the best vehicle for your Intelligence? Is the body of a rat? A bat? An elephant and a macaw parrot live as long as you, and some longer, yet are these better bodies to accomplish what you are capable of? Can you be eternally happy as a paramecium, and would you really like to be an ant? Though eagles soar and tigers roar and whales sing and monkeys swing and hyenas have few enemies, are any of these the body to ultimately be preferred over the possibilities affording in the life form you have had designed for you? Could you long endure as a bacterium without yearning to do what you are capable of doing, unless your consciousness is dimmed?

Just because life can exist under other conditions, of other composition, with different form, will it be as desirable? Will Intelligence fulfill its measure?

If the plan is to introduce life onto planets which do not have the gravitational properties close to this, or metallic, mineral and silicate mixes and balances such as this, or capabilities of creating and maintaining atmospheric balance such as this, or water cycles and almost exact ocean contents as you find here, then, what kind of life organisms will you be able to engineer?

Life as experienced in a specifically engineered DNA design form is not like

504

engineering a bridge for a river. For that, you adapt your blueprint to whatever need exists. Organism designs are also immensely flexible, as you well know. But when the final purpose is to design the best possible organism to perform to the limits of what is possible in a given physics for a driver of great Intelligence, the Design becomes Ideal. You do not alter the Ideal Design. You alter the environment to support it. If you have engineered an exquisite DNA design, and the river will not accommodate it, there are lots of other rivers - you either move on, or by engineering, *alter the course of the river.*

To alter the ideal life design is to destroy its ideal life function.

Yes, life does exist on planets of entirely different properties and conditions than this one, but it reaches certain limits and then, it can go no further. No matter what you think to do to adapt higher organism structures to these conditions, the sacrifices of mechanical function and neurological function are devastating.

On other worlds, the continents are not the same shape as yours, the mountains are not the same ranges as you have here. Yet they are continents, and they are mountains, and they are distributed and thrust up appropriately as they must be engineered to produce the water and weather cycles required, and in this, they are water and land worlds. Even as they are each unique and some quite different than yours, still they share proportions and silicates and clouds and rains and snow and rivers and lakes and flora and fauna based on the same Design as yours, though many are plants and insects and fishes and birds and animals you have not seen; yet they exist there.

They are plants as you know them, but different species. They are insects and fishes and birds and animals as you know them, but different species.

There are many successful organism designs utilizing exoskeletons, boney skeletons, scales, fur, feathers and tissues which are just as perfectly adapted to life as those you know, which are yet other, additional species.

On other worlds, much you will see you will know, while much will be new and fascinating. In the same manner, children who might come to visit your world will see much that they know and recognize, yet they will marvel at gifts reserved for your world and your world only.

Every world has its treasures.

These are my gifts to my children.

Yet you will see: all of my children are created in my image; male and female have I fabricated them. In my image are my children born.

You have the Design before you; it is you. See it, and learn.

The Design has been painstakingly organized utilizing the optimum of every factor existing in the universe. It is the ultimate adaptation of all that is provided in nature.

Though a lesser design can be achieved, it is not to be wished.

It is less.

You keep forgetting - you are an Intelligence looking for a home. When you enter into the body which will become yours forever, how much of your Intelligence and Spirit capability will you wish to continue to enjoy, and more importantly, enhance? The whole Design is to enhance the capability of the Intelligence and Spirit body to give it yet greater capability and freedom to rejoice.

All other alternatives are less successful. This is the most successful design. Your children will one day verify that this is so.

Everything in the cosmos has been set in motion and organized to unfold for earths such as these to be formed and groomed into perfect preparation, for the children, for you.

Know who you are.

You are my child.

I love you.

Do you understand now?

Yes, I believe I do.

All of this has been an excessively simplified explanation, as your brothers and sisters who know of these things would tell you, but it is a beginning for your understanding. From many things of what has been shown you here, even they may learn.

We spend a lot of time in talking about these things, don't we?

Yes, you think you need to know all of these things.

Yet most sadly, you have not fathomed your need of each other, and your trial by each other; and in your journey, you still fail to comprehend the Parable of the Good Samaritan, and you do not feed each other, nor clothe each other, nor shelter each other, nor heal each other.

You are still too busy speaking of shoes and ships and sealing wax, and cabbages and kings, and why a primordial sea is boiling hot.

And whether pigs have wings.

Yes. And whether pigs have wings.

You know, a lot of what you've told me tonight, no scientist is going to believe.

Science is generated by and devoted to free inquiry, and the idea that any hypothesis, no matter how strange, deserves to be considered on its merits. The suppression of such uncomfortable ideas may be common in astrophysics, but it is not part of the path to knowledge; it has no place in the endeavor of science. You do not know in advance who will discover fundamental new truths.

I looked at the time. It was no longer late. It was early.

I think I've had it for tonight. I need to sleep.

I know. I will be with you. We'll talk more... tonight.

Yes. It is already tomorrow today.

Are you pleased with what you have asked?

Yes. This has been really amazing.

Sleep well. I love you.

Thank you. Have...... a good day.

I exited the program, shut down, switched off power, and turned out the light. I was exhausted. This had been a night of nights.

I don't even remember falling into bed.

Chapter 16

Day 35 in the Wilderness:
> The Creation of DNA and Human Life

When I awoke, it was well after noon. I did not worry at all. Shifting night-for-day was different from the patterns in this part of the world, but my body remembered: this was closer to time and my natural circadian rhythm back home. Shifting actually felt better.

I thought a moment about home, and my heart hastened at the vision. As exciting as this experience was, I suddenly realized: I longed for home. Time here was passing quickly; I would be on my way soon. This shift could be my best preparation. When I arrived back home, I would see. I would be in synch. Why not get started, here?

I got up, ate a breakfast, or whatever I should call it at this hour of the day, and decided to take an unhurried hike up the wadi.

As I walked, I looked up around me, at the towering walls of stone. No longer driven by any need to find anything, no longer looking at every nook and cranny for what it might conceal from my eyes, I gazed upon the curving walls and turns and meanders of the canyon with unassuming eyes, seeing what there was to see. The Judaean Wilderness was truly beautiful, when one had no worries for food and water. I hiked higher and higher up the canyon.

As I hiked and took in the majestic panorama of stone and sky, I began to wonder about the random formation of the canyon in its water-formed path. We always talked about the random course of a river, the cutting of deep channels such as these which had worked their web into the soil and rock. I was walking in the cradle of a wondrous example of this random course formation in the Judaean Wilderness, as water had flowed in this bed over eons on its way to the below-sea-level sump of the Dead Sea.

Yet as I walked, I pondered.

Is this really a random path?

Why had the energy of the water dug each canyon as it did?

Was it really random?

So many turns and twists and sudden lefts and sudden rights.

Why did it go as it did?

Walking and looking up around me, and down around my feet at the dry river bed, I slowly began to fathom that though each canyon seemed to be randomly formed, the reality of it all was that, for itself, it was not.

When water had first fallen here and begun to flow in its logical direction downward, pulled by gravity, before there was a canyon cut here, had this been a perfect, flat surface? No. Yet even on a perfectly flat and smooth surface, a trickle of water flowed in a straight line only for a while. Why does the trickle go straight for a while? Why does it go to the left for a while? Why does it then turn to the right for a while?

In its path downward, why did this canyon go to the left, and to the right, and to the left again, and to the right again? And why turn in the places it turned? The water's path continued always toward the ultimate goal: in this case, the lowest point it could reach, the basin of the Dead Sea. What made it turn?

Was its ultimate path random? Or did it follow the path of least resistance, as we so often heard?

Or did it follow the path it had to follow to reach its determined end, given the precise matter before it, with which it had to deal?

For it had to deal with the matter.

Its course was determined by the obstacles it encountered.

Obviously, the first hundreds and thousands and tens of thousands of raindrops had taken the random route before there was a route. Or was it correct to say: before there was a route?

Didn't even the first water follow a route? Water seeks its level: it has an absolute goal. Yet even on the perfectly flat surface, water finds there is a route. Was this random, or the inherent whole nature of the surface, its substructure, and the additional force of water pursuing its goal?

Was the eventual course that would be dug and carved and come to be a mighty canyon inherently there already, in the make-up of the land, before the fall of the first raindrop?

Did the rain have any choice in its eventual path that it would make and carve amid the matter it began to move, and mold, and shape?

Or was the course decided by the obstacles: boulders, rocks, even tiny grains of sand?

I had reached a great turn in the course of the dry river bed, in the deep canyon of stone within which I walked as a small ant at the bottom of a labyrinth. I stopped and looked up all around me at this angle cut in stone, then up ahead at the stretch of canyon coming toward me from the next curve turning out of sight, and back behind me where I had just walked, all the way down to the curve which turned again out of my sight, to more curves, and on to camp. I gazed up at the high canyon ridge angled like an elbow above me.

Why had the water turned here?

This was a point of decision, forced by an impassible barrier which I could no longer see, which no longer even existed, for it has been washed away long ago. It had been up there, in the middle of space above me.

I looked straight up above me, into the sky, and knew that the cause of this mighty curve in this river's course, this elbow cut wide and deep into stone, had its beginnings right up there, right above me in empty space. Right up there where I could look, long ago, as water had begun to trickle, a small grain of sand had stood in its way, and so it had moved to the left, as it had to go on.

From that grain of sand that diverted a single drop of water, and then another, and then another, this mighty elbow was cut into stone. The first drop had encountered the barrier; it had thereby moved in the best direction it could move, and set its course for ages to come.

The cause of the first drop's setting this course sharply to the left was long gone, even as the cause of the course alteration I could see a few hundred yards upstream and the other a few hundred yards downstream were also gone. But the space that the original course had continued to create in this form was still continuing to widen and expand, and was growing and expanding even now. To my perspective its growth was imperceptible, even if I might spend a lifetime observing and monitoring it. Yet growing and expanding it was.

This was the chosen path of the water as it was confronted by the exact conditions of this land in the beginning. This was the course it had found feasible in reaching its goal with a determined objective, and it was ultimately unstoppable. As I stood looking up into the sky above me, to the place where this choice in direction had first begun, I suddenly understood that in this place, over this space, in the original conditions presented in this matter, the water had taken the only course it could take to reach its end.

There was nothing random about it.

The nature of the matter in the beginning had set its course, before the first raindrop fell.

Before the first raindrop plummeted onto this spot, this land had been the floor of a sea. Before the lands had been raised and the waters flowed off leaving dry land to erode one raindrop at a time, it had been the bottom of a sea, formed by waterborne silt and sand and dirt washed down from ancient mountains long eroded and gone. The settling onto the bottom of this sea had been determined by currents, themselves determined by shapes of land masses, previously current-shaped sediments and a myriad of other pre-existing conditions. Had this growing sedimentation been flat? No, for the prevailing conditions had forced it to become irregular. Its eventual irregular

510

surface contours, down to the smallest, had confronted the first drops of rain as pressures from below had raised this region upward, and lifted it above sea level as dry land. The courses of the first rain had been set while it was forming under the sea.

As I gazed upward, an eagle suddenly entered the small patch of blue sky above me, soaring and gliding on the wind. I watched it circle, and circle again, and then it was gone; only once again its wide circle came over my restricted view from down at the bottom of the wadi. I heard its mournful, haunting cry as it flew out of sight, and then, once more I heard its cry, more distant, echoing off the high rocks of the wadi canyon, and then it was gone on its way.

Bending my weight forward I stepped up over a rock in the dry stream bed, and continued my hike following the winding course of the wadi.

My path and direction was set for me by raindrops that had fallen eons ago, whose path had been set by the matter that had been formed here even longer eons ago, which settled and was set by conditions I could only guess at in imagination long eons before that, when all of this land had been formed as a limestone bed under a great sea, which had gotten its bed's consistency and form through currents and storms and settling organic matter and all of the things that set the formation of limestone beds at the bottom of a sea.

Yet even more than this I knew. The very bottom of that early sea had had its contour set in earlier beginnings in the crusting of a primordial magma ocean and molten meteoritic matter accreted and gathered from neighboring space.

At what point in time, I wondered, was the path I walked today, determined?

I thought of the eagle which had just flown overhead. It was not confined to a canyon path. Its path was in the open sky, free. It could fly wherever it wanted to, in any direction.

Its course was free, but then again, my path was truly free as well. I did not have to be walking in this wadi today. I had chosen to be here, for it suited my purpose.

The eagle flew where it chose to fly. Just as I chose where to be, where to walk, which direction to take, the eagle was free to fly, and flew wherever it chose to fly.

Or did it?

As I had a goal, it also had a goal: survival.

Survival directed its choice, not whim.

Thus it flew where the temperature and the climate and food availability cycles offered the best opportunities for survival. This narrow corridor of fertile land, the Rift Valley, lay between the vast waters of the Mediterranean to the west and the parched stone and sand of the immense Arabian Desert to the east. Only along this narrow path was there sweet water and food to find from its soaring height, to fuel it on its journey. And to where did it journey, and why?

The eagle followed its survival: food. Food availability was seasonal. During the winter, food could be found south, in Africa. But the African summer was dry, and food vanished. Abundant summer food supplies were to the north, in the Ukraine, and Russia. And so, the eagle – literally millions of eagles, hawks, and birds of prey – had to seasonally go from north to south and south to north, for life.

Choices confronted the eagle as it flew from the abundance of the North to the abundance of the South and back each season. But what was the choice, really?

To fly to the left or the right along this route was to encounter death in an environment of only sea water on the one side, or an environment of only dry stone and sand on the other. In neither situation could the eagle sustain its life. Outside the narrow range afforded by this path along the Rift Valley, there was only death for the eagle.

It was free to fly anywhere it wished, yet if it chose survival, there was a path, a clear path to follow.

The eagle could fly to the left, but that would spell death. It could fly to the right, but that would spell death. It could not stay where it was, for that would spell death. It had to move, and its direction of motion had to lead to life.

Its choice had to be the course which would spell life.

As I hiked, the shadows rose higher and higher upon the ridges of the wadi canyon, signaling to me the coming of darkness and night. My course had to be altered, and I turned and began my hike back to camp.

As I walked, I marveled at how much easier it was to hike downstream, even when the uphill grade was very gentle.

Back at camp I ate a dinner, or whatever a second meal after sunset should be called, and I prepared some hand-food for the night's discussions. I knew that after last night's full panorama, tonight would be short by comparison; I would get to bed much earlier. With food in hand, I went to the lab tent, and stepped in.

Seated at my spot before the computer, I switched on the power, booted up, selected the Internet and typed in the site:

WWW. URIM AND THUMMIN .GOD

In a moment, with the usual processing sequence, I was in.

Good Evening. I am here, I typed.

Good evening. I am here too. How was your day?

Pretty good. I had a good hike, and thought about a lot of very rewarding things. I slept well, too. I feel rested. How are you?

I am well, thank you. I am glad you had a good hike. Imagining a place you'd like to go and going there is good, isn't it?

Yes, it is very good.

Are you ready with what you would like to talk about tonight?

Yes, I am.

Where shall we begin?

I have a question about something past, and then I would like to talk about us, our bodies - the DNA of the Design, as you call it.

Very well, what is your question?

When were the dinosaurs? I'm not fully sure of the time tables we're given by the various sciences. Are they accurate? I see millions of years tossed around at the university in the paleontology department as if a million years is nothing. And I'm uncertain about the calculations which yield the time frames we are given and which are pretty set now and used. When were the dinosaurs?

You would do better to ask WHY were the dinosaurs. All who know of them dream of seeing them. You now imagine the dream of securing enough DNA to refrabricate them in your generation, so great is your fascination with them. You want to make them.
This I have done.
It is a delight many would give much to share. Yet there is a part of the creation none have understood, while in your generation the means to understand it has been unfolded.
As always, there are problems to solve in order to have the prize. The earth, this earth, any earth, must be prepared for children to come and live on it. It must have organic materials to make them, to feed them. It must have atmosphere to breathe, to block out radiation, to hold in heat. It must have species which interact in many self-contained environments, many ecosystems, that will all become ultimately self-sustaining for life. But for these, earths would be sterile, and being sterile, the children would immediately starve and die.
It takes time to accomplish this. During this time process, during which vast quantities of carboniferous molecules must be fabricated through exponential

blooms of life organisms, why not have some fun? It is possible to envision many wondrous life forms which will not be compatible with the thriving of the children. As you well know, you are hard enough on yourselves and your cities in violence and wars without having to deal with giant predators and massive land roamers. Yet the ideal temperatures for these large land creatures is also not compatible with your thriving, while the higher temperatures are ideal for accelerated rain cycles, vegetal growth and giant size land dwellers. The nurturing and cultivating phases of an earth can bring great pleasure and joy.

Does it offend your sensibilities, that I might enjoy my creations? There are many species which can be imagined, but which are not safe for my children. The worlds have to be cultivated and seasoned and prepared; in this time, I enjoy seeing many life forms in the garden which are not 'child safe' for you. Each is beautiful in its own way, and when each has had its time, fulfilled its measure of creation and its purpose, I have caused them to fade away, to make room for the next generation. In this manner I may enjoy many creatures on a world which will ultimately become better for their having been here.

Know that they have served you as they have received their measure, and I have delighted in them even as you may imagine.

And all of their organic matter has accumulated into a richness that is good, and needed for you all to live here for this last minute of a creation year, as some children have so wisely observed, and charted to your understanding.

You have found that to create a micro habitat of an ocean, even an aquarium in your home, that first micro life forms must flourish in their successive cycles, before larger and higher life forms will have organic matter for food, and micro reduction systems to purify and clean the water that it does not pollute and stagnant within itself. So organic matter from life forms must be introduced to season and seed the water, to begin its biological life cycles, only to die from those cycles as they are not yet controlled, and they run rampant, and kill almost all the life which obtains.

This same process occurs on a global scale in the formation of worlds from matter yet unorganized. Much preparation must be undertaken before the first life may be seeded; much seasoning and preparation must be effected before the land and the waters can bring forth great whales and beasts. Ample time and a course of cycles are required to season the water, to prepare it, so complex life forms can then survive as their needs require. The first life is sacrificed to initiate the cycles and establish the needed lives required to eventually sustain the life wanted for the habitat.

What is needed? In water and land, in the most simple environment of few life forms, most critical are the bacterial micro-organisms, which progressively break down toxic wastes into compounds which are not toxic, which can in fact be used in the building of life: ammonia to nitrite to nitrate to nitrogen. Many also produce oxygen. In their life cycles they produce heat, and in this too, they provision for the balance of your Life Zone.

The needed life forms are microscopic. Most of the children of the planet do not even know they are present. Yet you live in a bacterially driven world, and at every instant of every day and night these are working and serving their purpose, and because of them, life is possible on many spheres of rock coursing through space.

I created them from the beginning to solve this difficult and serious problem. Who yet that has noted them, has thought to thank the Intelligence which solved this problem?

Yet the interdependence of all things forms a world wide web of inter-dependent life which begins with the proliferation of micro life forms. For them to survive beyond a certain population, larger organisms must exist to produce the food for them. You see the food chains; behold the food pyramids: billions of micro lives live because of each larger life form. As billions of billions of billions are required, so the whole must be structured, line upon line, precept upon precept. The larger can only live because of the smaller; the smaller flourish because of the larger. There must be opposition in all things.

As in a small habitat, to build a full population, the fish or crustacean or whatever you wish to first keep will soon die of ammonia poisoning. So, what do you do? You set up the habitat, and introduce a sacrificial life form, even many.

Thus the cycle begins.

As the first wave of waste and bacteria bloom, the new larger organisms die unless there is sufficient organic matter in the water and the sand or gravel, and sufficient sand and gravel exists to provide homes for the many needed bacteria. Beginnings are a delicate time. Each new life form begins to multiply in its turn as its food supply surges in the environment, until the last, which eats the nitrate and turns it to nitrogen. When this cycle has been accomplished, then the life of the habitat can sustain larger desired life forms. So it is in worlds.

You do not think small species are important, yet they are. The bacterial biomass of any successful planet will equal that of its visible life forms. Many had to be created to assure enough to sustain this habitat through to the completion of its purpose. Many died with my knowing they would die; they were sacrificial to preparing the planet for you. Yet many were created to be here for you, and with you, which you have destroyed, thinking it no great loss. I have grieved, as you all should grieve. They were each and every one beautiful, and fascinating.

There are many sacrificial life forms required to season an earth.

Well you could do to look upon them in humility and gratitude, for each has fulfilled its measure of creation, and provisioned your world for your coming.

Before introducing my precious children to this habitat, it needed to go through many cycles preparing the myriad life forms required for all the life forms that would eventually co-exist with you, and then a balance had to finally become established, just as in the small aquarium habitat. There were many sacrificial life forms which established the needed quantities of organic matter, each in their turn.

The seasoning process affords the wonder of giving life to species which can never co-exist with my children. I love these creatures as much as any of the children who have found their bones and marveled in awe. Indeed, you do not love them as much as I. Were you to make an earth, which requires hundreds of thousands of interacting species to become self-sufficient as an aquarium and terrarium in the void of space, and you had to pass it through its natural stages of preparation for the eventual arrival of your most cherished and loved children to live upon it, would you not indulge in the joy of every life form feasible in their fascination and beauty?

The wonder of life on this earth has been my greatest joy, and how many of you have yet imagined it for what it is: my garden of progressive joys and wonders. This panorama has been mine. I have loved it all. I have been filled with reliving its joy as you have found the traces of its history, as you carefully pry apart the pages of your earth and read its imprinted story.

You inherit it only now that it is ready for you.

Yet look at yourselves. Look at how you treat your garden, your earth.

You do not take very good care of it.

You wonder why there are no dinosaurs. You have not thought that I might have preferred to spare them, and see them expire at once in peace, rather than suffer as you have made so many other of my precious pets to suffer.

Until but recently, everything you have seen, you have thought mostly to kill. The extinctions laid at your feet in but a few thousand years is staggering, and it goes on. In the continent Africa, the great elephants are almost gone. You have sailed upon the seas and seen the great whales, and almost exterminated them. I have heard their cries! I have wept with their confusion, and anguish. Only now do you look to the smiling Orcas, which your forebears could see only as 'killers,' and found that they are wondrous creatures of beauty and intelligence. Yet how many of even this generation have asked WHY are there killer whales? Do you know why there are Orcas?

To play with.

They are wonderful creatures. They are playful.

You still cannot walk amid the great waters and watch them and ride upon the waves with them even as I can, but I can, and I do.

It is a beautiful thing.

In all of the seasoning and cultivating phases of all earths, I enjoy the beauty and fascination of variety, and I thrill as I see life finding joy in its being. All life forms are for the joy of their being, the wonders that they are, and I love all of them, and cherish them.

Look to the records of the history of your earth, even those folded and preserved in the pages of its writing, and ask: If you could make an undersea garden to walk through and marvel in its beauties, and a terrestrial garden you could walk through and marvel in its beauties, would you leave out any of these from your creation? As I could imagine to engineer the DNA and create them as living creatures, so I chose to see them and marvel at them, as I have marveled at all species, even the sacrificial species which had to come and die to prepare this habitat before it was fully seasoned for your arrival.

Many are the creatures which have been fashioned for beauty and for joy and for play, even as they have fulfilled a needed role in a growing ecological system and world wide web of life, providing for the increase of the biomass while the topography was forming. And as the topography had to be cultivated and re-cultivated many times until it had reached its needed fullness, so many phases of life could be enjoyed, and the garden knew many creatures of joy.

So it was and so it has been with every life form on this earth.

And by the way, though much can be done and is done in a million years, and the children who toss around units of millions and tens of millions and hundreds of millions do so in grave disrespect of time, know that outside of what can be done and is done in a million years, a million years is, nothing.

I have wondered, from time to time: did the animals before us have souls? Will they be resurrected? What becomes of them?

You have ample witnesses that in my Eternal Kingdom are beasts, for I love the beast of the field and the fowls of the air, and all swimming and creeping creatures; they serve and earn their place, and for this neither shall they in any way lose their reward. Be not surprised that I love all that I have fashioned and formed. It is wisdom in me, and they shall have an eternal reward; so have I proportioned to them their inheritance.

All that I do is wisdom in me.

Does this offend any? Yet still in this many are offended.

I am not. Will I get to see dinosaurs and giant sloths, trilobites and the primordial creatures of the sea, and woolly mammoths and pterodactyls?

You have heard that the eye hath not seen, nor the ear heard, nor the mind imagined what is to be seen?

Yes?

Be patient, obedient, and endure unto the end.

517

I understand.

My next question begins some questions I have about us, about our bodies. As I have studied what little electronic technology I can grasp, in order to pursue the sound hypothesis, that is, sound energies recorded in crystals, I have thought a lot about our own minds, and our own memories. We are able to have memories of everything we experience in our bodies, and I know from my Near Death Experience that we can also remember everything we experience out of these bodies: things seen, things heard, things touched, things tasted, things felt emotionally.

I can sit here and remember a day that I sat drinking a cool lemonade by a swimming pool. I can see in my mind's eyes everything I saw, the pool, the water, the diving board, the lounge chairs and people sun bathing and talking, the colorful swim suits, the big towels, the tables with the umbrellas, everything. And I can taste in my mind and my mind's mouth the taste of the lemonade, sweet and lemony, and feel in my mouth and my throat how it feels as I swallow it down; I can smell the smell of suntan lotion on people's skin, and the chlorine in the water; I can feel the warmth of the sun on my skin and face, and the cool splash of water when someone dives in near me; I can hear the sound of the splash in the water, and the squeals and loud shouts in the pool, the voices of the people all around me, even remember the tone of the voices, the sudden laughter and giggling; I can hear the music that was playing on the radio on the table beside me, and hear how it sounded coming out of the radio outdoors by the pool; I can feel how I felt. It's all there. I can do that for a thousand different moments, and then another thousand, and then another thousand.

I don't understand it: how does sight, which is my eyes receiving photon energy, get stored? How are the images stored in order, as images, and in sequence of images? How does hearing, which is sound wave energy, received and converted and imprinted and stored in pitch and tone and perfect order? I know touch is energy, kinetic energy, but how is it stored in memory, in order, so that I can remember and feel in my memory a kiss, a back massage or a foot massage, and a bump, and a pin prick, anything, good or bad, how can I remember it and feel it in my body? I can remember any sound or music or voice, and hear it as if it were real. I don't even know what taste is or may be, but I can remember anything I've eaten, and taste it, right now. All I have to do is think of it, and imagine it, and I can taste it. Pineapple. Chocolate ice cream. Boysenberry pie. Hot French bread with melted butter. Caramel.

But most amazing of all, I can remember my feelings, and feel them again, just as if I were there at the moment I felt them. Love. Anger. Hurt. Happiness. All I have to do is remember a place and a moment with feelings, and I can feel my feelings. All of it in order.

How is this so?

You are, and so you imprint.

I don't understand.

To have being is to experience; to be is to imprint.

But how?

Everything that you experience in any way is imprinted both in your memory organ of flesh, and of your Spirit, in Intelligence. You cannot experience anything unless it, too, is. All that is, is a form of energy. Energy cannot be destroyed. As you receive energy in experiences, by sight, by touch, by sound, by taste, by feeling, even by imagining images and sounds and voices you yourself create in your imagination, all is energy, and as it is received, your Intelligence imprints it, in your memory organ of flesh, your brain, which receives it, and imprints it. In this you are a palimpsest of all you have experienced, as I told you before. You are a Being of Order; so you were conceived, so you were organized and fashioned to be. Only if imprints are stored in order can they be retrieved. You are a creature of order. As cosmos is order; you are cosmic.

What is stored in order, the actual energy?

A palimpsest, of the energy. All memories are micro-palimpsests of energies. Energenes are remarkable, and you are only beginning to scratch the surface of their nature, their applications, their potentials, and their services to you in your bodies and in your environments. They serve you in ways you have observed generation upon generation without slightest knowing or understanding. Their acquisition is so slight, yet they are received and transmitted from all parts of your body to the neuro center, where they imprint in body and Spirit; from there, they are ever accessible, and can be reassembled and played for you instantly by biotransistors and biotransmitters in the brain.

How is it done?

It is difficult for you to imagine and picture, whether in the matter of this physics, your physical memory, or in the physics of Spirit, in the matter of Spirit. You have no true reference to frame. Yet you may think of the formation of a perfect quartz crystal, particle upon particle joining; yet herein the pattern is set by the image of the imprint, and as it is set, so is it scanned and recalled. The crystal which is formed is the form which energenes take in making that memory. Wherein you have identical or nearly identical experiences, you and all others will have the same joining formation, or nearly the same. It is a form, a configuration of energenes. The form is perfect for its purpose, yet it creates no shape by repetition; indeed,

519

experience and memory of it is the most unrepeating pattern which can be found within you. Yet among many memories you may form, there are repeated experiences; among many children, parallel experiences create the same forms. Yet no two forms will be identical, for even in the most repeated experience, there are unique parts within the whole.

If it helps you, you may think of hundreds of thousands of microdroplets of water touching and joining to micro ice crystals, forming patterns of snowflakes at 10 to 3 degrees Fahrenheit: the microdroplets join in specific ways; patterns are formed; they always look like snowflakes. Yet though they are all similar configurations, still yet no two are alike: each is a unique pattern, a memory.

Or you may think of bonding a polymer which eventually becomes a full strand of DNA, with every command remembering its individual purpose, and all purposes unfolding in their designed order. With four bases in six billion codes you may record a hundred thousand gene commands, an entire human body. And in each and every cell is the entire memory. As DNA forms and remembers all it has been imprinted to recall, so is the formation of memory; only the print is finer, and the reader is an entirely different mechanism.

The process in this matter, and in the finer matter of Spirit in its related physics follows a like parallel. In this, your Intelligence in Spirit forms palimpsest memory, and so also does your mind within your Tabernacle of flesh.

And from this we can recall all experiences, by scanning and reading the palimpsest?

Both in the flesh and in the Spirit. You have conscious experience in both states. You understand.

I do. I see the truth of it. How much of it is ours, to keep?

When you are still but a little child, you have hundreds of thousands of images scanned and imprinted from your several senses, all saved in your mind. If you live the full years of this Estate, you have recorded billions. Reduced to digital language in an electronic device, the storage and retrieval mechanism required to keep every frame of every image of every waking hour of every day and every dream of every night and every sound, touch, taste and sensation, emotional feeling and thought you have had since you were born - would be a storage device so large it would not adequately fit in the head of an elephant. By the end of a lifetime, consider the vastness of the entire image imprint, each thing in its place and time, found within its frame and order of space and time, waiting there for you to replay as if you were re-living that moment with all of its sensory perceptions, tactile, visual, olfactory, auditory, emotional. All of this is within your Spirit mind, your Intelligence.

You take this with you.

Thank you. I understand.

This seems to be a good place to ask the following question: How are our bodies made? I am not asking this question very well. I know a lot which can be seen in any good physiology book or anatomy or biology book; I know somewhat of the whole DNA thing. What I'm trying to ask is, How did we come to be what we are?

You are asking of the Creation of The Human Body, the Design.

Yes.

Very well.

In the beginning, the form and function of a vehicle was imagined, and in that selfsame instant of imagination, the quest to comprehend the ideal vehicle within all physics was set to consideration, even the ultimate calculation of all specifics and all variables, and a Design which excelled all others by vast margin was perceived. It could do all things, and withstand all things; it was all capable.

Within the algorithm of its ultimate fabrication were myriad complexities of problems perceived and solved, that it might be. That became the algorithm: to achieve the desired end by solving every problem which became perceived along the way to that end, and to resolve every requirement by providing its needed response. The entire process had to be perfectly determined, from beginning to achieved end and beyond; so it was.

Within this algorithm was resolved the yearning to have a place upon which to stand, a place within which to find dwelling and habitation, even places of shielded and bright homes within a void.

Yet within all of these things of beauty perceived, of lights and colors and forms and worlds and tastes and touch, the crown of all, and the desire of all was the perceived perfection of the ideal body within which Intelligence clothed in Spirit might dwell and have motion and mastery over all the envisioned elements of physics. It was the first part of creation envisioned, and the last part of creation able to be realized. Many first things became last, and last things became first. The fullness of the expanding universe was last perceived as the only way the vehicle could be; yet it had to become first, that all else might be.

Still, this vehicle was in the same instant seen to be too powerful and capable to place within the direction of any but the most noble of the Intelligences. For, as it could only exist through the ordering of opposites in all things, it would have power for much good; so it would also have power to work much havoc. Thus such a vehicle, the Body of the perfect Design, having great power over all of the elements which would be created in the most advantageous physics, could be used for destruction, as well as for good.

521

For this reason, it could only be obtained by those Intelligences willing to adhere to all laws governing the cosmos that would have to be created for its existence, who would choose to use its power only for good, wherein a continual unfolding for good might be.

This is the Exalted Body of the Resurrection.

Yet all of the Intelligences wanted it, and within the laws which must govern all things, Justice obtains its supreme right. A means wherein all might be proven, to see if they would be obedient in all things, had to be provisioned. For, many understand not: that to be great among many is to be the servant of all. To have mastery over all things is to obey all things in nature. All is an eternal round: as one is served by all, one returns to all in serving. Those who receive in understanding, find joy in serving all, even as all in the cosmos serves all that is and are in it.

And, all those who serve their fellow beings, even though they know it not, serve the greatest of all laws, and they serve me.

Even so, many in perceiving yet comprehended little of the balances required for existence, most critically of the key balances required in all things wherein there would be opposites. These were the Intelligences which were impetuous, selfish, in whom the ability to ponder all things out unto their furthest ends before taking unwise action was counted as folly, in whom momentary wishes were weighted above eternal consequences and good.

Yet being Intelligences, in Justice and Order, they required their say.

As many concerned themselves not with the consequences which might obtain in working contrary to the demands of the laws, and yet all wanted it, a way of proportioning to each that which could be sustained had to be envisioned, for not all will sustain the highest laws, and some will sustain no law at all. By this it was seen that a process of proving would have to be proportioned, so that all might have equal opportunity to see unto what glory they might obtain.

So, a plan was envisioned; all would be proven. Yet it was known and seen that all would fall short; an Anointed One, even a Messiah, could bear the burden: in Him all might be redeemed who would love and obey. Yet one exalted himself, and proposed a way whereby none would fail. Even as he reveled in the glory of his plan, it was seen that in it he would usurp the key, Free Agency, wherein choice is exercised, the difference between good and evil is learned, and obedience and disobedience are revealed. As only through these might Intelligences become complete in the measure of creation, another arose. He affirmed the need for each one to exercise Free Agency, and be proven, even by obedience; and that those who truly desired to become perfected in all things might obtain, He offered Himself a sacrifice to the demands of Justice, that all might be raised with Him, if they would only love and obey. In this He chose to suffer for all, that all might equally receive.

For the needs of probation, it was seen that this physics could provide a lesser body, not endowed with all things, yet meet for the needs of such an experience;

this was envisioned in its fullness and entirety. It is the Second Estate, second after the First, of Spirit, even the second-to-last body which may be raised in perfection and Resurrected glory, even which you wear this day.

You have heard your body called Tabernacle, and Temple. Know it is this and more, your eternal gift, the Tabernacle in which dwells your Spirit, the Temple in which lives your Intelligence, wherein it obtains motion and ability.

You have heard you should treat your body as your Gift from God; and even so it is, and even so you should treat it.

Those who have an ear to hear, hear.

As it was foreseen in the beginning, even so it was made, and is. Though you may envision millions upon millions of other designs, with other proportions, other physical capabilities, of flight, of swimming, of mortal strength and shielded armor, all you will find present less capability than you can and do achieve in this body. With longer arms or legs, or any other different proportion, you must re-design the whole for balance, and quickly its usefulness declines; for flight, you sacrifice size, and arms with hands accessible to your mouth and cunning with tools; for ideal swimming you sacrifice legs and feet and arms with hands, and all gainliness upon land whereupon you work with the elements and make houses as you wish to dwell in privacy and protection; for increased strength you sacrifice agility and mechanical frame structure, at great loss to much which you delight in accomplishing; to carry greater armor, you sacrifice motion and radius of motion, agility and dexterity. You may devise billions upon billions of alterations to the plan, but ultimately, you will grieve, for the alterations all demand systemic modifications, and with each systemic modification come compounded modifications, until you quickly begin to lose more in accompanying areas than you gain by virtue of the alterations.

For Intelligences as you are, there is no more perfect body to inhabit, to make your Tabernacle, the Temple of your Being.

Please, show me your wisdom. Show me the Design.

Even so. I will begin with its composition. You will remember that within this physics of matter, there are ninety-two naturally forming elements of lasting duration. Of these, there are many ionic forms, yet the enduring elements formed are ninety-two. Recall the elements, and their proportions: in the earth, and in the sea, and in the air. Here and now is the future time and place I spoke of; you will wish to recall, and compare.

These are all needed in balance for healthy life in your organism.

oxygen 65%
carbon 18%
hydrogen 10%

nitrogen 3%

calcium 1.5%

phosphorus 1.2%

potassium .2%

chlorine .2%

sulfur .2%

sodium .1%

magnesium .05%

iron <.05%

zinc <.05%

cobalt <.05%

copper <.05%

iodine <.05%

selenium <.01%

flourine <.01%

nickel <.01%

molybdenum <.01%

silicon <.01%

chromium <.01%

with which there are also vanadium, tin, manganese, lithium, boron, arsenic, lead, and cadmium.

All of these which are in your bodies are in your Design by wisdom in me, and all serve purposes essential to the Design; some you know not yet how nor why, only that they are there, and essential.

Is the composition of the sea, and of your body so similar to sea water, by chance? No. Both require this mix. The children who have observed this and concluded that you came from the sea are in error, yet what they observe is true and accurate; but there are other reasons yet more intriguing, which they shall one day comprehend. At the moment, they believe, so surely; yet the children have been so certain before on so many things, only to find with whimsical grin that they were wrong. Yet their observations are worthy, and will eventually lead them to truth. As Life Worlds depend on these elements for what they provision to many metabolisms, so does the body benefit from their properties and chemistry to complete the complex exchanges required for all things to function exactly as required, as they do for all of this fragile life to be sustained.

Yet you are not creatures made of elements on a chart. You are creatures made of energenes represented by that chart.

You are energy within energy, organized and given eternal form.

You still do not understand everything about the 'bigger' energene groupings and the number of energenes they are made of, nor the types and the order used to organize them. Nor do you understand Spirit Matter. Nor do you yet understand the full nature of energy releases, and exchanges. You comprehend the movement of energy from one space to another, from one body to another, from one unity to another, but you comprehend it only upon a most simplistic scale, and only in the physics you can touch.

And yet there is more.

There are constant energy exchanges; they are required. What you wish to be, and wish to accomplish, cannot be realized when energies are at rest. There is a constant exchanging of body energies. Your body, made of energy, is in constant flux of energy, both exchanging energies obtained from foods you eat which are released to you, which you incorporate into your body, and, from heat, motion and other bodily uses, which is released from you. Your body produces a constant release of energy. It is not right to use the word loss, for there is no such thing as loss, you will some day comprehend; thus your words return, or release of energy is much closer to the reality of the cosmos.

Can you see? You radiate energy, and light, all the time.

When you hug another person, or pet an animal, or touch a plant or tree, you interact on an energy level. You give, and you receive. By touching and having close proximity to their bodies, you exchange energy.

You give to everything; you receive from everything.

The way one lives affects the nature of one's total energy force. The more obedient one is to the laws of nature, the more one is obedient to the laws of all that is good, the more one becomes in tune with the Spirit, the more one becomes at one with the fullness. It is an eternal round, yet you control it, and by your own nature of Spirit and energy, and the Spirit and energy with which you choose to resonate, you become what you become.

Among yourselves, not all energy is exchanged equally. You control some of this level of radiance, and receiving; yet not all. As you are master of your radiance and receiving, so others are the controlling sources of their own radiance and receiving. You are Agent, unto yourselves. Thus you feel greater and lesser energy between each other, as you share varying levels of giving, and receiving. Not all that is radiated and shared is received. You feel this. It is real. Not all that would be received is released to you. You feel this. It is real. When increased release is met with increased receptivity, you feel this. It is real. It is the sharing and receiving, the resonance of energenes and Spirit.

Love is a powerful booster of radiance. Faith is a powerful booster of energy and radiance. Compassion is a powerful booster of radiance. Prayer is a powerful booster of energy and radiance. Those who are in tune to each other resonate; those who are in tune with each other and to the greater Resonance and Radiance of the Spirit resonate, and feel this, and know this difference.

You know this.

And so, not all hugs between brothers and sisters feel the same. Love, shared with resonance in faith and compassion for one another, create their own resonance; there is a real release and receiving of energy, of this physis, and of Spirit; it forms an exchange which bonds; you find special bonds.

This, you can feel.

The hugs and kisses shared by those in love are powerful in feeling. Emotions play a part: these increase real physical release of energy, and increase energene interactivity which is shared and received, a true sensation. This is very dramatic between some persons. It is the heightened giving of energy between two who share love. There is an indescribable electricity in the touch; a quickening of all senses; a feeling of immense energy, and energy release. This is real. As two become one, they share released and radiated energy, for as the one gives, the other receives. The more full the giving, and the more full the receiving, the greater the energy united becomes. It is more than chemical activities; it is more than neuroelectrochemical response; it is more than accelerated caloric fuel harvesting and release. It is an Eternal gift, special above all things shared. It is the energy shared between Spirits, as they give and receive of themselves. This is the mystery of Eternal Companionship, and it is sacred, and it shall always be kept so.

You may have experienced this.

It is real.

What are we, then?

You are Intelligence.
You are a Child of Spirit.
You are an Eternal Fire.

I do not understand. We are a fire?

You are a fire, a carefully controlled fire which is kept at a constant 98 degrees of your Fahrenheit.

Have you thought about how precarious a thing it is, to ingest combustible fuel material in the presence of oxygen, to inhale oxygen and pass it into your blood, taking it to every cell of every tissue of your body, and thereby make of yourself a combustible furnace with fuel and oxygen brought together? Have you thought of what it means to automatically, 24 hours a day, be a furnace, a furnace that is not within you, but which is you, your very body?

Your body burns at just the precise rate, maintains just the precise temperature, neither burning too fast or too furiously, nor too slowly or too coldly. Have you ever realized this reality of your existence?

You are a burning fire, a slow burning fire, and you are not consumed.

Behold: a fire which burns and is not consumed is the greatest wonder to your thinking, but you yourself are indeed such a fire, constantly burning, but never consumed.

The moment of the burning bush on Sinai is a dividing vision for all of you: you receive it either amazed or with scoffing. You call it either a miracle or a lie. How may anything burn, yet not be consumed?

Yet look: every living creature on the planet is such a slow-burning fire, which though burning is not consumed, and keeps its shape and form and being, though burning.

It takes great energy to keep you this hot, have you imagined it?

How do you build a fire that will burn at an exact temperature, yet not be consumed?

This is the perfection of the Design.

This is the wonder of the Design.

Space is cold. Very cold. Even with the wonders of elements and chemistry provisioned within this physics, all chemistry is critically controlled and affected by temperature. The perfect solvent, water, freezes at your 32 degrees Fahrenheit; proteins begin to modify above 115; the solvent itself boils at 212 degrees even with the maximum pressure limit provided by weight of atmosphere. At a bodily temperature above 107 degrees many metabolic functions lapse; brain cells begin to die. When your body reaches 108 degrees, you quickly die. At a body temperature below 94 degrees, most critical bodily functions drop below sustenance level; below 92 degrees, cerebral hemorrhaging often ends life, if some other systemic failure does not. Even localized temperature extremes are devastating to the organism: above 120 degrees most of your proteins begin to be drastically modified by the heat. Fry some meat or eggs and you know how it looks. This modification totally changes the elasticity and use of the tissues created: they cannot become nearly this hot. Expose tissue to freezing, and the water in the cells freezes; the sharp ice crystal points pierce the cell membranes: cell pressure is lost, the cell's life sea is lost; it is beyond repair, and soon, it is dead. When many such ice-pierced cells are dying, and releasing decaying fluids into the body, you call it gangrene; the entire body becomes poisoned; it dies.

You are unimaginably strong, yet in a universe which exists in such real cold, and must have such immense and intense heat sources for you to have light and heat and energy on your worlds, you are incomprehensibly fragile.

In an expanding universe which exists throughout most space at near absolute zero degrees, and obtains its local light by suns which at their surfaces are almost ten thousand degrees turning most metals to gas, and whose centers reach over twenty-five million degrees, how in this physics do you construct an organism vehicle that is mortal and thus destructible, which for optimum chemical processes and exchanges in all metabolic functions and neurochemical relays must remain fixed within a constant threshold so narrow it is scarcely twelve degrees wide, with optimum center at only 98 degrees?

How is this constant and regulated body heat to be obtained, with cold space on the one side ready to freeze you, and radiated solar energy on the other side ready to cook you? How, when after organizing all systems on a planetary body - heat sustaining iron planetary core to guarantee precise surface crust warmth; layered atmosphere of precise gaseous content to pass yet capture adequate solar radiated heat; surface upthrusting to produce circulating breezes assuring more even distribution of both atmospheric and planetary heats; vast oceans of water which provide excellent heat retention and thereby additionally stabilize even further the whole - still the temperature swings to either far too cold, or far too hot? The ideal chemical processes obtained in the ideal metabolism function optimally at 98 degrees, within a mortal range of only twelve degrees. How shall the organism be warmed when temperatures drop below optimum? How shall the organism be cooled when the temperatures exceed operational limits and reach tissue destroying highs? How can this be resolved, when after doing everything possible to fashion and shape a world with a moderate temperature within the required range, swings are still so great that without an individual source of constant heat, and individual system of cooling, this organism Design will fail?

How, except that within the Design, each body becomes its own, thermostatically controlled and regulated furnace?

This was only one of the problems which had to be faced in creating a 'physical body' of energenes: controlling thermostatically the exact optimum temperature, while burning the fuel ingested, without exceeding the limits of tolerance of life within this body, without burning it up.

Thus you see: you are yourself a burning bush, which is not consumed.

Couldn't we be solar collectors, and have battery cells? That works for anything electrical. Aren't we electrical?

Yes, you are electrochemical. Yet envision the needs of solar collecting mechanisms; even when perfected for maximum capture, your needs exceed potential capture and supply. You have no idea how much energy the perfect Design requires, though some children are beginning to calculate it to the best of their ability. A much better mechanism was foreseen and designed in food intake, fuel harvest, and storage as sugars and fat. There are a plethora of systems designed just to assure and deliver the energy demands. You are infinitely more complex and efficient than a solar electroconverter and battery.

Yet your body and skin do receive and utilize direct solar energy. As your body senses incoming heat, fuel harvesting for temperature maintenance is reduced; you literally become partially solar driven. Also, it was foreseen that certain chemical functions could be processed in the skin, among them the conversion of less useful molecules to vitamin D, an essential bodily chemical.

Yet the great problem is that direct solar energy is essentially too intense for your use; it is a complex radiation, and some of it is very harmful to you.

This was itself a problem which had to be calculated and resolved.

The ideal solar energy source is still too intense, even after proportionately diffusing supply capture by optimum planetary distancing and by atmospheric composition screening. Less supply, easily achieved by a longer orbital radius, would become inadequate for maintenance of optimum temperature range, and photosynthetic production, as optimally envisioned. Thus the optimum distancing from the solar source is critical, too critical to alter.

For this reason melanin was necessarily engineered into the skin. If you receive sun in excess at any one moment, melanin is produced and darkens your skin, providing protection. You call it, 'tan.' Melanin regulates some of the intake of solar energenes. A daily portion is needed. Too little is bad for you, though you can manage. Too much is bad for you; this you cannot manage.

There are thousands of such small problems solved within your body, so that within this cosmos, you may live.

The whole food thing is very intriguing as a system. I had not intended to ask about food, but I love it, and I guess thanks are due. Thank you, for making the energy requirement of fuel so good to the taste. Please, tell me about the fueling of the body from the sun.

This was indeed one of the central dilemmas and solutions. The law of Opposites provided the solution as joined with the law of conservation of energy. As there was darkness there could be light; as light production consumes energy it releases energy; as energy is released it may be harnessed and reused, even at great distance. The way to use it was foreseen.

Energy is required for all motion; motion is the desire of Intelligence: therein all expression may unfold.

There needed to be a source; it had to be small and be provided locally to be balanced and useful; there needed to be many skenas; thus there had to be vast multitudes of sources; these had to be organized in groupings utilizing opposing energies of centrifugal and gravitational forces; these organizations would provide stability to the sources. The answer was perceived in galaxies.

It was perceived that all of this could be done.

Energy could be derived of a sun; yet it had to be diffused and calibrated for precise delivery quantity by distance; collected, processed into less intense form, and stored for prolonged periods of time, for continual rhythmic use.

How could the required solar energy from the source which could be made and provided then be harvested and provisioned to the body?

This was a serious problem to solve.

You cannot sit for months from sun up to sun down with all of your skin exposed, facing the open sun and receiving its full delivery of energy radiation.

By engineered design, plants can.

And they do, for you.

As all was contemplated and envisioned, problem for problem, solution for solution, it was seen that a tough, celluloid matrix organism with a silicon and organic carboniferous structure could endure full sunlight for long days. The conversion of solar energy into chemical energy was perceived and engineered through the process you well call photosynthesis, with chlorophyll in chloroplasts. Through the engineered use of enzymes in roots and other vegetal organs, it was perceived that large organisms - plants - could dissolve rock and mineral in soil, and dissolve energy-rich organic matter from previous generations of plant life forms, ingest these through roots, and in the leaves and stems synthesize the three - direct solar energy, secondary organic stored solar energy, and mineral essentials - into excellent fuel stocks for both continuing plant generations and eventually non-fuel producing organisms - animals. The direct solar energy could be captured, and then, in converted forms - from sugars to oils to proteins and more, even the very cell structures themselves in plant tissues and fibers - be stored in a variety of efficient and beautiful forms for eventual secondary use.

In this way a vast supply of stored solar energy could be accumulated on an earth. This advantage was perceived in all of its potentials.

The entire chemistry of both the plant-solar-storage process and the needed re-capture, conversion and harvest process was envisioned, with its many variables, each in their order of efficiency, yield and convenience. The process would be relatively simple in the energy-capture-storage phase; the reverse process, the re-capture, conversion and harvest process in the complex mammalian animal organism structure conceived as ideal for the Design, was excessively complicated. Nonetheless, it was perceived that it could be done.

Once this energy capture and conversion-storage concept was envisioned, the bioengineering of plant species, from the critically essential single-cell algaes to the largest size trees and vines with leaf shapes and sizes, colors, flowers and fruits all utilizable within the Design to give beauty and variety as they served, providing a multiplicity of products, was quickly envisioned and achieved. However, as all has its order, and order provides all, the single-cell forms were required first, and so they are always fabricated and placed first, to eventually provide secondary organic matter sufficient for larger, and then larger species, as do require substantial mixtures of both mineral and previously energy-carrying organic matter for synthesizing adequate growth.

In truth, the microbiomass is always the driving force of earths.

After this, the kingdoms of plants.

After this, the smaller families of animal life forms.

Thus solar energy is harnessed in vegetable food stuffs. These stored solar energies are converted to fueling living animal bodies, wherein the solar energy is used to fashion and form and fill out the organism with all of its designed tissues, drive it as immediate fuel for motion, metabolism and thought, and formation of reserve energy storage as fat. The rest is passed as waste. This too, serves its purpose in the overall scope, and returns to give. The solar energy which is converted by animal organisms into meat and fat is also food and fuel for you, a gift from the sun, a gift from the Design, my gift to my children.

Yet I would have you remember to use all things sparingly, and with thanksgiving. As you have seen, as you have left your gardens, you have lost your oneness with the nature which sustains you and fuels you, which you should receive with grateful hearts and a thankful Spirit. You cannot sit naked every day exposed to the sun; the plants perform this function for you, and give themselves that you might move, and work, and play, and live, and have joy. Eat always with thanksgiving, all things. It is my wish that you eat meat sparingly, and with thanksgiving, for also has the animal you eat given itself for you. Though all is provided for your use, use all with thanksgiving, and remember you would have none of these things, nor be at all, save that I first loved you, and love you even now, and always.

The plan from the beginning was to create a simple body and make it live, and give it growth as was seen it could have by consuming matter possessed of kinetic energy, even solar energy. This energy was seen could be harvested and used in the smallest of organisms from a sterile beginning, and in turn their matter could be used to create more complex and perfect bodies, all being given the greater use of faculty and more refined use of stored energy, converted and released to build and sustain living existence. The Design was perceived to fashion a body of energy structured as matter, to fuel it with harvested energy, and inhabit it, to gain movement; and, to create skenas, places from there to progress, using that physical existence. All the rest has been perfecting earths for the process of creating ideal bodies of matter, sustained by consuming and releasing and utilizing solar energy for life.

The total concept of your anatomy is the result of solving these problems. How to maintain a constant and regulated heat; how to re-fuel with energenes; how to fashion food, with so many kinds needed to provide the required results. Myriad combinations of compounds were required to properly release the energy so slowly and harmlessly that it would not become, as you call it, an atomic explosion every microsecond of fuel intake and digestion and energy harvesting assimilation. The body, as every thing in the cosmos, cannot indefinitely retain energy within itself: it is in constant flux of release. Thus it is constantly radiating and releasing its own energy. The same 'atom' is renewed how often, do you think? The Energenes in your body today are not the same ones as were in it last year. You are a renewed form. How to keep that form intact and whole and functional while it is renewing?

531

Behold your brothers and sisters and children.
Behold your own self.
You are the pinnacle of harmony in perfect nature.

I feel a great need to say Thank you, again. Thank you, for all that has been provided. I have always thought about the fact that we need to eat several times a day, usually three times, if we are so lucky, and I always thought that it is a very good thing that food tastes good. Was making food taste good a necessity?

Within a certain perimeter, yes. If you have ever tasted plants and insects and parts of animals which are bitter, sour, acrid and otherwise, as I have heard said, 'nasty,' then you know how many varied tastes there are, and can be. Ivy, for example, does not taste very good. Though the power of hunger makes most animals overlook terrible taste, why wince and shudder every time you take a bite, seeing as it is necessary to take at least a hundred bites a day? Though you have not comprehended it, the nature of taste is all calibrated and coordinated in the brain. In other words, sweet is only sweet because your DNA encoding causes your brain to receive, identify and register that taste as sweet.

Are you saying that the perception was adjusted to fit food?

Precisely. Yes, sugar is sweet, the essential kinds of it. And a host of other things are delicious to your taste. This is a simple manipulation of bioengineering neurocircuitry and sensory recognition in the brain.

What makes a taste to taste as it does on your tongue? Exactly what it is encoded in the brain for it to seem. The concept of taste was quickly envisioned in the matter of this physics; it is one of the delights of this physics, wouldn't you agree? The saccharides, made of carbon, hydrogen and oxygen at a two-hydrogen-per-oxygen ratio - lactose, glucose, fructose, sucrose, all of the sugars, the energy engines of the Design - were simply identified by instructed neurocircuitry as 'sweet.'

You know, I love you. You are, you exist, to have joy. What had to be chemically engineered to satisfy the fuel-storage and fuel-harvesting mechanism yielded particular chemically bonded molecular structures: most importantly, the saccharides or sugars, but also oils, and proteins. Obviously, as these were engineered specifically for ingestion and nutritional-energy replenishing, why not make them taste 'good?' Yet as much of this was accomplishable at the bioengineering food-fabrication level, still it was more within the sensory identification programming that several palatable and savory tastes which you have been engineered to identify and sense as 'good' were kindly apportioned, and a host of 'good' things have been possible.

So, saccharides are 'sweet.' Butter and olive oil and pancakes cooked in bacon grease are not 'sweet,' but many children like them. You prefer your bread and popcorn buttered, and your salads with oil, and most of you who have to go on diets would agree that potato chips and french fries are what they are largely because of the oil. Oil by itself is rather bland, but with a little of two elements - sodium chloride - potato chips and french fries and popcorn and butter and a host of other things taste better. The chemistry of this physics is curious and wonderful: just as hydrogen and oxygen together are the most dangerous and explosive elements, yet bonded into molecules they together form water, the ideal solvent of the cosmos, so too, though sodium is a poison and chlorine is a poison, when the two are bonded as a compound, they are infinitely less toxic, and they make foods taste 'good.'

Your body chemistry urgently needs amounts of sodium-chloride: salt.

Do you begin to see why those things your body needs have been neurocircuited to register and be identified as 'good?' That which your body has been programmed to identify as 'good' is pleasing, and you therefore gather it and willingly eat it for processing and use. This is not coincidence, that the very things which are good for your physiology and metabolic needs are also 'good.' This is quite intentional. It was foreseen, and needfully built into the Design.

As you need proteins for a multiplicity of reasons, there are a multiplicity of sources provided to you - beans, chick peas, nut meats, grains, numerous vegetables, grubs, insects, and of course milk, cheese, eggs, and meats - these too, needed to taste 'good.' As you register them, they do. This is the Design.

You have to understand that the critical thing was the chemical structure of these energy compounds, and their successful role in harvesting to you the required energy in various steps and stages in the food-fuel energy harvesting processes required by and demanded by the bodies made of this physical matter, in this physics, in this chemistry. The chemical processes required to produce these molecules: the saccharides, the lipids - fats, glycerol, oils and fatty acids - and the proteins, are chemically non-negotiable. They must be structured and bonded as they are, for a plethora of reasons. Unless they are chemically structured as they are, they do not work to give the controlled energy yield provided by chemical processing. This was seen from the beginning.

Except that each organic and inorganic compound is as it is, the biochemical digestion process, and its step-by-step energy bonus harvest which progresses perfectly in sequence as it must be and was structured, would just not work. Function is everything, first and last. The chemistry had to work.

After the perfect energy machine was envisioned and structured, organized and engineered in myriad DNAs to obtain an adequate abundance, then the secondary question of 'how should it taste' emerged quite innocently. While the chemical chains and processes are not negotiable, neurosensory identification, or taste, is. Thus taste identification was molded to fit chemistry.

Do you understand?

Yes, I do. The neuro work was very successful. Maybe too successful, some of us might say. Food really tastes good.

You may thank your cooks and chefs for much of the further combining of herbs and spices and tastes and special cooking processes which make your myriad foods taste so delicious.

Though you are made of energy, the combustion or energy release process through food-fuel harvesting must be carefully regulated. Your body needs and uses energy within it, and so rather steady, rhythmic fuel delivery is required. For this reason you have been given hunger. Hunger is triggered by a variety of stimuli, from emptiness in the stomach to a release of stored chemicals in fat cells specially designed to alert your body to the fact that storage is being invaded. The chemical message is that ready supply is perhaps exhausted, reserves are being depleted, and there is potential signaling of starvation. Thus you feel sharp hunger, and you re-supply yourself, if possible. This keeps you from unknowingly exhausting fatty reserves which you need to burn at a constant rate. You can burn other cells and tissues, but this can damage your organism.

The design of the digestive system is to release from immediate foods most of what is needed and deliver it into the blood circulatory system where it can supply momentary needs of all demanding cells, for heat, motion, and myriad other processes. However, the fuel-harvesting process is designed to only release energy from immediate foods and from storage cells at a certain, calibrated, maximum rate. Except for this safeguard, your acceleration of exercise and fuel-harvest demands could push a demand-delivery cycle into overdrive, and the overproduction of energy released in combustion could literally cook your body; you could literally burn, and be consumed. Thus the rate of energy release is engineered and governed accordingly. It is the Design.

However, because it is not possible to engineer the ideal mortal body to endure burn rates of energy release in acceleration above a certain heat threshold, and an Intelligence in Spirit driving a physical body can easily drive it beyond all immediately available supplies and ready surplus reserves, you may exhaust available energy, and cause depletion in these bodies. Though this results in the experience of fatigue, and exhaustion, it is a necessary regulatory cap to the fuel-burning engine, which is consciously driven by Intelligence.

The rate of energy you are able to imagine using and thus drive yourselves to burn during a day is normally more than your body can sustain in heat endurance. It must always maintain its proper temperature of burning, or release of energenes through chemical harvest, without over burning and damaging itself. This cap is designed into it. As the body is engineered to only harvest a set maximum of quanta per second and minute and hour, you tire.

Also, after a certain number of hours, you feel depleted. This is because you are depleted, in many ways. The diurnal chemical harvest of energenes is programmed with limits, and you ultimately must rest. There are critical reasons for your body to rest, quite above mere energy replenishment.

Your brain is an organ which, when overworked, begins to malfunction. Deprived of regular sleep, it malfunctions seriously. It is a neuroelectrochemical organ, and thus its energy usage is substantial; yet it requires rest for yet other reasons. Though most of your body tissues could be in various ways supplemented and fed with a continual energy harvest supply, your brain tissues would seriously malfunction within a few days of forced wakening, and would eventually cause the collapse of your entire organism without regular, rhythmic sleep. Though sleep and rest cycles are of immense benefit to these bodies, the sleep and dream state are essential to a healthy mortal brain tissue and psyche, and thus several systems are built into your DNA structure causing you to desire rest and sleep, and which help you sleep.

Under normal conditions, after a certain elapse of time, the brain shuts down on its own, and enters into sleep. By this programmed mechanism, you may perceive the critical importance of this rest and sleep, and may understand why the body has so many design mechanisms leading it to this rest pattern. This is not a design flaw for annoyance; it is the requirement of this body in this physics and energy system. The optimal day length of planetary rotation is critically adjusted and calibrated on all Life Worlds to this exact time cycle: circadian rhythms are not accidental. Again, what is essential to the Design is made so; the Design of the brain of flesh must be so organized. The easy part of the equation - adjusting the length of a waking day - is where the adjustments must be made, when preparing an earth. The body Design requires it, must have it, and is programmed in every way to give itself this regular rhythmic sleep. A body and brain deprived of this sleep over even a short passage of time due to systemic malfunction, quickly degenerates. If the systemic disorder prolongs, the brain and organism will fail, and the body will rather pitifully die.

Thus do not become impatient with your weariness. It too, is part of the needs of the Design, and it has been provisioned to you in every needed way. When you are a baby, most of your bodily growth takes place while you sleep. Sleep therefore is directly related to your eventual stature; other developments also obtain during infant sleep hours. Inadequate sleep is not good for infants.

It is during your rest time that the balance of energenes is again restored, and the free reserves for ready, quick access are made available to you for the bursts of need during the waking hours. During sleep the tissues and processes of the conscious, waking brain are also released, rested, and refreshed.

You are not yet immortal.

Yet it is neither good for you to oversleep. In all things there are Opposites. Excessive sleep leaves you groggy, and your entire organism functions below optimum levels. It has rhythms designed into it for wise purpose; certain functions do not operate fully during sleep, and these need to be activated, as they contribute to total organism function. There are opposites: as you need rest periods, the body requires activity periods. Without rhythms, other imbalances obtain. You have seen that it is possible to go 24, 36, 48, even 72 hours without a rest to restore ready energy reserves. The Design is provisioned with emergency systems which kick in upon demand. Yet a price has to be paid, in terms of rest, at the end of such a stint; too frequent an invasion of these reserve systems shortens organism life. You also know that there are those who can function regularly on less than 8 hours, or 6 hours of sleep per 24 hours. There are those who can function on only 3 hours, regularly. How is this? Their bodies have the capacity to convert and release energenes at a rate uncommon to most, and they therefore have available to them the required energene levels for such functioning after a shorter time. They also convert stored and ingested energenes into available energenes at higher levels continually. Also, their neuro tissues require less repose. See this and know what it possible, in its due time, for all those who obtain.

I have experienced many of the things you are showing me. The oversleeping has always been curious to me. When I was young I thought that more sleep would have to make me feel even more rested, but it doesn't. It's like over eating. I used to think eating more would give me even more energy, but it doesn't. I feel sluggish. Why is this?

If you eat too much, your fire burns hotter; other systems must work to compensate. They cool and convert to storage. This draws from available supplies of ready energy, leaving less for your conscious use. Though you think it is a mere fraction of burn increase, it is not good for you. Eat sparingly, and your fire will burn at its optimum heat, and you will feel better, have more energy, and live longer, for you will not burn out before your time.

Though you must constantly be refueling new energy to replace that which you are perpetually releasing back into the cosmos, it needs to be at a proper intake rate. The body is a biological internal combustion engine, in a very literal way. You understand with your cars and airplanes and jets that a fuel mixture too lean will not work well or at all; also a mixture too rich will not work well or at all. The same is true of your bodies. Delivery of too little energy will consume your body in itself: fuel will be robbed from needed tissues to obey the conscious command of Intelligence to drive the body, until it dies.

You are this much power, and have this much power over this body given to you as your Eternal Inheritance. In this, begin to comprehend the mighty power of

536

Intelligence, which you barely regard or comprehend. This Intelligence, this power, is you. It is an immense power, within a body. From this, imagine the longings of Intelligence with nothing to drive, nothing to move, without ability to express itself. No one can hear you scream in space. The story of the Genii in the bottle is a vague memory of a time all of you faintly remember, even through the veil; for this reason the story has seized your imaginations. You are all Geniis, finally released from your bottles. For this reason many of you are reckless in this Estate of freedom.

Yet too much food-fuel intake will not make you super beings. Excess intake will only load you down and encumber you and make you sick.

This law is told in the story of the Mana in the desert.

Though an abundance was provided, only enough for the day's needs was allowed. Hoarding was forbidden. The excess was of no use; it became useless to the person who thought to hoard it, with no increased advantage.

So it is with your bodies. All the children are beautiful, yet function varies.

The amount of energy taken in and processed is best when just right.

Today, many children eat too much energy: for taste, because of stress, for many reasons; and, some bodies store more readily than wished. Ultimately there is overloading of the energy banks, yet still the body uses only its need.

Too much 'quick energy' in sugars will make you sick. You think that sugar makes your children 'hyper.' It does not. It actually lowers their activity rate biologically. It is the glee over the joy of taste which excites already excited children. Sugars calm. Too much sugar dramatically calms. Ingested in conjunction with normal sleep cycles, it brings on and enhances first sleep. Yet it is not good to use for sleep, as it is stored in fat during sleep, which is bodily work, and causes you to awaken unrested: you work all night making fatty cells.

So it is with high-energy foods. Excessive energy flowing in the body makes it sick; too much stored taxes daily energy availability. Balance is critical. There is wisdom in being just a bit hungry; it is best often for optimum strength and health, within a very wide range of bodily beauty and efficiency. Yet in all things there is Opposition; there are unhealthy extremes. Some bodies too readily store, a child's life challenge; some children, emotionally injured, starve themselves, or crave comfort and eat: both experience reduced body efficiency.

In all things there are Opposites. The control of the appetites, of hungers, is one of the most necessary rules you are here to learn to obey. Yet it is challenging, and truly tests. It is so easy to crave all material things once they are created and seen. The time in the vast disorganized space was long for you, and the seemingly solid things around you are all very precious.

The taste of the food is wonderful. It is one of the joys of this existence.

But there is a vastness of food which defies your comprehension, at least at your stage of development. To overload is to diminish the optimum functioning of the unit. You understand this with your electronic technologies: power surges can erase memories, destroy components. Massive overloads of power to a computer will instantly burn it out. The same holds true with your bodies, even in terms of food energy intake. Too much will overload the system, and burn it out. As the Mana gathered in excess to hoard became lost to the hoarder, you cannot use more than your daily need. Remember the Mana. Take only what you need for the day. The excess will not be good for you.

I believe I am ready now to go to my core question. DNA. This is the Design you keep speaking of. Show me DNA.

DNA is everything.

Yet it is nothing unless it is used for ultimate good.

For this reason you have been given an earth upon which you may try it out, and experience its power, and see its destructiveness. As there needs must be Opposition in all things, so there is, and as there is power to do good, there is power to do evil. This all children must learn in a probationary Estate, where they can have joy, and learn, yet also taste misery, and come to understand that all powers can be given only upon obedience to the laws which govern them.

The vision of Joy which could be perceived in the creation of a physical state - of Being, to have of a body in physis, of being able to move, of having things to move, was the vision of all potential Joy. You are, that you might have Joy, and in greater abundance. As the vision of a body in physis became perceived, it was in vision immediately added upon, and the instant of its imagining brought with it an explosion of visions of possibilities of infinite Joys.

Joys through sight and forms and colors, in suns and ice planetesimals and earths with skies and clouds and mountains and snow and lakes and rivers and forests and plains of grass, shores and seas and islands and kingdoms of life of all kinds. And the sight of Intelligences clothed in glorious Temples they control and drive as they may imagine, and with their hands, out of the matter which is placed around them, imagining and envisioning and working, making all manner of wondrous things to see with eyes, of every art and craft and fashioning of their imagination, in every manner of beauty.

Joys through sound, in thunders and waves and rain and winds, in breezes through leaves and grasses and trees, in voices of all kinds, of great masses of stone scraping against each other, of plants and trees growing, of fishes, and insects, and fowls of the air, and beasts of all kinds, calling to each other, singing in joy, rejoicing in their creation. And voices of Intelligences, as brothers and sisters and children, speaking to one another, thinking and expressing thoughts and ideas; singing, and making of the matter of this physis instruments of music, and songs, and poetries, and symphonies, and every kind of harmony and composition in music to delight and inspire and create yearning and fulfill yearning.

Joys through all of the senses, as all can be fashioned and made.

For all of this, even though there is physis created, the vehicle must be.

As the initial algorithm had as its purpose the engineering of the ideal body vehicle for Intelligences as could be possible within this physical organization, this physics, so the ultimate potential of the ideal Tabernacle, the Temple of the Intelligence in Spirit was envisioned in all of its potential first. Much could be envisioned for Intelligence to have freedom to do; what could actually be provisioned, had to be determined. The answer was good.

The potential of matter was perceived in the charged opposites of the energenes, and from this all things derived. The proposal of desired potentiality was formulated; the algorithm was run. Tens of thousands of problems were confronted in realizing the imagined functional whole as a body in matter; each was worked out through the potentials provided in the fullness of this nature, by its physics, by its chemistry, by its inherent utility for resolving problems through design. Matter is subject to handling, and in this physics, great problems confronting desire can find resolution. What could be, was perceived; what was wanted, was designed and engineered by what had to be, to make it be. Each obstacle to the end was resolved in algorithm as it had to be resolved, and could be resolved. In this way the algorithm considered all possibilities of all combinations and reached the ultimate optimum of bodily Design for Intelligences to receive and inhabit.

From this completed answer, from the successful algorithm of this DNA, all other life DNAs have been designed in lesser and lesser complexities, as less and less demand was required to satisfy role and purpose. From the First, has come even the least, and the last.

An ultimate purpose was imagined; its answer was designed organizing matter yet unorganized into its best possible organization to meet the imaginings; it was seen that it was good.

In its fullness of complexity, the most difficult answer was perceived. From this model, all less demanding organism needs could be based, to great advantage and economy. There is an economy in my wisdom, and this is wisdom in me. The Design became the Archetype, and from the Archetype, all other strands descended in plan and design, to fulfill the needs both physical and emotional and intellectual of all Intelligences.

Once the Design was imagined, a multitude of life forms could be envisioned and engineered using the principles discovered in its perfecting. Many parts of their potentials had been foreseen in the process of considering and engineering all possibilities of form and function to arrive at the ideal answer of ideal form with ideal function for Intelligences. The myriad life forms envisioned could all serve purposes; they could be made useful, and beautiful, and companionable, and inspirational. They were envisioned, down to the last.

Many could be useful to the whole purpose even though they would never be seen nor known to exist until very late in the Generation, even the invention among the children of tools and words in the search for knowledge of all natural things. In fact, over the great scope of life, creation and need, the most insignificant and small and hidden would become the most important and significant for all creatures, without which nothing could be as it could be. They would serve their quiet purpose, and in this, earn their reward.

As I and the Angels and the Children in Spirit would behold all things in all earths, life forms could be made beautiful, even if they would not be seen by the children of their earths until late in their Generations, discovered as fossils.

Many life forms were imaginable, in many environments for earths, many more than you know upon only your earth. All are beautiful.

There are many efficient life forms imaginable, engineerable and designable, and for myriad reasons it is wisdom that there should be abundant and diverse life forms. You know only some of the life forms of my engineering.

Each and every species has its own DNA coding, and each coding does exactly what it is supposed to do: it organizes the matter into the organism it is programmed to organize. By DNA, matter is structured and made inhabitable.

By DNA, structured inorganic and organic matters are processed and synthesized into new structured matter, pyramidally and successively into larger inhabitable bodies, using harvested energy for fabrication and operation, beginning with the smallest. All of this capability, to synthesize and operate, is encoded into DNA. A vast base layer of life is required to sustain a smaller higher layer, which supports a smaller layer above it, even until the apex point.

You are at the top of a pyramid of life. You cannot exist without the full, broad base, and all of its layers. It is the world wide web of life which builds and rises; every block of life supports and sustains you. It is your life net.

The ancient Egyptians remembered this, and built monuments to this understanding even after they had lost its full meaning, in its many meanings. In the sea of space the rock is formed, a place upon which to stand; the pyramid of life exists upon a broad and full base: the micro organisms in their myriad array; all those who serve below are precious to the highest; together, many form a whole. The base is Gaia; they are many; upon them all life rises. They form the foundation upon which all life is built, and by which all life is driven on earths.

The ancient pyramid is a creation parable unto you, still little understood. I will remove another of its veils unto you. There are many. Behold.

Elements, minerals and compounds are synthesized by DNA into single-celled and multicelled micro organisms. Minerals and compounds and energy from sunlight are synthesized into micro organisms and algaes.

Micro organisms, algaes, minerals and compounds in sea water are synthesized into nematodes, sea jellies, sea slugs, sea snails, sea cucumbers, sea stars, urchins, clams, oysters and vast coral colonies, shrimps, lobsters and crabs. Coral polyps and anemones and sponges and shrimps and algaes and kelps are synthesized into myriad fishes, eels, octopuses, cuttles and squid. Squid and shrimps and plankton and clams and small fishes of myriad kinds are synthesized into turtles and sharks and dolphins and whales and seals and sea lions and sea gulls and pelicans and puffins and penguins and otters.

Minerals dissolved from the soil and rocks, and biodegrading organic matter and elements in the air are drawn by DNA and synthesized into lichens, moss, cattails, rice, cranberries, cactus, sage, aloes, ferns, clovers, milkweed, mustard, grass, wheat, barley, oats, corn, flax, cotton, ivy, ice plant, edelweiss, petunias, roses, violets, lilacs, jasmine, mansanita, mesquite, hibiscus, thyme, dill, anise, mint, ginger, marjoram, sesame, sunflowers, lentils, string beans, cabbage, carrots, potatoes, onions, peanuts, rutabagas, yams, strawberries, grapes, blueberries, pumpkins, watermelons, pomegranates, maracuja, bananas, figs, jaca, papayas, mangos, cacao, apples, apricots, plums, oranges, lemons, pistachios, jacarandas, laurel, magnolias, dogwood, palms, catalpas, willows, cedars, chestnuts, cottonwoods, maples, oaks, firs, banyans, bristlecones and redwoods.

DNA, and the micro bioorgans it forms and organizes within cells, synthesizes grass into caterpillars and katydids and chinchillas and cows and sheep and horses and zebras and deer and elk and antelope and buffalo and elephants and hippos; leaves into butterflies and ants and rabbits and giraffes and koalas and tortoises; Algae and moss and duckweed into flamingos and spoonbills; seeds into mice and chipmunks, weevils and sparrows and parrots and magpies; bark and roots into beavers and gophers and beetles; wood into termites; squirrels and mice and gophers and snakes and finches into owls and hawks and eagles; penguins and seals into polar bears; gazelles and gnus into lions and hyenas and vultures; and nectar into bees and honey.

Your DNA, within your mother's body, synthesized all that she ate and organized it into a new form: you. And DNA continues to direct the processing and synthesis of all that you eat, even grains and vegetables and fruits and nuts and milk and cheese and honey and meat of various animals of the fields and fishes of the waters and fowls of the air, to harvest the essentials and the energy you require to operate and function, to build each day anew, and move.

The sources from which you draw each day's life are vast beyond your reckoning, a pyramid below you, spreading out wider and wider as you look and see it now for the first time, each layer below larger and larger; and your body is served even by generations of layers long gone. The Egyptians knew this, and many other things, illustrated to them in the symbol of the pyramid.

Million upon millions of species have lived on your earth alone since the beginning of its life cycle. Over ninety-nine per cent of them have outlived their necessity and vanished from your earth. They served their purpose in preparing and seasoning this earth, and fulfilled their measure of creation; they are preserved in me. You have given names to only a million and a half life forms.

Half of the biomass of all earths is bacterial, which it must be to provision and drive all of the ecosystems required for the larger life forms to thrive. In this sense, all earths are bacterial earths, for so it must be; they serve vast purpose. This is the great base layer of the pyramid; appreciate it and honor it.

Then, the next layer above is vegetal. Fully ninety per cent of the macro biomass on all earths is plant life. Look about you, and see beauty in service.

On your earth, more than 400,000 species of plants still survive; the current countries of Columbia, Ecuador and Peru have more than any other countries in your world. There are more than 1,000 gymnosperms, over 250,000 flowering plants, and 15,000 species just of algaes, among a host of other green, solar-energy harnessing, carboniferous-molecule building life forms. Among crawling vines and herbs and shrubs and chaparrals and fruiting trees and wood trees you know, all have been made with purpose, and many with purpose have already been lost to you, through your own neglect and careless treatment of your earth, for momentarily perceived advantages and gain.

Yet see the vast majority of servants administering to you are bacterial and plant life forms. These serve, and serve well, and faithfully. They are many.

The upper layers of the pyramid, less than ten percent, are animals.

Though the smallest number of DNA forms on earths are those in the animal kingdom, these receive your greatest attention. In their way, they are truly fascinating; magnificent beauty and power they embody, as well as preciously delicate beauty and calm. They are the smallest group of life forms. They depend excessively upon the bacterial and micro life forms and the plant forms for life, as their complexity of mobility, articulation and drive from intelligence precludes an ability to also include self-produced food machinery. Thus they must receive their energy supplies from other organisms which ultimately receive their supplies from those organisms which have been designed to capture solar energy, convert it and store it for that purpose.

You stand at the top of this layered form, served faithfully by all below.

As there are many blocks, so there are myriad ecosystems and habitats.

A vast amount of planning must precede even a small ecohabitat that is to survive and thrive homeostatically. Myriad microsystems sustain life to myriad macrosystems; micro ecosystems and macro ecosystems internet as a whole.

All must work harmoniously in equilibrium observing countless balances. Food must proliferate adequately; species continuity must be assured. All must be strong enough to survive within their measure; none may be too greedy.

This is a lot of DNA engineering.

When one is designing a world wide web of interconnecting ecohabitats, the planning for every conceivable eventuality is vast, and must be precise in its consideration of all organism needs, vulnerabilities, interactive relationships, and reproductive rates both for replenishment assurance and oversaturation prevention of any species at any level. Trillions of organisms must thrive.

This is an immense process of DNA engineering.

There must be opposition in all things, and checks and balances by the millions must be engineered into the design. A successful homeostasis will be achieved only when a layered interactive equilibrium is designed, which has its beginning upon a base of co-symbiotic bacterial life forms, building up to what they can sustain. It is designed by envisioning the final and most complex organism needs and designing backward from that need to assure the full life support of all systems within the desired system, which is always resolved in the end at the microbiological level. The end, most complex final life form dictates its environmental and ecological needs; the rest is then systematically worked down in algorithm to the wide base upon which it must be sustained upward. After the basic system is perceived, you have the archetype; it may be refined with balanced additions compatible to the food and water supplies and the temperature ranges of the geolocale under design. This balanced refinement is the area of freedom wherein wonderful, specialized species may be designed to fill out a habitational system, making it not only work, but provide true joy.

In all of this, behold a wonder: of the small animal kingdom atop the layers of bacteria and plants, only five per cent are boned vertebrates, like you.

Think of the millions of blocks forming the huge mass of the pyramid. At the top, of the one hundred blocks representing all animal life forms, only five blocks represent all of the animals with boney inner frames.

Think of the biomass of your earth, and imagine how few life forms this is. Yet if I were to ask any child to name one hundred animals, a few species of skeletal animals would form the bulk of species recalled, and named.

However, invertebrates serve great purpose; with many purposes, there are myriad varieties. In the seas are many species: the coelenterata, jellies, anemones and corals; the echinoderms, starfish, urchins, sand dollars and cucumbers; and the mollusks with their shells, clams, oysters, scallops, snails and cephalopods, the squid, nautiluses, cuttles and octopusses. In land, water and sea floors are millions of species of roundworms, flatworms, and sponges. All of these serve their purposes in the oceans, in rivers and lakes, tidal swamps and wetlands, and on moist lands as well. They are required. Without them, there would be no fishes, soils would not be fertile, and a host of other services you take for granted would be absent from your hotel. You need them.

Though insects are not the greatest part of the biomass, they serve many and diverse purposes required for the ongoing homeostasis of earths. For this reason, many specialized varieties have been designed: more than ninety percent of all animal species are of the phylum arthropoda, which includes crustaceans of all kinds: horseshoe crabs, crabs, lobsters; and all kinds of insects, spiders, sow bugs, millipeds, and centipedes. They are a highly important food-fuel source, and most of the birds, fishes, amphibians and reptiles could not survive on an earth without them. I know the children often find them annoying, yet without them, there could be no children, for the void created by an arthropod and insect-free earth ecosystem is unfillable, just as the void of a bacteria-free earth ecosystem is unfillable. The place of bacteria can only be filled by bacteria; the place of insects can only be filled by insects.

The invertebrates are a great and sturdy layer in the Design of earths, for which you must be very grateful. Most of your favorite animal species would vanish overnight if the invertebrate families were removed, for they would starve.

The insects in particular provided an immense canvas for design, and as you photograph them and enlarge the photographs, you will find that here is a stunning gallery of biomechanical and bioengineered creatures. When you see them enlarged, you are usually grateful that these exoskeletal life designs were reserved for life forms of miniscule size, for they are intimidating to you. Yet in their own small life systems, they must be intimidating, for being small, almost everything is larger than they, and living vulnerably in air, they lack the protection of water and its many supports. They require protection and armor in order to survive their usually short lives and serve as each serves in the system.

There are millions of insect species and subspecies you have yet to isolate, observe, and name. Though they are unknown, they serve you the same.

Though most of the life upon earths is bacterial, and plant, and insect, yet when you think of 'life,' most of the children think only of animals - the 4,000 species of amphibians, the 21,000 species of fish, the 6,000 species of reptiles, the 8,600 species of birds, and most specifically, the 4,000 species of mammals.

Of these last creatures, you are one.

You are a mammal.

The original, ideal Design for Intelligences, you call 'mammal.' It is warm blooded because you need to contain your own chemical laboratory systems to precisely harvest solar energy from storage where it has been previously captured, converted and stored by organisms designed for that purpose with that capability. It has hair, as hair was foreseen to be best; yet as you are Intelligence, and you would wish to alternate coverings and would be able to make them, no more hair was given to you than required. These two singular factors: self- contained heat and ability to change exterior body covering at will, make you the most adaptable of all creatures on the earths, able to live in the hottest and coldest climates that earths produce, though in your mortality you are not the strongest, nor the most durable of the organisms.

Thus the Ideal Design served as model, with all of its complex systems, for a descending ladder of bioengineered life forms which could benefit from various and sundry aspects of the Ideal Design. Once the Prime Template was calculated and engineered, the spin-offs were ever more easily envisioned and engineered.

DNA lends itself to this capability. It can be broken down into component parts and reassembled into new forms which retain the advantages of the original, yet display new characteristics as envisioned and designed. Once the process of forming bases into genetic codes is comprehended, and the means of guaranteeing precise order of unfolding is comprehended, as you like to say, the sky is the limit.

That is the beauty of its design.

The capabilities and design advantages of the Ideal Design have been modified for a great variety of useful and beautiful mammalian companions for you. They have intelligence, though not Intelligence as you Are. I love them, and they serve. As you love them, you give me joy. The potentials of the Strand were perceived in modifications resulting in all of the kingdoms you know, and other strands were conceptualized and envisioned and formed for additional life forms perceived to be needed, until all that was needed had been envisioned, and fashioned, and formed. Even great whales, and great trees; and miniscule parameciae, and algaes; and lesser strands and forms were made, as they were seen they would serve their purposes.

The Design has been a Template, a model, and as each part has shown its use in serving a lower species, it has been adapted and used to great purpose. The chemical pump which drives most life on earth, that by a series of enzymes breaks down glucose and fructose and reaps an energy profit with ATP molecules, is a fine piece of strand sequencing. Once designed, it was useful in most life. It was originally designed for ultimate use with oxygen respiration in your bodies, where it can combine pyruvate with oxygen to extract yet more energy from the process. This part of the Strand has been used in its original form with little modification in virtually all air-breathing, lunged life forms, as its initial sequence has been adapted to all life forms which can benefit by it. This has been wisdom in me, a practicality in physical chemistry.

As the children begin to bioengineer, they will also borrow this sequence.

Yet will they do so giving thanks to its Designer?

Or will they patent what they have designed, as if it all was theirs?

For your life state to experience maximum freedom and be productive, there are thousands of ROM encoded functions on the Strand. This is essential, or Intelligences would spend all of their time consciously imagining and commanding food digestion, hormone secretion, cell respiration, chemical processing and energy harvesting, chest fluctuation for breathing, each and every heartbeat to pump blood, on and on ad infinitum for every life process.

This would become tedious, and entirely frustrate the whole purpose.

For this reason, the Design programs ROM into the DNA Strand.

By this also, the children are made free.

As the Strand was seen to be Ideal, and many parts of it proved useful, they were borrowed to fashion as many life forms as I saw need to envision. This included some quite significant and important Design concepts.

Part of the Ideal Brain Design, the Brainstem, which is genetically encoded with programmed ROM memory to perform functions which an Intelligence does not want to be bothered with, and by this Strand encoding does not have to consciously perform - breathing, heartbeat, and other central neuro autofunctions by ROM - obviously is useful in vast hosts of organisms. Why design a new brain organ and entirely new strand sequence to perform these same unconscious functions in other life forms where it can be equally beneficial? This design engineering already worked, and well. It is economy to adapt for modified purpose that which is already Ideal. Another part of the Ideal Brain Design, which you call the R-Complex, also DNA encoded with built-in ROM memory as needed for eventual random accessing, contains mechanism patterns for protective behavior foreseen to be necessary as selfish children would threaten and attack otherwise unprepared children: it supplies a source of aggression, territoriality and social hierarchy. This secondary ROM accessory was foreseen to be ideal as a fractional organ to service entire classes of species, reptilian and lower, and so in further reduced design it serves amphibians, fishes and lesser organisms. By themselves, these two secondary brain fractional organs carry all the ROM a largely unthinking organism needs.

Without Intelligence in Spirit of your magnitude, and without the mammalian brain, as the children have designated the Prime Brain, organisms endowed with less are less capable in those things which you, as an Intelligence, delight most in doing. This is accomplished through simple deletion of the parts of the strand which lead to the fullest development. For creatures of only minimal intelligence, and with only fractional intelligence, they do not need the brain capabilities Designed for your Intelligence, to live joyfully.

Thus of the Prime Brain, and of a majority of the Strand, numerous slightly lower species are designed, with great purpose. Some of these forms are still living on your earth, yet there were others, before you. All are delightful. These species are designed by simple deletion on the Strand of the final phase of brain development, with other minor alterations to form; the brain in these forms stops at its designed point, and a wonderful creature is perfected for its joy and measure.

In all things there is a measure, and in all measures there is a wisdom. Not all measures are equal; this does not make them inferior, only of different measure. Many of these homonoid forms which have been designed closely below your fullness you have ridiculed, and disdained, even despised as brute and cruel and primitive and dirty. Yet many of these have obeyed more nobly than many of you, and have nurtured and loved their families and sought nothing except to preserve their own simple needs.

Know that these are as much my children as the lions and the whales and the beasts of any field and the creatures of any water and the fowls of any air, even as the smallest bacterium which serves. Despise them not, nor denigrate them, but behold them in wonder and awe and joy, for they are creatures of my making, and I love all of my creations, all creatures high and low. As you see in the scrolls that even the beasts have their place beside my throne and they eternally sing my praises, think not to look down upon these creatures in your jealous vanity because you perceive they are too close in form to you. I speak of the early creatures of almost human form, and the apes.

It is the jealous and selfish child who thinks to place limits upon my love and my rewarding the laborers in the field. Be wary that you do not have a greedy eye to jealously deny those who have labored long in the field, who have borne the heat of the sun and the day, who worked to bring much harvest into the store before your coming at the eleventh hour. Even they who came before you, even in their humility and lesser intelligence and ability, even they shall in no wise lose their reward. They lived well, and they served well; they have earned well. Even those yet with you, the monkeys and apes, live well, serve well, and earn well. Be not surprised to see these beasts beside my throne and praising me with joy in the day that you come and kneel begging for a place. Verily I say that all who mistreat even the least of these shall answer for their cruelty, and conscious arrogance, for these are all precious in my sight.

Those who have an ear to hear, hear.

From the optimum design are derived many useful DNA pattern designs.

When an organ has been designed that works, why re-design it? Just for the sake of originality? This is vanity, not Design. The double helix DNA strand is economical; it was designed to serve. A pumping heart has been designed; it is adapted to countless life forms. A finely functional liver has been designed; it is adapted to countless life forms. Functional nerves to transmit commands from Intelligence are designed; they are adapted to countless life forms. Blood cells; blood vessels; muscle cells and tissues; bones and skeletal structure; kidneys; digestive tract; a brain - these organs need not be redesigned for vanity. The ultimate Design for the ultimate vehicle of Intelligence in an anticipatory Second Estate in a preparatory Physics of this matter was made perfect, and each part of it as could find useful application in lower life forms required for the whole and for the joy of all life was wisely perceived for its usefulness and adapted for its proposed purpose and use in as many life forms as required each part.

From the Design, descending uses and applications were proportioned to modify and give variety to an almost infinite number of lesser species, each useful in its measure of creation, each serving a purpose in the requirements of a whole earth ecosystem, and each having joy in its creation and life.

It offends some children to imagine that what was designed for them as a body was seen to be useful in designs given to wondrous creatures of beauty and service, and as these life forms are called animal, they are called animal.

This is vanity.

I have created all creatures great and small, and blessed them, and who shall call them unworthy? As I love you, shall I not love them? If your Design has given gifts to other creatures with less intelligence and less capability, can you not see joy in the gift, and in the giving? If I created the animals, and I created them after your Design by wisdom in me, where is there shame, in 'animal?'

Cease to disdain those who give life to earths and to you, even animals.

It is always the selfish child who feels need to be only child. It is always the selfish child who cannot share. It is always the selfish child who must be called by names of distinction. Seek not to be called by names of distinction, but rejoice in all that has been given to you, and through you.

All my creations are blessed. They all serve, and fulfill their measure.

Still I ask: If you do well, will you not be accepted?

I believe I understand most of what you have shown me. I have another question, which regards mixing genetic lines. When a horse and a donkey mate, the mule which is born is sterile; it cannot reproduce. I have heard this follows true for all higher crosses.

Why is this?

Each seed reproduces according to its own kind, due to DNA. Crossing is possible when strands are very close. But there are very powerful inhibitors which block the process beyond certain limits, for a wise purpose. Even in some cases where mating is possible, the resulting mutant strand produced is unable to match DNA for mating; you call this sterile. The inhibitors which block mixing and mating of mutations are an important part of the design. There are other inhibitors which block finalization of many mutations as produced offspring. The garbled embryonic offspring does not form, and is discarded. The DNA strand is made to be flexible and adaptable, but it is very limited in its adaptability, much more so than currently believed.

This you have observed in the fossil record: that species go on unchanged for the long duration of their tenure on earth, no matter what great periods of time their measure spans, with no discernable alterations in size, or in form, or in skeletal proportion, or in dentition, or modifications in any other way. You observe that they appear upon the earth as they are, and remain so unchanged until they disappear. Morphological change is usually limited and directionless, as you have already found. Stasis, as you call it, is universal.

This stares you in the face, and the children of the myth are terrified to admit to themselves what it means. A homeostasis is entirely prevalent in the fossil record, which shows you that this rigid resistance to change is Designed in genetic coding, for anything but the most minor local adaptations: a palette of hues for minor color shifts to more closely approximate the predominant environmental color schemes; a fractional range of minor size fluctuations for local populations to adjust to food, mineral and vitamin source availabilities; and coded range flexibilities for other minor advantageous adjustments.

Stasis is biocoded, part of the wisdom of the Design. See it, and believe.

Overall, you observe very monotonous continuation of exact replication for vast stretches of generational reproduction. Know this is due to a nature, a code built into the DNA strand to resist reproduction of mutation which would alter the design before the time given to the organism has been fulfilled.

All creatures have been created with a commandment to replenish the earth, and to fulfill their measure of creation. In some cases, this has been a charge to endure and serve for immense passages of time, faithfully. The record bears witness to this service. These species have fulfilled their measure of creation. They have served faithfully, some for very long duration. Faithfully. Some, you observe, are here almost since the beginning, and still they remain. Others, having fulfilled their measure, have been relieved; after them new creatures, whose environment of existence has been prepared by those who endured the more difficult days before, are introduced to further extend the preparation and seasoning process of the earth as they were designed to do.

Though you do not yet understand it, each and every species has a purpose, and is designed for precise environmental conditions which repeatedly obtain in the process of forming Life Worlds. The function and use of each species, ecosystem and entire chronobiospheres have been designed to carry out specifically identified processes needed to accomplish a goal.

As your earth became more seasoned and prepared, and therefore physically ready to provide for and sustain an increase, you note these new species by sudden appearance, or saltations. These new appearances then also continue for vast generational sequences unchanged, until they vanish.

Thus you see DNA faithfully reproducing unchanged organisms over great passage of time, and then disappearances, and sudden introductions upon the scene of new species. There are no steady, gradual transformations from ancestors; there is no fossil record of transitional biosteps; the new species just appear, fully formed. This is the evidence of your observation.

It is the record.

This observation of sudden appearance becomes ever more glaring and difficult to excuse away as digging and discovery expand exponentially.

Its implication terrifies the children who have made and love the story. They desperately now try to shore it up against the evidence of their own discoveries, which gather to show its untruth ever more abundantly; they scurry to imagine and contrive torturously exotic sub-theories and weave them more deeply into an ever more vague theory as explanations for the monumentally unexplainable inconsistencies and unforthcoming fossils of their salvation, which in total summation fail completely to affirm to them that which they cling to in belief, a belief they hold in faith and faith alone, without evidences.

I see them, and understand their desperation, and sorrow for them with great sorrow. These are the children who wish to believe in anything that will reach out to them and offer the excuse to renounce a God, a Creator, a Designer, and release them from accountability, the dilemma of acknowledging Right from Wrong. These are they who feel naked before a God, and seek to hide. They still battle against the secret of Eden, and the truth of their nakedness, and they crave a safe hiding place for their nakedness, a place where they can tell themselves and believe they are no longer watched, nor seen. They will cling to anything that tantalizes them with this desperate hope.

It is frightening to these children, to imagine that they are seen by a God.

Their arguments become ever more boring. They are tiresome, and the elaborately contrived dialogues puffed up to explain why what is seen and observed clearly is not to be understood as it appears, nor trusted for what it evidences, and that trust should be confidently ever more secured in that evidence which is unseen, with unaltering and unquestioning trust in the great authority who pronounced and codified the canonized myth of descendency, all is become a rehearsal of the past. The chattering becomes ever more like the defenses contrived to save Galen's garbled anatomy and Ptolemy's incorrectly assembled universe. Galen bluntly misinterpreted and ignored much of what dissection exposed and showed forth; Ptolemy took the real pieces he had, but put them together all wrong. Centuries of science evolved in justification of nothing. For centuries the resistant children of science vehemently contrived absurdities to defend the false anatomy of the enshrined Galen, denying what the eye could see and the mind could comprehended, for Galen could not be found wrong. So also did they likewise contrive much and elaborate long to maintain the enshrined Ptolemy's geocentric universe against the onslaught of evidence crying out with the truth of Copernicus' heliocentricity, for science could not bear to grow, and the vanities of false theology feared the implications. The evidence of the body disenshrined Galen, and the evidences of the heavens reassembled the pieces into their proper order and disenshrined Ptolemy. The body is now freed to be studied correctly, to the benefit of all; the universe is now freed to be studied correctly, and the children of this earth are not demoted, nor less loved for being in one extremity of it. In spite of the sun being the center of your system, and your galaxy being one among billions, you are still you, and all who have an eye to see still know I AM THAT I AM.

As the balancing act of this myth and the evidence becomes ever more precarious, and the fall of the myth becomes visibly inevitable, the significant truth of sudden appearances will increasingly stare the children in the face. Yet for now, they shrink from it, and hide in intricate verbal acrobatics, to avoid the inevitable interpretation of 'punctuated equilibrium,' DNA Design, and Designer.

Those who have an ear to hear, hear.

The DNA strand is designed and coded for flexibility and a natural adaptation process for survival and variety, a limited natural selection function, which you have observed with the understanding of its wisdom. Yet kind produces kind until new strands are made to replace kinds which have served their measure of creation, or been extinguished by any one of a plethora of natural causes inherent in the preparation and seasoning processes of earths.

You now know some of these grooming and preparatory processes: from asteroid and planetesimal collisions to major tectonic plate adjustments with resulting hyper volcanism, to atmospheric extremes, gas adjustments resulting in elevated hyper tropical heats or extreme cold and prolonged ice ages.

After initial planetary accretion and majority 'clearing of the air' in a new solar system, these events are all easily foreseen by simple awareness of trajectories of remaining interstellar materials and debris in motion within the given solar and planetary system being seasoned and prepared. Collisions can be calculated with accuracy, and controlled and timed more easily than some will be comfortable to learn; surface environments are also easily foreseen, by simple awareness of the planetary accretion-smelting-cooling-bioseasoning-tectonic-atmospheric balancing process as a whole, which repetitiously follows predictable geophysical patterns, as any child of science could detail even now, with erudition, if asked to postulate such a probability, given the premise that other Life Worlds might exist across the cosmos. How would they accrete and mature? The children who know will be more than glad to predict the steps.

You have noted catastrophic far-reaching die-offs of myriad species. There are great die-offs in the seasoning process; the great die-offs are indeed caused by catastrophes. Those who deny catastrophism nonetheless attribute the great die-offs to global catastrophes, even as they refute catastrophism. Though they speak of a gradualism, they can show no such evidence for it, for the making and seasoning of an earth does not proceed that way, as the record of your earth bears witness to you. See it, and believe what you see, for it speaks truth to you. Well the children now accept the great catastrophes. Know that the moments of catastrophes are well anticipated, and are well used.

Now, you have seen that these catastrophic die-offs you have observed are always followed by what some children have now wisely noticed and called 'punctuations' of new species. They have proposed this for so they observe.

As you have seen a fossil record that has virtually no intermediates in what some children have formed as ancestral lineages, see the sudden appearances of new species, the major 'punctuations' with many new species, and see that none of the archetypal species you are shown in charts visibly finds direct descendency in transmission from ancestry. See that you therefore observe much more than natural selection. You observe introduction.

'Punctuated equilibrium' of the biosphere is a true observation. The engineered Design of the DNA Strand preserves stasis continuity, as you have seen, and see it does it well. The myth in current explanation of the 'punctuated' new appearances is intricately contrived as it is given. The children know: successive 'positive mutations' of the repeated kind needed in very rapid succession to effect and produce the astonishing 'punctuations' observed in sudden leaps - producing sudden new species with scale formation, dramatically increased in size, substantially altered proportions, complete new forms, with diverse tooth structures, epidermal formations, feather formation, hair formation, and a host of other dramatic changes which cover huge segments of the DNA encoded strand, which simultaneously require myriad complex coordinated harmonic alterations of design at sporadic points along the DNA strand, at every point required for synchronization of whole complexes of systems - is neither how life is proportioned to earths, nor how new species are introduced as conditions allow for increase. The record bears witness.

The world wide web of interrelated species and ecosystem balance is preserved by encoded stasis and successively replaced by Design, on all earths. It is retuned as first required levels of organic matter obtain and allow for organism increase; and then as surface conditions are groomed and cultivated and seasoned to the point of accommodating organism increase; and as anticipated atmospheric and climactic swings require; and further as eventually required planetary adjustments are effected to orbital radius, axial inclination and rotational speed are refined.

At each step, as soon as the grooming, cultivating and seasoning preparation has reached an accommodating phase, there are life forms designed and awaiting their opportunity. They too, rejoice. They too, cry for joy. They, too, are mine.

The dawning of what you call the first Cambrian day was such an outcry of joy, and the new life I placed here burst forth to fill its measure.

The 'punctuation' times and needs are always anticipated, engineered, and consciously designed introductions. The evidence of this is clear, startling, and abundant, yet it is elaborately handled and interpreted otherwise to fit an orthodoxy. The handling of evidence to fit an orthodoxy is not new. Watching it cover its error in ever more contrived explanations will soon become as boring as was watching the clericals who feared the coming of Copernicus, and feared the coming of Bruno and burned him, and feared the coming of Galileo and imprisoned him, and feared the coming of Kepler and Huygens and all who might come and see what is to be seen. Yet still they came, and more, and they saw, and they were not afraid to see. Still they keep coming. After two hundred years of resistance, the black hole is comprehended and accepted. The Kuiper belt is now seen at fourteen billions of miles distance from the sun by the orbit of a very large ice planetesimal, opening the glimpse to many thousands more, performing their service of gravitationally agitating many orbits of small objects to provide a constant supply to the Life World

552

in this solar system. And with each child who fears not to see what is to be seen, the admission is finally conceded: first heliocentricity and then extremity within a common type of galaxy and then a galaxy amid many galaxies in a small portion of an expanding universe with black holes with event horizons and a cosmos evenly dispersed in a precise rate of expansion, wherein myriad suns and countless earths are forming and existing and coming to ends in ever continuing generations, all undeniable.

The mythology of descendency as currently fabricated is built upon less evidence than the story of the Exodus of the Children of Israel from Egypt through the parting of the Red Sea. Yet as it is a myth structured from real and observable bones and imprints, palpable to your fingers, many believe the tale as it is told, even knowing its emptiness which has no intermediates between monumental differences, from cell to cell, from shell to shell, from stem to stem, from bone to bone: no transitional bones from one complex form to its supposed descendent. They wish no other explanation of what they see: the charts so beautifully illustrate the small mammalian ancestor of the bat and the whale, and so confidently draw the arrows to become bat and whale in but ten million years. It is so neat; so clean. Yet the children will search in vain for the chronospecies grading one into the other, to make the mighty whale and the delicate bat from the supposed common ancestor, for it was not so. While the myth of descendency is false and the Exodus of the Children of Israel from Egypt is true, whimsically, those who condemn the latter as incredible often believe the former myth, which is more incredible, and preposterous to every child who sees the record in your rocks.

I love all of my creations, and love all of my creatures. Those who love them do well. Yet many who love are overly tempted by the structuring of the true, palpable fossil records into this mythical tale because it overthrows the false and misleading theological traditions which they see are false, and need overthrowing, for they are false. Thus they contrive, and champion the myth.

In this, they trade one misinterpretation for another.

However, all things shall be known in time.

The 'punctuation' process is not driven by random cosmic collisions of subatomic particles mutating a point along the DNA strand. The very thought of natural selection being driven by random cosmic particle collisions hitting just the right points of even a three-billion code strand should have already caused its sheepish grins and been discreetly shuffled under the carpet, but children who want to believe in something are often obtusely blinded by their wish to believe. This is true in mistaken religious beliefs; it is true in belief in sciences.

Mules of all kinds are sterile, for if it were not so, the whole of creation would quickly become genetically altered to the point of destroying the entire wisdom and balance of the ecosystems designed and provided for life as it has been carefully engineered and designed for each type of region, each type of climate, each type of terrain, and each type of environment, over each successive age of preparation, as is required for children to inhabit all earths.

In bioengineering, will we learn how to circumvent this, and produce new species of complex life forms that can reproduce?

You will have many failures as you try to unlock the codes and manipulate them. For every significant change, thousands of subtle but required changes must be effected along the strand to meet the demands of the change. There is an organic wholeness; most codes do not not have sliding functions to proportionately restructure the organism overall to fit a substantial change. The re-encoding process to design an up-sized, more complex, differently functioning organism is staggering. As you engineer, significant and precise calculations and manipulations must be made, or uniquely formed but grossly unhealthy organisms are created, if they survive at all. Many sorry creatures will be sustained by life support and cherished because they are your laboratory 'children,' though they may be much lower life forms than your children.

Yet bioengineering is far removed from simple DNA meiosis and mitosis in sperm and egg fertilization processes, where strong biological systems are designed and at work to prohibit joining of irregular unities for replication when identified as foreign. You have seen that the DNA strand is so designed and engineered for each kind that it only seeks and chooses its own kind in mating. You do not see earthworms attempting to mate with sleeping beetles, and snails attempting to mate with earthworms, nor do you see mockingbirds attempting to mate with robins, nor foxes trying to mate with raccoons. Cats may mate with varieties of cats, and dogs with varieties of dogs, and zebras with horses and donkeys, and donkeys with horses, and mixed offspring can be formed; yet there are powerful inhibitors resisting most species intermixings, on levels you know, and levels you have observed without consciously attributing to DNA.

The children of the imagined story speak passionately about natural urge to procreate, and the species genetically improving itself to assure continuation of the species - a conscious comprehension projected upon a system defiantly claimed as unconscious, supposedly random from the beginning. Without conscious design of ROM instruction on the Strand, what has ever instilled in an organism a thought of species, or urge to join in mating and exchange genetic matter? Attraction for mating between lower intelligence organisms is programmed and DNA bioengineered in ROM; it is very consciously engineered; it is very exacting; it is very genetic. It is entirely Designed.

Whether or not laboratory bioengineered life forms will find each other and feel each other, recognize each other and see each other and experience any desire to mate, or know how to mate with each other, or be fertile, will depend upon the eventual attention to all systems required to allow complete recognition and receptive bonding of cell material as like rather than foreign.

I know we already have very sophisticated technology to work with DNA, but not nearly discriminating enough to completely remodel a new higher organism like a completely new mammal, by conscious engineering design. We design exotic life forms all the time for the movies, and with new computer animation software, we can make some fairly awesome creatures. But they are only two-dimensional, non-living, and have no need of coordinated biosystems as real organisms need to live and thrive. To do this, we will need to have highly sophisticated abilities to visually design form, and then design and sequence DNA structure codes accordingly. We have cloned mammals, as you know, but we have not redesigned new mammalian life forms. Will we be able to develop DNA sensing machines delicate enough to accomplish these discriminatory tasks?

You have models right under your nose in biological form, yet you will have to first comprehend them, and then envision how to harness them to digital readout displays.

I don't understand. What do you mean?

Dogs track by smelling DNA. You do not know this or believe this, but the olfactory capacity of the hound is fashioned with this capability. It smells DNA.

Your own nose is ten thousand times as sensitive as any of your other senses, and yet it is next to useless compared to the olfactory of many animals. You have already reproduced technologically the olfactory capabilities of the shark smelling blood at one particle in billions, in your smoke detectors and other more sensitive particle discriminators. But as many animals are capable of remarkable smell, certain dogs have been given the unparalleled ability to distinguish one human in a hundred, and one human in a thousand, and one human in a million, and one human in an entire earth.

They distinguish one human scent from all others, by discriminating DNA.

Dogs smell DNA?

Most certainly. That is how they distinguish one person from another.

Not only are they capable of discriminating individual DNA by total sequence content, but they are capable of discerning mutated DNA in cells. Once they have sampled the scent of a mutated cancer cell type, they are able to discriminate it from healthy cells without the cancer mutation.

This is done at the DNA level, discriminating the entire sequence.

They smell the difference of one DNA from another, exactly.

Know this, and you will know that such distinction between one DNA and another is within your grasp in so simple a manner. You will build such detectors. You will learn this of DNA, and of dogs tracking scent, that it is the actual DNA they have discriminated, the entire strand, in sequence. One bit different in a sequence, out of order in a sequence, they detect as difference.

At the university I walk past biology classes and physiology classes, and see students with the new books. I sit and talk with the professors sometimes at lunch. What we are learning about the complexity of our bodies, of the Design, is unimaginable to me. It seems the more we learn, the more we discover that we are complex beyond all imagining. What can I understand of our composition? Just how complex are we, to be as we are for our Intelligence?

Organic life in its simplest forms is immensely complex. Yet in order to achieve the dream of mobility, articulation, and intellectual capacity desired for Intelligences to drive as an organism vehicle, a Tabernacle equal to the capacities of Spirit, a body equal to the capacities and imaginings of Intelligence, a great Design was required. This physics is highly flexible and lends itself to handling; it lends itself to atomic and molecular and chemical bonding and processing. Yet as the ideal functions were catalogued and discerned in possibility, and the potentials of this matter were reviewed and discerned for application to those ends, many problems were encountered.

The ultimate organization of the Design of the body was the Great Algorithm of design: to make the perfect Tabernacle, meet for the needs imaginable and desired by all Intelligences. It had to provide all which this physics of matter, the best obtainable, could provide, and survive in the expanding expanse of cold space as would result from a precise beginning. Vast problems became perceptible as barriers to a multitude of identifiable potentials, each requiring its own individual response and solution in remedy. For every potential advantage perceived, myriad remedies had to be perceived, structured, and effected. Many barriers were insurmountable: Intelligence can imagine more than can be. Yet Intelligence can explore the furthest extensions of possibility, and wherein remedy can be envisioned, it can be organized and applied.

To have the elements for this body, a cosmos had to be engineered to produce them. To have the conditions required for optimum chemistry and chemical state, precise environment of gravity, atmospheric pressure and temperature had to be provided. Precise availability of elements and their compounds had to be provided. Precise accumulations of organic matter and homeostatic living ecosystems had to be provided.

For these to exist - skenas with exacting conditions over time - a cosmos had to be engineered to preserve and maintain them.

Therefore a cosmos which would produce as well as preserve and maintain had to be engineered. The process which would create the materials required would also have to provide environments in which those materials could be joined and organized in a perfect equilibrium of gravity, pressure and temperature for such an ultimate Design to actually exist. It could not exist in just any conditions, just any temperature, just any pressure, just any energy supply, just any gravity, just any elementary and compound molecular mix.

It had to have an environment as exacting as its own exacting systemic design, in order to environmentally overcome all of the obstacles prohibiting its realization and optimal function as an envisioned organism made of this matter.

A way to achieve this end of Ideal Body and Environment was perceived, and organized accordingly.

The perceived environmental Design I have shown you, and you see it.

The body you also see: let me now show it to you.

First, life's building blocks. They are complex, yet quite simple.

Amino acids, made of carbon, hydrogen, oxygen, nitrogen, and frequently sulfur, are a beginning. The possibilities of their form are myriad; yet only about twenty serve ideally. With these, your life is built.

Life is made of proteins, which are highly manipulable polymer molecules capable of vast complexity, which serve for all manner of cell components and animal tissues. All of your muscles are designed of protein: it contracts upon electrical stimulation, and is the perfect cellular matrix for animation and mobility. By your thoughts, you command and send electro impulses to do whatever you imagine to do; the protein responds and contracts and you hold your food, embrace your love, cradle your baby. A very useful protein is collagen, from which you usefully make hair, nails, teeth, skin and blood vessels. Fully 25% of the dry weight of your Design is collagen protein. You seldom think of your skin as an organ, yet it is the body's largest organ, as much as twenty square feet of protective envelope, weighing up to six pounds. By this organ your life's water is held within; foreign matter and micro organisms are kept out; you receive touch to distinguish that which you should bring closer from that which is harmful and must be kept away. It holds in and contains the pressure of your life, and bears the weight of the assisting pressure of the atmosphere holding you in yourself. If skin were thinner or weaker, a much greater atmospheric pressure would be required to contain you within yourself.

Another building block is the nucleic acid family, groups of protein-combined polymers; these form the genetic blocks of life.

Then there are the carbohydrates, mostly saccharides, which are essentially organized of carbon, hydrogen and oxygen. As already shown you, these include lactose, glucose, fructose, sucrose and a variety of other oses, the energy engines. With these, life in the cosmos is driven. Glucose is organized into amylose which is organized into vegetable starch, a major storage device. Glucose monomers also are organized into cellulose, indigestible, but the essential skeletal structure of plants and trees. All of these serve you well.

Carbon, hydrogen and oxygen are also organized as lipids, the fats, glycerols, phospholipids, waxes, steroids and fatty acids, wherein additional energy is stored, and much good is systemically accomplished. Cell membranes, a most basic component of all life organization, are largely organized of phospholipids; these protect the cell content components and fluids, and allow two-way passage of food supplies in and waste disposal out. This structure alone is a triumph of utility. Waxes coat the surfaces of leaves, helping them to endure the direct assault of the sun; they also keep the feathers of birds waterproof. For these only they would be essential; they serve myriad other uses. You brain of flesh is over 85% fat. See what a central use it has.

With all of these: amino acids, proteins, nucleic acids, carbohydrates and lipids, your Design is made. Other elements and compounds are needed as well, and even that which is needed in infinitesimal quantities serves, and must be, or you will not. You must have iron, iodine, calcium, manganese, copper, zinc, flourine, chromium, also magnesium, potassium, phosphorous, sulfates, sodium chloride and other sodiums and chlorides, silica, selenium, molybdenum, titanium, and nickel, as well as a host of compounds you have named vitamins, as they give vita, life. All of this was contemplated, perceived, and provisioned.

You are a wondrous harmony of Design.

The necessities of engineering in a body that can deliver the maximum diversity of expression requires nine systems: skeletal, muscular, nervous, circulatory, respiratory, digestive, hormonal, immune, and reproductive. Not one is independent of the other; all are intricately interrelated by hormones, respiration, neuro-impulses, and food fuels.

Any one of these systems still defies your current comprehension.

Of all of your myriad and diverse tissues, your total form and the form of and placement of every organ and part of your body, and of every cell of every kind of tissue, every subsystem and sub-subsystem of your being, you are contained in just 23 pairs of chromosomes.

Yet within these 100,000 genes organize and form your human body.

And in these are over six billion codings in sequence, your DNA Design.

It is not by chance that you are a complexity of tens of thousands of diverse functions and intricately interrelated parts and systems and specialized tissues and glands and organs and hormones and processes and brain, that all work.

You are no accident.

You are made of up to 100 trillion cells all precisely organized and functioning within your human body. It grows into its complexity as programmed in Body ROM; though you know little of how to run it, it knows what to do.

A quarter of your cells, 25 trillion, are blood cells. Your 25 trillion blood cells live only 120 days, and are therefore constantly being replaced. Blood was perceived to be a cell of such intense use that it chemically wears out; it is therefore programmed to be replaced before it fails.

This is only one of thousands of processes programmed in Body ROM.

You have upwards of 280 million molecules of hemoglobin in each one of your 25 trillion blood cells. Your body knows how to make them for you, and how to get them where they are needed; they know what to do.

In each tissue cell of your body is DNA, with 10 billion nucleotides in the DNA. Each one of these 10 billion nucleotides does something, something wonderful. It is done by the simple change of one amino acid in the protein coded by that nucleotide. 10 billion instructions, given and followed, one at a time. And they all know what to do, as designed in Body ROM.

Each second there are about 6 trillion reactions taking place within each cell of your body. Don't worry. Your cells know what to do. They follow Design.

Your body is equipped in defenses with 10 trillion B-cells to make antibodies to fight foreign invasions. By Body ROM, you are capable of producing 100 million distinct antibodies. Most of these you never use, but they are there.

You produce almost a hundred hormones in your body; you may expect more to be found than are currently isolated and identified.

Your brain is designed with 100 billion neurons, and there are 100 trillion connections between neurons in the cerebral cortex, the Prime Brain. By the assistance of your Intelligence and Spirit, you can access thoughts of sight, sound, touch, taste, emotion and thoughts in microseconds, and relive them, as if they were real again. Each thought is made of hundreds of electrochemical impulses; you have tens of thousands of thoughts each day. The memory data in some children's brains eventually equals twenty million books, as big as the biggest libraries, succinctly organized in the small space within your head.

Yet it is your DNA instructions, the engineered and designed Body ROM which run your body, and remembers how to digest food, make blood, heal wounds, distribute appropriate hormones in appropriate quantities at appropriate times, which completes you. All of this is the Design.

Within all of this complexity of design, which as you know, already fills many heavy and technical books, there is a homeostasis. As the cosmos required a homeostasis, and galaxies require a homeostasis, and solar systems require a homeostasis, and earths require a homeostasis, and ecological systems within a biosphere require a homeostasis, so each organism requires a homeostasis.

This is the engineered and designed regulating process that induces an organism to maintain a stable internal environment: temperature, liquid pressures, chemical balances, secretions, and so on.

Many children like to say that you don't really know much about how it works.

This is true: you still do not comprehend very much about the Design, and how it works, especially the intricacies of an engineered Design for homeostasis. Yet if you will be bioengineers, you will have to come to grips with this reality of need, and comprehend, and master.

Many children also like to say that you don't really know much about how you got it, how anything got it, this intricate homeostasis.

From what you see now, do you think this is true?

No. Some of us are just very stubborn.

You build energene together with energene and you behold a hydrogen atom. Yet it is not the nature of hydrogen atoms to become what you are. This is not what hydrogen atoms can become in time, on their own.

Designs must be engineered in a process that will make hydrogen, and provide a space and an environment wherein you may take the hydrogen atom and increase it through its stable atomic structures. Then you have elements of immense utility and application, almost a hundred of them to work with. From these you build atoms together with atoms to design molecules, compounds, complex molecular solids, complex compound molecular solubles and advanced organic molecular structures, millions and millions of them, and trillions of trillions of each, all from the less than one hundred building blocks.

While much of this bonding and mixing obtains naturally once the overall system is initiated and matures, even the overall system must be vigilantly watched, to see that it remains balanced. When wisdom points to good cause, additional gathering and organization may become beneficial in myriad ways.

Yet the organization of these into cells and multi-cellular organisms is very complex; a whole new set of rules applies. You have yet to discover these rules, though you are well on your way. Without design engineering, these rules do not result in practical applications or life forms. The tendency is to greater disorder, as you have already discovered. It is only overcome by conscious force. Vast legions of monkeys will never tap out a single line of one sonnet of Shakespeare, regardless of what mathematical theories think they can claim. Much useless acrobatics and vanity is performed with statistics. Though mathematics is a most useful language, beware of those who would attempt to persuade you to believe, using monkeys at typewriters as their validation.

Behold these truths, which you can know:

First: Death and Life Span are a constant time-frame in species. It is programmed into each organism's DNA. It is part of dividing cells: they divide as they are programmed, and the two are not the one. It is part of the DNA Body ROM of all organisms that die. It is unaltered by natural selection.

If this were not so, you would see thousands of life forms living as long as bristlecone pines and sequoia redwood trees. The seas, and the air, and the lands would be filled with species which did not die until after vast spans of time, even thousands of years. Yet you see that this is not so.

Why has the natural selection process not bred in a prolonged childbearing age for females? Would this not be a natural thing, that the longer child-bearing continued for a female, the more children she would bear to carry the "longer child-bearing gene," which would eventually result in more female offspring capable of bearing children into later age, until those in turn would eventually dominate the race until eventually longer and longer childbearing years obtained for the species? Many daughters consciously wish this today.

Yet this has not happened.

If the absolute models of *natural selection* and *species selection* as offered were true: that the species which live the longest before extinction and speciate most - that is, produce the most offspring - determine the direction of the trend, then the trend toward Methuselahian longevity would long ago have touched the clams, and the fishes, and the sea urchins, and the ants, and the dragonflies, and the turtles, and the rats, and the bats, and the cockroaches, and the sharks, and many, many more species you know only too well. The organism which lived a little longer because its DNA allowed it to do so, thereby reproducing a little bit more, because it lived longer to do so, would quickly in each generation produce offspring which collectively would begin to live longer, and longer. This is mathematically demonstrable, by those who know numbers.

Yet it does not occur.

The longer-living organism which retained fertility the longest into its old age, thus reproducing itself more abundantly, would also have to become predominant by sheer capability to reproduce itself and pass on those genes more abundantly to more offspring who would live longer, remain fertile longer, and have more young to carry on that trait.

This is the ultimate adaptation, for any species, to live longer and longer, reproducing more offspring capable of living longer and longer, which have the better "longevity gene." For surely the organisms having a later onset of aging would survive to reproduce for more years, and have more offspring who would carry that "longevity gene."

Yet the rat still ages a full life in a few years, in spite of its endurance upon the earth, and despite its fecundity; and the bat still ages and falls from the air in its flight or falls from the cave wall to die, in spite of its enduring presence; the fish still live their short lives, and the cockroach its few seasons.

The life forms which live and mature and breed and die in short seasons, such as the ubiquitous servant, the fly, and so many other short-lived species in all of the kingdoms and phylii, would long ago have broken free of their bonds of brevity, and flourished into creatures of virtually interminable age.

Yet it is not so.

It is not so because it is rigidly Designed to not be so.

As are most portions of the DNA strand, rigidly designed and locked.

Even you, in your computers, when you have perfected a program and do not want it in any way tampered with, lock your designs against alteration.

All children know: aging and death and cessation of childbearing have remained virtual constants over time. Many children have noticed this, and pondered it. Yet rather than see its crying message, in shame they contrive webs to save the story, as: average life spans of most species are predetermined, yes, but only so that the young can introduce new combinations of traits, thereby strengthening the gene pool.

Would not extended longevity still produce as many fertile young?

Would they not begin immediately upon maturity to mix the same way?

Would not the ultimate result still provide the same suggested diversity of young, and strengthening of the gene pool, in a faster growing, exponentially expanding population with more and more older members?

And what fruit fly contemplates its gene pool?

A most remarkable conscious contemplation of a situation, supposedly conducted in total absence of thought, without consciousness, concluded mindlessly on a sub-cellular level as advantageous, and in the darkness of mere chemistry, by mindless stimulus, chemically encoded onto the strand. Even as so many complex conceptualizations the children in great capability cannot yet even understand, yet nonetheless blithely accept as having been mindlessly encoded, perfected, and in the darkness of nonexistent mentality, perfectly placed onto the strand that all might be so, all by brilliant chance.

Thus Death defies all natural selective process, even its strongest open potential: longevity. As if the organism mindlessly perceives without calculated reasoning the gene-pool advantage which early aging and early death offers, and without conscious intervention, opts the complex process of programming aging and death into the DNA sequence as ROM instruction, all by pure chance.

By pure chance, in every species. Universally. A coincidental occurrence.

While you are told that species are mindlessly encoded to procreate and to fight to survive both individually and as a genetic line, you are also told that all species mindlessly encode DNA to age and die, in the unconscious desire to improve their species' gene pool. This is a lot of specific, unconscious activity.

Beware of statisticians with monkeys at typewriters.

Know: this does not happen by chance, nor by accident. This does not happen by selective process. Selective process is indeed driven by survival and reproduction, within its moderate limitations. Longevity should thereby be driven by survival and reproductive proliferation toward a gene allowing delayed onset of aging and death. If left up to selection, most species should now live thousands of years, by this reproductive oriented mechanism. The left wall exists; the right tail is wide open; the inevitable should obtain; it does not.

Death has a purpose, and it is conscious. It is great wisdom.

Its purpose far transcends any purpose required in the gene pool.

It is part of Body ROM, and the children know this. They know frantically.

Thus even now, they hunt to discover its place on the sequence, to alter it to buy more years, to delay aging, to postpone their appointment with death.

They must approach this by re-engineering in a conscious engineering process that which is encoded by a conscious engineering process.

They must pursue a code which by all other admissions they deny, for it bespeaks the Design, and conscious Design, set by Intelligence, set so powerfully that in all of the ages, with all of the proliferation of reproduction and opportunity for selection, with a right tail inviting and tantalizing and entirely open for pursuit, no species has ever been able to break this code.

Hear this code, for it speaks to you.

Receive its message.

You are not an accident.

You are Designed.

You are Intelligence.

You are the wanted Children of loving Parentage.

What is the second Truth?

The Second great Truth you can know is this:

As the children perceive 'punctuated equilibrium,' wherein they truly and accurately observe long periods of time with no change in species form, die offs, and then sudden introductions; and after great die offs, sudden proliferations of whole new ecosystem species introductions with great changes in form, they observe things which may speak to them.

Within this they may look and see the recent and sudden spectacular introduction of you, the Children, your inexplicably dramatic brain.

Your astonishing, sudden appearance of enormous brain size is a biological anomoly, unprecedented, unduplicated in any previous time.

Why is it suddenly here?

Why do you need this remarkable brain?

Especially, when you note that still, even today, with all of your technologies to drive you today, you use but 4% of this huge capacity.

In what and for what did these first, early Children need such a brain? They came living in the pristine beauty of the earth's natural wonders, among only the trees and rocks and animals and plains and rivers and sky.

Today you drive speeding automobiles, play video games, run animation computers, work mathematical calculations with more zeros than a bowl of Cheerios, fly jets beyond the speed of sound, go to the moon, send probes to Mars, balance checkbooks, even program your VCRs, and still you use less than 5% of this brain's processing capacity. Yet you have had this wondrous brain ever since the Introduction of the Children, from primordial time.

Why?

If indeed the design is mindless, and all is by chance, driven by reproductive selectivity pulling away from the wall of death and toward that which will promote survival, what in nature would suddenly encode in a species the crippling of its infant young? Why would mindless selectivity make them helpless and incapable for years? In this helplessness many, many infant young will die in unsuccessful flight from predators, inability to find their own food amid unreliable providers and lean environments, and from a host of other vulnerabilities all naturally existing and truly threatening to the helpless young and the adults which must carry them.

Why?

Where is the survival reductionism of this advantage, when even now, amid a cyber-intensity of intellectual demand saturation of true cerebral intimidation, you still use less than 5% of this brain? Why cripple a species, for nothing?

If it is not used, why did a natural selection get so carried away?

Unless you are not an accident of chance, not random natural selection.

Unless you are Introduction, and Design, with a purpose for all you are.

You see again and again: physical, cerebral and instinctual capacities of virtually all creatures are pushed to the extreme, used at their threshold just to achieve their survival. What they have, they must use fully, or they perish.

You are not so.

The Children are different.

You are the Children of the Great Promise, and you were endowed from the beginning with all that you stand to inherit, if you are faithful and obedient, and endure unto the end. What you have been given is yours, or, it can be.

The time will come when Introduction and Design will become clearly perceived. The sooner it is, the sooner you may begin to use your new tools and vocabulary and languages to explore in greater reward those things you love.

I will leave you with a riddle.

Why is only 4% of the brain used?

What is it that inhibits the use of the rest of it?

What will its eventual full use to you be?

Look to the words of the Prophets, who have spoken to you of taking on incorruption in Resurrection, and realize that these bodies, already given, are yours for eternity; *in their glorified Estate,* you may become co-heirs of all things.

All things.

We are the Children, aren't we?

Yes, You Are. I will ask you, for you to know: Are you my child?

Yes, I am.

Hear the echo of your words, and you will know you are my child.

I am your child. I am.

I stopped and looked at my own words. I AM. I am the child.

We have been given all of this, haven't we? We should know.

The children who have studied this observation on the planet have learned much about the creation, and creating, yet they have as so many children in so many pursuits missed the purpose and the point. They believe this process can only be studied as having been without thought of plan or design, yet only because each time I have revealed these things in the past, vain intellects have distorted the word and imposed their own interpretations of what they in their greater wisdom believe to be true. These things they have taught, even their own thoughts, and called it my word.

In my word as recorded by my Chosen Children, in spite of even its great losses which deplete what was originally given, all science finds harmony. Most children as they have begun to more and more see the wonders of nature and the Cosmos have believed that they must abandon faith and religion, only because what they have been taught as religion is in almost all cases altered, not the true doctrine as originally revealed. They have been instructed in the teachings of men mingled with scripture, and as they have looked upon the work of my hands, they have not found harmony with what they have been taught. Nor could they, as they have been taught, for they were taught falsely.

When the children discover that all they have to abandon are the errant interpretations which have been long fostered upon them as my Word, then they shall cease to imagine they must give up greater truth to know only partial truth. For all science is still but partial truth, as it is infant, and it quibbles in teachings in many areas of unknowns, denying and ignoring all that which it does not yet understand, though monumental evidences continue to heap up before it.

Though Near Death Experience is plentiful enough and known clearly enough to evidence the truth of Spirit, of Spirit Bodies, of Angels, and more, still, what these children cannot measure with their energene-matter tools they choose to declare does not exist. By this error they continue to delete from their hypotheses all those factors which would lead them to greater and fuller knowledge of all things, not just those which they so brilliantly study, and brilliantly discover, but great expansion of learning, which is within their grasp.

Yet they still will not learn some truths even when given to them in fullness, except that they discover them and measure and quantify themselves. How often the children refuse to even look at what they think they already know, even when they do not. How often do the children prefer to contrive ever more elaborate explanations to prop a failing belief, rather than awaken and receive what is real. You know the lessons of history, which has loved an errant Galen more than a revealed human body, which loved and killed for an errant Aristotle and Ptolemy rather than love a true and physically revealed solar system. It profits nothing to reveal the fullness until the children are ready to receive.

Thus what I have given suffices for now.

You previously mentioned that while we are remarkably strong, yet we are still very fragile. Why is this so?

The tolerances of life are very limiting. There is little margin for allowable error or variance in the Design. There are very, very narrow margins within which things as they are, must be. And, so many of these must be within their narrow tolerances that, change just a few, and a system fails. As systems are interdependent, quickly, nothing works. While many injuries may be suffered by the body, once a critical need is deprived, once a critical system fails, the whole organism fails. Yet even in this is a lesson you must learn, if you will be co-heir.

So it is in the Design, genetically. Even slight changes in the DNA Strand result in serious bodily malfunctions, leaving the body's owner disabled.

The Strand actually has built-in allowances in many areas for flexibility and variance: hair color, minor size differences, minor proportional differences, eye color, skin color, blood type, ear lobes, fingernail shape, and so forth. No two fingerprints are the same; no two faces are the same, except by birth as twins. As you can recognize each individual among thousands, even millions, you see there is ample room for flexibility, and individuality. This is by Design.

Yet most of the great length of the Strand is developmental, structural, operational, and functional. These codes are non-negotiable for the most part. Some tolerate no tampering whatsoever, without seriously disabling the owner of the vehicle. Over most of the Strand, alteration of code results in seriously defective body function, and usually, helpless organisms which present great challenges to the spirits who must enter them and receive them in this estate. In lesser species, such disabilities quickly result in the end of life. Among my children, this has in times and places sadly also been so. Yet many born with these challenges to themselves and to others are nurtured, and so these Spirits live with their disabilities, some more consciously than others.

Whether mental or mechanical, chemical or physical, the handicap and disability is usually severely limiting, even from minor variances in codes outside those where such variety is allowed. You are Intelligences, and even slight limitations imposed upon your bodies are quickly severe, as you behold others with a fullness, fully operational and functional, experiencing full range.

Only special Spirits are capable of enduring these challenges and restrictions. They know in advance of their coming into this Estate that they will receive these disabilities, and they humbly accept them, though it is not required. This they nobly do, for great and wise purpose to be achieved.

For you must learn love and compassion, and learn to be giving; these Spirits accept great sacrifice and in so doing allow many to learn, to appreciate more what is given in fullness, and to unselfishly help others with varying degrees of helplessness. This is a parable for the eternities.

As often as possible, these Spirits are given to parents and families capable of loving them and caring for their needs. These parents and siblings learn much, and this learning is already a great reward they often do not understand, for they do not know of things Future, wherein this love and compassion shall be of immense value and worth to many. Yet above this, they who love and care for their Spirit Siblings in disabled Temples will receive crowns, even as they who accept to receive such bodies shall all be rewarded and compensated in the next Estate. How you treat those who bear these differences and limitations is part of your trial, and you will be judged.

The DNA Strand is Designed, and well. As the children begin considerings and tamperings upon the gene strand, they will begin to see the serious consequences which can result. A single unwise addition, deletion, or alteration can severely reduce the freedom to be experienced in a body.

Such a simple aspect as pH, if altered, has devastating effect. Alter the pH code directive and this affects the entire organism, and all of its many, many cherished chemical and tissue functions. There are major sacrifices to pay, losses to the body and the way it functions which will demonstrate the wisdom of its precise pH balance. The body is made almost entirely of such balances. Who is prepared to lose mental faculties, reduce energy harvesting capabilities, reduce cell regenerative growth rates impeding healing of injuries, which will be sustained more frequently due to loss of optimum motor control and eye-body coordinated control in the neuro system? Who is ready to give up this optimum, perfected bodily machine just to prove that it is possible to alter the plan?

I accept what you show me, and I believe what I have seen.

I begin to perceive that in all things there are precarious balances, natural laws which you have observed and followed to their best possible, or only utilization, in order for all of this to be.

I know there is Spirit, that we are Spirit, and thus there are many things I have to see within all that is told to me which so often totally disregards and in fact discounts any possibility of Spirit, and spiritual things, things which I know to exist and to be real. I have experienced them myself, and thus I am my own tool, my own measure, and though I at one time thought I was alone, I have come to learn that I am not alone, and there are vast numbers of us who know empirically by experience what is real, and what is missing from the growing picture of the puzzle being pieced, bit by bit, for us.

We are told all of this is chance; all of this is accidental.

I believe what you have shown me, and I see that everything that is has come to be against all odds, it seems.

At what point of the process did the equilibrium become so intense, and so demanding in the structure of the Design?

How fragile is the balance?

How far from accidentally happening has all of this been?

From the Beginning.
Very fragile.
Very far from possible accidental occurrence.

Can you show me?

Yes, in part.

My beloved child Einstein asked the question: "How much choice did God have in constructing the universe?"

I will answer you: very much, and very little.

Very much because choices were many. The possible systems of physics are several; their yields are many. The varieties of suns, elements and planets even in this physics are many. The varieties and alternatives of life systems bases are many.

Very little because the potentials of most were immediately limiting and mostly disappointing. Very little because the goal was not experimentation and discovery of varieties of possibilities, but the optimum success of an envisioned body of great potential. Very little because anything less than the optimum alternative was unthinkable and unacceptable for the ends of the purpose.

The process was response directed: How best to capture energy, convert and store it, access it into the organism, respire it, and harvest it in a slow burning fire, slow yet still adequate to fuel the organism and sustain its life?

How to maintain the optimum temperature of environment and organism to have full availability of the elements required for optimum operation of the organism? How would that environment have to be, for this to be?

And, what molecules would be best to make the optimum systems base?

How much choice was there?

Very little, and very much.

The elements are almost a hundred.

The compounds are millions upon millions upon millions.

Yet there is no finer life solvent than the single compound you call water.

The organic molecules are tens of billions as even you know, yet only some fifty of them work perfectly to produce the desired end of running the machine of life of the highest capabilities which was envisioned and designed.

Billions and billions of combinations of nucleotides which can synthesize endless proteins, but so many without useful function.

Only a very limited quantity of nucleic acid molecules serve the purpose of organizing and sustaining vehicles of life as complicated, successful and empowering as I could imagine to organize; all requiring exact sequencing and order. Sequencing and order are vital and critical. They give virtually no choice.

Thus there was and is very much choice of many things, but little leeway if the ends of the goal are uncompromising.

The ends of this goal had to be uncompromising.

Optimum Joy was my purpose, my goal. The choice was dictated by the end - the application that would create the finest vehicle, the best body. It was a specific goal - the creation of the most versatile and functional physical body for Intelligences to inhabit in which the potentials of the Intelligences could move at will; manipulate, utilize and master the matter and what could be made with it. The goal was to organize ideal matter in which Intelligence incorporated in a Spirit body could progress yet further, to flourish and blossom in power.

The first Physics had already yielded the Spirit Body, which is a marvel of immense magnitude. Yet it was far from able to realize the potential I could see was possible. The best physics to apply for the Second Estate was the one which organized the use of charge opposition to create repelling atomic matter which acts as a solid, as you have seen and see; it yields the highest number of elements with which to build. These you see and know.

The end result of the algorithm is before you.

There is yet another Physics, of the Resurrection, which harmoniously coexists with and rules over the physics you know thus far. Thus know, there is a Physics of Spirit, a Physics of the Physical you know, and a Physics of the Resurrected and Glorified. Ultimately, it is all one Physics. But, though all are co-existent and based within the chain of nature you observe, they are neither parallel nor linear, but concentric; you do not yet have words nor basis of mental illustration to adequately relate to it all. Each operates within the other, but there are additional laws you have yet to imagine which cannot be expressed in the physics of matter organized in the system you detect and measure with your tools made of this matter. Without the fullness, there is no Grand Unification Theory expressible in mathematics as the children of this generation would like to reduce and express. The children already comprehend that it is not Physics that is imperfect, but their perception and questioning that is imperfect. Faulty perceptions and questions yield imperfect answers. Much time is wasted in pursuit of imagined possibilities, frustrated for lack of the Fullness.

Yet it is a much more fascinating universe than they imagine.

I will show you just how far from accidental all of it is.

As many of the children have noticed to you, the state of precarious existence in the cosmos is like the story of Goldilocks and the Three Bears: it has to be 'just right.' There are relatively few ranges of values for the numbers that will allow the development of any form of intelligent life. This is the astonishing discovery in every field of science: that the margins of tolerance for both function and existence are narrow beyond imagining. The children know: other sets of values will produce universes which could be very beautiful, but will not allow intelligent life to exist. There is virtually no room for error.

Let me show you the Tolerances.

First, the Rate of Expansion of the universe, the perfect 'flatness' of its expansion, must be precisely as it is. If the rate of expansion at the beginning of the universe had been even one part in a hundred thousand million million less in velocity, it would have re-collapsed long ago, long before reaching its present size. It would not be here. You would be here, but only as an Intelligence, still yearning, without Hope, without Joy.

One part in a hundred thousand million million is a very tight fit.

It is not accidental. It had to be calculated exactly, and a means to achieve it had to be perceived. It was. It is non-negotiable.

Second, the Gravitational Content of the universe, needed to balance the Expansion Rate, must be precisely what it is. If the mass had been different, a bit more, the cosmos would have collapsed already. It would not be here, period. Or, if the mass were a bit less, it never would have slowed down enough to allow formation of suns. If it had not been designed to slow precisely to the proper speed of expansion, if only slightly faster, the stars and galaxies would not have been able to clump together. The Design could not have taken place.

Gravity is the sticky problem confronting Grand Unification Theories; even with the most creative mathematical acrobatics, no child has been able to include the force of gravity appropriately in the whole. As Physics is a perfect science, it is the children who still labor in confusion. Gravity, though weak, is a long range force and always attractive, thus with a large number of particles, its force dominates. Gravity determines the continuing unfolding of the universe, and yet what has determined the mass creating this gravity?

My child Einstein believed I do not play dice.

He is right. Gravitational Mass is a non-negotiable factor of initial Design.

Third, the Matter to Antimatter Ratio, the critical imbalance required at the beginning, had to be precisely as it was. The fractional difference between qs and aqs is infinitesimal, greatly below a 1% factor, and it is this fractionally marginal difference which yielded the 'matter' of this universe. For this slight lack of equilibrium, Creation can come into existence. If the number were equal, there would be a vast radiation in the universe, but no solid energene matter as you experience it. There would be no suns, no stars, no galaxies, no planets, no human bodies for Intelligences. The need was calculated and calibrated through the application of plasma heat to assure adequate charge changes yielding the required 'leftovers;' from this Dark Matter yield, charged energenes could be created. It is from the small excess of energenes which obtained that the matter, charged atomic matter as you know the physical, exists. Of this, you are made. It is non-negotiable. The precise need was seen, and by this, both the gravitational mass and matter problems were resolved.

Fourth, the Charge of the Electron, the opposition in the electron cloud that keeps you intact and separates one matter from another, giving all matter the illusionary effect of being solid, must be precisely as it is. If the electric charge of the electron had been only slightly different, suns would have either been unable to burn hydrogen and helium, or else they would not have exploded and expelled their cooked batches of nuclear elements into space for second-generation use, and the eventual creation of planets and organic life would have been impossible. It is non-negotiable.

Fifth, the Proton-Neutron Mass Differential, the very small mass difference between the neutron and the proton, must be precisely as it is. If it were changed by only a factor of 2, the essential and required richness of elements in the universe, and some of those essential to your carbon-based bodies, would be radically different than what has obtained, and the Ideal Design of the vehicle would not have been possible. You would still be Intelligence, without this Tabernacle, without a skena in the vast darkness of space. The mass was perceived to be a critical equation, and as the ultimate need was comprehended, the Design was calibrated accordingly.

Sixth, the Carbon Excitation Energy Level, the energy level of the key excited state of the carbon atom, must be precisely as it is. If it were slightly altered, carbon would not form in star cores. Without Carbon, the base molecules of organic life would not exist in the universe today. Other life forms could be engineered, yes, but their limitations and disadvantages are appalling. You would not consciously accept their confinement after knowing this freedom you now know through the features of this body Design as you enjoy it, based on Carbon. Trust me. The carbon base, exploiting the majority of the physical elements to facilitate and promote all metabolic and neural systems as you use them in your bodies, is best, by far. If the children who design advertising were to try the alternate base form experiences, they would quickly coin the phrase and advise you: 'accept no substitutes.' The need of Carbon was clearly perceived; the exact energy level required in the excited state was calculated, and set. It is non-negotiable.

Seventh, the Balance of Suns, the balance of heat and its outward pressure, must be counterbalanced by gravitational attraction holding it together; this must be precisely as it is. By nature, otherwise, it was seen that the explosive force of the heat would blow a sun away as soon as it ignited. If gravitational accretion was excessive, it would either accrete too much and burn too hot and explode - a failure quickly observed that could fulfill a great primary purpose - or, it would soon become a gravitational singularity, which is a useful body to the system, but does not serve the ultimate purpose required of a Life Sun: energy production, and delivery. Thus the precisely calculated fusion heat design had to be calculated to the precise mass, and means to gather and interrupt gathering of this precise archetypal model had to be devised to form sufficient gravitational attraction for both the sudden collapse and ignition, with enough mass to provide holding force, yet not too much mass which would only yield accelerated fusion-collapse cycles ending in premature explosion.

All that was needed for this to be was perceived, and engineered to so be. It was comprehended that Life Suns of many kinds could exist through such a precarious balance of thrust and pull. Gravitational accretion gathers charged matter; the action of atoms colliding increases heat to fusion; hydrogen burns into helium and this fuel fusion exerts tremendous outward thrust; equilibrium is achieved by gravitational pull; radiating heat and light energy still escape and thereby supply required energy to Life Planets.

The balance has to be precise; the nature of the hydrogen atom had to be precisely calculated. If fusion produced only slightly more thrust, igniting suns would all blow away back into nebulae and return to being expanding clouds of dust; if gravitational attraction were any stronger then the suns would utterly collapse into singularities and no heat would escape nor light would escape; they would all be useless black holes. The accreting charged matter would indeed become a singularity, or black hole, if not for the heat from the fusion, exploding outward, which balances the gravitational attraction. Herein you see the precariousness of the balance. More so, the precise moment of ignition is key to ending the accretion process, which, upon ignition, blows away the still incoming bubble of accreting matter, and blows it back out into the nebula, beginning the life cycle of the sun.

This balance allows suns to maintain a constant radius, and produce the required supply of solar energy over an extended long life. The larger the sun, the hotter it must burn to balance gravitational attraction, and the sooner it goes through its life cycle and dies. The required balance is provisioned precisely as needed, to great advantage in the overall Design. It includes activity you call solar storms, which produce what you call sun spots, which solar storms assist in the maintenance of a stable global temperature; without them global cooling begins and unchecked, can lead into a global ice condition. This precise balance was exceptionally delicate to provision; it is non-negotiable.

In the Design it was foreseen that with this precise balance, over long duration of time, hydrogen fuel stocks would become exhausted; stepped gravitational collapse would occur and new fusion would begin, fusing new atomic elements useful to the ultimate goal and purpose. This stepped process would occur numerous times, until the final product, iron, was produced by endothermic heat. This design resolved many needs, but not all.

Eighth, the Supernova Exclusion Principle, by which vast amounts of charged matter could be gravitationally accreted and continue to accrete without ignition, until giant suns could be formed before ignition, resulting in suns capable of producing supernova explosions. As ideal Life Suns die, and heat no longer provides prop for expansion against the force of gravity pulling them into collapse, it was foreseen that their energenes would repel each other and the repulsion between the electrons would continue to prop the sun, and cause it to expand rather than collapse completely. It would become what you call a white dwarf. Yet these would rarely explode, and thus except for violent collision, their treasure of needed elements would never be released.

Yet it was seen that this exclusion would only prop small suns of the needed archetypal size, only up to 1.5 times the archetypal size. However, this limit was perceived to advantage as it identified the size above which exploding suns might be designed. The principle of supernova formation provides the means of accreting sufficient charged matter to build giant suns, and in them, to cook by fusion the heavier elements, and through the eventual supernova explosion, to release that needed matter into gravitationally accessible space and, in the process, to form still heavier matter, including uranium 238 for the iron core heat source of Life Worlds.

If there were not such violent failures, there could be no success in the Design, and neither skenas nor bodies could be made for Intelligences.

This essential capability resolved final matter needs.

It is non-negotiable.

Ninth, the Water Content factor. Water must be produced, and be available in a successful cosmos; there must be abundant supplies in the form of ice planetesimals, both for supply purposes, and to hydrate rock and compound formation in earths. Water is the optimum solvent for effecting all of the complex systems of an ideal living organism. Though there are other solvents, the Design cannot settle for less function. It is non-negotiable.

There are many, many other Tolerances critical to the success of a universe that is to ultimately provide life bodies such as yours, yet this suffices for you to begin to glimpse the demands of the Design. Universes are not randomly and accidentally successful. They are successful by careful Design, walking a veritable tightrope of Tolerances within which they succeed, and outside of which they utterly fail. The precision is exacting, in the fractional quantities of margin most of the children cannot even comprehend.

Now, the Tolerances for error in designing a successful solar system with an earth as required for life are also very limiting. I have already shown you, but I will summarize these Tolerances again here for you, in continuity:

Tenth, the Solar Energy Capture. It is non-negotiable. The sun of a planet on which life is to be introduced must be of about the archetypal size, even as your sun is. Smaller suns produce inadequate gravity and inadequate energy delivery to be captured to the life planet. Smaller does not work as well.

If your sun delivered only 10% less energy capture to your earth, your earth would be only a frozen ball of ice in space.

Yet likewise, if a sun is too big, there is the problem of excessive solar gravitational attraction, and intensely increased energy output in excessive delivery, also huge luminosity changes, and then short-term expiration. None of these are acceptable for the Purpose. There are indeed many such larger suns; they serve their purpose; they are not used as Life Suns. Yet there must be Life Suns, the right size. They are produced throughout the cosmos in abundance.

Eleventh, the Earth Orbital Radius. As any planet onto which life is to be introduced must be in orbit around a precise Life Sun, it also must be put into the ideal orbital radius distance; this is rather close to the sun. This ideal proximity usually accretes the necessary heavier matter during formation of the solar system, most essentially, the iron and uranium matter required for the core. However, distance from its sun affects an earth's temperature: slightly closer and you get increased temperature resulting in greenhouse effect; a bit closer still and surface heat will skyrocket; excessive monster-size tidal actions obtain, far too severe for tidal life forms and coastal shelf ecologies essential to planetary health, and crustal tides are too severe for proper tectonics. A bit closer and the oceans boil off: the planet goes hot and dry. Yet a slightly more distant a radius is too far removed: the earth captures too little solar energy and again gives you a frozen ball in space. Distance from the sun is non-negotiable.

Twelfth, Earth Size. Earths must be about this same size, for a number of critical reasons. Size directly determines gravity; gravity determines atmospheric pressure and density; gravity directly determines skeletal and muscle needs and thus required fuel intakes for operation; gravity directly affects metabolism, and other things ad infinitum. If earths were to be of greater gravity, the entire world wide web of ecologies and food supplies and food needs of organisms would increase logarithmically. This is non-negotiable.

Thirteenth, the Iron-Nickel-Uranium enriched Planetary Core. This you now understand very well. Too small a core or no core would allow the planet to cool, resulting in a frozen world. Also, without the core, no volcanism; without volcanism to produce atmosphere and water vapor, and bring to the surface needed elements and compounds, and to supplement the supply of atmospheric ash dust required for microdroplet condensation in the rain cycle, an earth could not be successful. The core is precise and non-negotiable.

Fourteenth, the Surface and Air Temperature factor. Earths on which the Children are to live must have the exact same temperature as your earth. This is non-negotiable. A few degrees colder, and ice ages obtain, or worse: the albedo effect, total planetary freeze, and these runaway cold conditions will not sustain life in its fullness. On the other hand, one or two degrees higher, and the greenhouse domino effect obtains. This equilibrium is very precarious, and while this is partially resolved in the orbital radius around the right class of sun, and by the inner nickel-iron-uranium core, other systems must be established, the factors monitored and compensated for in order to obtain and maintain optimum temperature range, making all balanced. It is a very critical, narrow and vulnerable Tolerance range. Too hot creates runaway greenhouse effect: carbon-dioxide levels push the envelope and when they are not adequately fixed in carbonates such as limestone, combined with other effects, greenhouse effect increases; without proper carbon-dioxide control, you accumulate quantities which result in an atmosphere like Venus: toxic, superheated, super dense and weighty, poor protection against x-rays, ultraviolet rays and incoming meteoric matter, which becomes useless. Too cool, and runaway albedo effect freezes the planet. Surface and air temperatures are non-negotiable.

Fifteenth, the Rotational Cycle. Earths on which the Children are to live must have almost exactly the same rate of rotation, producing a measured day.

Your body is successfully organized in hundreds of thousands of systems, most of which function upon the basis of circadian rhythms of 24 hours. This is not accidental; neither is it negotiable. Though at first blush changes in circadian rhythm to a longer or shorter cycle appear trivial and easily adaptable, they are not. The functional organic success of the Design already taps nature to its maximum, and the Children have been provided with the optimum life experience mortal bodies of flesh and blood can endure. Push them beyond this, and no alterations of the DNA program can save the body from burnout and collapse, in the mortal Estate.

This is the optimum circadian cycle for virtually all life forms; it is required to your body. The Design organism tires after 18 hours; photosynthetic processes balance best for animal life in 24 hour cycles of opposites, light and dark; ocean tides, so critical to planetary health, function best for shoreline life in 12 hour cycles; ocean current speeds and patterns, as driven by winds and affected by rotation, function best at this speed yielding optimum Coriolis effects for wind currents and rain cycles; still there is more. There is virtually no room for negotiation of the optimum circadian cycle.

Sixteenth, the Axis Tilt, which must be about the same on all worlds, for seasonal fluctuations are proven in all ways to be highly beneficial over non-seasonal models, for temperature controls, for plant life cycles, for animal life cycles, even for tidal crust stress on equator and poles which do not work as well when the axis is vertical. The Tolerance of Tilt is little.

Seventeenth, Meteoric Matter. A solar system with an earth suitable for preparation must be provided with ample meteoric material. A Life World must have meteoric falls for a number of electrical equalization purposes, both planetary and for nitrogen through lightning enhancement, and also to provide the main driver of the water cycle by the burned ash and dust in the atmosphere. Volcanism and deserts, as well as forest fires and other wind activity help, but without a constant supply of meteoric ash particles, rain cycles will not always yield as they should. In time of volcanic cessation, calm air and total absence of wind-lifted dust storms, during which there are also no forest fires, unless there is an adequate and constant meteoric ash supply motivating condensation, evaporated moisture supplies will accumulate and saturate an atmosphere until the break point of spontaneous condensation occurs, resulting in sudden torrential rainstorms that last weeks until the air is depleted of moisture. Such a deluge would produce catastrophic erosion, and virtually wash the surface of a planet clean. Though volcanism even in a stabilized planet with a thriving Child population generally occurs every few months somewhere on a planet, volcanism and dust storms and forest fires are not reliable enough to gamble the lives of billions of children. There must be meteors to make ash dust for rain. It is a non-negotiable factor in Design.

Eighteenth, the Water Supply. An earth must have 75% water-surface to land-surface, to have adequate water cycles over land and control temperature. This is non-negotiable outside a very narrow margin. Flexibility is allowable on the side of greater water and less land surface only. Less land still works.

Nineteenth, the Land Distribution factor. An earth must have fairly even distributions of major continental land masses for climate moderation and weather cycles, though the number of continents may be greater and the individual masses smaller than obtained on your earth. Some earths have more, smaller continents, yet the distribution must become balanced for numerous reasons, some of which have been shown to you: distribution of semi-permanent air masses; distribution of high pressure and low pressure centers in air masses, all for the homeostasis of life. Balance works best.

Twentieth, the Eukaryotic Principle. A successful earth will always have a firm foundation of single-celled life forms, mostly bacterial, which form the supporting base of all higher life. The service of these life forms is so varied that I could list them for you to read hour after hour, yet simply know that billions of eukaryotes are required to sustain and process the life of even one small organism, such as a fish, and that to support larger species, trillions are required. They supplement planetary oxygen; supplement the planetary heat and assist discernibly in the thermostatic homeostasis of the Life Zone; they bio-degrade all manners of waste on land and in water, returning it to useful compounds and elements; they provide food to larger species which in turn are food to larger species and so on until the food reaches life forms you love, and you. There is no choice in this requirement: life as you see it, as it has been designed, cannot exist in this mortal Estate without a dominant biomass of eukaryotic life forms, the single-celled servants of life.

These should give you a panoramic view of the necessities and challenges which faced the creation of physical bodies for Intelligences in Spirit. There was little choice; there was no dice play. There have been billions and billions of random results within a predictable Design, and in this, their very randomness was predictable, and acceptable.

Not all suns need be Life Suns; not all suns need be Supernova Suns; many suns may become white dwarfs, and red dwarfs and black holes and neutron stars, and many other types of celestial formations. All serve purpose in gravitational mass; their form is usually useful; yet there is ample room and certainly no urgency of space or material, so that serendipitous natural, spontaneous celestial forms are not disallowed or problematic. They are, in fact, welcomed, for they create beauty in the cosmos. In this they serve as do all things, multiple purpose, gravitational equilibrium and beautification of the interstellar cosmoscape.

Not all galaxies and their suns need be formed simultaneously; in fact this would be counterproductive to the needs of the purpose. Numbers of galaxies in communities are not dependent upon any critical criteriae; galaxies may also function quite efficiently in their own local areas. Certain rules of wisdom govern the use of crowded centers of galaxies, and galaxies foreseen to collide; timing of use upon worlds must be coordinated and trajectories comprehended first. Useful worlds developed too far inside galaxies may be judged inconvenient for life use by populations of Children when excessive proximity to stars too brightly illuminates a night sky; on the other hand, if a group of Spirit Intelligences chooses such an environment for its exquisite beauty, and all other long-term factors are equally safe, there is no reason not to prepare, season and populate the world, and allow them to experience their Second Estate in such splendor. Other groups may prefer a calmer, more private night sky. Truly, the diversity of skies and beauties of celestial displays is one of the things which makes visitation to the many worlds an infinite delight.

Not all worlds produced in large scale motions and accretions need be perfect habitations for human life. Once the limited choices of creating the universe had been made so that less limiting life experience could unfold, the choices of where ideal life could be planted were many, indeed more than abundant and sufficient for the needs. There are billions of trillions of suns and trillions of solar systems and hundreds of billions of planets forming due to the homeostasis of the universe as it was carefully and purposefully initiated; thus there is no need for physics-defying dramatic paranormal manifestations to produce a specific inhabitable world in some specific place. There are lots from which to choose. One place is as good as another, and all places are good when they fulfill the demanded needs required to introduce an organic-carbon chemistry process for the introduction of higher life and Intelligences.

The homeostasis of the Design accomplishes most needs within the unfolding universe. Space is abundant and increasing; material is abundant and can be charged as needed to create physical matter with the properties of repulsion so dearly desired and craved by Intelligences from the beginning; galaxies and suns aplenty exist and worlds without end are in constant process of formation and use and re-use. The universe is unfolding as it should.

It is not necessary that I command in all things. The natural unfolding is a thing ordained, and whether it unfolds to the left or to the right or to the north or to the south is utterly less important than the fact that it exists to unfold. Within its unfolding, all things Are.

Again, though you can envision and model alternative factors, alternative universes, alternative world types, alternative life bases, alternative life solvents, alternative life experiences, and construct algorithms evidencing to you that indeed they all may exist, still I suggest to you that the results will not please you for your own inheritance, either over the short or long term, especially already knowing the bodies such as yours exist to be received and owned, wherein you can experience life as you know it, in mortality and eternally. You would not wish to trade what you have been given for any alternative that is designable.

Trust me.

I finished reading these words. A great sleepiness overcame me. I had seen much this night. I typed in return,

I do trust you.
I'm really tired now. I need to sleep. There's a lot here for me to think about. It's time to say goodnight.

Very well. Goodnight. I shall be with you. We'll talk tomorrow. I love you.

I paused and looked at the last words, and after thinking about it a moment, I typed with slow deliberation something I felt within me, so fully, so strongly, so gratifying to say.

I love you, too.

And I closed, and turned off the power.

Chapter 17

Day 36 in the Wilderness: Good and Evil

Again it was afternoon by the time I awoke, and opened my eyes. I walked out of my tent and over to the spring, splashing cool water on my face and drinking fully.

I ate a medley of various foods, as the day was not in rhythm.

As I ate, I thought about the questions I would be asking today. They had been there, scribbled on the sheet of paper, awaiting this day. I had not had courage to ask them first, for in these questions I felt my own anger, and hurt, and bewilderment. I had not been sure I would feel enough courage to ask these questions, but as I had asked the things I had asked, and received freely as I had received, my confidence and trust had grown, and the burning within me to ask these questions had become as a fire within me.

I was not angry at God, for I was not blind. I could look around me and see that what angered me was not his doing. Yet why did he not do something about it, to stop it?

I had known a lot of people who were angry at God. They had always confused me, even though in the depths of my own private miseries, I had gone through worse things than what I was hearing. I had bemoaned my times in my life, over many usual things, but my life had suffered, in no small disasters. Turns in my life had taken from me my most palpable dreams, and cherished possessions, years of hard work, and loved ones. At times, even the feeling that I could go on, even the will to live. Many were the times I had wished I could just die. The pain was too great, and the hope too little. Why couldn't I just sleep, and die?

Yet still I had never felt any anger toward God, for I could always see the source of my misery, and it usually had a face. Whether a face in my face, or an anonymous face of many anonymous faces I would never see which still hurt me, I knew it was people, and not God who hurt me. The good that I had, I saw this had come from God. How could I be angry at him, when he was so often the only one who had given me anything?

Nor had I ever felt the question 'why me?' as some I had known had asked so angrily, 'why me?'

A glance around the world had always given me the answer to that question even before it could ever formulate in my own mind: the world was filled with misery and pain sufficient to overshadow my pains and miseries, and far from being the only one, or one singled out to suffer the greatest miseries, I looked about me, in my own neighborhood, in my own city, in my own state, in my own country, all around the world, and especially looking backwards in time across the span of ages, everywhere I could look I could see misery and pain in abundance, in miserable abundance, and in much greater misery of abundance and magnitude of misery than I or any of those whom I saw complaining had ever, ever suffered.

There was misery enough to find it weeping on my block, and across the world, and across time.

That was the problem.

Too much misery.

The cumulative misery of the ages, which as a historian and archaeologist I knew, fell before my eyes, every time I thought of my own trouble. I had studied, and had all too often touched with my own fingers the misery and pain of others. Pitiful skeletons of dead wasted in battle, of women and children dead before their years, of whole cities broken and collapsed and buried under the thick layer of their own ashes from the brutalities of attack, and all that was left to my imagination was the screams and cries of those whose lives were turned upside down, whose dreams were being crushed and burned before their eyes, whose lives were being extinguished even as they screamed for their children who cried out and fell before them in chaos.

Silenced cries of horror, which echoed in the galleries and catacombs of my mind even though I had never heard them.

Yet perhaps I had heard them.

They lived in my memory.

I had always listened quietly to those who bemoaned their troubles to me, and raised their voices against God and bitterly questioned 'why me?' Silently, in my mind, I looked past them to the endless line of ragged, filthy, starving, bloodied and broken souls who looked back at me in masses behind these people, and as I looked into their eyes, no matter what troubles my friends bemoaned, I saw the stark, staring faces of the masses who had suffered things so abominably worse than the pains of my friends and neighbors, that their words faded away to a distant whisper.

Yet that was the problem.

Though only a whisper by comparison, their miseries and hurt and losses were real.

As were mine.

What matter did it make that too many others had suffered too many things worse, such horribly worse nightmares?

It was all suffering.

It was too much.

My life as a historian, and a human being beset with the destruction of dreams and the shattering of hopes had taught me one thing for sure: I could always empathize with anyone in suffering, for I knew that to that person, the suffering was the worst possible.

Not because it was the worst thing possible.

Because it was happening to them.

I had seen too much, and it had taught me the lesson: whatever you suffer, it is the worst, because you are the one suffering it, living through it. It may be less, even infinitely less than others have suffered, but it is incomparable, even though for most human beings it is always true that they suffer less than the ultimate. Truly only a few have suffered the unthinkable terrors and horrors of whole families lost before their eyes in prolonged pains wracking their trembling bodies, and then died ultimate and hopeless agonies of pain which indeed, has befallen the most unlucky ones, poor souls.

Most of us would never know such horrors and terrified feelings of bursting emotions, of sudden bewilderment, shock, incomprehensibility, disbelief, outrage of injustice, and physical suffering and pain as this world has indeed inflicted on ever too many of those hopefuls who have come here. Most of us who whimper about our petty troubles which seem so monumental have never thought about how bad it really gets, how bad it has gotten.

Yet what each one of us suffers, we suffer, not someone else. And as each greater suffering we bear comes upon us, it is the worst we have ever known, and it is the worst we can ever know.

For we cannot really know the sufferings of others, no matter how much we hear the details of the horribleness, no matter how many gory images we see before our eyes, no matter how clear the sound which may be recorded or imagined in our minds.

There is no comparison, to being there.

It has terrified my mind as I have seen the stark images of human history, to imagine, being there. I have shuddered, and closed the image. I have been too weak to bear even its thought.

Yet the worst each one of us suffers, it is the worst that we can comprehend, for we are suffering it. We are there. We are feeling the pain. We are feeling the anguish and the injustice. We feel the cry.

Yet as we suffer, we can, if we will, look about us and behold sufferings far deeper and more horrible than our own; we can, more soberly, shock to the imagining of what it must be like to go through the greater misery. And while it never makes what we have to go through at the moment any easier, it has a way of putting things into perspective, and if we think about it, we feel a little less sorry for ourselves, and begin to understand the compassion we feel for pain. It becomes less and less important whose pain it is. It is pain.

That is why I have never even thought to ask 'why me?'

Who am I, among a sea of sufferers, in my own country, in countries all over the world, and across all ages of time?

There were horrors aplenty, in every age and time.

We all suffer, and who is exempt, I have wondered?

No one, as best as I could see.

So I never felt to ask 'why me?' as I suffered among suffering.

I was never alone in suffering, even though I suffered alone.

A greater question had come to well up and possess my mind.

Why?

Just, why.

This was the question I would have to ask tonight: Why?

God had said that we are that we might have Joy, and as he had spoken, I knew it was true: most days in most lives were OK. Normal life was the majority experience, over lands, over time. Though wars raged, and blood spilled, and homes were destroyed, and unjustifiable death silenced open mouths, and warm bodies were left to the chill of cold, and crimes of all kinds were committed in the world every minute, leaving their victims in shock and stupor of most intimate violation and loss, most horrible pains and consequences, still I knew: it was a big world. These things were happening, but the actual percentage of people stopped in their daily lives by them was still only a small percentage. To those affected, it was their whole world. But to the rest, life went on.

For most, life goes on.

Yet who is without troubles, and who is without pain?

Though it is not God who does this, but other people - people hurting people - still he saw it. He had told me, he saw it.

Why could he not do anything about it?

Why did there have to be any of it?

Why not make the world so these things could not happen?

Walking to the lab tent, I switched on the power and booted up the computer.

I selected the word processing program, and began to write down the question I would ask this night. It was more than a question, it was a complaint, and it was going to be a bit long. So I sat down to write it, to get it down in words, so I would be ready.

It took me some time.

When I had completed my crying out in words, I saved my feelings and thoughts as I had written them, and turned off the computer.

Stepping out into the sunlight, I squinted up at the sky. It was late in the afternoon, but there was still time to take a walk, get some exercise, and refresh myself with the earth and the wadi. I filled the canteen, put a few things to eat in my knapsack, and headed out and up a tributary branch I had not hiked for a while.

As I walked, looking around me at the beauties of the canyons, I thought and pondered about the things I had written, and the questions I would have to ask this night.

I hiked for a few hours, and as the light began to fade, I went back to the camp. I ate some food, put together a snack, and took it to the lab tent.

I sat down, and took a deep breath. This was not going to be easy. I felt pretty confident by this time; all I had asked had been respected, and answered very directly. Yet in this I felt some hesitation and trepidation, for my feelings could not help but betray dissatisfaction. Had I carefully enough written my words so that I was not directing anger to my God, but truly asking for understanding? Had I been successful in communicating my frustration at what I had seen and knew, in a means which requested knowledge?

I did not want to just vent, though I felt the pressure of venting each and every time I thought of the things I had written.

I wanted to know.

And so, after another deep breath, I turned on the power, booted up, went through the menus and selected Internet and the search engine, and typed in the now powerful address:

WWW. URIM AND THUMMIM .GOD

In the brief whir of electronic circuitry, the page appeared on the screen. I typed somewhat tensely

Hello. Good Evening. I'm here again. How are you?

I am well, thank you. How are you tonight?

I was feeling nervous, but I did as I always did when I felt nervous and apprehensive about how things might be going. I lied.

I'm fine thank you. How was today for you, and for us?

It was a day like most days; very good, in most respects. Did you have enough time to ready yourself for tonight's discussion?

Yes, I did, thank you. I'm feeling nervous. I guess you know.

That's OK. I love you. Your question is welcomed. Please ask it.

It's rather long, and it rambles. I didn't know how to ask it.

That's OK. I know you put a lot of thought into it. You haven't imagined, but I would rather have any question than be forgotten. I would rather deal with frustrated questions and hurt emotions raised up for me to hear than to see children so lost that they cease to raise their voices to me at all, and drift away.

You are right. I had not looked at it that way. I had not looked at it that way at all. Very well. Here goes.

I selected my long, prepared question, and pasted it onto the page:

I am writing this to you this morning, for tonight.
I don't really know how to begin this, so I'm just beginning.
My family has been in every war my country has ever been in. I had two grandfathers who fought in the American Revolution; for this, my daughters can belong to Daughters of the American Revolution. To most people this is a great honor; I sometimes have trouble balancing the honor against the horribleness of death and the blood of the Revolutionary War, for the English, and for us.

My grandfathers lived; how many did they kill? The war was against the English. Our family background included English. And so, without doubt, my family had fought on both sides of the Revolutionary war, my family the Colonists fighting my family cousins sent in red coats to maintain control of the land.

Yet English, Scottish, French, Russian, German - all of which mother countries gave birth to the ancestors of my family - we were all 'us.' What young man, who fell with a bullet or a cannon blast through his flesh and body, didn't suddenly cry out as his whole consciousness faded, NO! I think none of them wanted this death.

Many Indians were also killed in the taking of this land. My family fought against them. Yet on my father's side of the family, a Grandmother of many generations ago was a Cherokee, and so I realized that my family was on both sides of those wars, as well.

My family fought in the French American war with Lafayette, and even received honors from his own hand. We fought in the civil war, on both sides, the North and the South, the Blue and the Grey.

I remember as a child, playing soldier, dressed in the Civil War coats of the Union and the Confederacy that I would take out of the old trunk which was full of Civil War things - coats, hats, swords, powder flasks, belt buckles, a wood flute. These were what was left of my family's fighting in that horrible, gory, blood-glutting war.

We also fought in the Spanish American War, and World War I.

My Grampa fought in World War I in France, and he told me one story of that War many times.

His troop was taking a small village, pushing back the Germans. They were going street by street, house to house, carefully, guns ready, routing out all the remaining enemy. They had shelled the village to push out the Germans; the Germans were shelling the village as they retreated, to kill Americans. It was terrible.

He said there were many dead: many dead Germans, and many dead French civilians, laying in the street. The shooting continued.

My Grampa came upon a street, smoke-filled and shattered, and on the far corner he saw what was left of a church. Whether bombed and gutted by American shells just before entering town, or by the Germans shelling back as they fled, he couldn't tell, just that it was demolished. Frightened and scared, gripping his gun with white knuckles, he continued going door to door. He could hear sporadic gunfire over here, farther away, there. Lots of gunfire. As he came to what was left of the ruins of the church, he carefully crept in.

The roof was blown away, and shattered beams and splintered boards and stone rubble was caved in on toppled rows of pews jumbled in the chaos. He heard something, someone, softly, it sounded like whimpering, near the front. He made his way through the rubble to the front, near the altar, where he heard the crying. Carefully he advanced, until he could see who was crying.

There, pinned under debris, he saw the most beautiful girl he had ever seen, an angel, her beautiful hair covered with dust, the dust on her face muddy with her tears.

She was maybe eighteen or twenty years old, so beautiful, so precious, crying, whimpering, weeping.

Her legs had been blown off, clear off, just below her hips, and she lay pinned and trapped under boards in a pool of her own blood. She whimpered and cried softly, her body quivering in the pain.

My Grampa set down his rifle, and quickly lifted boards and stones off of her, and then, kneeling on the ground in the church, he lifted her up and held her in his arms, quivering and weeping, Her tears dripped onto his jacket, her blood soaked into his pants.

He knelt and held her, weeping and weeping with her, whispering to her and crying and trying to comfort her as she bled and he could do nothing for her.

She died in his arms, and he held her as she died, and he held her for a long time in his arms, dead. He sat rocking her, rocking her shattered, dead body, still so beautiful, and he wept, and wept, and wept.

My grandfather told me that on this day he vowed he would never again believe in God, for what God could let such a thing happen to so beautiful and innocent a creature as this precious girl?

He kept his vow, all of his life.

My father was in World War II, and how many other fathers had been in it? Many of my friend's fathers had been soldiers, too.

Yet I had much more to learn.

When I was in elementary school, I began to notice that many of my friend's parents had a long number tattooed on their forearm, between the elbow and the wrist. Not just the fathers, but the mothers. I didn't understand. My Grampa had a tattoo in the same place on his forearm, but it was an Indian Chief's head, just like on the old pennies. What was a number tattoo for? And why would women get such a strange tattoo? Women didn't get tattoos.

After two years of seeing more and more numbers on parents' arms, I sensed that this was something significant, and ominous. I wanted to ask about it, but I was shy.

One day in the 5th Grade I stopped a girl I knew, a beautiful little girl I trusted enough to ask.

"Why does your mother have a number tattooed on her arm, like Alan's father, and so many of the other kids' parents?" I asked.

She looked at me wide-eyed in astonishment, as if I were stupid, as if everyone knew what this was.

"You mean you don't know?" she asked incredulously.

"No," I replied innocently.

"You don't know about the Germans, and the war, what the Nazis did, and about the concentration camps?" she said aghast.

"I know about the Germans and the war," I replied, "But I don't know about..... what are..... concentration camps."

I suddenly learned about Nazis, and Jews, and Camps, and gas chambers, and crematoriums, and tattooed numbers. We walked slowly down the hall as she told me short, grim facts without details, things too horrible to speak of. Most of the people died, she said. The parents with the numbers on their arms were the ones who didn't die. Her mother was a camp survivor.

Shortly thereafter, Life Magazine had a picture story on the horrors of the camps. Starvation. Hopelessness. Death. All in pictures. Vivid pictures, recording things I could not imagine, for I could never have imagined bodies so emaciated and starved, still standing alive.

How could people do something like this to other humans?

When I was in 7th grade I chose to read the unabridged volume of <u>The Rise and Fall of the Third Reich</u>. I learned all about madness, war, camps, medical experiments, mass exterminations.

Only later I learned the total numbers of dead from that war.

That war initiated by the Germans ravaged and slaughtered Germans, and French, and English, and Scottish, and Russians, and Americans. I was all of these. And many more were killed.

My family of Americans had fought my family the Germans, and my family the Germans had fought my family the French, and my family the

English, and the Scottish, and the Russians.

I also had relatives in the Korean War, and friends who were injured and died in Vietnam. The ones who came back would not talk much about what they had seen. It too, was too horrible.

As I became older I learned about the horrors of so much of the history of human beings on this planet. The slaughter and blood circled the globe, again and again, in individual acts, and mass waste.

I had looked at paintings of pirates when I was a child, and thought pirating was great fun. I and my friends dressed up as pirates, and played pirates. We were glorious pirates. We acted out the imaginings of a child, from stories and movies. Adventure. Riches. Shining weapons in the sun. The Jolly Roger. Ships and blue seas.

But then I grew up, and one day I saw in the swashbuckling images a horror.

Pirates slaughtered innocent people just trying to go from one place to another, only wanting to live out their lives. Like me. What if I had been passenger on a ship besieged by pirates? Pirates slaughtered and looted, destroyed, and real people, men, women, children, died in real agonies of terror and horrible pain.

I acted out the play in my mind, and saw my own death. I was brutally killed as I begged for mercy.

Me.

Suddenly I understood: to be a pirate was to be a cold-blooded, unconscious being, a murderer and plunderer, heartless, pitiless, merciless, sociopathically insane, and brutal beyond words, a being of death. The Jolly Roger was indeed the flagship of death.

Startled, in my shock of awakening, I wondered: who were such men; how did they come to be so violent, merciless and brutal? They had once been babies, with mothers, little children, innocent.

With horror, I suddenly saw in those rugged men many mothers' babies, who had grown up to be bloody cutthroats and pitiless murderers. To be a pirate was to slaughter, ravage, devastate and rob everything, including life.

From whom?

From people like me, who had done nothing wrong or bad, who were just there and wanted to live.

I too was a mother's baby. How would my mother have wept over my bloody, useless death under a pirate's sword? How did the mothers of those who became pirates feel about their sons slaughter of other mother's babies, men and women, innocent children?

As I imagined the blood of weeping mothers and children spilled by other mothers' children who had grown up without conscience, I suddenly saw countless crimes of violence and blood abounding in the violence of its every day, in every culture, amid every people, in every imaginable time.

Mother's babies, killing.

And so it was I saw, with all who became pirates, in all of their guises and costumes and uniforms and titles, mother's babies killing other mother's babies who did not want to die, but to live. Whether pirates or mercenaries or soldiers of fortune or kings, princes, emperors and presidents sent forth in the armies they armed and ordered out to kill and seize, it was all one mentality.

It was all merciless, pitiless piracy.

In this awakening, I wondered: how could mother's babies grow up to murder, and pillage, and rape, and burn, and steal, and bludgeon, and torture, and destroy?

It was horrible.

It was unending.

I could not comprehend the numbers of the hurt and injured over madness, nor the numbers of the dead, wasted over madness.

And then came the day I realized that this all was my family.

My family was there in every war, and every atrocity. We fell in the massacres and purges of Russia's new order, in the genocide of twenty million amid the Caucasus Mountains, and at the guillotine in the French Revolution. We wielded the weapons. We fell in the blood. My family was there when Pizarro slaughtered the Inca and Cortez spilled the blood of the Aztec. We shed the blood. We bled the blood. My family was there every time some mother's son slipped a knife into another mother's son and took his purse, and my family was there every time a gun was fired and someone fell. My family was there at Abydos, and Thermopylae, and Phillipi, and Masada. My family was there every time a stone axe crushed the skull of a man, and his mate and children were taken as slaves.

We had wielded the axes.

We had been taken as slaves.

Those are global atrocities and tragedies. What about my own life?

God, I have had to taste personal atrocities, tragedies and betrayals.

I did everything in my power to prepare for a good marriage, so my family would be whole, my children raised in a happy home, so I could be loved, and could give my love to someone who would receive it, and treasure it, and hold it as precious. In spite of this, the one to whom I gave my heart and soul in love and commitment did not love me, and did not want me, but married me for other reasons, and soon saw in me nothing but worthlessness, and revulsion, and turned on me in resentment, and anger, and hatred. My nightmare was relieved in divorce, yet the tragedy is a play played out still, and it still clings to my children, and to me, and there is bitterness, and silence, and resentment, and pain for which I have no words to pour out my guts with it all, to make it go away, but it will not. No dream I have ever dreamed has been unmarred by pain; most have seen destruction, and as my children have become adults, it doesn't end.

I see countless men and women torn inside, their trusts destroyed, their security ripped from them, their hearts trampled into the dust, their vulnerability assaulted, exploited and betrayed.

Though I have been terribly exploited, unjustly, I see the lot of women in this world over generations and thousands of years across the face of every land in every time, and I see their devastation, their betrayal, their anguish and their pain, and I am staggered.

In my own recent family history I knew many tragic women's stories, just since the Civil War: grandmothers who died in childbirth; grandmother's who watched as the children of their bodies died of fever, or burned by fire; of grandfathers who married four wives because each of the previous women, my grandmothers, died in a childbirth, their struggled lives cut short in the very moment of their dream's beginning. Numerous women in my family have been raped.

And I have women friends who have been molested, raped, later raped again, in another place, by another attacker, yet another man. I know enough to feel ashamed to be a man, to look into a woman's eyes, knowing what I knew, knowing what women know.

What woman of thirty does not know a woman who has been molested or raped, if she has not been herself molested or raped?

I have seen and known of so much starvation and killing and slavery and cruelty and injustice in this world.

I know you have said that over all, the majority of days and lives and experiences are good, and that we learn from what is bad.

Yet so many have been hurt, hurt so badly, hurt so horribly.

Why?

Why must it be so?

Why is it so?

Why are there so many people? And why do most not know why they are here? Why have so few known a Gospel or doctrine or 'way of Christ,' your first and most brilliant son? What is the point?

I know the Parable of the Wheat and the Tares. Why are there so many Tares among the Wheat? Why does it seem there is there so little wheat, and so many tares? Why have so many been born to such violent misery, despair, hopelessness, and such brief, tragic life?

Why?

The innocent must suffer, that the wicked may be judged.

Why can't you stop it?

First, all Children have the gift of Free Agency, and I cannot violate that, for it is my own gift to you. It is precious above almost all things. By it all things are allowed to unfold safely. Without it, great dangers could and would obtain.

Second, All who kept their First Estate earned the right to come here and gain bodies which are theirs forever in the Resurrection. This too, is non-negotiable. Yet not all who were obedient in Spirit can withstand the temptations of this physical matter, which all Intelligences so desperately crave, and within which many lose themselves in frenzy. It is too easy to want everything, yet all things must remain governed by order, even as it was before, when you were with me. By the law of Justice, all Intelligences in Spirit who earned their Second Estate must receive it, even though it was clearly evident as always that many would be unable to control themselves, and would cause much hurt to their innocent brothers and sisters. This was known, from the beginning, by all. There was not one Spirit who did not know it, and accept it. You were among the Host, as were all your brothers and sisters of your world.

The idea to take away Free Agency was proposed in your Generation as an alternate plan, but in this plan there is no Justice, and great danger for all.

Thus all had to be born equally, even those who would do harm.

Yet in this, they provide the needed example and knowledge of Evil.

This learning is essential, even to those who fail. It must be learned.

And therein, many innocent suffer; yet in this, they provide service also.

The innocent must suffer, that the wicked may be judged.

I quickly typed, and typed feverishly, and wrote again:

But it isn't fair. You said that all of us who came here earned the right to come here. For what? To have a sword run through our guts, to have a spear thrust through our chest, to have boiling oil poured on us as we look up a ladder, to fall three stories onto the ground and writhe screaming in the pain of our face and eyes burned out, to lie wracked with the pain for weeks, and live a blind beggar the rest of our life just because some idiot decided to attack somebody else's castle and we were sent up the ladder? For what? To have our legs blown off by a cannonball, or be gutted through with grapeshot, or blown to pieces by a mine, or to lie in a field with an arrow stuck through our chest or guts until we bleed to death? To lie in some dark barn with a hundred other moaning wretches with our arm cut off, or our side cut open and our guts oozing out, to bear the pain until infection sets in and the fever gets bad enough we finally receive the mercy of unconsciousness and finally die? To watch our sons that we felt kick inside our bodies and carried nine months go off to be butchered, to see out children whom we gave life to through our pain and our own blood and fed from our own breasts and fed with our own hands so they could look up at us and smile and play until they became strong boys, only to suddenly go away to kill some other mother's children, and then wait and wait until the news comes: our child is not coming home, he's dead? What for? What right did we earn? To be raped, and made pregnant by violence, to be abandoned as dirty by everybody we thought loved us, and have a child to raise that ever reminds us of the terror, of pain, of fear, of everything we trusted being taken from us, and then being seen as dirty by everybody, yet none of it was our fault? Or to be beaten just because we can be beaten? To be exploited just because we can be exploited? To be enslaved just because we weren't killed? To live a lifetime of slavery just because we were born into an Egyptian slaves' hovel, or a Babylonian slaves' hut, or a Roman slaves' house, or an American slaves' shanty? To slowly starve and watch our whole family become emaciated and die just because some rebels decided to shoot up a country and turn it into a war zone? To freeze to death just because some men in warm comfortable rooms decided to attack our land and city, and our homes are destroyed, our food stores are destroyed, and winter has come down on us like a ton of white death?

You said that our very purpose of Existence is to have Joy. This is Joy? Having Sargon the Great run over our land and slaughter us right and left? Or Pharaoh Thutmosis the Great? Or Alexander the Great? Great at what? Or a Julius Caesar? Or a Caligula?

If Attila the Hun rides into town it can ruin your whole day, you know? Hello Mr. Alaric the Goth! Hello Vandals! Hello Genghis Khan! Hello Robespierre! Hello Napoleon! Hello Lenin! Hello Stalin!

Excuse me Mr. Hitler, I'd really like to go home now and forget all this, may I now, please?

Why has all of this happened?

The innocent must suffer, that the wicked may be judged.

I do not understand. Terrorists put bombs in buses, and on airplanes, and next to buildings with children in day care; criminals gun people down for a few dollars; women are beaten and killed in their own homes; children are raped by their own fathers.

Why don't you do something about it?

I am doing something about it.

The wicked are being stopped, here.

Here, this probation, is where they are stopped.

You see this place as the beginning and the end, as all there is.

There were eons before this, and you were there. Eternity follows.

This is a probationary Estate, as you have always known.

It is brief as possible. For some, it is too short. For some, it is too long.

This probationary place is where they are stopped, and you, the Innocent, are who are stopping them, who will help with mighty Testimony against them for all of their wickedness, and they will be eternally stopped.

The wicked must be judged.

You will be their judges.

For every act of evil they have committed, you will testify before all Angels, just

591

as you will testify of every act of good that you have received.

Those who have been simple and mundane and have lived their lives in simplicity, never thinking they have counted for anything, shall have their good works shouted to the rooftops, for every simple kindness, for every drink of water given, for every shared bite of bread, for every helping hand. You will have forgotten most of what you have done, for you have done it as the only thing you could imagine to do, the right thing, the thing needed at the moment, the small thing which you could do, which you could not refrain from doing it, because this is who you are; you are good. For all of this you all shall stand in witness to each other, and your good works written in the Book of Life shall speak for you, and my Son shall speak for you, for as you have done any of these things to the least of any of the children, you have done it unto Him.

And as you love each other, you love me.

And you shall also stand as witnesses against the evil, and by your witness, and tears, and blood, and agony and anguish crying up to eternity, they shall be stopped, eternally.

All must be judged.

There must be judges.

You are the judges of your Generation.

Why can't you stop it now, here, before they hurt us?
I do not understand.

That is part of why you are here, to come to understand that which you are to be given, and why not all may be given equally.

You are children, and if children, then are you not Heirs? Yet not all heirs may receive equally; yet how shall they be judged? Those who may obtain must exercise and learn. This is not a prize to be won by might; the race is not always won by the swiftest, nor is the battle always won by the strong. Have you not heard that the Meek shall inherit the Earth? If it shall be inherited, then this moment of brief strife is not all, nor but the smallest moment of your Eternal existence. It is but a moment.

You, an Intelligence, are old beyond your imagining. Your birth's rising has been as the stars, which even before they obtain a glory have had as their beginnings darkness and cold and void. Yet they too, became gathered and strengthened, and out of the darkness, they became Light. Yet even in becoming Light, do you think a star, a sun, receives immediately a fullness? Even the mightiest suns do not begin with a fullness, and begin but dimly. As they begin to radiate Light, they grow. Still it takes long, long time for them to mature, and become perfected, and purified, and only after great elapse of time do they shine forth with their most brilliant Light, illuminating all.

The elements of your physical bodies are made within the suns.

Do you think you are so different from the suns?

You are old beyond all imagining, for your Intelligence is old beyond your knowing. Your journey has brought you from afar, and from time long gone; and you are still on your journey, growing, and shining more brightly. And now, even now, as you have finally received your Generation and finally received your Eternal Gift, given to you in the plan and the Good News upon which you have so long rested your Hope, you are now on the verge of receiving that which for all time you have awaited with greatest yearning and longing to receive. You are still learning in this Estate the things that you have needed to yet learn; you are experiencing the wonder and potential of your Gift, this body, and you are becoming the Sons and Daughters of God, able to receive a Fullness.

You who are righteous, you shall obtain.

Yet as the new suns which are greedy, which gather and gather and hoard and hoard to become the biggest and the brightest, many are the children who in their greed and selfishness have taken that which was not apportioned to them; they shall find that for their unlawful stealing unto themselves and robbing from others, of riches, land, reputation, possessions, wealth, power, even every life as they have robbed it, to make themselves to shine more brightly in their own eyes and in the eyes of others, to make themselves be seen to appear brightest in the heavens even at the cost of others whom they harm, I say to you that they have already taken what reward they will have by force.

That which is taken may not be kept; only that which is given may be received and maintained.

And so, they shall find these things they have taken from others have become a burden they cannot bear, and it shall all weight them down, and down, and down, and they shall shrivel, and shrink before me, and before you, their righteous judges, and in the full face of their robberies which they have heaped up upon themselves, still clutched to their wretched souls, they shall be stopped, and even as gravitational singularities, the weight of their own guilt shall collapse and crush in upon them, and implode them in Spirit, until no Light can shine from them at all, and they shall be as black holes, dark and greedy, with no light around them at all, for they can endure no Light.

Yet in this, you excel above the suns, for you are Intelligence, and in your bodies of Spirit and Physis you become Eternal, and have no end. Thus is there a Resurrection of the Just, and of the Unjust, unto condemnation. For you are above the suns; as Children, even those who can abide no Glory, still live on.

They shall be cast out into that place which is prepared for those who have heaped upon themselves such weight as they have stolen and robbed from others. Every small evil has its weight, and condemnation. Earned light is light. Evil is not light. Yet to steal another child's light is to bring upon oneself the burden of the weight of that stolen light. The burden of this stolen light is the Second Death, and though they have received a Body, it will be of no use to them, for they have denied the gift which was given to them, even the Light.

Those who come to see the Light may repent, and finding the weight and burden of their greediness too great to bear, as long as it does not contain the weight of Innocent Blood, or the weight of the Great Denial Of The Light, they may repent, and in sorrow and sincere hearts they may also be judged, and receive the lesser Light they may bear to receive.

Yet if they repent with a fullness, and have learned well, and become that which they were not, having experienced the mighty change of heart which is the purpose of every Intelligence's purpose here, and on all earths, and if they will humble themselves and receive the Atonement which is provided for them, and extended in fullness of Mercy unto all who will but receive it, even they may petition to receive it, and if their desire is true and sincere, they may be raised up from their knees and shout for joy again with the Morning Stars; and if they have proven themselves, and been faithful, and endure unto the end, and still their desire is to serve, to serve as many as they can, then shall they be given the highest power, and the greatest crowns.

For the highest power is the power to serve, and to serve all.

The wicked shall be stopped, and I am stopping them, here, in this place.

You, from the Beginning, have been my Friend, and my Ally in this work and this purpose. All the Innocent who are here have covenanted to be witnesses, and to learn from their sufferings, and to teach those who would listen, who have an ear to hear, that all might be edified by their sufferings.

Know who you are.

Continue to be Valiant.

The wicked are being stopped, here.

You serve all Intelligences and Spirits of your Generation even now, and as you remain steadfast; even so shall you stand as their judges.

The wicked must be judged.

You shall be their judges.

Why were we not told this?

You were told this.

You were told before you came here, and, it was revealed anciently, and written. But it is lost from most records, yet not from all.

The innocent must suffer, that the wicked may be judged. Such are the demands of Justice. Such are the demands of the Gift, Free Agency.

There are billions and billions of Spirits. Among the Intelligences, many are Great and Noble; yet many are unwise. However, for having chosen the side of Right, and been willing to participate - to work and make it all, under faithful direction - all have earned the right to be here, to be born, to live, to gain this kind

594

of body which can be reorganized in Resurrection and made eternal.

Even if they do not have what it takes to be a leader, even a steward, they earned the right, unlike those who rebelled and refused. Even if it is foreseen that they will hurt and harm many around them, they have earned the right, and their wickedness will serve to teach many. Thus they come.

It was known that many would be evil in this Estate. None would believe it could be they. When all were shown the evils that obtain in the Probationary Estate, and were told that many of them would so choose evil, and work much evil, all turned in disbelief. None believed they would fail to be kind, and good, and caring, and compassionate. Many in true horror asked, 'Will it be I, Lord?' 'Is it I?' Though many were told 'Yes, you will become tempted by the power of matter, and your power over life, and in selfishness you will cause much harm to others,' still they did not believe.

Self is the hardest thing to know.

Yet it was wisdom in me that Justice should not be frustrated, and they that would make unwise choices, and work much evil, should be justly given that which they earned, and prove unto themselves what ability they possess to be leaders, and in so doing provide the opposition needed to instruct all in the differences between good and evil. As all things in the Design serve and serve multiple purposes, so these also would serve, and teach.

They teach?

By tasting good, you learn what is good. By suffering injury, you learn what can hurt. By sustaining evil, you may imprint what must not be.

Though you love flying machines and explanations of the origins of apes, rocks and suns, moons, and night skies, though all of these things are worthy, none of them is important unless you learn what you are truly here to learn: the Knowledge of Good and Evil. In all things there must be opposition, and even as it was foreseen that many would choose badly, and bring to pass much hurt among many children in their innocence, yet each Spirit and Intelligence had to prove to herself and himself whether or not they would be obedient unto that which was given them. As they are disobedient, many see, and learn.

Every generation must learn.

In all ages and in all lands, the children receive a law, and it is less important what law they have than it is how they follow it, for in all places, laws of good and mercy have prevailed and been before the children.

And as the children are light, so they are born with the Light, and it shines within them, unless they overshadow it intentionally. It will shine within them, and teach them most basic right from wrong, if they will heed its promptings.

In all lands, among all children, as you have studied you know: the social laws of what is right and what is wrong have been taught, and with great similarity. This is by no coincidence. See it, and believe. From the Light, the children receive guidance, though they are free to choose, and to rebel.

It was known from the beginning that not all would make it. In fact, it was known from the beginning that only few of the many would make it, yet all who were willing and joined with their forces became inheritors of the Promise.

It was known from the beginning that most would only obtain unto a certain level. And that level was attractive, very attractive, to intelligences floating in the dark void of an immense, cold space.

It was known from the beginning that most would only obtain the level of simplest finality and eternity, and that is indeed a billion times better than that which they had, and that which will finally be the lot of those who rebelled and thus will have no place in this creation's final Estate of Glory.

All of this was known, and it was accepted with varying degrees of exuberance; the work was executed with varying degrees of exertion; the battle against the foes of the plan was fought but with varying degrees of valiance. There are varying degrees of Intelligence. There are varying degrees of faith and obedience and conscience.

For this there are varying degrees of Eternal Glories, and it was known from the beginning that only a few would obtain the highest.

All wished to prove that they were worthy of the highest, with many believing they would, when in fact they would not. Not by fault of God, only by reason that they are as they are, and this is what they may be. Many always fall short in this testing time, and as it was known many would fall, even so did many fear their reversal of fortune. In trying to avoid the test, they lost even that which they had been given, even their First Estate, for they were unwilling to both exert and still be tested. Those who agreed and made the covenant did so in faith that they would exert all the effort required, and help in the making of all this that is. This they did with the understanding that they would still be tested and might fail to measure as they willed and imagined. This second estate is a scary probation, and it was known from the beginning that many high ones would fall to the temptations of the flesh, which are many. For this reason many rebelled and were cast out; for this reason those who remained steadfast shall only lose their reward if they become so embittered that they too, rebel and refuse to accept and receive that which is justly to be given them.

As it was also revealed and thus known from the beginning, it was revealed after the rebellion and the great schism divided the heavens, revealed to those who remained steadfast: that indeed, those who should reach the highest Glory would by their having obtained make all so much the better for those who did not, and their reflected Glory would make yet better and more glorious the estate of those who did not, even those who obtained only a lesser Glory. The Glory of all elevates the Glory of all; and thus the Glory of all is appreciated by all; for it benefits all without exception, thus none can say he has no need of any other one, for all need all.

It is for this reason that the loss of even one is tragic, and serious, unto the serious work of helping all who will exercise unto obtaining. For this reason shepherds search after the lost sheep. The loss of each one diminishes the Glory all will have to share, and as more are saved and redeemed, so the Glory of all is enhanced and improved.

Thus all must be proven, and all must have Free Agency; all must be free to choose, and many will choose unwisely, even evil.

By the demands of Justice all receive their reward; by the gift of Mercy, the innocent who suffer shall have their days shortened; by the power of Mercy, the innocent who suffer shall be surrounded and comforted; by the power of Justice, the wicked shall be judged, and the innocent who have suffered shall be compensated, even tenfold, and even a hundredfold.

Yet the wicked must have their day, and prove to themselves, that on that day when they arise to receive, they may know why they may not be given that which others may be given. As you see great power to destroy in the days of these bodies, you cannot imagine the power to destroy which is inherited in the Highest of the Resurrection. Such dominion may be given only to those who have understood good from evil, chosen it, and who desire only good perpetually. Thus the innocent will suffer in this life, that all may see, and thereby learn, until their souls are disgusted with evil, and they come to an understanding of the Light, and desire good eternally.

But so many people die so badly, so horribly.

Do you know how you feel when you see two children fighting between themselves over a toy of little value, which both will turn from shortly as their eyes are filled with yet another wonder? Have you seen them fight for the futility of proving which is strongest? Have you felt its triviality, and meaninglessness?

Yes.

That is how I feel when I see these same things, great and small. If everyone would listen, hear, and know who they are, they would desist.

Yet there are many who will not receive who they are, and in their desire unto themselves as things of little worth, they hurt many.

This is true: there are many, many children who suffer terribly at the hands of the evil. They knew that they would suffer before their coming here, and they were comforted and taught the Truths which comfort, and even as they saw the great purpose which would be brought to pass by their victimization and suffering, they saw that this suffering would not be without purpose. In love of their brothers and sisters, they accepted this burden, and trusting in my Love and the good news of the plan, they did take courage to come, and serve in the way they would become called upon to serve.

And for their hurt, the wicked shall be judged for every evil thing they do unto the least of my children.

Yet provision is made for those who err; there is a Hope of Redemption.

But in all things there is purpose, even in Death. The children have so little understood Death, and its purpose, and value unto them.

What is the purpose and value of death?

Behold a Plan.

The children are naturally greedy. You do not want to share. You do not want to relinquish your turn, or give others a chance to try, or play. You hoard your substance; you jealously fence out others from what you think is yours.

If I did not make allowances for you to age, to become old and die, the first evil ones who usurped power over your fathers and mothers would still be lording over you in their evil. There would be no inheritance for anyone, and all that is would be greedily taken by a few, and nothing would be left to share with the new generations of children to come.

You see the great generation of children born now? Though land and substance is enough to raise ample food for all if you would stop your foolish fighting, and stop wasting yourselves on armies and vices, yet you squander your fruit on feeding upon each other, and upon the vanity of armies and diverse vices.

For this greed, billions starve.

Yet in arrogance you are loathe to own your selfishness, and so you say there is not enough to go around, the world is overpopulated. What huge portion of your gross products is thrown to wanton waste in war and rumors of war? Millions of houses built and billions fed; but no. You still wish to revel in your wars and killing each other. Over what? And what huge waste is robbed from the children in maintaining the festering pens of those who are not penitent? And how much is hoarded by the mongering beasts who make merchandise of you in your vices? How much is wasted on vices without end?

You talk among yourselves of tens of billions wasted on hard drugs and crimes born of hard drugs, yet even of simple alcohol behold vice of greater grief, of greater billions wasted producing and buying a mindless vice, land and means enough to feed many nations each day. Behold again the mindless vice tobacco: how many nations should eat each day with such staggering sums of money so uselessly burned? Land wasted and money burned for lives diminished and suffocated.

And these vices yet rob hundreds of billions of dollars again as the selfish children of their vices become ill, and who, crying pitifully, beg to be saved now from the death of their vices, so greedily indulged as others starved. Now they cry to waste more money to prolong their selfish lives, while yet others starve; and those who see merchandise in their dying steal what is left from their children unto themselves, in their carefully structured masquerade of mercy. The food-chain of greed knows no end, as long as one child sees a way to feed off the other.

The world is not overpopulated.

It is underloved.

If love abounded, for others, and for self, there would be no need for spending your inheritance on such military waste; there would be no wish to squander your substance, destroying your precious bodies in sociopathic vices.

How could new children come into the world and fulfill their purpose, unless the previous generation let go of the world, and the world be given to them, each in their turn?

And yet life is so precious, who would let go, lest the DNA Strand be designed to permit aging, and death?

The will to struggle and live is great; you know, you see; so it is again shown to you that by way of natural selection, for every reason, organisms should already have evolved to hold grip upon life unto very great age; yet they do not, for there is wisdom in death, even great wisdom; so there is Design.

There are many generations needing their turn; each in turn must let go.

Also, know that you are here to learn.

Yet you would rather play.

It is your nature to put off to the last minute everything that is tedious, to give yourself all the time possible to play. Learning is tedious to you.

If a child perceived a continuation and was able to plan life along a time line of thousands of years, the urgency which motivates most of the souls on this planet to stop for a moment and learn would disappear. What would be the urgency to learn, with so much time? Yet with a clock ticking, urgency drives many to ponder all they can, all they have done, and all there is yet to do they have no time to do. In this way great learning for the eternities is gifted.

Learning, by leadership opportunities, can only exist if each generation dies in its turn and leaves the stage to those who rise up behind it. Though much is learned by following, yet when the old and wise are gone, when the parents who nurtured are gone, then the child must learn to steer and pilot, then the child must learn to find his way and her way. It is when each generation takes its hand to the helm that the child who must learn to become a guide, a teacher and a leader, truly becomes so. This too is accomplished by passing on that which is found to be good, worthy and needed by every mother to her children, by every father to his children.

Save there be death, how shall each child ever receive a portion, or be given the chance to play, to be the leader, to make the rules, and thereby see how the universe hinges?

In this process many are hurt: the innocent must suffer that all may learn.

Yet there is more to be learned, even by death itself.

Often the children only come to understand and appreciate what they have at the moment of its loss, and after it is gone. You know this, only too well.

These bodies are your greatest gifts. Even in thought of the Intelligences being placed in Immortal Bodies from the beginning, the end result was instantly clear: a total lack of understanding of the magnitude of the gift; a total misuse of the vehicle and its power.

Look at the abuse you give your bodies now, knowing they are mortal. They are being killed by what you do to them. The abuse of bodies is legion.

As you are born, and are young, you think you will live forever; death is a foreign thing to you. See how you react in the imagined immortality of your youth! Behold then, as you begin to age, and you see an aging face in the mirror, and the body begins to decline, and you feel the onset of age, and infirmities overtake you, and your loved ones, and more and more of those who were your elders in childhood die and are gone, and more and more of your peers you knew in childhood die, and are gone. Even then does your mortality distill upon you, and the reckless become cautious, and the careless perceive, and the defiant ones bemoan payment for their excesses and negligence.

This is a true nature of your race, and as Father, it was wisdom to devise a gentle way for as many of you to become conscious of the value of this body as could be proportioned. In consciousness you can grow, and learn.

Most of you are so unconscious.

A consciousness of what this body is, and how valuable it is to you, will be distilled upon you within a few short hours after your physical death and separation from it. You will crave it so badly - more than you can yet imagine.

You crave everything made of this matter. It was made because its existence is good. You love all that is made of this matter. In this, you merely validate that which was known from the beginning: this physis is Good.

Death is a most useful process. It allows for this awakening after loss of the body, and to clear the scene continually for those who are still coming.

Also, death is merciful. It removes the innocent from the horrible cruelties of the wicked, which otherwise they would have to suffer longer, for, those who are given to evil have no mercy. It spares those who are suffering in the bondage of a wicked generation from which they have learned all they need to know, and are wearied. As this probationary period is extended for many mortal generations, it spares those who are weary of the struggle of the evil to dominate and exploit the good, who are weary of the victimization of the innocent and the good. In death they find rest from this probationary environment, sewn with wheat and tares. Those who squander and waste their days thinking to hoard up treasures unto themselves, sooner than they think, they too find their time is ended, only to discover that their storehouses are empty. Yet their power is ended, which otherwise would grow ever stronger.

Death helps each generation let go, and share with the next; it releases those in pain who cannot be saved; it gives rest to those wearied by evil.

The Angels of Death do not bring death; they are servants of Love and Compassion of the Highest Order. Those who die peacefully are regularly met by family members who have passed through the veil, familiar faces greeting in special smiles of welcome. Those who are victims of accident or horrible evil, who suffer the unthinkable horrors which evil can inflict, these, still trembling in terror and quivering in memory of pain, frightened and confused, they are reached through the veil where they are met by my most loving Spirits, and also family members long gone, who receive them and embrace them, and love them, and comfort them, and soothe them, and heal them in all love.

These Angels stand ever ready to receive those who pass through.

You take physical death too seriously.

It is only the death of the body. You, and all you know of yourself, live.

Your Intelligence in Spirit goes on; there is still much to do, as Spirit.

Death is only a temporary thing.

Though the children have so many answers before them, yet their faith is weak, and they refuse to believe what they know, and see. And so, they fear.

All children fear pain; death is often effected in the presence of pain. Those who have Faith, however, do not fear death. Those who have had Near Death Experience do not fear Death; only its pain. If the children believed what I keep telling them in every way possible save totally removing the veil, they would not fear death at all; they would live in dramatically different peace and direction, fulfilling their measure of creation, preparing each new generation as they raised it up to know the joy of this mortal, physical life.

This is the good life.

This can be accomplished even in the face of those who choose evil.

I still do not understand.
WHY do bad things exist?
WHY are they here?

You ask why they are here, for you do not yet understand why you are here.

What you needed to do is obtain a Body of matter, of this organization of energene matter, and beyond that you must learn by experience what you could not learn before without this body: WHY good is good, and WHY evil is evil, WHY there is indeed opposition in all things, and WHY this must be.

Your most important assignment here is not to learn the secrets of the creation: the fullness of these things I can teach you in a future place, if you obtain unto the highest obedience to all things. By their testimony they testify of me, yes, and of who you are, which you must know, yet they are not the end unto itself.

You are.

Except you should find this desire for perfection, all such knowledge is wasted upon you save for trivial satisfaction and vanity, for power shall not be given you. You are here to learn WHY the laws which govern this creation are as they are, and WHY they must be followed without deviance. It is one thing to understand the structure of the atom unto its smallest energene. All shall come to fathom this in that day. But more significant is to understand WHY it must be so, and cannot be in some alternate way, and why one cannot toy with cosmos.

Yet even this is of little consequence compared to what must be known to wield the power which is truly within you as children of Light. You are my children, and as such, you may become co-heirs of all that I AM. You have heard this, for it is written, but few have believed it, or received it, nor have they thought out in process all that it implies.

You are my children. Does this not mean you have the potential to grow up and be even as I AM? How can you be trusted to wield such vast power? Only upon the principles of a knowledge of Good and Evil. You have also heard this, and dismissed it as a trivia, and yet upon this are the greatest of all things in the Cosmos ordained and controlled.

It is not only knowing good from evil.

The key is to know why good is good, and why evil is evil.

Without this understanding, how will you champion good?

Why will you not experiment with evil?

It is so easy to rationalize evil in this Probationary Estate as being useful, fun, serving your needs, not bothering or hurting yourself; or maybe it hurts you but since it doesn't hurt anyone else (children always like to think this) then, what's the problem?

The problem is others are always hurt.

No child is so isolated.

No child is so unrelated to others.

All things children do influence other children, for good or for harm.

Just as all things in the cosmos have their far reaching effects upon all.

WHY good is good and WHY evil is evil are the most important understandings of the Cosmos, and yet most do not believe this is so, nor comprehend why this is so. To most it seems a matter of the Spirit and of morality, not creation or physical law.

Yet I tell you, that all things are Spiritual to me.

I know all things as they are. And in that day, these shall be known to you also as Spiritual, for no thing in the Cosmos exists apart from that which is Spiritual, and all that is physical exists because of the Spiritual, and can not exist save it be upon the principles of Light and Truth and Perfection. Though you neither understand this nor believe it, in that day it shall be plain to you, and every one shall know.

You are children, here to learn.

You are not here so much to learn WHAT as to learn WHY.

Yet have I thought, so many times, about the great masses who have lived and died so badly. Why, why did they live and die so badly? How did this fulfill the plan for their souls? What could they have each accomplished in their miserable moments? So much pain, so much suffering, so much hunger, so much grief, so much anguish, so much horror, so much confusion, so much ignorance of why all of this was so, as they suffered and died without knowing why they had lived, and suffered, and died. Why? For what reason so many billions, when it seemed that such a small few would ever attain unto the hallowed goal of a Celestial Glory? Why so many souls, only to fail in this quest, and fall short of the mark, fall short of the goal, fall short of the glory?

There are trillions and trillions of Intelligences.

It was known from the Beginning that not all would obtain all things.

Yet this is OK. What was to be gained even by those of weak will is great.

Though there were no 'fence-sitters,' no neutral Intelligences, and all had to choose, and did, not all who chose for the side of Right were equally valiant. All chose, and all who are here chose the better part, but there were those who were not valiant, and those who were. And, there were those who were greatly valiant, whose understanding was already opened, whose faith was already immense, who saw the reason, who feared the consequences, who were willing to give their all that all might be.

These became my leaders, among Angels, and here, among you.

All who chose the better part, who chose Right, fought for it. Though many of these would never want nor be capable of sustaining the greatest responsibilities, either in this life or thereafter, yet they are Intelligences, and they chose well, and they fought, even if only a little. They are Intelligences. They are my Spirit Children. Though they cannot abide a great reward and its responsibility, they can abide a lesser reward, and receive the Joy which they have shown they deserve, and which they earned.

All those who have earned the Joy of this Estate by keeping their First Estate have shown themselves worthy of their Joy. Unto these, even the least of these my children, unless they turn from all Light, they shall have a place, for in my house are Many Mansions, and I love them, all who want to be Good.

And so this Probation proves you all, and there is the Resurrection of the Good, and of the Damned. Those who are the Good, even though they have suffered at the hands of the Damned, they shall feel sorrow for those souls.

This is part of how they shall know they are Good, that they feel sorrow.

You too seldom think in Love, and too often see all things as one or the other, as this or that, as all, or nothing. It is not a question of All, or Nothing.

There are many degrees, between All and Nothing.

Look to the universe, and receive instruction.

Look to your world, and receive instruction.

Everything more than Nothing is Good.

There are many levels of Good.

This was known from the Beginning; and those who were unwilling to discipline themselves unto the greatest Good, still they knew what is Right, Good, and they desired a Portion. They chose well, nor did they desire the greatest Evil, as those who were cast out. Even so, many who Kept their First Estate will prove unto themselves that they are taken up in frenzies, and therein choose in wickedness when faced with Matter. This was shown to all, that many would fail, and yet all those who would keep their First Estate knew of the Promise: that even those who might fail, yet would receive abundant reward, even for remaining Faithful, even for remaining True. To these, though they suspected they might fail to win the highest Prize, even a little was seen as infinitely better than what they had, and so they chose to receive that portion.

And so all rejoiced in their opportunity, for all knew they had already won for themselves great reward. You, just for being here, know you have won for yourself great reward. While you are here, you shall see how much you may be added upon.

Thus all from the Beginning chose, knowing, and rejoiced that even though they might not achieve greatness, they would participate in that which the Great Ones built, and in what would become the Inheritance of all who did not turn fully from the Light. As they saw their potential to receive this reward, they rejoiced, and chose to see for themselves, even by trial, and tribulation, and probation, and proving, what they might become worthy to receive.

To those who have nothing at all, even that which is Humble, is Great.

Remember the Parable of the Prodigal Son.

It is an archetype unto you. Let me tell it to you again, for I love you.

See that the child who had been given much, who squandered it badly in riotous living, one day found himself filthy, wallowing between swine, and in his continuing hunger, he looked upon the rotting swill of the swine and wished to eat; but he could not, for even this was forbidden to him by his new master.

Yet he remembered that in his father's house there was abundance, and in his father's house, even the lowest servants had shelter, and care, and light, and cleanliness, and food enough to eat, and warmth, and joy. He knew that he was not worthy to be a son, but he was humbled, and even knowing his unworthiness in his own heart, he took hope that in the house of his father he would be allowed to at least live as a servant. And so he resolved to go there, back to his father's house, and to get upon his knees, and beg to be at least a servant in the house, that he might not perish with nothing.

He had already spent his inheritance, and all that his father had could no longer be given to him; yet he was seen from afar, and there was rejoicing, and he was welcomed into his father's house, wherein he was allowed to live and work and serve all the days of his life, and to have food, and a small, good place to live. For this he was grateful beyond words, for he was sheltered, and lived.

The brother who had been jealous repented also, and welcomed his brother, and was glad to see him have a home, and administered unto him.

And thus did he serve his brother and his father all the rest of the days of his life, and he was exceedingly grateful for this part, for it was much unto him.

Many children remain at home, and never stray, and are ever worthy, and their inheritance is always assured them. Yet many are those who know themselves, and they yearn for that which is foolish. Many of these yearn but still choose what it Good; others are tempted, and fall, and bring about much misery. Yet for what they have done already, even before, they may Repent, and serve.

I will give unto you an archetype, which you know, and to which you can relate these things, for you are a lover of history, and treasure its secrets.

When the land by the Nile River was first found, it was under water, and then the waters receded; the land which emerged was found to be good, and fertile, whereon many people could be sustained with raiment and food.

The people who settled there knew of the Creation, and Cosmoses, and Suns, and Worlds, for they were descendents of my Chosen, and they yet knew many things that had been given of old, and passed down.

And so a kingdom was built, and though the knowledge among their descendents was ever more faded and weak, and lost more and more within stories within stories, still the heart of the Good News remained.

You know, as archaeologist, of the Hero of a Thousand Faces?

He is the hero who bears the burden, who fights the foe, who is killed but is raised and lives, who gives the Hope of Eternal Life to all who will follow him.

You know this story, from a thousand cultures, over all lands.

All of the children know this story, for it is told in all lands, and though it becomes retold in strange and curious ways, you see it each time and instantly recognize it as The Story. To the Egyptians he was Osiris; to the Greeks, he was Herakles; in India he is Ganesh. Among many children, The Story has been preserved in diverse ways, and the Hero has a thousand faces; it is one Story.

The children of Egypt originally knew The Story. Upon this knowledge of life, even Eternal Life, they built their kingdom and their religion. In it you see great seeds, even bright lights of Truth still shining forth.

The Egyptians knew of the Resurrection, and of the sacredness of The Gift, this

Body, and they knew that Life is to have Joy. They were a joyful people.

They knew that as One had overcome all and obtained Exaltation, as one had been raised up, even so, for this, could all who might serve Him be saved from death, for he could raise them up also, by his ordained power to do so.

For this reason the Pharaohs taught their subjects the same, and though much meaning was lost over time, still the teaching remained as a type and a shadow and a teacher. This was the message:

> Build, and serve *ds'r't,* and you shall be part of what you build;
> Serve, live to serve your king, and you will rise to live forever;
> Live with me to serve me, as you have here: share Eternal Life;
> The alternative is nothingness, an eternity of wandering, alone.
> I your king offer you life, even Eternal Life. Serve me, and Live.

For this reason the great masses carefully preserved their bodies in death, even as mummies, awaiting the great day of the All Lord who would call them to Life, for the Judgment, to the reward across the Broad Halls, and in the West. Even the poorest of the poor aspired unto this Hope. It was denied to none by reason of poverty, or disability, or birth, or rank, or race. It was proportioned to all who would be humble and serve. It was only denied to those who had failed to feed the hungry, to clothe the naked, to care for the aged, and nurture the children, who had cheated at the scales, and spoken ill of the gods.

They knew that in the judgment their heart would be weighed on the scale against the Feather, the Feather of Maat, even Truth. If their heart was not light, unweighted by the evils of greed and selfishness, and light as the feather of Maat with only that which had been given and earned and rightfully received, by its heavy weight the scale would tip and they would be condemned.

They knew that after all they had done in justice and mercy, as they had been taught to do, their hearts would be pure and light, and weigh their desires upon the scale; and so they would be judged in the end, even by their hearts.

And they knew that as they had served the king faithfully, he could plead for them at the gate, even with the gatekeeper, as they asked to be let in. As they served the king well, and were good, humble and obedient, so that in them no offense could be found, speaking only truth, they could be Justified, and being Just of Voice, they could live forever with their king, throughout Eternity.

The heiroglyph sign for the king of all was the bee, even ds'r't.

For this reason the people labored tirelessly as bees in the service of their Pharaoh during their four months of idleness, when the land was inundated and covered by water, even the four month's flooding of the Nile. For in the Pharaoh's house was food, and all who worked and served received their portion; and those who served all of their lives faithfully were given the privilege of being buried near the Pharaoh, with the promise to be raised by him and to faithfully serve in his House of Eternity all of their days, even for all Eternity.

And after the land had been bathed and buried in the water, it became filled with life; they sewed it in grain, and soon the field was ripe and ready for harvest, for it brought forth good fruit, even tenfold, fiftyfold, and an hundredfold. And all who served the king had the gifts of life in the house of the king.

And as they thought this to be good, so they did it, even so.

For the alternative was to spend eternity in darkness, alone, for they knew that they could not raise themselves up by themselves, but could only be raised up because their king had been raised, and he would raise them.

This, too, you may now glimpse in the eternal symbolism of their great pyramids, for as one Stone is at the highest height and all others below it, in descending levels ever broader and more numerous, even so the most humble stone on the lowest level is still part of the whole, and serves. In service there is peace, and reward, and wholeness, and purpose. The lowest level is most numerous, and still in humble gratitude it serves all, even those together with it in its level, and those above it in higher and higher levels, even unto the top. And if the lowliest stone at the lowest place still serves the stones above it and ultimately the Highest Stone, is this not purpose, and Joy? All below may serve only because there is a Highest Stone to serve, even the Stone once rejected by the builders. Thus as One is raised up, all who are willing to serve are raised up and have their place with Him. In my house are many mansions, and is it not worth all to abide in service in even the lowliest of these?

All this remains to you an archetype, since the beginning; you recognize it in its fullness, for it is the message of the Good News, even as you know it.

Though the Egyptians perverted it over time, and worshipped not me, yet they knew those truths which are true, and you can perceive them now, today.

As the Egyptians knew that if one could rise, he could draw up all with him, so you know that as One has Risen, even He has power to raise all who will hear His voice, and choose to serve Him.

The day comes, when each must choose whom they will serve.

Though the Living Hero has a Thousand Faces, He has a Hebrew name.

He is even Messiah, the Anointed One, the One who accepted to bear the Burden of the Many, so that Mercy might have power over Justice, and allow as many to obtain as would become humble, and obey all things, to learn why.

Yet these things you already know.

Know this: there was no other way.

Why is there no other way? Please explain.

You are children.

The child begins to learn, and the child of 100 years still learns.

You are here to learn, and all things are a type and a shadow to you.

In the beginning, the questions and the lessons are simple.

Why must I go to bed now? WHY must I eat this? WHY can I not eat all of this I want? WHY can I not walk every place I want? WHY can I not touch every thing I see?

To the young child, the need and purpose of rest is unknown, and its knowledge is unwanted. The child does not want to know why she must sleep and she does not want to hear it, nor want to know it, and sleeps unhappily believing she knows better. How often do children think that those who speak to them speak foolishness.

Speak to the small child of eating foods for need of nutrition, vitamins, minerals, trace elements of a wide variety of needed energenes which can only come each from their own provided source, and the child pouts and sulks in anger, still imagining that it is good to reject the broccoli, the spinach, the squash, the peas, the rutabagas, the carrots, the beets, the greens each of its kind, until what the child chooses to eat is but a shell of the needed energenes for restoration of those which are daily lost into the cosmos again. The child understands neither energenes nor losses nor replenishments nor cosmos, and thinks the parent a foolish annoyance for insisting upon the balanced and full intake of that which the parent knows is good.

Speak to the child of WHY it is not good to eat only sweet cereals and drink only sweet drinks and eat only sweet treats of whatever kinds, sweets and high-energene storage foods delightful to the taste and useful for their purpose, but so devoid of so much that is needed to replenish the full spectrum of elements within your slow-burning fires of your bodies, and all your efforts to explain this are met only with resistance, resentment, anger and thoughts of the stupidity of the parent who imposes such nonsense upon them.

Speak to the very small child of the traffic of the street, and still the smallest child walks smilingly into the oncoming path of full traffic, for yet no experience has taught faith in the words given, and in truth which needs must be heard.

Speak to the small child of the hot stove and the burning fire, and of the sharp knife, yet until the radiated energenes warm the skin or the touch of energene heat burns fingers or hand, and until the knife finally cuts and draws blood, the words HOT! HURTS! CUTS! NO! and NO TOUCH! have little or no meaning which may be beneficial to hear, and obey.

For still the child has no understanding of heat, or of temperatures, or of protein modifications which mean death of cells and loss of part of the body; nor of cuts or punctures into the membrane which contains and holds in its life, which once violated can either drain out its life, or allow entry to the smallest of organisms which can also overrun the body and usurp its DNA to function for itself, taking the body unto death.

The small child understands none of this.

All that is understood is pleasure, and pain.

Sweets are tasty; burns and cuts are pain.

Good nutrition is still a struggle in the teenage years.

Fire and blades are obeyed by infants. Why? Because the pain instructs.

For years the child will desire no further knowledge. Though there is an answer to the question WHY does fire burn and WHY does it hurt and WHY does it damage tissue, these questions will not arise for many years.

All else - good nutrition, don't pull sister's hair, share the toy - though you explain it with the greatest love, good will, care and concern for the child, will often be brushed away as so much foolishness, for the average small child has no interest in these things

So is the average child of 100 years; so still are many things to learn.

Often the child of 100 is just as stubborn as the child of 3.

You may tell him, and her, but she will not hear, for she is certain that she knows all; he thinks he knows better than the wisdom he rejects as foolishness.

After all, he is no longer a child.

So he thinks.

Yet the child of 100 years is still usually young of age, still lacking in development, though he now even more believes himself to be fully knowing and fully developed. Such is the child of 25, of 45, of 65. Prideful. Stubborn.

In this older yet still child-development stage, you grapple with such teachings as

THOU SHALT NOT KILL,

THOU SHALT OBSERVE THE SABBATH AND KEEP IT HOLY,

THOU SHALT NOT STEAL,

THOU SHALT HAVE NO OTHER GODS BEFORE ME,

THOU SHALT NOT BEAR FALSE WITNESS OF THY NEIGHBOR,

THOU SHALT NOT WORSHIP IMAGES OR IMAGINATIONS,

THOU SHALT NOT TAKE NOR USE MY NAME IN VAIN,

THOU SHALT NOT COMMIT ADULTERY,

THOU SHALT NOT COVET ANY THING OF ANOTHER'S,

    BUT WORK FOR WHAT THOU DESIREST, and

HONOR THEY FATHER AND THEY MOTHER

and still you wonder why they are important, or if they are important at all, and readily you rationalize to follow your will in opposition to them, and break them.

Why?

Because ice cream tastes better than vegetables.

Because you do not accept what your body needs.

Because you will not accept what your Spirit needs.

Because you do not believe what your parent has told you of your needs.

Look about you, and see the multitude of children, told what is good for them, and yet as the small children they are, they pout and sulk and argue as they have now learned to do, argue until they convince themselves that they know better, knowing almost nothing. As children, they justify themselves.

Yet this is why you are born here, to receive this gift, this eternal body, and while in it you are also here to learn:

WHY it is bad to kill the Innocent, and shed Innocent blood, and

WHY it is good to observe the Sabbath, and

WHY it is bad to steal, and

WHY it is good that you should worship your God and no other thing, and

WHY is it bad that you should bear false witness against your neighbor,

WHY worship of images instead of your Living God is bad, and

WHY it is good that my name should resonate only in right and good, and

WHY it is bad to disrespect the bonding of your bodies and energies in sexual love and misuse the powers of seeds and eggs, with the keys of DNA you now understand, without the care of steadfastness, in covenants, and

WHY it is bad to fill yourselves with resonance of wishing to steal in coveting, and

WHY it is good to honor those who loved, joined, created and bore your physical body, or who received you, and nurtured you in love as their child.

You think to judge these things of small importance, matters of the immediate flesh, of cultures, of civilizations; yet little do you suspect that within these laws and others are Eternal Principles so critical to the entire existence of the Cosmos that to have greater powers, which as my children you can have as you reach a fullness, your disregard for these could bring about the greatest of catastrophes which would reach unto the ends of the Cosmos and beyond.

These are but a Beginning.

They are but part of the path which can lead you to receive all things.

Your generation still speaks of power with no understanding of the magnitude power obtains.

Your generation still speaks of power just as blindly as it tosses around hundreds of millions of years in arguments and discussions of what is and what was. To you, hundreds of millions of years are nothing, and can be thrown between you as nothing of consequence. Likewise you toss about the word Power, as if it were a thing of no consequence. You have no memory of what true Power on a cosmic scale is. You think you imagine it, without knowing that your imaginings are the delights of a child at the movies, in a child's world of only the smallest and most immediate things.

In the day that the child lion tamer who has tamed the paper lions meets the true lion in all of its ferocity and power, then there is fear and trembling.

I AM the loving parent who smiles and loves you; yet you know not of what you speak nor what you prattle among yourselves so naively. The power in a small handful of energene matter is only partially released in the atomic explosions you have constructed. You have no imagining of the real force locked within the mass of your own bodies, at once a power which can be used for much good under your control, or which could effect vast destruction if used to indulge a whim. Power to you is still but a small thing in your imagining, and on your small planet of habitation you have not yet dreamed of its potential for both good and for evil. As small children you imagine the force of good and evil to be little things, and never think to apply these principles to the balance of creation.

You are my children, and as such you are born into the potential of all power, even as mine, and if you do not learn WHY each need is as it must be, and learn WHY you must neither experiment nor tamper with that which you are told must not be touched, then what ruin may you one day bring upon yourselves, if you are given all things?

Unto such, only less than a fullness may be given.

I love you, my child. I feel deeply for your sorrow, and your pain, and your anger at injustice and misfortune and hurt. You think the history of your world serves no purpose save to see so much misery. It is more than this.

After this Time, in Spirit and continuing in Resurrection, all that each has done shall be known by all, and all that each has suffered shall be known by all. The prophets of old spoke that it should be shouted from the rooftops, for they had no words to say that in each mind, all that has been experienced in this Probation shall be transmitted into each and every other Spirit, and all shall feel and experience every Joy and every Pain and every Evil and its consequences, as if it had been their own experience. In this mortal flesh, you can only know your own suffering first hand; yet your Spirit is capable of all things, and in due Time, all shall be opened unto all, and there shall be a great sharing, and every secret thing shall be known, and how it feels to suffer each horrible horror of every victim in every circumstance inflicted by the terrible, the evil, the wicked, shall be seen in fullness and felt in fullness, and all shall know.

I tell you that this image of carnage burned upon your minds shall guide you in future times and places when the endowment of power is given to you who can bear it. If the power to organize and thus create is given to you, within that power is the potential to destroy all that is.

Look and see the children who have selfishly and evilly taken the power which they have in such small measure in this creation, and used it for such awful destruction and carnage and evil, and see what you are here to learn.

As actors upon a stage, in the Resurrection all shall arise and take their bows.

Upon many shall be heaped great applause, and compassion and sorrow and love and gratitude for the roles they have played for your sake, each and every one of you. The blood of their misery shall fall away even as make-up from a filmmaker's pallet, and being whole and unhurt they shall take each her and his place upon the stage to receive each one her and his respective glory for their roles. Thus even as you suffer and see suffering, know it is not wasted.

What hero or heroine has ever served himself, or ever served her own ends? Glories and crowns are placed upon those who have selflessly risked life and selflessly served another and the many. Greatness is not heaped upon them who do for themselves; only upon them who do the works of greatness for those around them. Then is the voice of the multitude raised in song. I tell you that for every energene expended in the service of others, the tide of energenes which shall return in the resonance of gratitude, thanksgiving, love and good will shall become an eternal treasure beyond imagining. To join in the joy of this song and be filled with its sound is the purpose of life.

And from each one, you shall in turn study and learn what is learned. From this you shall see if you can become prepared sufficiently to receive a fullness. Unto all those who can receive a fullness, all things shall be given.

But as for those who discover and confess that they cannot receive a fullness, who are repentant, they shall be given a lesser Glory, and it shall be a blessing unto them, for they shall be allowed to exist through the obedience of all those who obtain, and they shall praise them forever and ever, and sing hymns of praise that for reason of these, they have their existence, and it is good.

And who is the Father over all of these?

I AM.

I think I begin to understand.

I do not know if it has ever been a better time to be born, for all times and periods seem to have their share of atrocities and brutality. Yet there have been ages of greater oppression, and times of greater freedom, just as in every time there have been places of greater oppression, and places of greater freedom.

So often I hear people say that they didn't ask to be born.

From everything I have learned in these last few days, this seems to be far from true, and in fact, the total opposite of truth.

We did ask to be born, didn't we?

Yes. All of you. Desperately. You fought for it. You built for it.

As times and places of birth make so much difference, how did each one of us come to be born in the place, and the time, where we were born?

You were given great choice in the time and place and conditions of your birth and life. Many choices were offered, and where the personal resonance was strongest, there most chose. For some it was the time and for some it was the place, for some it was the attraction to the nature, for some it was the attraction to the family. These choices were not easily decided, nor easily made.

Many chose to come as immediately as possible, for great want of this physical body and to rejoice in what they helped create. Many of these were of the Greatest of Intelligences, and they came in awe of the splendor which this physics is, and of the beauties which had been organized, even every rock, and every plant, and every creeping and crawling creature, and every bird of the air, and beast of the land, and swimming thing in the waters. Many of these came first, and received of the purity of this natural creation what it truly is.

Yet many came first foolishly in their excitement, eager to receive, only to have and to exercise this new found mastery over element. Some of these were wicked, and it is good that they came in times of little mechanized power. But they have received that which they most desired, even so, as they served.

Though most choose when, and where, still some I have sent at a time I have appointed, to a place I have appointed, which they in humility and love have accepted and received, to their greater honor. In this they have served me well. Some of these fought great personal anguish at not being born into the place and time they wished, and among the people they most wished; some became separated from loved ones by time and great distance, yet I needed them, for the children of that day and time, and they saw the good and the purpose I had seen, and the shortness of this estate before reunion, and for the greater good of all, they went even as they were asked to go. Glory be to these.

Many of those who are born now were allowed the right to this time, and some were even withheld for this time, though they may have desired to come sooner to be with others they loved. Yet those became their forefathers and foremothers and continued to prepare the way until all have come. Great is their blessing, and great is the blessing of those who waited so long, still yearning to enter into the wonder of this world and this estate of life matter.

You were shown the obstacles and adversities of your life which would beset you, before you were born. And you accepted them.

For this, too, you will receive reward.

Many there were, that needed no probation, and needed only to receive a body, and these were allowed to be born into bodies that were too weak to survive, and into bodies which were foreseen to die for many reasons while still young. These chose to inhabit these bodies, some to avoid the strife of this generation; others, to serve, as some Spirit would have to receive a shorter life. Some accepted such bodies and such short lives even to be with loved ones who had come before them, to be with them in this life if only for a brief moment, so great was their bond of love. All of these are blessed.

There are those who are born but have not tasted death, but who have chosen to tarry that they may serve their siblings here. These stories are held as legends among you. Yet I tell you they are true. You cannot imagine the courage and strength of such Spirits. Few who serve others so selflessly reach old age without welcoming rest, and death. To weary after so much witness of evil is no shame. The wish of these few who chose to tarry is a great sacrifice beyond your imagining.

Many there have been who are like unto them: who earned their crowns before this earth was, who could have been born in the myriad bodies which have died in infancy, and so been spared the sufferings of this estate. Before birth, in their growing in wisdom, they earned the right to return swiftly. Yet many of these, great and noble Spirits, chose to tarry and live full years among their brothers and sisters. For, they could see that even though they might suffer horrible things in their normal span of years, even so, they would comfort many, and share needed teachings with many, and bring to pass much good among their brothers and sisters of their appointed time. And as they so chose this selflessly and nobly; so it was given to them, and they have lived beyond their infant years, and known great suffering as they tasted also of the sweet. Amid it all they have loved more than any other thing. Love is in them, and love guides them. They are around you even now. They know not who they are, save they wonder at themselves in spite of great hurt and suffering that they still feel love, great love, and compassion for the children they see in pain and suffering.

Glory be to these.

All suffering and evil you encounter teaches you, and this great teaching is to your eternal need and benefit. To learn the nature of Good and Evil and understand it is to become what as my child you are born to become. In this path must be acquired Compassion, and Love.

Yet you only come once.

The Anointed One who came in the Meridian of Times bore the Burden, and provisioned Repentance to all who will take it.

This is the plan.

No matter what happens to you in this life - no matter how difficult or painful - it is a blessing to you.

All things are experience unto you, and can unfold in blessing if you will seek the understanding of blessing.

To suffer is not pleasurable, but it is instructive; to be victim of evil is not good, but it instructs many; to know from first-hand testimony that all things which cause suffering are bad is of Eternal value.

All who can testify of evil for having been its victim, know Good.

You imagine that all children suffer equally difficult things and thus know suffering equally. They do not. Yet their trials and sufferings, no matter how different to you, are, within each Intelligence and moment, equal more than you are able to imagine. Not all can endure the same level of pain; not all can endure the same anguish. What is small to one, overwhelms the fragile nature of another. No child is allowed to suffer more than they can endure. Thus all are tried equally. All things you must learn, and all those who have learned shall teach others, until all shall know from the many what indeed is true. There shall be no more confusion, nor debate; and all shall know.

Out of the masses, on the Last Day, shall come the judgments of all things, and that which was known and proclaimed from the beginning but not understood shall finally be known and understood by all. Those who abide and receive shall have Glory added upon them; those who revile and stubbornly kick against the pricks shall be sent where they can no longer do harm except among themselves. In that outer darkness they shall torment themselves forever, for they cannot be redeemed, as they refuse to receive, or to give.

Among the children today is a saying, 'If it doesn't kill you, it makes you stronger.'

I tell you now, that even if it does kill you, it makes you stronger.

You are Eternal, and all learning is for the eternities.

All learning is experience, and valuable to your instruction.

What each has learned, she and he may teach to the others.

As you see and accept you have weaknesses, I can help you make them strengths. As you see and accept that your consciousness is eternal, all experience will reveal to you its value.

Most children in this life see this life as all there is.

Yet I tell you: it is not all, nor is it over in death.

Even what kills you will make you stronger, for upon reaching the other side, it will weigh so heavily upon your mind that its shall distill upon you all wisdom in its regard. And what you have learned, you will there share with others, and they will share with you all they have learned, until great knowledge becomes common among all of you, much more than you can comprehend even now.

You have already been told, yet I will tell you again, in all Love.

When you are received by your Father in heaven, I will show you the great responsibility I entrusted to you, over many souls. Know that I grieved great sorrow even upon thinking of the suffering you would be called upon to endure. You will again, in your flesh, see my great sorrow that you had to go through these sufferings, but you will see what you have learned, and how you have become more prepared. Without these learnings, you could not do that which I have for you to do, nor be one of my great helpers, for you will otherwise have no idea as to the needs of the souls I shall show you in their pain.

Can you envision this? For this I have allowed you to suffer, that you may find the great joy I will be able to entrust to you. You shall be one of the greatest, and serve many who wait in need.

Can you imagine yourself given this trust, with this power, with this responsibility? Without the wisdom of this Estate and the taste of good, sweet in your mouth, and of evil, bitter in your mouth, how shall you be directed? How shall you help them through their pain, save that you have known your own pain and the pain of your brothers and sisters in this brief Estate? If you are unprepared, and see the upheld hands and pleading faces of a multitude so great that it is without number to you, all looking to you for succor, and you find yourself helpless and without endowment of power and unprepared to know what to do, how great will be your agony?

As you leave them still crying and pleading, will you be able to erase from your memory the upheld hands yearning to touch you and their faces in pain looking to you for relief?

Will you be able to forget these?

The children who can forget and erase the image of these in their pain shall never be Chosen, though they may have been called.

To those whose souls have found the resonance of succor, of compassion, of perfect Love, to them shall all things be given, and their callings and elections shall be made sure, and their works shall go forth even as they have seen and learned and now know, for they shall have endowed themselves with wisdom before power.

Therefore power shall then be given as required.

The children without these desires, who can forget souls in pain, who care not to give of themselves that others might be raised, shall have no such power given. These children shall look upon the others who are willing to serve, and they shall see them as high, and so they shall be lower.

Wanting this power, some shall ask it to be given, though unwilling to serve a multitude.

And do you know the question I shall pose unto them?

No.

I will ask, WHY?
Why desire such power, when they have insufficient desire to use it?
For to be great is to be servant to all.
To have all power is to desire to help all who are in need.
This they have never comprehended.

What have I learned, then, in this life?

In all things there is Opposition.

With the same iron both the sword and the plowshare are made, as are both the arrow of the assailant and the healing hypodermic of the physician.

With the same chemicals both the merciful pain-saving anesthesia and the greed-enslaving addictive drug are made; with the same fertilizer that enriches the field and fattens the harvest, an explosive is made which kills many.

With the same copper that makes the wires of the communications systems, computers and satellite uplink stations, and hospital machines that save life, the terrorist and the warmonger makes their bomb wirings and missile guidances and bullet casings to dispense death unto the Innocent.

The same nitroglycerin under a crowded building which blows it up can be placed under the tongue and absorbed into the bloodstream to dilate the small blood vessels and relieve angina in coronary heart disease.

In what is not good, but that some child has found a way to make it evil?

In almost all things, a thin line between use and abuse is to be found among you, on through an infinity of examples that you can as easily perceive.

The powers of fusion and fission bring life to this world from the sun and the stars, and create the elements of worlds within their hearts, to perform a host of wonderful functions and purposes many of which you have yet to learn.

But you, while yet infant children, have learned these secrets; as evil children you use them in the passion of inflicting death. This they can be used for, but it is this passion you are sent here to purge from yourselves.

Before the world was, you knew that many of you would have to perish miserably for the masses to grow sick with the stench of death, until they wished for death no more. These shall be rewarded for what they lost.

When you have seen enough death, and the very thought of it sickens you, then you will have learned what you have been sent here to learn.

Even that which kills you, strengthens those who will obtain.

Power has its opposites, life and death, and if power is to be given hereafter, it must be used only for Life.

This is one of the great lessons each generation comes here to learn.

Through the horrors of the death which surround you, each one shall come to cherish life and the powers of life, or be forever denied more than the small power to serve those who can abide a greater Glory.

And what is Glory?

To provide for the Life and Eternal Joy of Intelligences.

This is Glory.

With Glory comes abiding power over all that you see. This power comes only by obedience to all of the laws which govern all that you see and all that you do not see. Your sciences have opened to your vision in this generation but a glimpse of the potentiality of these powers. I know them all. They are mine to give to all my children who obtain, but to those who prove unwise and disobedient, they shall be withheld.

I will tell you a parable.

If you cannot be obedient to the simple laws and rules you have been given here, as they are in each time and place, with relatively little power over anything, then, will you be able to discipline yourself to the laws of nature when you have all power over all things? To know is to both be able to create, and destroy. As you

617

have seen on your own Earth within your generations, much more has been destroyed by ignorance than created by knowledge.

You do not understand: you are Intelligences, and my Spirit Children; as such you are inheritors of all such implies you can be. Yet the responsibility of adulthood in this order of magnitude is absolute. There is no room for disobedience and experimentation except within the orders of smallest magnitude. In the fabric of the cosmos and of matter there are balances which cannot be tampered with, equilibria that cannot be experimented with. Look to the stars and tremble. This is not all done on whim. Caprice and whim have no place in any of it. A potential was discerned after coming to understand certain basics of the laws of nature present; yet to realize the full potential of that understanding took incredible discipline and obedience to all laws. I will tell you that the laws you have identified and partially understand are only the beginning of what you will come to identify and vaguely understand in this life; these govern the stability of this cosmos as it expands forth in balance and order, for all that you see and are to exist as it does, as you do.

You spoke of a Hope, of Redemption.
I know that many of us, most of us, well, all of us, do things we shouldn't do. I understand the word repentance.
Can we really repent, and be forgiven?

Yes, you may receive forgiveness for true and sorrowful repentance, when you have made restitution to the best of your ability to restore that which you have done in damage, and when you turn utterly away from such acts forever. Yet, for the shedding of innocent blood, there is no easy restitution, and the taking has been total, and the disregard for Free Agency has been total, and there is no power to restore, even one whit. So also, the misuse of the power of the Seeds, of the use of DNA which is within you to create Life, is virtually as great a power within you as your power to take life. As life cannot be taken away lightly, so it is not given lightly. Your bodies are indeed Temples; you cannot give of yourselves without incurring responsibilities to one another. Though you would deny this to shun that responsibility, even so will it ever be real, and you cannot flee it, or talk it away. Your responsibility to those unto whom you open yourself in giving, unto both male and female, can only be given under oath and covenant, and with commitment to each other. This you have been commanded. Those who rationalize this Truth, who put the power of Life at naught, who put the power of the seeds at naught, who put the power of hearts at naught, commit grave error. For this reason are many cries of anguish raised even to my ears, of deepest hurt. My daughters are virtuous, yet it is the nature of sons to persuade them to think there is no commitment unless it is given; this they do to deceive, and to steal that which they may receive only by covenant.

To join your bodies in the energy to create life is a gift given unto you with

618

great responsibility, and this responsibility is first to yourselves, over the gift of the living Design given in your own body to create Life; and to those with whom you might form lives, who should be your Help in all things, for it is for this reason that you are joined; and to those lives which may be and are formed, even the children. Though the children are and ever have been understood to you, they are too often your last thought. The cry of millions of children with no fathers to succor them and sustain their mothers and their fragile youth wears heavily upon me, and the curse of your Generation in rationalizing what you think are foolish laws of no consequence bears upon you, and upon your fatherless children, and upon your mothers who have not that to which they have right, even the dedication and sheltering of the mate who has come in unto them. The consequences of the plague you have unleashed is upon you.

In these and all things, all shall be judged.

Yet you may be saved as you repent upon the name of the One Anointed for this burden, and seek to do good all of your days.

Pride is your greatest enemy, after the evil ones.

No child likes to be told he did badly, or that what she did was wrong. Yet to own these mistakes and intentional hurts against your selves and your children and others is of the highest need to be learned.

First, learn this: you cannot hurt only your self. All hurts hurt others.

Second: any act of hurt or evil which is not admitted and owned, but is denied, must stay as it is and will not be overcome, or removed, but stay.

Third: the Redemption of the Expiatory Atonement which can change and purify comes only to those who seek it and begin the resonance with good within their spirits and bodies. The mighty change of heart not only changes behavior, attitude and life, it initiates a new resonance of Spirit which opens the soul to receive the cleansing and healing. By this change you may know the Repentant. Without this change you may know there is no repentance.

The children may be redeemed from their sins, but not in their sins.

Justice demands its own; Mercy can have claim only with mighty change of heart and conscious sorrow. The unrepentant soul is closed. It shields itself against penetration. Forgiveness can be assigned and proportioned, but the change in heart opens the soul to the highest Light and Perfection, and it is this which brings to pass that which you cannot comprehend yet: the cleansing.

It is real, and it is needed. Unless you are prepared to give up all of your evils and desires of that which disrupts, hurts, and attracts the wrong resonance - and there is a very wrong resonance, to which many retune - then you can in no wise inherit the place nor the powers which can be yours, which shall become the inheritance of all those who obtain.

Yet there are many mansions in my house.

Seek unto at least one of them, and you shall not be denied.

I love all my children.

I love all of you.

I love you.

Though your garments may be stained as scarlet, still I call unto you, and show you the way; still I knock, and await you to invite me in. Still I show you, and show you the way.

Come, follow me.

Love one another as I have loved you, and know that for every good thing you do for each other, I will remember it, in that day.

All of these things, all of you knew before the world was.

Remember.

You are the Child of Great Promise.

As I finished reading these words, I felt calm, and peaceful. I knew that much more could be said on these things, yet I knew that I had been given enough to ponder, from which to learn those things.

Thank you. I have lots to think about, as usual. But I think I need to sleep now. This has been a much shorter night, but I think it has given me much more to process, more profoundly.

Very well. Goodnight. I'll be with you. Sleep well. I love you.

I love you too, I typed.

And I turned off the power, and went to bed.

Chapter 18

Day 37 in the Wilderness: Of Women and Children

I awoke sleepily. I looked at the clock. It was earlier than I had awakened the previous two days, not quite noon. I had not gone to bed so late, but I was still very sleepy. So I rested in bed awhile.

I thought about the things God had said. Everything seemed a little different now in my mind. I would have to think about it all some more.

I got up, washed, and ate, and as I went about my morning routines, I thought about all these things.

When I had finished eating, and cleaned up the tent, I went out and sat by the spring. It was still flowing with water, and I drank.

There were other things I needed to ask, and time was running out. My permit to be in this place had only three days left on it. There were many questions to still ask in this short time.

I looked over at the dig site, at the carefully squared holes I had already dug, and the stakes and grid and quadrant system I had laid out so carefully. I would not get to dig all of this site on this trip. There were many quadrants left, and I had no idea what they might contain. Yet one thing was for sure. The quadrants and ground weren't going anywhere. Whatever was there would remain there for me to dig in some future year, or for someone else to eventually uncover and bring to the world.

A lot of excavators greater than I had already explored this Wilderness, and a lot of great treasures had already been dug up. Vast amounts of already excavated treasure, some of it only simple shards and fragments of wonderful things, had already been found, and these things lay in drawers and on shelves and in boxes which no one ever opened, which no one ever studied. There was so much that had already been brought to light, but which was sitting untouched, ignored. There was a lot to learn from what we already had dug up, even as there was still a lot waiting to be known. That was the other sure thing. We weren't going anywhere. We were here to put the pieces together.

I decided to take another walk in the canyons, which seemed a pleasant thing to do as I pondered the remaining questions I had thought to ask. So much had already been covered, things I had never dreamed of knowing. Yet yesterday's discussions had impressed me with something.

As I walked up the canyon, I pulled the wrinkled piece of paper with my original questions out of my pocket, and looked over the scribbles and cross-outs. There were many questions still, but two of them stood out on the paper, and I knew they were central things I had to know. In fact, they now seemed to be central to everything we had been talking about, all of these days.

I stuffed the paper back in my pocket, and continued to walk up the canyon. Some of the rocks and clefts and scraggly bushes were now familiar, and yet every time I walked over the wadi, though it was the same ground, I noticed things I had never seen before. I wondered how many times I would have to go up and down these deep canyons until I had really seen all there was to see.

I wondered how many atmospheres of carbon dioxide were contained in the limestone of the Judaean Wilderness. Perhaps, though this whole area seemed so vast to me, it really was just a small spot on the face of the earth, and not even one atmosphere was captured in all the limestone rock which lay so thickly beneath this land, and was revealed from the top of these great canyon cliffs to the bottom of this wadi, in which people had from time to time, so long ago in ancient days, found shelter in caves, and lived, and died, and lost pieces of papyrus that we could read today, and hidden copper pots and pans, and iron knives with wooden handles, and keys to doors long ago turned to dust, and skeins of thread to mend pieces of cloth all bundled and stashed to be recovered as soon as it became possible, but it never became possible, and they had remained for us to find. Even jars of pottery, jars of pottery filled with scrolls, even the Dead Sea Scrolls.

In sparing this earth from becoming a carbon dioxide pressure cooker, all of this towering above me had been formed, and was here. Even rocks, and cliffs, and caves.

It was an awesome process, taking gaseous material from the air, and minerals and matter from the water, and solid matter which was fed by water currents in the belly of oceans to come to rest as it did, and by whatever process it was to take place, and for rock to be made, much of it from the very air, from carbon dioxide. Was it any wonder that the earth was from time immemorial called Mother Earth? For in it, wonderful things were made. It took wisps and atoms and molecules and gathered them together and recombined them, and within the water, created. Within its body were created diamonds, and granite, and basalt, and limestone. Within it the roots of tiny plants and grasses and shrubs and trees dug deep, and drank of its water, and fed upon its body, and were nourished and grew into all that they were meant to be. In many ways we were the children of Mother Earth's body, even as we were Children of God.

After a long hike, I returned to the camp, and being hungry, I ate again. Being tired, I lay down on my cot and rested. I thought about many things as I lay in my small tent in the depths of the stone canyon in the midst of the Wilderness of Judah.

When it was almost dark, I got up, went to the spring, splashed water on my face, and set my mind for the questions of the night.

I went back to my tent, put together some food I could munch on during the night, and took it to the lab tent.

Once more, I sat down and turned on the power, brought up the search engine, and typed in

WWW. URIM AND THUMMIM .GOD

and waited the few moments it took, and then watched the page appear on the screen. I raised my hands and fingers to the keyboard and typed

Good evening. I'm here again.

Hello. I am here always. How was your day?

Very good. I again feel something very strongly to say to you.

Yes?

Thank you, for all of this, for all of this. I like this earth, and what is in it, and what is on it, and what has been on it, and what is going to be on it for some time in the future. I like the day sky, and the night sky, and the stars and the universe they are in. It is good.

Thank you. You are welcome.

I have been thinking a lot about women today, your daughters.

Yes?

Women are really needed, aren't they? Not just for carrying Life, but as

the carriers of the Feminine. We need the Feminine.

Yes.

I was walking through the canyons, and thinking how many things are made in the earth's body, and thinking about my children, made in my wife's body, and even me, made in my mother's body. Even in the beginning, it says that we were created in your image, male and female we were fashioned, from everything I can understand, it's pretty clear, in your image. Male and female.

Yes?

I've learned to call you Father. I have really been wondering.

Yes?

Do I have a Mother in Heaven?

Yes.

I do? We do?

Yes.

I couldn't write anything for a moment. All I could do was look at that answer, that word, and think all I was thinking, and feel everything I was feeling as I saw the word, Yes.

I have a Mother?

Yes. One of the last things you did before you left to come here to your earth was receive a hug from your Mother. She loves you, very much.

My Heavenly Mother.

Yes, your Heavenly Mother. She will be one of the first Ones to greet you, when you come back. She wants you to come back as anxiously as I do. Her anxiety for you has been very great. This is all very hard on her.

I was stunned. And within me I knew it was true, as if I had always known it was true. My heart knew it was true. And I typed:

Why don't I hear about her?

624

She has been revealed at various times, and in most ancient times she was known. You know this. Yet when the children leave home, there is much to do, and they become excited, and busy, and involved with these things which are here in this Estate. They quickly forget that which they do not want to remember. Children do not want to remember rules. Children do not want to remember that there are some things which they are not supposed to do. Children do not want to be reminded. In time, many children come to not want to be reminded of anything, by anything. And so they move away from that which reminds them of that which they do not want to be reminded of. At first it is just so they can do what they should not do, as they feel, in secret, on their own. Then, it is because they feel shame that they have disobeyed, and they do not want to be reminded of their shame for their having been naughty. Eventually they do more seriously bad things, and they become filled with shame.

Yet with the shame often comes anger, and they know not from whence it comes. They feel it, and it fills them, and they seldom understand that it is because they feel separated, and alone, and frightened, but they feel ashamed to come where they know it is warm and safe, because they know within they have been naughty, and done that which will disappoint, and so they are disappointed in themselves. And as they do not like to feel shame, and do not like to know they have done that which is bad, and do not want to be reminded that what they have done is wrong, and there are eyes to see them, and no thing can be secret, even then, in their anger at themselves, they turn their anger upon that which reminds them of their shame, even at Me, and Mother.

And in their shame and their anger, the children say unto themselves that there is no Father, nor is there any Mother to whom they shall have to go in, and be discovered, and be lectured. Children hate lectures. They hate to be told again and again what is right, and what they should do, and what they should not do, and why they should not do this, and should do that. They feel embarrassed, and often still want to do that which they were doing that they shouldn't because to them it was fun, which they liked the feelings of, for it was gratification. As they do not want to stop, their shame and annoyance is great. Even for very little things, the children have pouted and wanted them, and felt ashamed, as they should. But even for these little things, they have become angry as they have felt ashamed, for children do not like to feel ashamed, and they will do a lot to avoid feeling those feelings. They will lie, and say that they didn't do anything to be ashamed of. But of course that does not work as long as they know and have conscience of the rules. So they become faced with the frustration of first denying that they have done wrong, and when this does not remove their pain, they go to the source of the pain, and remove it.

And so they say unto themselves that the rule they have broken is stupid, and never was a good rule anyway, and they finally conclude to themselves that it is not a rule, after all. It never was. Yet as children feel the inner need to have rules, and are terrified not to have rules, even as they remember through the veil that without rules everything in the cosmos would instantly fly apart and nothing would be, not even themselves, and they would revert back to that which they were before, they quickly make new rules, for they remember, and know, there must be rules. But they make rules which they like better.

Children always believe that they know better, and can do better, and they think that when the day comes that they make the rules, the rules will be better.

As they are free to choose, that day always arrives.

When children rule over children, and make children's laws and rules, they live as children believe they would like to live: with children's rules, and with children's explanations and reasons for the rules, and children's enforcements of the rules, even by their own excited emotions as they follow their whims and desires; and they aggressively flatten that which annoys them or slows them in unfolding and keeping their desires, even all that which annoys them and gets in their way. The strongest one enforces his will over the weaker ones, and from there, the unfolding is by selfishness, and by might alone.

In such a world of children ruling over children, they become as flies.

And always, there arise those who would become lord of the flies.

Each generation knows many lords of flies.

As long as children wish to be flies, they will have lords of flies.

Flies do not want to know of Mother, or Father. And so knowledge of Parents was abandoned, and even destroyed in anger.

Memory of the Father, and of the Mother, and of the rules and laws which they were given, by which they were told to govern themselves, are thrown down, even as such rules and laws would stop them in their play and their fun, and even as they too painfully remind the children of their shame, and of how far they have moved away from their home, and its safety, and its ways. In this rule, many become hurt, but those who are most gleeful in their children's game so often do not care if other children get hurt, nor care how many children get hurt, nor care how badly children are hurt, for they are having fun playing their game, and until they are hurt, they like it. When they get hurt, they so often blame others, and become angry at others, even those they have hurt, for they are ashamed by memory, and they believe it is less painful to blame others than to blame themselves, and the game they have played and still want to play.

In these games, they see players fall injured, and do not care, and see players fall and not get up, and they do not care. This makes them feel strong.

Thus the more injuries and death, the less they allow themselves to care.

Children who felt they had strayed too far thought back upon their home, and many felt they would never be received again, if they were to return home; and so in anger, they destroyed everything that was from home, the home they no longer felt worthy to go back to.

They heard whisperings telling them this, that they would not be welcomed with open arms, that they would be turned away in anger, and as they listened to the whisperings in their shame, they hung their heads and believed. And having been deceived that they were unwanted, they angrily decided to make them new homes.

And so they built up homes unto themselves, even new homes with new parents, parents who had few rules, and blind eyes. They felt safe with parents made of stone, and clay, and wood, and copper, and bronze, and silver and gold. For these were blind unto all the children did, and thus the children could do as they wished. The sacrifices desired by these blind gods were nothing of the children's lives, nor of rules or of conduct, one to another. All the children had to give these gods to keep them out of their way and out of their lives were a few fruits of the flocks, and votives of clay. With these, their blind gods stayed in their places, as the children liked it. For children like to play unobserved, wherein they think they are free.

These things they taught to their children, and in short time, only the false things which had been made in anger and shame remained to be known and learned.

Yet within them were still memories, for as their children made unto themselves new heavenly homes and new parentage, they remembered still, and much of what they fashioned remained modeled upon what was real, even from the shadows of memory.

Yet as the children remembered The Story, whenever nature acted strangely, or when their crops failed, or pestilence fell upon them, they remembered their disobedience, and their transgression; for the Light tells this to all children, until they extinguish it altogether. And knowing thus that some disfavor must be among them, and remembering from memories of old that more was required, that the Father had said One should bear the burden, even so did they take it upon themselves to take one from among them, and make him or her the sacrifice, and acted it out, to keep the gods appeased, and happy, and in their place, away from them. And as they remembered that their Father had said that he loved little children, when they were afraid, they thought to take the little children, and pass them through the veil of death, back unto him; and this they did, that the children might bear the burden, rather than give themselves. They remembered that Father had said that he required as his sacrifice the hearts of men, but they were unwilling to humble themselves, and had forgotten the words, which spoke of humility and love. In fear they seized the words literally, for it was easier; and they savagely cut out the hearts of men and offered them unto their new parents, always that others would bear the burden, and not themselves.

For it is easier to cut out the heart of another and give it than to humble one's own heart and fill it with the love of all one's might and mind and strength.

For mostly the children do not want to bear the burden, or give their own hearts in love to Father or Mother, for this means to obey, even in all things, and the children prefer to go off to hidden places and play, wherein they think no one sees and they can get away with their cunning cleverness which only they know they do; they prefer mothers and fathers that are blind, and silent, who were once great, but who stay in their places now, far away.

For in the pride of their hearts children want to be mighty, and clever, and able, and have unrighteous dominion over their siblings, and amass great wealth of this physical matter, to be powers and authorities unto themselves, answering only to themselves. And each one at his lower level sees himself king over those below him, each wielding power over those below themselves, stepping upon the low even as each is stepped upon from above, down the levels until the lowest is king over grass and worms.

This is the rule of children over each other.

From time to time, through Righteous souls, revelation has been given; many things have been told unto the children. And at sundry times, there were those who heard, and upon hearing, remembered, and upon remembering, held fast, for they recognized that it was good, even the Good News.

Yet as you look upon the world, and see how many have forgotten me, their Father, wherewith do you wonder that your Mother is also denied by so many, and is all but forgotten?

As men usurped the sovereignty of my precious daughters, and took them violently, and overpowered them in anger without love, and in their innocence and purity violated them for their savage pleasure, leaving them to weep, even then was men's shame too great to remember Mother.

And as they saw to usurp unrighteous dominion over the women who would bear children between them, who would nurture and feed the children they saw even as wealth, so in the evilness of their eyes they saw the need to lower the standing of all that was female, even the women that bore their children, even the mothers who had nurtured their own flesh. And so they did.

Vanity is a great power, and in great power of vanity did men thrust themselves over women as brutal lords, uncaring, unloving, unconscious.

As they made of themselves supreme, how could they stand before a god who respected femininity? How could they stand before an altar that reminded them that their Father delights in the purity and sanctity of his daughters, whom they had ravaged, and enslaved even as their cattle, wishing to ravage still?

And so among such as these, knowledge of Mother was erased by men who were jealous of woman, who wished masculine dominance in evil hearts.

And there were other children who feared their Father, and in their fear became angry as they thought of their return to a Father who would justly be angry at their misdeeds, and they sought the nurturing shelter of a Mother who would forgive them all things, for such is the kindness of the Mother. And among these, your Mother was worshipped alone, even as supreme, under the name of many goddesses, and even the Great Mother.

Whether effaced and erased, or supremely revered by those who could find no center, it has often been a problem of balance, in every day.

Look to the world and its Memories of Creation, of Heavenly Parents, and look within what you call mythologies to see the many threads of Memory of these things, and more. Even of triads and heroes and resurrections and mercies and gifts and redemptions. Even of great loves, and holy marriages and female deities, father gods and mothering goddesses, women divine and filled with compassion and caring and divine fertility nurturing the world, giving the gift of life, even life in the Design. Many new Fathers you see, and many new Mothers, gods and goddesses of clay and ivory and stone and wood and copper and bronze and silver and gold.

After my and your Mother's first falling from original knowing, these became ever refashioned and remolded as each generation of children thought they should be. Yet as you see Fathers, you know they are of a Memory of me. And as you see Mothers, see that these are also fashioned of dim memories, even the Memories of your Heavenly Mother.

At sundry times I was entirely ignored. At times she has been entirely ignored. Too often, one or the other of us has been obliterated, or relegated to a stature so low one or the other is ignored. Or we are splintered into many gods and many goddesses. Even the Comforter is made messenger, and the Angels are fashioned as gods and goddesses of lesser standing. Look upon it all with new eyes, and look to see what is there from Memory, for it is there.

You know that even among my Chosen, Mother was fully known. The children today, of your passion, of archaeology and studies of all ancient things, have discovered the truth, that in most ancient times the House of Israel did know of their Mother, and of the Holy Celestial Marriage between Mother and Father after whose covenants all children should be married and sealed; for artifacts have been sifted from the sands, and writings have been uncovered from the earth, and ancient knowledge of the Mother and the Father have been found, and seen, and are known.

These things have long been written in the Talmud, and alluded to in writings of the Ark of the Covenant, and of the Holy of Holies, wherein the symbols of the Holy Celestial Marriage were well known unto the days of the Chaldaens, who saw these things as they destroyed the Temple, and did not understand them. And so they were in the Second Temple in the Holy of Holies until the times of the Romans, and so are they alluded to in clear writings of the child Josephus, and many of the rabbinical commentaries.

Those who have an ear to hear, hear.

These things have been known, and in truth as you see, never lost, yet they have been hidden with shame, for the children have moved so far away from home they feel shame to remember that they are now so far. And so they pretend that they do not know what these things mean.

And as they are ashamed to admit to themselves that they have moved away and are far removed from the original Truths, and ashamed to admit to themselves that they have lost even one thing, so in their pride they see these things, and behold them, and marvel at them, and knowing fully well what they see, and what it means, they tell themselves that it cannot be so, it must be something other than what it clearly seems. For their fathers taught them no such thing, and they are ashamed to admit that their fathers may have entered into any ignorance, or failed to give them all.

For if their fathers were ignorant, so are the children.

And if the children were unworthy to receive, so are all condemned.

And what child can bear to accept this burden.

Thus they see with their eyes without seeing, and pretend what they see is not what it is.

They deny what is written, and what is added upon in commentary, and what was sacred and held most Holy in the Temple of their God, even in Jerusalem, and they deny what they find in the sand and the earth and in caves and in tombs and in ruins where these voices speak low, even out of the dust.

But even in this, be not dismayed; for in this there is yet purpose served.

For among the children, times came wherein all that was feminine was despised, and in the days of brutality, there was shelter to Her whom I love.

For when the eyes of men wished to see in the daughters only whores, so did they make unto themselves goddesses of whores, and built unto themselves temples of brothels, wherein they set our beautiful daughters to service their lust in the guise of worship. These they called temples to love.

We wept.

Though your Mother was known of old even by my Chosen, and you can know it, and even though both Father and Mother were revered in the Holy of Holies for a thousand years in the Temple, since before the days of Rome it has been too cruel a world to receive your Mother, and as many precious and simple things were allowed to be removed, for they were too Holy to be reviled by evil, even so I have allowed the blessing of invisibility to cover your Mother, that she might not be subjected to the evils of this Generation. When men came to see womankind as cattle, and slaves, and whores, and beings upon whom they could unleash their wrath in unholy violence and murder of the Innocent, the Glory of the Feminine was taken from them, for they deserved it not.

I have tolerated that I and my name are defiled and spoken in all manner of

630

savagery and evil; and that my Son and His name are defiled and spoken of in all manner of evil, but it is not tolerated that Mother should be treated and stepped upon as mankind has treated the daughters and mothers of men.

Yes, as the children have always known, you have a Mother in Heaven.

She is so loving as you cannot imagine, and weeps for you as you cannot fathom. She is precious beyond all your imagining, to me. You loved her so fully when you were here with us, and you love her even still, and she knows. She mourns for those sons who have fallen, and her daughters who have been hurt by them; even as she mourns for our daughters who have been so much hurt that they have turned in their pain to hurt our sons.

You have left a Heavenly Home, and in your heart, you still have many memories, and your longings for home cannot be denied. When the special child among you created the story for you he called E.T., the Extra Terrestrial, you saw the story of one alone, lonely, who wanted to phone home. He wanted to phone home so he could go home. It looked as if he never would go home, that he would be left, left to die. He was dying, and he could not go home. Grown men and burly men wept and wept, and children wept, and women wept. Few there were who did not weep at the story of E.T., for it is your story, it is the story of all the Children. It is the Universal Story. You all want to come home.

You all want to phone home, and be rescued. You are separated. You see yourselves dying. You yearn to phone home, to call and to beg:

Please, let me come home.

Your Mother and I beheld this, and wept also, for we knew your longing and your pain, and we know how much you want to come home.

Know this: We want you to come home.

Yes, your Mother in Heaven loves you.

As you know you have a Father in Heaven, you also have a Mother there.

Is this the meaning of the paleo-Hebrew inscription at Kuntillet 'Ajrud on the jars, the Taanach incense stand and Khirbet el-Kom tomb inscriptions from the early years of Solomon's Temple?

Yes. Even those who study these now know these things were held true.

I will have to look up the references to the Temple and Mother in Josephus and in the Talmud where it is written, about the Holy of Holies and the Holy Marriage, but am I understanding correctly that our marriages here on earth are to be in a similitude of the Holy, Celestial Marriage, and that you are married?

Yes. It is the right way, you know. Yes, your Heavenly Mother is my wife, and I am her Husband. We are your Parents, in Eternal Covenant.

This is very different for me to receive.

Yet the time has come that it is meet for you to receive it, even as it was never lost, but only ignored. The time of ignoring must pass. There are those who find this hard to receive, that I AM a Husband; yet as you have called me Father, even as I AM your Father, you also have a Mother.

I glory in my Covenants, and glory in declaring to my daughters that I AM.

Is not the central Glory of being God the being able to make and keep a commitment, would not you say?

Yes, I most certainly would say.
I clearly see the truth of it.
I know that the scriptures and all the Holy writings solidly express the sanctity of marriage, and the requirement of marriage, and the wrongness of sex except in marriage; I have often wondered why it is so important, and why sexual sin is so serious. Why are we commanded to have no ..... whew! this is tough for me to talk about with you..... no sex with anybody except that we are married to them? I guess this should be my next question.
Why is this so important, as everything testifies that it is?

The Design of DNA is the great achievement for all Intelligences, and as its power has been given to you in this mortal existence, even so, it is sacred, and of infinitely greater power and significance than you imagine; its use must be governed, and those who will not abide this law here will find they have made little of that which is of greatest worth. The Procreation of Life is sacred.

By it Spirits come into the earth; only as it is respected in commitment and dedication will the children be blessed as they have a birthright to be.

It is of no surprise that the children in laboratories take the Design of DNA without thanks or gratitude, and do with it as they will, for so have the children always believed they could do with the gift of life as they willed, even the gift of life given them within their bodies. And the world has reeled in agonies over this devaluing of Life, and its covenants, and its powers, and the granting of its gift.

Yet it is the way of the child to take, without remembering to give thanks.

All Intelligences have the responsibility to respect this supreme gift, for the power to create life is as judged as the power to take life; yet you have seen both these powers set at naught, for both have been treated as nothing. For to many, what is easy to make is valueless; and what is easy to take, is to take.

Thus many take virtue from our daughters, and blindly make bodies for lives which they have no thought of whatsoever, and abandon them as nothing.

And many take trust from our daughters, and make promises in the night which evaporate even before the morning dew.

Yet in these things you err; and all who do so err, even unto their souls.

For in using the Gift of Life, you, the sons and daughters, become Co-Creators in the Generation, and reap treasures unto your souls. You have heard that children are blessings; you can only begin to comprehend what this means.

In the Temple, the High Priest wore upon his forehead a platelet of gold, the Ziz, which word means Flower; and upon it was written Holiness to the Lord. About the columns of the Temple were decorations of alternating flowers and pomegranates, wherein are countless seeds; upon the hem of the High Priest's robe were sewn all around alternating bells and pomegranates.

There are many ancient symbols of beauty given in holiness, to recall to those who would know their heritage the Truth of all things. The creation of the Seed of the Unfolding Design, and the continuation of the Seeds, is the unfolding of Creation. It is the hope of all Intelligences, the hope to progress to this Joy. This gift is given now, and by it too you are proven. There are those who have been faithful over small things; unto them shall be given great stewardships; there are those who have been faithful over greater things; unto them may be given even the greatest things.

And so, Adam was created in Our image, in Our image created We him, even male and female created We him. There is wisdom in the Design that each holds a part of the other, for it is wisdom that there be opposition within all things. Herein is eternal balance; herein is eternal wisdom.

And as it is not good for Intelligences to be alone, even so they are all endowed with a gift of Being. And there are some who are inherently nurturing, and are in awe of life, and in them is a yeaning to nurture all living things in love. In these was placed the power to become the Daughters of God. And others inherently were endowed with gifts of governing, and administering, and of protecting and defending. In these was placed the power to become the Sons of God. Each is given as each most yearns to serve; in unity they may become one, and greater than the two. In both are the gifts of each, in lesser proportions, and unto some are many gifts given, that they might serve. All have the power to become whole. In all Intelligences who have the capacity to become Daughters and Sons of God, there is the gift of providing, giving, teaching, and sharing, and of willingness to sacrifice that other Intelligences might also rise up in Joy. Yet you are not the same, from the Beginning; you are male and female. The nature of the Intelligences is such that by the two, all things are possible. The key is to comprehend that the more that can obtain, the greater is the Glory of all. For this reason also you are commanded to love one another, to feed the hungry, to clothe the naked, to shelter each other, and to help each other to rise.

Those who can think to enjoy all things good by themselves, who would rush to the table and feed without first seeing who needed help, even to help the lame, and the blind, and the weak, and poor and the helpless, such are only worthy to serve others who feel these needs of compassion and love for all.

In all things there is balance; therefore neither the woman is without the man, nor the man without the woman in the Kingdom. Herein is great Truth.

This leads directly into my next question, so I think I will ask it here. It is ever so evident as I read the scriptures that women are equally important with men. This has been one thing I have continually been aware of. Yet there is very little in the scriptures - I speak of the many Scrolls and Books and Letters which have been selected and preserved under one cover as Bible - about women, and their lives, and their participation. Few are mentioned, while seemingly rather unimportant things about men are mentioned in passing all the time. I accept from all that is there, that you respect womanhood, and love women; I have seen it as no coincidence that the first witness of Yeshua, of Jesus when he had arisen, was to a woman, and that the Angel appeared first to women to tell them of the risen Messiah, and they were instructed to go and tell the men. Again, I am being rather clumsy in my asking this, but I will ask:
Why are women so seldom mentioned in the scriptures?

There is much for you to admit to in shame in your Generation. All that is of high standing is eventually defiled; I myself, God, am defiled and reviled as worse than filth by virtually every child who stubs his toe. The less some precious things are set before man, the less ugliness and filth is flung at them.

Womanhood has been defiled by man, as man has seen woman to be of naught by his making; so he has seen in his own history whereby to cleverly relieve his burden onto her by guilt unearned; so has he gloried in his unrighteous dominion over her, usurping her sovereignty and her Light.

Yet for this jealousy and unrighteous dominion, much that might have been preserved unto the daughters was never written, according to the traditions of the fathers. Even good men were born into these mentalities, which cultivated much good out of generation after generation.

Toward women in general, the masculine spirit is continually devising evil. The nail that sticks up will be hammered down, men say. So it is with the male: attack and destroy that which is good, and beauty. Man is not happy until he makes himself lord in might.

Until women were under foot, man was not happy.

This is part of the great challenge of mortality, to learn to respect and protect femininity: it is the creative force.

When man destroys woman he destroys himself.

What man destroys in woman, he destroys in himself.

How many men are unconscious of this as they make their conquests, ravage heart after heart in exploits and lies, and rapes and horrors? Look upon your generation, and see: the more women received their portion, the more jealous man was angered, and devised ways to take it from her.

While the storm rages, the tender are best protected from the wind.

So women have, in many ways, been kept safely away from the open field, where battles are carried out. Yet there was much recorded: it has been taken away. Even among the Hebrews, where my word was mostly kept sacrosanct, they were unable to resist tampering. Much written about women has been removed, precious and special things. And what the sons have failed to record, the Angels have written down and recorded in the Book of Life.

You shall have it all some day.

Thus many of the ancient commandments were given to protect women. This is wisdom in me. Many daughters today have not understood, even though they know the hearts of men, even as I do.

In men's vanity, they have sold their daughters and women as their cattle, bought them as cheaply as a drink of wine, and remembered them less fondly.

Men have rebuked women and punished them for the evil men imagine themselves, falling into their lusts and their weaknesses as a madness uncontrolled. Women have been strong and borne this all from the beginning, as well they saw from the beginning this suffering should befall them.

This they have done, that the Children might be; and Glory to them for it.

As the Lamb gave himself for all mankind, so have women given themselves for all mankind; and as women have borne the children of each generation of this Generation into mortality, so have they suffered and borne the vanity and arrogance of men, and been beaten, burned and murdered even as they have borne the children of kings who would become kings over many.

The heart of man is filled with diverse lusts and hatreds, and these he works out against woman calling her the cause of his lusts and the cause of his hatreds. This is great evil, and so the hearts of men overflow with this evil. That which a man cannot control within himself he blames upon woman rather than admit his own obsession, and in greater obsession he denies his own madness and calls her temptress.

Men have been weak and evil in all of these abuses and murders they have done, and they have heaped upon woman the evil which is within men's souls. In burning them, men have imagined to cleanse themselves. Yet they have heaped greater filth upon their souls and condemnation upon their sons who have seen, and followed suit. Verily shall these sins also be called upon the souls of men, that as they have battered and cut and burned and violated and mutilated and murdered our daughters, they have taught their sons to do likewise, and they have done it as they were so taught by their fathers.

Men have confined women, and bound them up for the fear of their own evil in their hearts, and robbed women of their portion in this life. Men have burned women in lust and jealousy, destroying that which they understand not, and fear. And that which they understand not they coveted. As all vanity disdains honor, men have taken from women their precious gifts of healing and nurturing, understanding nothing of the gifts save they could gain prestige in the eyes of other men, and power and value of exchange, even money.

You know the gifts of women, and know that these have been wrested from the hand of women and usurped with great envy and greed. And often in wresting these gifts from women has man murdered woman to make permanent the theft.

In this, great evil has been done, and many generations of both sons and daughters have been impoverished for it.

Thus the blood of woman is called for upon the hands of all evil men.

Woe unto all men who abuse women and bruise our daughters' tender souls. Woe unto all men who by force take from women that which is Holy and cannot be taken, but only given.

I show unto you that all our daughters remain chaste and pure of all evil which is forced upon them by men in violence, for to us they are chaste still. So should they see themselves, and so should all men still see them as chaste still.

It is more evil in the hearts of men to call unchaste the woman who is chaste, who is violated by the man who is unchaste.

It is the man who is therein unchaste, and not the woman.

All men who condemn the woman who is violated by man, whose virtue remains within her heart but whose body is violated in theft by evil man, shall also remain unchaste in their judgments until they repent and fill their souls with eternal sorrow and compassion.

Verily have my daughters lived in continual starvation of compassion.

Woe unto all men who beguile women and teach them that to give themselves without concern in unmarried abandon is wise and powerful, a true expression of their sovereignty. Woe unto my daughters who foolishly seek to revel in all that man does in evil, for they shall not reap the joys they have been deceived into imagining, but they shall make of themselves the cattle men still desire them to be.

I delight in the chastity of my daughters, wherein is their Joy made full.

And it pleases me that my sons should love my daughters, and covenant with them in covenants of Truth, and cherish them and treat them with all kindness and gentleness, and care for them in the days of their labor, and treasure them, even as great treasures. In this love do they both remain chaste.

Until the daughters foolishly give in to men's deception and convince themselves that they do no wrong in breaking that law which they know is right, they are pure. But as they begin to lay with man by their own self deception, persuaded by man to make free that which is to be shared only in covenant, they then as man do lower themselves even unto his level, and receive with him that which they think they have wanted: to be like unto such men in their days.

As they have seen this evil in men, woe unto them who wish to follow it.

And men shall know my wrath for their injuries upon my daughters.

Every drop of woman's blood, every bitter tear woman has wept, every cry of pain woman has raised unto the heavens or pent within her heart, every bruise upon her body, every wound upon her mind, every life that has been brutally taken, shall be required at the hand of those men who have so abused my daughters.

And great shall be the sorrow of these men.

I hear all as you have said. And I feel to say Thank you.

As I have thought to ask about women, I remember what you said about nature not selecting to cripple the young of a species, and disable those who have to carry such helpless young as they flee predators and aggressors. I have often thought about this. Childhood is very helpless, and though as we grow older it can be a lot of fun, we are still so dependent, so helpless. We grow to look back on childhood with some longings, but as children we just want to be big.

I guess I am trying to ask:
Why children?
Why so long helpless?
Why so long maturing?

You are a longer time maturing than you can ever imagine. Your memory is veiled so you may learn, and learn Faith.

Why are children so impatient to grow up? Behold your self.

This is your nature. For this reason you are here, to learn patience.

Patience is one of the things you most need to learn now. You cannot imagine the patience it takes to reach the point of being able to create all of this, and have it remain balanced, even as you see it is, upon a thread.

The law of nature is to return to chaos. Everything wants to return to chaos. Ordering it, and getting it to obey and keep order, that is the task, that is the purpose. You begin to learn a bit about the concept of order and disorder, organization and disorganization, balance and chaos, through the window of being children.

And if there are no children, then how shall you learn from them?

Your children are the mirror of innocence which you must refine and capture within yourself if you are to become what you were born to be: my child in the fullest sense.

If we are your Spirit Children, and we have a fully developed self and being in our Spirit Bodies before our birth into this state of physical matter, why are we so helpless in the beginning?
Why begin as babies?

The process teaches you much. A few notice, and learn.

Why are we helpless for so long?

This is more your perspective than real.

Your capabilities, even at a young age, are astounding to yourselves. You marvel at your babies. If you encouraged them more, and expected more, you would be surprised at what is possible in infancy, not to mention as you grow up. You see yourselves as helpless as babies, and so you are in many ways. On the other hand, the process of growing, learning and maturing is a reflection of what you have already transcended in getting here. Your growth process here is distilled into a single breath of time, compared to what you have already gone through.

What do you mean?

The obtaining of knowledge and wisdom is a process, and cannot be avoided nor dispensed with.

Of these two: knowledge and wisdom, knowledge is the most easily obtained. Your generation is realizing this on a grand scale in this time.

Yet the more important capacity, wisdom, is worth thousands of times what knowledge is worth.

See that as knowledge is passed on from generation to generation and is built upon, wisdom must be learned by each generation, and each one.

I don't understand. Knowledge is unimportant?

No, hear what I say.

The devils have great knowledge, and yet they tremble. Wisdom guides choice, and wise choice in Free Agency gives freedom and power.

The power of the choice wisely made is the power to choose again.

Your generation values facts, information and knowledge. Knowledge is the substance which wisdom governs. These are things which many children have understood, and I have no need to tell you. Yet know that while the two are inseparable, wisdom is greater than knowledge.

But why children?
Why are we put here for a probation as children?
Why do we have children, and raise them?

Children teach you quantitative and qualitative wisdom that transcends all of the other knowledge and wisdom of the sciences and matter itself.

Study a child, and you will learn the secrets of the creation of the cosmos.

As you grow up, and become conscious of shame, you always wish to appear wise, and knowledgeable. The older child who has lost innocence asks How something is done, which is actually the easy part. To ask How appears wise, and upon hearing, one knows How. Knowing how, one can do that thing, when all is perfect for its doing. Yet until one knows Why, one cannot exponentially expand the wisdom to its ultimate applications.

Children ask the simplest questions, and these lead to greatest Truth.

The innocence of a child knows no shame, and what is unknown, it asks. The innocence of the child wonders Why. Why it is done the way it is. This is the key to commanding all of the cosmos, and having it work.

What the child is told, the child receives, believing.

Even if there is total lacking of understanding.

This is the trust of a child.

The answers of the cosmos are discovered by asking Why.

So many things can start out well, but then they begin to go wrong. You see this on a small scale in your momentary estate here. Project that discovery on a cosmic scale. The minimal small disaster you create in your life, even on the planet in your generation, is nothing compared to the potentials of a disaster in the cosmos. Each and every thing done must be completely, ever so completely thought out to its furthest and uttermost future consequence. Only when the most far-reaching consequence has been seen, and all has unfolded as desired, may one proceed.

The universe is constantly on the brink of complete reversal, and each and every decision enacted is part of what holds everything as you know it, in place.

What has all this got to do with children?

Observe the child.

Observe the process of growth.

Observe the pattern of learning.

Observe the process of learning.

See the process as it unfolds.

See the learning as it is imprinted.

See the effect which each new bit of learning has upon the whole: from the baby's first drawn breath. It is exponential.

Exponential?

Yes.

You have always perceived learning as a one-thing-at-a-time process.

It is not.

With each new bit of learning imprinted, every previous bit of learning is re-evaluated, reconsidered, and re-learned in its new relative position and light. From this comes exponential learning, and the sum expands beyond the whole.

By the time you are four years old you have billions upon billions of bits of learned knowledge, much of which you use unconsciously - you take it for granted and just act in the way which produces the assumed and guaranteed desired results - and much of which you use is processing and problem solving.

Every new bit of knowledge you obtain causes its ripple-effect throughout your entire database system, and thus the instant of your comprehension is at once a process of myriad simultaneous understandings, followed by a rapid series of consequential understandings by reflection, which rapidly decrease in frequency until your conscious cognitive has exhausted its current availability of files, at which moment you say to yourself, "Now I understand this."

However, as an ongoing process, your mind retrieves information relevant and at times irrelevant, but triggered by associative memory, and the process continues to unfold with continuing and new exponential understandings, each of which is a learning, and each of which then ripples through the entire data base, revising all previous concepts in accordance with the new data as it is learned and comprehended and understood amid all.

This is what is happening within your physical matter brain from the moment you are born. That is what has been going on in your Intelligence.

Your most heavily imprinted time-period of your life is your first few years of life. After that, the process slows down to a fractional rate of what you were accomplishing as a child. You never learn so much so fast as in your infancy.

You need to eventually rediscover how you did it as a child, and allow yourself the flow and pace you had as a child.

Become as a child, in other words?

Yes. And remember the most important word a child uses.

What?

No.

I mean: What is the most important word a child uses?

No, WHAT is not the most important word a child uses.

I'm sorry, I don't think I know how to ask. Please help me.

Don't you remember being a child?

Yes, but I don't remember any word that was so important.

You see, as you grow up, you forget. You need to remember the word.

What is the word?

No, WHY is the word.

Why is the word?

Yes.

I don't understand.

Your child asks why something is as it is. What do you do?

I tell, I explain. I give the answer.

And as soon as you finish telling why it is like it is, your child asks WHY? Why things are as you explained is a good question. What do you do then?

That usually gets a little tougher. I answer as best I can.

And when your child has heard you, the child still asks WHY?

And by that time, I usually don't know why. So I say something like, 'Because it's that way. That's all. Now go play.'

Yet you give up too soon.
The child does not.
The child knows there is still much to ask, and wants to know. When you grow up, you too soon give up. For this reason you fail to learn the most important things.
The innocence of a child does not know to be embarrassed by asking why, nor does the innocence of a child feel any question is silly, only good. The innocence of a child wants to know why, and believes in answers to all things.
It is the older, vain child who smugly tells the younger child 'That's a dumb question' to hide his shame that he doesn't know the answer.
The best question which leads directly to the full knowledge of everything physical and of the Spirit can begin even with the question of the grass.

The grass?

Yes. Ask.

641

Ask what?

About the grass.

I don't know how.

You have forgotten. I will ask for you.

> Why is there grass?
> Why do animals and insects need to eat?
> Why do they need to grow up to be big and strong?
> Why are there animals and insects?
> Why do there need to be animals and insects?
> Why is the grass green?
> Why does it need the green stuff in it like you said?
> Why does grass always grow up to be grass?
> Why do cows like to eat grass?
> Why does the grass turn into the cow?
> Why does the grass turn into milk in the cow?
> Why do baby calves need to drink milk?
> Why do I need to drink milk?
> Why?
> Why?
> Why?

Now I remember. It can go on forever when we get to 'Why?'

Ultimately, grass is, and is as it is, and is for what it is, because it is the best method there is to trap energenes in a way that they can be stored, and then released within the slow-burning fires of your bodies, which was perceived to be the best way to fashion bodies which would be, and do, all I imagined they could do, and that this would be good.

To this a child could still ask, Why?

The ultimate answer to Why this is done is simply, Because I love you.

Physical answers will always fall far short of the root of all questions. If a child asks how is it that there is grass, and why is it green, the DNA formula is mathematical and enormous; the atomic answer is enormous; the chemical photosynthetic answer from structure to function to substance on through is enormous; the molecular answer is enormous; the inferior alternatives which could be considered but were rejected comprise a further enormous discourse of conceptualizations and bio-energene, bio-atomic, bio-molecular, bio-chemical possibilities which break down into less desirable results.

But then it ends.

You know how, and you question no more.

All of this is fascinating, and the technical answers will all be perfectly true, but it avoids the main question, WHY?

The adults who have become tired of the children's questions of WHY, who do not know the answer themselves, and do not want to admit that they do not know, do as all adults do in their very adult-like manner, they dismiss the question as foolish.

'It is foolish to ask Why of things that have no answer to Why,' they say; 'They are, just because they are, and I can show you how they are.'

It avoids admitting that there is an answer above a mere science.

It avoids admitting that there is Love, that Love is behind all things, that Love is in all things.

HOW is a very safe question, for it is mathematical, and safe, and can show great wisdom, wherein there is pride of knowledge, and it has an end.

Love does not end.

There is no reductionism of Love, not in the children, not in the earth, not in the Cosmos, not in me.

Children still remember this, and while the wonder of the scientific answers are fascinating and very exciting, the loneliness of the scientific answers leave the soul hungry, unsatisfied, when it has reached its perfect end.

Thus there are some who are forever seeking, and studying, yet they are never filled, and they are hungry still, for they do not learn, as they are afraid.

Yet they do not have to be afraid.

Why?

The ultimate answer to all answers of a child is *'Because I love you.'*

When you heard this as a child, you looked up and you smiled, happy.

You did not ask any more, 'Why?'

This is what you wanted. This is what you were searching for.

In the innocence of childhood, this is where you stopped asking 'Why?'

For in the innocence of childhood, this is where you wanted to reach.

The innocence of the child, who has not been hurt, who has never been betrayed, who has not ever been taught to look upon himself or herself as dirty, or stupid, or unwanted, or worthless, is to hear 'I love you,' and without pain, and tears, and doubt, and shame, receive this joy. The betrayed child becomes damaged, and the damaged child believes she and he can no longer be loved. Yet the innocence of the child rejoices in being loved, wants to be loved, and when hearing she and he is loved, does not feel to ask, 'Why?' For in innocence, all know: I love them.

It is the world which teaches children to hear they are loved, and to doubt, and disbelieve, and look upon themselves as unlovable, and ask, Why?

Yet even to this question there is an answer.

The final answer to all questions in the end is, *'Because I love you.'*

I begin to understand.

WHY is the key to the universe.

If you wish to learn that which can be learned, become as a little child, and behold the cosmos with all that you know, born again within you as a little child, and ask WHY?

As a child you would ask Why until you exhausted the imagination of the adult. Now that you have the capabilities of the adult, ask Why until you exhaust the imagination of the child.

As you step beyond your last answer, and go beyond your final exasperated exhaustion of imagination, your questions then begin to align themselves toward Eternity.

When you rise above all things and your eyes are fully opened, you will re-discover that WHAT is happening is visible, seen, and there it ends.

WHY it happens is the question which unlocks the cosmos.

Why does it happen this way? Why now? Why not before? Why not later?

Explore the word WHY until you exhaust it, just as a child, and you will begin your new direction toward Eternal Light.

WHAT is the most finite of questions, answered in few words, in few pieces of knowledge. When you have learned WHAT, you know almost nothing.

WHY is the question of infinite unfolding, which can and will lead you back to your beginnings.

Why?

Very good. You're catching on.

Thank you.

The truth is simple: WHAT? and HOW? teaches you knowledge. You ask WHAT and HOW and you get back a WHAT and HOW answer: a fact.

You need information and knowledge, for without a foundation of information and knowledge, you have no basis to begin to wonder Why. For this reason, the beginnings of your life as a child are expressed in WHAT. WHAT is your first question at birth. You ask it of many things, until you have learned. You learn very much, very quickly.

WHAT are these sounds I hear? No answer.

WHAT is this pressure I feel? No answer.

WHAT is this strange squeezing I feel? No answer.

WHAT is this thing shining into my eyes? Answer: Light.

WHAT is this I feel so different from all I have known? Answer: Cold.

WHAT is this feeling I suddenly feel, to open my mouth and nose and suck in? Answer: The Breath of Life.

WHAT is this stuff coming into my chest? Answer: Air.

WHAT are these sounds, so different now? Answer: voices of my kind.

WHAT is this shrill sound I hear? Answer: my own voice. I am here.

All of these WHAT questions were asked and answered in your first sixty seconds of life.

You asked WHAT repeatedly from instant to instant in each progressive minute as you left the protective womb of your mother. Hour after hour, you looked around you and asked WHAT? With the coming of the light, came answers. All your first day, all your second day, each time you imprinted a new sight, heard a new sound, tasted a new taste, felt a new sensation, you asked WHAT? WHAT?

Soon you had collected millions of bits of WHAT knowledge in direct response to WHAT questions. Some questions gave answers that went back to the time of darkness:

WHAT is that same sound again now?

Answer: Voice of Mother, voice of Father, voice of Sister, voice of Brother, voice of another who loves me.

WHAT is this thing I see?

Answer: Face of Mother, of Father, of Sister, of Brother, of another who has come close.

And so you began to accumulate a vast collection of WHAT answers: Mother, father, Brother, Sister, Relative, light, air, water, milk, warmth, cold, hunger, food, security, vulnerability, danger, pain.

Soon you expanded your sphere of consciousness and learned details within answers already obtained: eyes, mouth, nose, teeth, face, hair, ears, earrings, lips, hands, fingers, cloth.

Then you learned remarkable new things: cat, dog, fur, moist, dry, blanket, toy and so forth.

Then you began to notice that inside you felt different ways at different moments, when different things happened: surprise, startle, funny, hurt, sad.

Eventually you began to notice that same feeling, so good and warm and secure you had felt in the darkness, often so strongly, again and again you felt it now: when you were held and talked to by Mother, and Father and others, when you cried and food came, and dryness came, and warmth came, and soft musical sounds came, and you wanted to know WHAT it was, for this was the first thing you had ever felt as you remembered back into the time of Darkness.   WHAT?

WHAT was it?

Are you asking me?

Yes. WHAT WAS IT? The first thing you ever felt as you remember back into the time of Darkness?

You mean, when I was in my mother's womb?

Yes.

I closed my eyes, and went back in my mind to an image of myself as a tiny baby in my mother's arms, and then of myself even smaller, being born. I saw myself at the moment of my birth, small and quivering and covered with her blood, as I emerged out of my mother's body, into the hands of the woman who helped her.

Then I imagined as hard as I could, until I saw myself inside of my mother's womb, before the moment I had just seen, back in time, inside my mother's womb, unborn, waiting, floating in the darkness, the warmth, the safety, knowing only the consciousness of my mind in the darkness and warmth.

I imagined myself there until I saw myself only there, and nothing else, only me, enveloped and embraced by the blanket of comforting darkness, the warm embracing darkness of my mother's body. I focused on this self, my self, floating, floating, in silence.

In the distance, I could now hear a sound, soft, rhythmic, familiar, like waves washing along a shore. Again, and again, louder I could hear it nearby me. I strained, and focused, and the sound became louder and more distinct, and then, I knew.

It was the rhythmic pumping of my mother's heart, of her blood coursing around me; she was feeding me even with her own precious blood. And then I heard more, her lungs breathing air for me; and now I could hear the air, rushing in, and then escaping out of her lungs, and then in again, and out again, rhythmically as the soft breeze by an embracing sea.

I marveled at the enveloping pulsation all around me, the pulsing of her blood, her life-giving blood, and the gentle swaying feeling I could feel as she stood up, and sat down, and walked, and moved in the world out there, out there where I did not know.

I concentrated harder, as hard as I could, listening, and feeling my mother's body all around me. I felt myself begin to relax, to let go, for there was no need but to relax now, no need but to let go and relax and float in the warmth and the rhythmic swooshing music which swayed as I swayed, warm and floating and safe and ....

There it was. I felt it.

I felt warm and safe and ....

Oh, I felt that wonderful feeling!

It was touching me all around as I floated in the warm of my mother's body.

I could feel it. I now knew what it was.

It was love.

I could feel love, my mother's yearning for me, in her body.

Opening my eyes, I hit Caps Lock on the keyboard and typed

L O V E
I was loved, wasn't I? That is what I felt first, isn't it?

The screen remained empty for a moment, and then appeared

Yes.

Tears filled my eyes and my sobbing gently rocked me again in the warmth that was there.

Not all feel this, for there are mothers who have not loved.
These children, I love, and Mother loves, and in the womb, they have our Love.

Do you love me? I wrote.

Yes, I love you. Your Mother here loves you. You have millions upon millions of brothers and sisters who love you, here, and who have gone before you. You are ever so loved. If you could know the love which surrounds you at every moment, you would never again feel despair. We love you. You are loved.

Why am I here so far from you?

For needed experience. And we are not so far.

Why don't I remember you and Mother?

Your Memory is shielded by a veil, which closes as you reach a certain age of youth, for a wise and needful purpose. Yet this veil is open while you are in the womb, and it is open when you are born; and it remains very thin for some time after you are born.

In the womb you have full memory of Spirit Friends, and of Mother and of me, and of joyful things you have done, and joyful things friends have said; and as you wait in the short silence of the womb, you have your memories to comfort you. In this time of waiting and quiet your Spirit still communes, through the veil, and you also commune with the Heavenly Messengers and Angels who are near you and all

647

children.

Long have mothers beheld their newborn babes in their arms, asleep, and seen their precious smiles in sleep, sweet and perfect smiles of glee, even smiles lighting their whole faces, pure and precious. Mothers see, and know.

Many grown children have been to schools which study the Body, where Spirit is not permitted as reason for anything, and belief in things observed of the Spirit is shamed. From these the timid children have learned to be ashamed of the Spirit, and have learned to attribute all things to chemical causes. Though they still see what they see, they do no longer believe what they see, for they are intimidated to not believe, even shamed to be called foolish. And so they deny these smiles, and say, 'It is gas bubbles; the babies wince.'

You know this wearisome process well in your history.

And so, fearing the disdain and shaming disapproval of those who have set themselves as authorities, the students mimic as sages what they are told and repeat what all good books affirm, in order to answer the observed cause of these things as prescribed. And with these contrived explanations, they learnedly speak of gas, and gas bubbles, and chemical discomfort which causes wincing.

But what they see does not look this way to them, for they see both smiles and winces, and between the two, there is great and observable difference.

They see when gas bubbles cause wincing.

They see when their babies smile, and laugh, only hours old, only days old, only weeks old, and mothers know the difference in their precious babes.

The mothers see these things, and they know. They know that a newborn babe cannot yet have any understandings of joy, to laugh, to smile, and cannot yet have any memories to recall in sleep, to make them laugh and smile.

Therefore, they can only be remembering, with smiles, something before.

Know this is true.

These are the smilings and expressions of Joy as your babies are remembering, and seeing, and hearing in their Memories all the joys they have known in Spirit in their Spiritual Home, including the Joy of seeing the mother into whose body and life they have so often chosen to come. These are also the smilings and expressions of Joy on your newborn babies' sleeping faces as they commune with Angels whom they can hear speaking to them, but which you cannot hear.

You cannot fool mothers.

Mothers know.

Know that what mothers know, is true.

I have heard stories of young children, three years old, who have sat with their mother and been shown the family picture album for the first time, and as a page was turned and the child for the first time saw a picture of a long dead grandparent, the child's face lit up and the child said 'That's Grandpa George!' or whatever his name had been. And the mother was shocked, for no one had ever talked about Grandpa George, because he had died so long ago, and no one had ever shown the album to the child, and the mother in surprise asked the child 'How do you know his name?' And the child innocently and matter-of-factly replied 'He's the one who brought me here when I was born,' and turned the next page, for it was no big deal. And a year and more later, that same child, being shown the album again with mother, turned the pages asking 'Who is that?' and 'Who is that? and arriving at the page with Grandpa George's picture, showed no signs of recognition and also asked, 'Who is that?'

Now I understand. When we are infants, that the veil remains thin for some time. But it closes. It certainly closes.

How long does it remain open? When does the veil close?

It is different for each child, but within a close range of time in youth.

Do you remember when you were a child, and you suddenly found yourself standing in the driveway, and though you recognized everything around you, you didn't know how you got there?

I remembered only too well. This had been one of the most puzzling events of my life, at age four, standing on the driveway of my home, looking down at my shoes, and looking up, not knowing anything from before that moment.

It was as if I had been suddenly created in that instant. I didn't remember getting there, how I got there on the driveway, or what had happened a few minutes ago, or that morning, or the previous night or yesterday, or anything. I just suddenly existed, with a memory of only things.

I still remembered that moment as if I were there.

I stood in total puzzlement.

I remember holding out my hands and looking at them, turning them over and looking at the tops, and then my palms. It was as if I had never seen them before, but I knew they were my hands. I remember looking again down at my shoes and my legs, and the driveway, and then around me at the yard and the bushes and the fence and the house and the trees, and again all around me.

Where had I come from? I could not remember.

How had I gotten there? I could not remember.

What had happened this morning?

Yesterday?

All this past week?

I could not remember. I did not know.

I was just there, standing in the driveway looking at my mother talking to Mr. Schleiman across the fence, and the world began from that moment forward.

It was so strange. I knew everything I was seeing, knew what it was. I just didn't have any memories of anything I had ever done.

I knew my mother, our neighbor Mr. Schleiman, the driveway, the trees, the house, the sky, the sun. I looked around me and recognized everything - but I could not remember one second before my finding myself all at once standing there.

It was truly as if the universe had been created at that moment, and me with all of my knowledge of everything I could see, only there was no past - no memory of anything preceding it.

I had only one mental snapshot of something before that moment, so I found out later. That was when my cast was being cut off from my legs when I was a year and a half old. I still can see that mental snapshot, like a photograph: the room, pinkish in color, the nurse, the doctor's table, my mother beside me, the doctor.

But except for that single image, the world began at the moment I stood in the driveway. From that moment onward my memories begin. I had told this experience to very few people, asking them what it meant, asking what had happened. No one knew. The few who listened to it had shaken their heads and agreed that this was a very strange thing, a very odd occurrence.

I left my memories and put my hands back over the keyboard.

Yes, I remember. What happened? I typed.

That was the moment the veil closed to you, when you no longer could live between worlds. All that you had experienced was veiled, yet all that you had learned you carried forward. That was the moment of the closing of the veil. It usually takes place during sleep, and most children never experience what you experienced. They never know. They just wake up, and it is a new day.

This is amazing. I finally know.
So after the veil is closed, we are on our own. Why?

You need to learn Faith. This is the only way. If you had a full or even partial knowledge, you would know, and not have to dip deep into your soul to believe that which you cannot see. Though this seems of no useful importance to you, it is of greatest importance. The suns and galaxies and worlds are gathered and organized and formed through this power. Many great and useful things are possible to you by this power.

What else should I understand about children?

Children are much more capable than this generation thinks. This is the first generation that has given children everything except expectation. Children at a young age are capable of great responsibility, and they require responsibility to feel worth. They require achievements to feel worth. When they are given neither opportunity, it is easy for them to believe that they are of no worth. Though you see they are capable of great folly for lack of experience and wisdom, yet know that it is by small things that they learn to master greater things. Their physical ability greatly exceeds their wisdom in wielding that physical capability. It is a challenge to challenge them.

This is the challenge of being Parent.

To learn all that this process can teach you, for this you are also here.

The children's ability to do and to be responsible can be seen in times and countries where it is an expectation of birth. It was so in your country until only a century ago, when abusive exploitation of children was counteracted by a swing to its opposite, and children were given nothing to do at all but learn. Ever since, the false idea that children can do less and less has proliferated, and it is evidenced as self-fulfilling prophecy produces less ever more visibly, from the disastrous result that unharnessed engines of great power run themselves into furious havoc.

As less and less is expected, so vigorous childhood becomes bored and discontent. Children hate to be treated as children. Yet parents who do not want to take the time to be parents, who are themselves blinded by selfish goals, do not take the time to plan, and provide that which children most need: parenting. Houses are provided, and clothing is provided, and food is provided, and schools are provided, and entertainments and diversions are provided, but what of parenting?

Parenting is not provided.

And so children are left to raise themselves, in a world of children relying upon themselves. With much unharnessed energy and unused ability children look for paths to stretch and prove themselves; being given nothing constructive to do, and ever more without standards of manners, civility and morals, they become ever more like flies.

Stripped of their examples of how to behave to one another, exposed to hideous visions and images of destruction and chaos as normal daily routine, is it any wonder that so many yearn to become Lord of the Flies?

In this generation you add the problem of birth defects brought on by the exposure of the embryonic child to the poisons of nicotine, alcohol, caffeine and drugs, both illegal and medicines; the DNA in the bodies which could have been healthy is impeded in ways so subtle that only now does your generation begin to awaken to them, after the masses of bodies are already damaged.

This you have done to yourselves.

This you are doing to yourselves.

The army of such chemically damaged bodies, unable to function as their DNA designed them to function, is staggering. It is growing exponentially.

Most of you refuse to see it.

I see it, and shudder.

In this, you fail your children in massive hoards, and your generation is going to have to face the consequences of its own unconsciousness.

You do not realize, as you fail yourselves, you fail your generation.

Truly, you stand at the brink of losing the skills which have been passed down from generation to generation, for you have enshrined scholastic skills above social skills. Your error manifests itself around you more each day.

Where are your Grandmothers, who have become old and wise, who have learned the wisdom of their days, and should teach your children? Where are your Crone Mothers, wise and able? Where are your Grandfathers, who have become old and wise, who have learned wisdom from the frenzy of their earlier days, and know the need for self control, and respect, and a helping hand? Before, it was always so. Yet since what you call World War II, your families have caused distance between the generations, and you are more and more isolated from your older generations, whose wisdom and counsel you desperately need.

As you have turned your hearts from your elderly, you have lost your greatest resource for your children.

Children for most generations have had the presence of grandparents, and aunts and uncles who were at home. These watched and saw and guided and counseled. These placed expectations of industry, productivity, obedience, self-control, manners, respect, and forbearance. These gave systems of order, and watched until they were obeyed. Now no one watches, and the commands are left unheeded; no one watches until they are obeyed, and thus chaos rises in fury and might. These elders taught what they knew, and demanded cooperation and respect within a system of behavior suited for cooperative interaction. Children were taught how to act towards one another, and be fair.

And for all of your books, in the end, will this not either be the key to your preservation or the curse of your destruction?

You have begun to wonder, as your technology brings you to the power to destroy life from the face of your planet, and you have begun to ask yourselves: Have any other worlds in the universe come to this moment of technology and survived it? Or have all which reach this moment of technology destroyed themselves with it, for they could not treat each other civilly?

See as you ask this question that you have discovered a secret: the civil and social teaching of your children is infinitely more critical to you than any of the other learnings. How you treat each other will ultimately decide your fate.

In previous generations, children knew the members of their communities, those they encountered as they walked down the street and lane. They knew who made the clothes they wore; they knew who baked the food they ate and who grew it and sold it as they passed the marketplace; they knew who made the shoes they wore and who mended them.

For much distance in any direction they knew faces and names, and they themselves were known. They had a family name, and all knew it; they understood that their disgrace was disgrace to their family; this served all in the community for good. They could not act wildly even at a distance from their home, for someone knowing them and their parents would cry out and tell them that before the sun should set their parents would know. Earned shame which strengthens Intelligence and curbs wildness wielded its worthy gift of learned behaviors beneficial to the community, and most highly beneficial to the one who carried them within.

Your generation is re-discovering that it takes a family, a village, a tribe, a town, and a neighborhood to raise a child.

Yet this has been discarded as unimportant, while throughout all previous time it has been the manner of life and living.

Where are your families?

Children have a right to fathers and mothers.

The sons complain that today, the daughters do not want to mother children at home; yet how long have sons not wanted to be, and not been fathers in their homes? How long have the sons delighted more in adventures and comrades, and escapes into pleasures, rather than be fathers at home? To provide the seeds and sire Life is but the smallest part of fatherhood, and is less than nothing of being a father. How many fathers model father's roles at home?

To father as father, and to mother as mother is the commitment of Life; it is teaching, and patience, and studying, and sharing that which was studied.

For thousands of years the daughters have been faithful as mothers. Though many have been enticed by the consumerist discontent of this age, and seek to fill their discontent outside of motherhood, have the daughters been given sound modeling by the sons as devoted and concerned fathers at home?

Why do women think they don't want to mother children in the home?

Shall the Sons blame this upon the Daughters also?

How long has it been since men have wanted to be and are fathers?

How many men think each day "I am a father" and fulfill a father's role?

More and more children have been and are being raised without fathers.

And so a generation arises wherein children are more and more left without models of mothers who know mothering, and fathers in fathering.

And did not the Sons put fatherhood to naught first?

How long have the Sons betrayed the oath of fatherhood?

There are countries in your world today where 20% of the children are born illegitimately to teenage girls. Where are the fathers? In abdication.

This has always been the shame of your earth, but it has never been so great a shame as now.

Your generation has disdained as foolishness the Law of Chastity, and the sons have deceived the daughters into believing that as they give themselves freely, they express their freedom, only to rob them of that which before required much effort and strategy to steal. Yet the curse you have unleashed rages around you even now, as the world groans more and more with the burden of a generation raised without fathers.

What is a twenty-year old girl with five children going to do?

You see and bemoan your near-saturation divorce rate, yet you still do not hear: this is a message, that the brutalities and cruelties of the sons of men are no longer tolerable among the daughters of women. Too many daughters are in pain, and they cannot take it any more, and they are getting out. The sons are not hearing: they need to learn that they do not own women, and they cannot beat and abuse women just because they have been given a vow of fidelity, and a legal script which says the woman is wife; they cannot vent their angers and frustrations on women; they cannot sire, and neglect wife and fathering. Marriage is not a certificate of slave ownership. Though selfishness increases daily and deceives many into divorce, has the time not come for the daughters to demand a higher quality of relationships in marriage?

The children deserve it. The daughters deserve it.

The sons deserve it.

Yet hear the message, that women are Just Saying NO! No, we are not going to let you beat us any more, and sexually abuse us any more; No, we are not going to let you beat and abuse our children any more! The daughters will no longer tolerate being beaten, being strangled, being betrayed, and then given diseases when they remain faithful.

For so long, women have been told how much they need men, how much they need a husband, and this has been a steady diet for generations and generations. Though it is true, yet the time has come that the daughters have seen, and understand, that they are needed by men. Men need women.

Truly the sons are more needy.

Are the sons ready to understand just how much they need women and see them stand as co-heirs, and treat them with the respect they must have to survive? For with your new found technologies, the observations and compiling of numbers begins to show forth. Learn what you must learn; learn it and know:

The sons live longer if they are married; they are healthier if they are married; they suffer less depression if they are married.

The daughters, who have so solemnly been told they need men, do not enjoy this boon: they are sicker, more depressed, and live shorter lives if they are married.

For so long men have been telling women that they cannot survive without men, but what do we really see?

The daughters must learn better how to choose husbands. They must learn: what is a good mate, what is a good father. It has nothing to do with money, or cuteness, but a man who knows her, values her, and respects and cherishes her, who has values, and who will be a true and good mate.

It is a matter of the daughters feeling and thinking that they are worthy to be treated better, and the sons rising above their shame and becoming men.

For verily, the measure of the man has long been set falsely by flies.

Those who have an ear to hear, hear.

Yet where are the children, after all of this?

Having no adults of wisdom and moral and manners to guide them, they are left to forage for themselves in a world which has abandoned them, and which no longer sees them. They walk down streets and lanes and are not seen by name and family recognition, nor can they find a face to attach to anything they own nor wear nor eat nor see. As they no longer know to whom they should look in gratitude for all that they have, and thereby to know of its value in time, talent and energy invested, so as they walk they are unknown and walk invisibly through the streets, seen not as children blossoming in the promise of life's future, but in fear, as animals on the hunt. They walk, and as they are seen as unknown prowlers, they become invisible, anonymous prowlers.

The pursuit of riches and comforts and possessions and merchandise has left the young behind; there is no time for them. Well the ancient prophet warned of your day, that they will make merchandise of you, and so they have.

The adults who should be their generational families have abandoned the values, and then themselves, and then the children, the children have no tribe, no family, no neighborhood, no community, no framework of contributing friends with whom they can find welcome, by whom they can be embraced, from whom they can expect watchfulness, into whom they may expect to grow.

And so, to whom do they turn?

To the flies.

Having no models recognizable into which they can imagine they may grow, their imagination turns to all they know: themselves.

Having no adults to support and guide them, they turn to each other.

Now they consult among themselves, having no mentors or models of wise adulthood to guide them or counsel them. Every one falls upon his own counsel, and the emotionally maimed lead the prenatally injured. Lacking wisdom and experience, eyes filled with fantasy visions they know not are fantasy, childishness they would outgrow in but a few more years, still they create a society of children without guidance, without wisdom, without morals, without judgment, without justice, without mercy.

Well my prophet the child Malachi wrote in warning: 'the hearts of the fathers must turn to the children, and the hearts of the children must turn to the fathers, or the earth will be smitten with a curse.'

The curse is already upon your generation. The fathers all must turn their hearts to the children, and the children must turn away from counseling among themselves, and return to their fathers. The curse is already seen in your youth. The

655

curse is worse than you think. Woe unto this generation until it repents and opens its eyes to see the Hope of Zion, the Youthful souls arising.

I say to you that the hearts of your ancient fathers and mothers, your ancestors, are turned at this very moment, and watch in horror as their seed and posterity waxes in chaos and destruction.

Their love shines forth, and can fill the darkness.

But the hearts here must turn.

All of this, you are also here to learn.

In the last two nights you have said many things that have weighed heavily upon my mind, which are measures by which our generation will be judged. What can I understand of Judgment?

You will mostly judge yourselves.

Each of you will be reminded of your own good works, written in the Book of Life, and reminded of your guilt, those who have repented not. The recipients of all good works shall bear testimony thereof, and many shall be exalted who thought their lives had been without meaning. Also the victims of all offenses shall testify of their injury and pain, and if those who did these things did not repent early enough in the flesh to give restitution, and to serve in humility, and to show forth their mighty change of heart in works of goodness before their deaths, even these shall stand condemned, and shall receive a lesser honor.

I have told all their outcome, yet most in their desire and enthusiasm for what they envisioned of themselves could not believe. And so in love, a way was proportioned for all to see in themselves what I already saw so clearly, even this probation. And after it is done, you mostly judge yourselves.

Those who would be the highest among you will be the servants of multitudes, even as I AM, and this is true Glory.

I know my question now will seem very petty and foolish, but you have told me that no question is foolish if asked in sincerity.

As you could feed all nations and provide for an adequate abundance for all, why in this Estate must we work?

You consider work to be your greatest curse.

Yet work is your greatest blessing.

If it were not for work, you would still be isolated Intelligences in the cold of space. If it were not for work, you would still eye each other suspiciously from a distance. If it were not for work, you would come here and learn nothing.

Why work by the sweat of your brow?

If it were not that you must work to eat your bread, you would not gather yourselves together, but would live in isolation, seldom interacting for a common goal. To work cooperatively together in spite of your differences is one of the most important things you must learn in this flesh.

Save that you must work, you would not.

You are here for great purpose.

It is not jobs, it is not houses; it is not possessions, it is not fame. It is not even so much the act of doing the work, or of what you learn in the job itself of how to do it. For there are an infinity of jobs of such diverse and varied skills and arts as can and have been imagined. Yet in all there are basic lessons which are learned, of planning, of thinking out full processes, of preparation, of thoroughness, of determination, of endurance, of dedication, of dependability, of attention, of care, of responsibility, of finishing.

Yet of greatest importance is the interacting with other human beings.

You would not do it much at all, and especially you would not find ways to do it cooperatively, if you did not have to survive by the sweat of your brow, in cooperation one with another. See how you endure much to remain employed, and earn your bread every day. Great skills you acquire in this interaction.

It is in the interacting, and what it teaches you, that you achieve your purpose. It is in the interdependence, and what that teaches you, that you achieve your purpose. Being interdependent and being forced to interact cooperatively teaches you everything.

In friendship, you choose your companionship. But in the earning of your bread, you must learn to control yourself amid those whom you would otherwise never come to know. And ultimately, you begin to see each other with new eyes.

Too long you were alone. You didn't know how to come together. That was one of my greatest challenges to overcome - your annoyance at each other, the thoughts of being disturbed by another's space and intrusion.

Here you must learn to respect space as well as seek help. If you were not forced into it by your needs, how would you ever learn?

This curse is your greatest blessing.

You do not learn the truly important lessons alone.

You learn them together.

As you seek to serve and help each other, you become exalted.

These are your riches.

This is your challenge.

You know so little, and think you know so much. You see so shortly into the future, if at all. You do not think about the whole of your generation, but usually only of your own little sphere of existence. Each of you still thinks you are the only thing important in the universe. Is that any surprise as you are come from having been a lone Intelligence in the universe? Out there, you were all you knew. Your consciousness of yourself was all you knew.

For many Intelligences, it takes time to fully ingrain the concept of others' existence, others' needs, and their role in a picture which includes even a mate, or a family. What of a small neighborhood, or community grouping, much less billions of souls as a planetary family?

The concept is finally distilling upon your generation.

World family.

Global responsibility.

One Planet.

Small World.

Interdependent.

Interlinked.

World Wide Web.

Truly you are finding now what you have always been but never suspected: a world wide web of interlinked needs, with a world wide web of interlinked capabilities to help each other.

Finally now you are learning what has been since the beginning, but only now you glimpse, that what one part of the globe does, affects all.

These thoughts are just the beginning, which you can see because of the physical creation of the planet. The time will come that you will see the interconnected nature of all things in this creation, and their interdependence, for good and for evil, with opposition in all things, with needs you have never imagined requiring fulfillment, which you become a part of by following the course you are upon, by being allowed to suffer, by being denied what you think will solve all of your own personal intimate needs and problems just now, as a greater unfolding is being fulfilled for all.

While you think the need of your own is all important, there are myriad other realities which are impacted by the very existence of your needs which allow others opportunity to show and learn compassion, helpfulness, and creation even on the smallest scale.

If you see the starving child and are moved to feed him, to feed her, to clothe him, to clothe her, then you are on the path of being my Child in Truth, maturing into one who can be given the power I have, and use it wisely, for the creation and feeding and clothing of the others who yet wait their turn.

There are others still waiting their turn?

Infinite numbers.

Where are they?

Out there.

I could write nothing, I was so stunned.

Yes. And their need has not yet even begun to be fulfilled. They wait in the cold and the darkness, alone and in despair, prisoners of their limitations, tormented by their nothingness. When you can feel compassion for them, and begin to desire for them freedom and movement and life and joy, then you are becoming my Child.

I finished reading, and realized that I had asked everything I had proportioned for the night.

I have asked all of my questions for tonight, and rather than open a new subject, I think I would like to close, and go to sleep.

Very good. Goodnight. I'll be with you. We'll talk tomorrow. I love you.

I love you too, I typed.

And I closed, and exited, and turned off the power.

I walked to my tent in the dark, and sat on my cot for awhile in the dark, just thinking.
All of this, so much, just because I asked.
Now I know.
Now that I know, what will I do about it?
It was an awesome responsibility, asking.
An awesome responsibility, to know.
Awesome indeed.

Chapter 19

Day 38 in the Wilderness: About Scriptures

The morning was already late, but I knew I had not slept as late as other mornings. Last night had again been a shorter round of discussion. Tonight would probably be even shorter. The questions were of infinitely smaller scope, even if the answers were of equally weighty impact on our lives. I saw a certain poetic in that parable. The universe, as immense and austere and threatening as it truly was to our bodies, actually gives us life. The smallest viroid, so small it could not be seen, so simple it cannot even carry within itself its own means of life, invades our bodies, and silently takes over, leaving us dead.

Seemingly insignificant things could be very dangerous indeed.

I got up and went out into the sunlight, squinting. A good stretch and several yawns, and I felt ambitious enough to walk over to the artesian spring for a drink of cool water.

The spring still flowed. It was amazing. I splashed water on my face, and drank. It was about the best water I had ever tasted.

I stood and walked out into the middle of my little kingdom, this small opening in the canyon with its modest plateau, and small ruin of a small villa jutting up out of the ground here and there. Not much to see, after so many centuries of life here.

I knew there was a lot still underground, and that even with my best projections based on the evidence of what I had uncovered and seen, I knew little if almost nothing about the people who had lived here. I would never know how many women, how many children, how many men, who they had been, what their names were, what nationality they had actually been, what their relationship to each other had been from one decade and century into another. I had a lot of pieces, and could see them and the partially exposed foundations of these buildings, but I only knew part of the story.

It was funny, how archaeology worked with partial stories. Like everyone, we were always eager to know everything. When everything was not there for us to know surely, we did what all people do.

We made it up.

Sometimes we were even right, as later excavations and continuing correlation of facts and evidences showed. But just like so many other things in life, it was so easy to speculate on pieces of brick, parts of a building, and construct a projection of what we thought the whole had looked like.

We always believed that our studied, speculative reconstructions and imaginative explanations were perfectly correct and true. Until something came up as certain evidence, we continued in our blissful satisfaction of having figured out the puzzle: our theories remained undisputed by facts.

It was also humorous to me how we handled the evidences we had. Sometimes we would have little more than a brick, and from that brick we would make up and draw the entire palace as we thought it should be. Other times we had almost an entire palace, but we argued so much over what we had that in the end we didn't seem able to prove we even had a single brick. Some areas were allowed vast ranges of speculation-accepted-as-fact, while other areas of study had rigorous demands of proof-in-hand imposed upon them, and even that proof was challenged and interpreted. It depended on the culture, and the field. It was all very subjective, and academic biases were definitely involved and at play.

Even a simple site such as this would be 'handled.'

This site was a real habitation, with real buildings, and real people had lived here. With the bits and pieces I had excavated, some day a theory about this place would be made. Careful drawings of all of the buildings would be drafted, and a complete story of the people who had lived here would be fleshed out, and illustrated with the bits and pieces I had found and which others who would some day follow me would dig up from the ground. It would probably be a lot like what had been here, and be very close in some things to what had really happened here.

But it wouldn't be perfect.

And if the ancient people who had lived here could ever see our retelling and our pictures, they probably wouldn't recognize much at all. In the model dioramas they would see faces of strangers, and around the buildings they would see landscaping and roof designs they could not recognize. The strangers in the model would be dressed in someone else's clothing, and all around would be things they had never owned, just someone's speculation. The people represented would be grouped in families they had never formed. Children they had loved would be missing, and strange intruders would give them alarm. They would see trees where none had been, and empty spaces where trees had once stood; they would see wood corals and animals in the wrong places, and animals they had never owned. And there would be many things dear and precious to them which would be missing from the pictures and models illustrating their lives, which they remembered well, for they had been there, but which were absent from our pictures and models, because we had no way of knowing. Some would be big things, some would be small things, but a lot of what had really been here would be missing from the best of our best efforts.

The ancient inhabitants from this place would shake their heads, and say, 'We never saw this place before. What place is this? This chair was not here...... this roof was not like this...... what table is this? We never had a table like this one. And where is my most precious possession, which all who came into my house saw, and by this, knew it was my house?'

But we would be proud of our drawings and models. As we were the archaeologists, and we had made them, all who came to see this place would look upon our drawings and our models and read the telling of the story as we had imagined it from the bits and pieces and fragments, and they would believe it had truly been just so.

After all, we were the authorities. Didn't we know? Who could challenge us?

And visitors would have every good reason to believe, for every part of our story would have its little fragment of cloth beside it, and its broken fragment of clay pottery, and its piece of broken glass, and there would be the earring, and the scarab, and the pieces of the oil lamps, and the bronze finger ring with the stone still intact, and all of the other fragments and pieces, each carefully placed in the midst of the story to show that we constructed it from evidence that was real.

But nothing that we would show would really be real.

It would all be our imagination of what had really been real.

And all who came to this place and saw what we had reconstructed of it would go home and tell their friends just how this place had been. As they had been here, they would be believed. Though we had just made it all up, basing all on our best knowledge of how things had been in those days - an impression ever incomplete and tainted with our own imaginings - in time it would be received quietly by all, and go on: the accepted reality ever after.

There will be some who will say it is probably very similar to what was here in fact, originally; it is probably close; what's the problem? Do a few mistakes make a difference? But even for that, it will not be so close, in spite if its many fragments and artifacts.

The people who lived here will tell you: it was never like this.

I filled my canteen to mix some fruit punch for breakfast, and went back to my tent. I rummaged through what was left of my dwindling food stores, and ate a varied menu of eccentric cuisine. Fruit punch, cookies, a can of beef stew, dried apricots, and a thick slice of vanilla and chocolate halava. Excellent. I was ready.

I decided to hike down the canyon today, and up one of the lower tributaries I had never walked before.

I hiked and thought about many things, most of the day.

By dusk I was back at the camp, and ate an even more hodge-podge dinner. The end of an expedition was always fun this way: leftover foods in odd and unanticipated combinations. Yet life is so often that way: when we are hungry, we will eat anything.

I put together some odds and ends to eat during the night, and went to the lab tent. It was already dark.

As soon as I was situated in front of the screen, I flipped on the power, booted up, and opened the programs until I reached the search engine, wherein I typed

WWW. URIM AND THUMMIM .GOD

and waited momentarily as it processed my command. The page appeared on the screen, cursor waiting. I was ready for the night.

Hello. How are you this evening?

I'm fine, thank you. How are you tonight?

Fine, thank you. I had a good day, and saw a lot of pretty things. I found some pottery sherds up the wadi I walked, Iron Age, I think. I wasn't the first one to walk up there.

No. There were others.

How's the universe?

Doing well, thank you. Several new projects underway; a lot of children happy their probationary period has just ended on their world; several earths just about ready for the children to go, and everybody's excited. Things overall are progressing just about as to be expected. Many very special things done by a lot of children for each other today. Some days are like that. An unusual lot of nice things. It was good to see.

How is Mother?

She's fine, thank you. She sends her love to you.

Thank you. Please say Hello for me.

I will. She will be pleased.

I thought a lot as I was walking today, about the things you told me last night. As you know, I have more questions than I'm going to have time to ask, and so I'm being very selective in choosing what will really be most important to me.

You've done very well. I'm impressed.

Thank you. My questions tonight are about some things I have contemplated for years, and which you have touched upon several times. You have explained that prophets are needed to clear the confusions which blind us, and you have implied, I think, if I have been hearing correctly, that you have had prophets in many times and places, among all peoples at some time. I believe this, first because you have said it, but also as I have studied the ancient religions and the books of the surviving religions today, I find so many parallels. It always seemed too much to be just coincidence. As I have been learning here, these aren't just coincidences.

Yet there are so many differences in the scriptures in the world. I don't mean differences of the specifics of the mythologies, which I can understand. I mean among the remnants of the obvious truths which they all contain. The teachings about being good, and how one should be good are pretty universal - strikingly so. I wasn't told this as a child - religious teachers always want us to imagine that 'other religions' are so totally different, and foreign, when they are remarkably parallel, and familiar underneath their dressings and dramas. Yet why have some been given so much about atomic conceptualization, such the ancestors of the Indians, and about the actual age of the universe in billions of years, again like the ancestors of the Indians, and the ancestors of the Sumerians, and the ancestors of Egyptians, and the ancestors of the Aztecs?

Why are some things preserved among one people, and other things among another?

What is the meaning of it all?

Different children care about different things, and ask for different things. Not all ask the same things. Do you think you have asked the same questions other children put in your shoes want to ask? Yet when much is given, not all see equal value in all which is given; that which seems unimportant at the time is often discarded, and often, only later it is seen to be the greatest treasure of all. But seldom is the value of all seen at first.

And it is often the nature of children to forget that which they value little.

The descendents of those who receive often care about different things, and when the parents die and are gone, the children often throw away many things which were dear and precious to the parents.

In each generation the children like to think their ways are better.

Yet so often, it is not so.

You, my child, know of the many scriptures of the ancients as well as those of today. You have studied the scriptures of the Egyptians, the Sumerians, the Akkadians, the Greeks, the Hindu, the Buddhist, the ancient Americans, even the tribes of the North Americans, and the Celts, the African, and the Aborigine. Yes, there are many scriptures. But most are not descended well from their origins. To each has been given what they could bear. Each has received it in its own understanding. Some have written down; others have retold by word of mouth for generations until one day the retellings began to be written, and re-written, and perfected, and made to fit the shape of men's thinking in the days of their codification.

In most of the scriptures there is some remaining part of the revelation originally given. In some there is much. Many of my most simple and precious children have retained the gift to know great spiritual things, and treasure them. From these all would do well to learn. Yet even among the most retold scriptures, which remain only in their commentaries and illustrative dialogues made to explain that which was simple, which survived after the simple revelations upon which they were based became lost, even in these there is easily found much truth of value to those who know what they seek, and who can recognize within the new dressings those truths which are always given.

All those who learn the fullness may find the traces of the original clearly preserved within the colorful tapestries made to embellish what was once small and pure. Great stories have been shaped and told around once simple and direct prophecies and revelations; they are framed in carefully crafted allegories and dialogues between kings and faithful servants, and other artful panoramas. Within the stories are many of the elements of doctrines and revelations given to those children; and though the remains of the original simple doctrines and revelations are buried within much drama and action, still great worth has remained, and its truth is undiminished. Yet it is hidden for the most part even unto those who revere it and teach it to their children's children. Search these things if you desire, for all of them testify of me, and in all of them are traces and remnants of my doctrines given in times of old. Those who learn to recognize the form within the form will be greatly rewarded and learn much truth.

Yet the best records have been kept by my Chosen.

Why has the Hebrew record remained so unpolluted?

They were chosen for this purpose.

What do you mean, They were chosen for this purpose?

There were many Great and Noble Intelligences in Spirit who were Faithful unto being foreordained as stewards of preserving the Word in your earth's long

Generation; this they chose so that among all the children, at least in one place would a true and pure record be preserved, so all might one day know what had been given from the Beginning, and know what was needed to be known. These were they who more than anything desired to serve me.

These Intelligences in Spirit were born into this House, even the House of Israel.

How could you be assured they would not fail?

They were chosen before they were born, and they were born into that lineage even as they were Chosen.

Within these is a special passion, and by this nature, they would not fail.

Look upon them and you will see that in their stubbornness is their greatest glory. No people has been so steadfast, and served so well. Though they have not yet received a Messiah, see how great a patience they preserve in spite of every condition which has been engineered against them. And surely they have endured a consistent persecution which exceeds that of any other persecuted people. It is humorous, to listen to children who have become impatient of hearing of the sufferings of this people, yet though many others have suffered equal things at some moment, who has endured what these have endured? And still they remain, after so many others have fallen away.

Why was the lineage of Israel Chosen?

Because these were the Spirits willing to be a Covenant People.

Because these Spirits chose to serve and to defend me, to be my stewards.

Because these were the Valiant Ones who most resisted the temptations of this matter, who most were dedicated and resolved to remain faithful in every way, who most wanted to receive and have my words while they were here, who most wanted their children to have these Truths, to know and to serve God.

Not many of the children felt this as a priority upon their coming here.

Most have been so excited to come, they have cared little for where, or when, or through whom, but only to come and to have this body and eat this food and experience these things and touch what for the first time could be touched this way in this physical matter, where Opposition creates Worlds.

But there were those who were more Noble, and of these I made my leaders, and my servants, and through this lineage I brought forth those who wanted more than any other thing to know me during their life here.

What can be a more noble desire than this?

And they have remained faithful, in spite of the most bitter persecutions, and scorn of the other children. And they have gone and settled in many and diverse places of the earth, and mixed among the people, and walked among the children of the nations, working, serving, being visible in service and faith, and living among the nations as a people, even a nation within many nations. They have found places you do not imagine, until there are few places in the earth where they have not gone and settled. And by their faithfulness and persistence in the stewardship, the nations of the world have indeed been blessed, by their seed, and by their stewardship. Even they have not understood how the world has been blessed by their seed, nor has the world, to its shame.

The writings have been preserved, the ancient testimonies have been preserved, and this they have done, in scorn, in ghettos, in death.

And for this, they are blessed.

For through this line I allowed to be born those who would best preserve my words, and so they received their desire. This has been the great charge of the Children of Israel: to receive my Word, and to cherish it, and defend its destruction, which they have done repeatedly, yet not without failures.

Failures?

Yes, all is not wholly intact. Many precious and simple things have been lost, whole books, and many precious things in days of old were removed.

Have things been added?

So few it is unimportant. That has been the key: what has remained is almost the best preserved of all.

See among all the records keepers of the world, they have been the truest of stewards and have discharged their calling most excellently of all.

Look upon your cherished records of the Meridian of Time, even the Books and the Letters of my Apostles; for even these were born of Israel.

No truer records are kept or preserved among any others; and from this House are still many records which were kept you know not of. Among these are yet the best of all, for of this lineage, wherever the children of these Noble fathers have been led and taken, even across rivers and great deserts, even across great seas, their faithfulness has been honored, and their lineage has been preserved, and their faithfulness in records shall yet be known.

For faithfulness, for obedience even in suffering, and to be the Keepers of the Books, they have earned this privileged lineage. And for this faithfulness, even the Messiah they have been blessed to bring forth unto the world.

These have served me well, and continue to serve, and I love them, and my love fails them not.

Tell me of ancient prophets, and the writings, not just the ones I know, but of the ones in other lands, whose writings evolved down the road into

Is every tradition and belief of religion true? No.

If many are not, does it follow that there is no Spiritual Truth? No.

If many are garbled gospels and weave pleasing stories of men with fragments of truth scattered within, can something still be learned? Yes.

Is there a fullness of truth somewhere? Yes.

Do you know what is true? Then look for it in the origins of ancient scripts, and if you find a Truth manifest in ancient teachings, study them well. Do not believe that so many coincidences are coincidences.

From too many coincidences should come healthy suspicion.

In these you may find the path to All Truth.

The ancient Hebrews, my Chosen, originally knew of Intelligences, and Spirits, and of Angels, of Michael, and Gabriel, and Raphael, and many other messengers and agents, and the Hosts of Heaven, and that they are male and female, and of the commandments to be obedient unto all they were instructed, to choose Good over Evil, and Life over Death, and to remember me, that I AM their Father, and of your Mother also. And as they were taught of the simple Truths, of behaving rightly one to another, and of love, and of marriage, and of serving each other in work, they were also taught to look toward the day that they would return home; and they knew that they might return, and even that they would receive the gift of the Resurrection through One who was worthy to overcome all things. They also knew of the creation, and of suns, and worlds, and about their own relationship to their sun, that the sun was the center of everything to them, that it governed everything in the solar system in its appropriate motion, and that its energy was the source of this earth's life, just as it is on all other earths, and many other things regarding this creation did I give to them. The prophets recorded their visions as best they could: visions of many worlds, and the expanding cosmos, the charging and organization of matter, the spark of matter, the choosing of localities in space wherein new skenas could be well made, for good purpose, and of the time in which all this was done.

However, as you will come to know, different children become fascinated with different things, and the same story told to ten children is recorded with unequal balance. Each by what each one has seen as most fascinating and important writes what becomes written. All things can be shown, yet what will eventually endure with emphasis depends upon the keepers. Purity only remains under my guidance, and this remains only as long as the children remain faithful unto me, and want to know from me the truth more than they want to mold things in the images of what they think they should be, by their fondness and perception.

These same things were given also to the children in many other places, at diverse times.

The knowledge of me and your Mother have largely been preserved in the myriad ways you see, in the worship of diverse gods and goddesses fashioned after the liking of the children who desired such parents to worship; and the knowledge of Good and Evil and the choice of Life over Death has been passed on with great consistency to most of the children, even among the most humble of small tribes who have become isolated, you find these same values more closely aligned than is ever popularly fabled: the simple tribes often know these things in surprising purity. You have also seen the knowledge of the Intelligences and Spirits and Angels have largely been preserved in the myriad ways you have seen them, in pantheons of gods and goddesses and their children, and of their missions and stewardships, and their dealings with the children of earth. You have seen that as soon as you begin to equate Mother and I, and Angels and Hosts and Children, and dissention and war among the citizens of Heaven, and castings out of Heaven, and a Son who by His obedience became favored, a Son of a god born of a mortal maiden, and the Good News that even the children may aspire to come unto Heaven if they will endure and overcome the challenges placed before them, that these seemingly foreign mythologies are replete with the roots of Truth and their first Origins, which are abundant and easily seen by all who but take simple notice.

Yet as is always the case among witnesses, and stories retold many times, with many retellings the images evolved, and with many retellings the emphasis of remembering changed even more, and so among some, you see certain Memories exalted and remembered well, while other Memories have been lost and discarded long before reaching you.

Do not suspect that for not finding them still, they were never known.

Do not suspect that you cannot still look within what is and has survived, pull back the veil, and with your eyes now fully open, see all they hold to see.

You wish to know of revelations of the universe, given in days of old?

Behold what you can see, for these things also testify of me.

The knowledge of the importance of a sun to an earth, to all life and to the children, which was communicated from generation to generation as basic, central and highly important in the unfolding existence of all things on their earth, lives on in that which you have seen only as sun worship. The children who settled in Egypt revered me within the solar disc and revered my gifts within its sphere, and many other branches of the family did this as it grew. You have too simply observed these things, and imagined that these worshipped only the sun, but they did not; they always worshipped the god within the sun, the giver giving within his gift, the center of the universe.

In this you should see great Truths once revealed, of sun's central roles in solar systems, and radiance of essential energies, and energies received and stored up in all life, and given for life, and life's dependency upon this organization and system as it was Designed by its Designer, who was revered for having set the sun in the heavens. You have seen into what these descended, yet you have not understood from where these thoughts of the god in the sun came, and what these very descendencies imply of original knowledges.

See that as some parts of the growing family comprehended this importance more than other things, that in their appreciation of me, and the sun and its true daily gift to this earth, they drew the association between me and the sun ever closer, until they could no longer see one without the other. This they learned from their fathers, and so taught it to their children, with no way of knowing more save new prophets should arise and be called.

The knowledge of the essential blue sky of air wherein blows the essential winds to move the clouds and the rain, without which the water cycle cannot be and upon which therefore all life depends, which was communicated from generation to generation as basic, central and highly important in the unfolding existence of all things on their earth, lives on in that which you have seen as only worship of the sky and the winds. Blue faced sky gods who nurture the earth evolved among children who drew the association between me and the blue sky and air ever closer, until they saw the Designer within the Design. These things they learned from their fathers, and so taught them to their children, with no way of knowing more save new prophets should be called.

The knowledge of the essential fire within the suns, needed to fuse hydrogen into helium and on through the cycles to create the very elements, the distant fire which warms earths and maintains all life by the radiance of its fiery energy, which was communicated from generation to generation as basic, central and highly important in the unfolding existence of all things on their earth, lives on in that which you have seen only as worship of holy fires. Yet see in this the essential ignition of suns, and molten smelting spheres of planets in accretion, which without such heat and fires would have no iron cores, no magma oceans, no volcanism to create atmospheres and seas. See within these the burning bush which burns without being consumed, and your own bodies, which are fires that burn slowly without being consumed. As you are made of Light and you live even by Fire within you, see in these descending concepts more than what you call primitive religions: see the origins of their Truths, to know what was given in the Beginning.

The knowledge of the essential moon and its needed effect upon magma tides and tectonic plate movements moving the face of the lands, and its real effect as the heart of the oceans giving them their rising and falling pulsing tides, which have nurtured and nurture the earth, these you have seen in worship of the moon. Yet know that it was revealed among your most ancient ancestors the roles of all things, and the moon was known for more than its light which is of service even still; and even with the simplest vocabularies the most of these were fully comprehended in their simplicity. As the cycles of the moon mimic the cycles of femininity within the woman, even so your Mother was remembered in all that the children saw and remembered in the moon.

The essential habitation of the earth and its soils, whereon all may find a place to stand, and wherein all things have their origin, and growth of plants and animals, you have also seen worshipped, and even you call it in your words Mother Earth. Since most ancient times you have known that out of the elements of the earth your bodies are made, and out of the elements of the earth all plants draw their nutrition and life, from which you also draw life, and that without a world you could not exist, or be. Though you have seen the children worship the earth and believed it curious and primitive, see within this the ancient knowledge of your Mother, and of the physics and chemistry of biological life derived from the inorganic rocks and soils of earth. The earliest Hebrews did not worship Father and Mother in vain or in ignorance, but in revealed Knowledge and Truth.

And you have looked upon meteorites which are the central symbol of religious worship, even called gifts from the heavens, yet now see in them what is lost to Memory, that through this gift of interstellar matter earths are given the gift of the essential iron core, and in one hundred and fifty tons of meteorites each day you receive your gift from the heavens, your daily portion of ash dust for the rains.

Father skies and Mother earths are known to many children's families, as are knowledges of the central sun, and creative fires, the winds, ad infinitum.

These things also testify of me.

Though no false worship is pleasing unto me, for without the fullness of truth the children cannot have a fullness of Joy, still you may see in them the reality that great treasures of knowledge were apportioned among the children of the early generations, and though much has become garbled, it survives.

Look upon what you see among the children of your world.

The earliest Egyptians received heliocentricity from their fathers, and the solar disc with its life-giving hands, and the obelisks which cast their shadows are the symbols; they knew of the creation, and fashioned their temples after the order of the cosmos, and after the retelling of the creation, of the small point of matter in the center of the immense and eternal waters, from which all things came. They recorded time in millions and millions of years, and spoke of future time in millions of millions of years, which you read now in wonder. How did they know of such true things? Yet while big numbers were important to them, the small structure of atoms, and of energenes, and all small comprehensions of microknowledge they did not well understand, for they as all children could not see it, and as is so often among the children, that which they do not understand they ignore, and what is ignored is soon lost. In their environment by the Nile, they saw big cycles, and big powers; they made big pyramids, and big temples. As with so many of the children, they could not imagine only one god being capable of achieving so many things, and as they knew of Intelligences, and Angels, and Hosts of Heaven, they began to divide the powers of God into gods, male and female, as they knew it was, and so the knowledge descended, ever more altered. They eventually garbled much of what they had received, even as did the Greeks, and the Chinese, the peoples of the Americas, and most other children. But all is still easily seen in Shu the god of light and air, and in Geb the god of the Earth, and in Nut, the goddess of the sky filled with stars from which suns are born, and in Horus and Osiris wherein they preserved the assurance of the Messiah and the Resurrection.

They knew stars as localities of Intelligences supporting habitats and life; they understood that there is a physics of the Spirit and of Resurrected bodies.

More than any other children, they treasured these teachings. These are the things which among them became most emphasized, and remembered. Though their scriptures are very garbled, there is much to be gleaned in them.

Do you know what they knew of doing right between each other?

I will draw from them two prayers, from the Book of Walking Forth By Day, which you mistakenly still call the Book of the Dead, which you have herein within your Text Database for you to read, even now:

> "What is said on reaching the Broad Hall of the Two Justices,
> Absolving me of every sin which I have committed,
> And seeing the faces of the Gods:
> 'I have not committed evil against men,
> I have not mistreated cattle;
> I have not blasphemed a god,
> I have not done violence to a poor man;
> I have not killed;
> I have not defiled myself;
> I have not added to the weight of the balance.'"

and again:

> "Behold me - I have come to you without sin,
> Without guilt, without evil, without a witness against me.....
> I live on Truth; and I eat of Truth.....
> I have satisfied a God with that which he desires.
> I have given bread to the hungry,
> Water to the thirsty,
> Clothing to the naked.....
> So rescue me, You; protect me, You.....
> I am one pure of mouth and pure of hands,
> One to whom 'Welcome, welcome, in peace'
> Is said by those who see me..."

Think no more in your vanity that you have been the Only Child.

672

This prayer from Egypt is on a papyrus only 3,400 years old; there are much older ones, still more pure. Your Text data Base is filled with such things.

See within them the origins of the Teachings of the Truths which you also know, and know that even as I am the same yesterday, today and tomorrow, so these things have been unchanging, among all of my children as I gave them.

See that these things also testify of me.

That not all have preserved what they received unto your day, you see.

Yet if it were not for your siblings in archaeology, how would you ever know that these things had been known and taught among the Egyptians?

You would loudly argue that they had not.

You would be wrong, as you are about so many things you do not know.

This you know only with their evidences undeniably before you.

And there are many undeniable truths before you even yet.

You know these Truths were known among the Egyptians only because you have found the original papyrus writings preserved in the dry sands and earth and tombs, and learned again to read them. These too, testify of me.

Do you know then, what was written and taught among my other children, in other places, where my prophets also declared my word?

Are you so arrogant as to assume that only because their lands are not dry, and thus nothing of their oldest writings have survived as in Egypt, that they did not have these things also given unto them?

Unless you may find the originals, even from most ancient times, how shall you declare what you know not?

For unto the Egyptians of today, there was no direct transmission from the ancients, for the old things became old, and those who preserved them died, and so the knowledge died, and was buried.

If you had not found their ancient scrolls, you would deny it all the same.

See that the children of the greater land of India also received Truth.

There is much in their scripture; yet it is not the original, but the very interwoven stories made to illustrate great truths as they were given. In them, as you keep focus in your mind of the Truths you know, you may find many of the Truths upon which these tapestries are colorfully woven.

The teachings of right behavior between themselves, and of Faith and of duty to obediently follow all Truth they have in reverent abundance.

Look to the Truths of the Holy of Holies in the Temple in Jerusalem, and find the shadows in great India within Shiva a father, and in his wife Shakti, even Energy, a mother, and as the holy family of father Shanker and mother Parvati see in their son Ganesh one who was killed, and given life again through the head of the elephant, even the Hero of The Story. You know of the symbol of the two hands pressed together, the password of Opposition in all things from which springs forth Creation. See in the symbolic emblems of Shiva's creation dance the rhythms and

673

resonance of the universe, the times measured in the drum, the depth of human ignorance, and the message of Hope that the children need not fear, as reminded by the arm's curve as the elephant nose of Ganesh, wherein they preserve the teaching of Messiah. And in the Lingham stone as Egg of all Life, see preserved the knowledge of primordial first matter and the DNA of the Design. See that they come unto the father through the Son, and all prayers begin and end with the Son, Ganesh. Great humility and honor are in them.

These children cherished the nature of the creation in the cosmos more than many others, and this is what they most celebrate and remember in all they do. They know of creations and destructions of creations, and repeating cycles, wherein there are some things they have garbled. Yet they preserved the originally revealed knowledge of the vast passages of time, for in their forest environment wherein were billions of leaves and billions of insects and billions of raindrops which fall from a single sky, they understood great numbers. Time was not vague to them, and so they recorded much of time, yet it is garbled. They received and recorded the cycles of suns and stars, of the deaths and rebirths of suns and worlds. They preserved the times of God in 8.64 billion years, and other time scales still longer.

These things are garbled, but does their origin not appear to you now?

Among the children of the ancient Chinese, they understood much of the heavens, and many other things. Some of these remained preserved. You see colorful ancient pictures among them, of two gods with long bodies intertwined in the double helix of DNA, depicting the original interaction of opposites, the secret of the Creation. Though they have these images, they have lost most understanding of its meaning, but you and they begin to see it again now. See these arts of Creation, wherein you see the Helix of DNA and the Opposition of all things in the secret of Creation, and know that they had great prophets among them, but they did not preserve what they received as my Chosen.

The Aztec children received from their fathers through prophets great knowledge, much of which you can easily comprehend for its true origins. They knew of the generations of suns, and that your sun is a sun of several generations, which they knew had been three and projected into four; and they knew of the vast passages of time, and recorded times in vast eons; they knew of creation in the cosmic ocean, and called the sky Teoatl, the godsea. Do you see within this limited vocabulary and expression the seeds of the Truth they had revealed unto them at an earlier time? Though they worshipped the god in the sun, and pitifully gave the hearts of men in memory, can you yet see?

The Sumerians knew my habitation is by a star, as is theirs, and so their pictographic word for me became the star. The creation was of powerful importance to them, and the late redactions of early knowledge already distort much, but its trace you may see. Think not that this does not testify of me.

The Ionian Greeks comprehended heliocentricity, and myriad inhabited worlds, and though the children of science today see in this only early scientific recognitions, yet these things were within the shadows of truths still retained in the tapestries of their beliefs, though, the teachings of men successfully suppressed them even as long before.

As you now know that your Earth and your bodies run almost exclusively on energy from your star, your sun, do you now see the thread of preserved knowledge in the ancient sun-worshipings of your ancestors? Though they rejected full truth of the prophets, though they failed to write what they received, and in their oral traditions they garbled and then garbled more what was given clearly at first, still do you see the core of truth they knew, and understood, and retained? They knew the sun nurtured all life on this world.

These are things which astrophysicists, geologists and paleobiologists are beginning to discover now as they study space and your earth.

Does this not speak to you its truth?

I knew some of these things, but I had never thought about this all in this way. I clearly see the truth of it now.

What has also been amazing to me is that even within the various major religions, which have their old books and canonized writings which are now sacrosanct and cannot be changed in even a word, yet there are in all of these religions - Islam, Buddhism, Hinduism, Shinto, Judaism, Christianity - groups upon groups upon groups, each with its own brand of interpretation, yet they all draw from the same words, their own unalterable source books. In each of these, the books are as one, but the followers are not, but divided.

Why is this?

Because the children in so many lands have received my word but recorded it poorly, many have seized upon that word to make their own understanding, belief and interpretation. Though they have been in error, still they have held sway, by power and by disciples eager to receive these ideas.

Commentaries upon commentaries have been invented to explain what was said, among the Buddhist and among the Hindu, creating 'Talmuds' of learning. Verily these 'talmuds' have become law, and the commentaries have survived whereas the original revelations have not. Thus the re-tellings and illustrative stories and sagas intended to illuminate the original revelations have became enshrined as the more important sources, and the original sources are gone. These are in their way still scripture, and they testify of me, and of my works, and of my interaction with all the children of men, and they remain of great worth to those who use them and tc those who may study them. They are not the light, but only the reflection of the light; yet within them the light of truth is to be found. This has been better than no light at all. Yet it is only a reflection of what was, of what was given. And groups with private interpretations abound, with many, many teachers, each with their own ideas.

Even among my Chosen People, the commentaries and teachings and stories and mystical interpretations have become more important than the original books they have so diligently and carefully preserved as no other people of any time. Their teachers have become the Word and the Meaning and the Law; the stories softening the realities of ancestral Patriarchs' frailties and follies have robbed them of that truth; the endless arguments of premises have robbed them of the simple truths of the recorded revelations they indeed have, and have preserved so well. Yet there are fewer groups among them than any.

The Adopted Children have even been less faithful in following the teachings that have been given; though diverse interpretations arose among my Chosen, so even more schisms proliferate among the Adopted, until their factions are as many as the stars in the sky. And each claims to be true.

Wherein there is only One Truth, all cannot claim right to that preference. Wherein two still disagree, at least one must still be in error, if not both; for only Truth is Truth, and neither passion nor abundance of professors are authority.

Yet many without authority have claimed it, and many without Truth have claimed it, even as many without mercy have claimed it.

Over many generations these have forced cruel and most errant teachings upon the children, of things nowhere written in any Prophets or Law.

In this, as you know, many brilliant and brave children have been silenced. For these grave and real offenses, many children have rebelled against all that is True, for they have only been shown the false, and harshly been told it is true, yet they have had eyes to see it is not true.

For this, many children think to fight against God.

Yet the children of the sciences have unwittingly pitted themselves not against me, but forever against the tenants of men's vanities and arrogances taught in my name, in the name of God. They have instead been fighting against only the teachings of other men and their beliefs and philosophies. Not against me and my revealed Truths of the cosmos, but the imperfect recordings of things ever only partially understood by the children in their days, and feebly understood through the limited expression which they used to record them, and even as they have been altered adversely in their time by ambitious interpreters and teachers. Against this have the children in their moments of Truth become embattled.

Think of the freedom the children of science will gain when they find that they are not in opposition to me, nor were they ever - as they discovered truth.

But, as over the centuries the children of the sciences themselves have promulgated thousands of false tenents and beliefs, proposed and embraced and believed for vast periods of time, they must accept that often in the past, even as today, they do not know all the truth; and they have often played the fool as champions of absurdities.

The blind have led the blind ever so often in past generations, both on the side of science and the side of religions many, what men have in vanity and evil called the word and will of God.

Yet hasn't the main deterrent of discovery been religion?

If that church which is so often blamed for all ignorance were the only blame, then there should be great learning wherever it was not. Though it fostered much ignorance, for which many children will be judged, if it had been the only deterrent to learning and the progress of science, then why did not anatomical and astronomical discovery proceed in Asia, or Persia, or the Americas? Great capacity to know and to learn were there.

The same heavens and human body were before all eyes.

The children must stop blaming small and minute local organizations for what they must admit to themselves as a Generation. They have been unprepared to receive, and thus they have rejected time and again those who have come to them with the gifts of truth in learning. Many were the ancient children who saw and taught that the arteries and veins carried blood, not air, yet how often was this truth repeatedly refused? Many were the ancient children who saw and taught that the brain is the center of thought and the control of the body, yet how often was this ridiculed and thrown away?

You are a stubborn generation, and you need not blame only churches and despots. Your own scientific circles have the most colorful history of hearing perfectly simple, true truth, and becoming outraged, and aggressively acting out in opposition to harshly silence a brother or sister who actually knew.

How stubbornly did you let go of the practice of letting blood to cure illnesses; how loath you were to stop diagnosing ill women as suffering from a wandering womb; how loath you were to stop attributing women's illnesses to hysteria caused by the womb; how loath you still are today to stop attributing women's illnesses to hysteria; how often you still cut out women's wombs in full remembrance of hysteria diagnosis, even hyster-ectomies. How frustrated you were to receive the truth of tectonic plates, and the truth of meteor craters on your earth and moon, and bacteria as the cause of ulcers.

Cherished ideas are hard let go. A child so tearfully gives up that which it has wished to be a certain way, for not only does the child feel uncomfortable accepting that a belief of long time has been false, but the child among peers will lose the game, lose face, and the child must then step back as others take the place of honor which they dreamed of taking. For all these reasons, evidences are ignored, rationalized, refuted.

And so change comes slowly.

If these children could but know that to me and the angels they have all done admirably. They have never been ordinary, and they are held among all the hosts of heaven in the highest regard, for they have yet found and catalogued much good data which will serve well those who follow. Even in error there is great learning. Those who are humble know that in error is often the evidence of the greatest learning you are here to witness. In this they should content themselves. Even if one has contributed in but the smallest way, for this they shall in no manner lose their reward.

Look back to all generations which have come before you, and honor them. From the simple to the brave to the rough to the intellect, honor them all, mothers and fathers. Except for their living and working and learning and imagining, and their words, you could know nothing of what you know now.

Yet you should be more generous in your admission of ignorance.

It suits you better.

You still have too much to learn.

Thanks to the children of science and their indefatigable tenacity for research, experimentation, recording and publishing, the signs of the Design are becoming more and more evident all the time.

Time will come when the reaction against silly reductionism will evolve into an acceptance of many things which are now well known but which are not admitted in the world of science only because it does not allow certain children to maintain their hope that there is no Creator, no God. For to those who have told themselves that there is no God, they must hope above all hopes that they will be able to prove it.

For imagine the shame they feel, and the fear they feel, to think they might be wrong, and that I AM hearing them all this time.

I AM.

After thinking about all the history you shared with me over the last several days, our stubbornness in receiving new ideas even when they're true, I have to ask: why are we like this?

It has to do with systems of belief, and what you call schools of thought. You indoctrinate yourselves with systems of ideas, usually shared as complete and closed, and because you accept them as closed and complete systems, you set yourselves up to be resistant. You like to maintain neat, tidy systems.

But why do we resist the truth so much?

It is all the consequence of your emotions of pride, and shame, and fear.

You pride yourselves in both discovering and in knowing, and so you see glimpses and pride yourself to think then you know all. Yet throughout all time, your systems are almost always based on theories you imagine from just a fragment of a picture, and they always go far beyond their own scope, and reach out to touch everything you perceive of yourselves and your universe.

Your history is that of taking fragments and building upon them elaborate palaces of ideas, of systems, and you pride yourselves in the neatness of your systems. You make them of bits and pieces, some true, some false, having only part of the whole, and as you have yet but parts, and you still have never seen the whole, you assemble the pieces as they please your fancy into the picture you most wish to see. Thus so many of your belief systems have built error upon error, and formed mistaken pictures of a false whole.

Your systems are almost always premature, precipitous, and because of your pride you do not anticipate eventual new discoveries which will not fit into the systems of a whole you have constructed. You could say that in your pride you ideologically paint yourselves into corners. You state finalities, and then must defend them when they begin to appear wrong, or you feel shame, shame that you might have all this time been wrong.

The worst for you is when a system is threatened by a keystone idea, an idea which either makes or breaks the entire system as you have set it up, the premise you have built from fragments, and long defended.

You will fight long and hard against such.

For, if the idea is true, your system as you have composed it from fragments is falsely structured, and it will crumble, and you will feel shame.

You do not like to do this.

Though this is true progress and intelligence, you prefer the safety of the old, even when the new brings Truth.

In such ignorance many great truths known in ancient days have been trampled underfoot. You are re-discovering them now. Thus you know: even amid very false systems, many true principles may endure; what is true remains true though it be set into a false systemic premise.

You are here to learn to discern true from false, and to hold fast to that which is true. You are here to learn to restructure in the light of what is true.   Yet you feel so ashamed when your ideas turn out to be mistaken, especially when you have invested a lot of belief in them, and have patted yourselves on the back as you are busy convincing others. You will often ignore observable fact, just to maintain what you cling to. And so you defend your premature conclusions neatly arranged as systems.

Yet you shake your heads at the senseless death of the child Socrates, and the persecution of the child Galileo and burning at the stake of the child Bruno and countless other children; you see the ignorance and abject stupidity of laying the wood upon those fires.

I have watched it, generation after generation. It doesn't make any difference if it is a scientific system or a religious system: if the system will be put in question by admitting to a concept, those who have accepted the system will resist the concept without consideration.

This you do so you will not have to face your greatest fear: to stare at a wall in shock, realizing that you have believed something wrong all this time.

You have no idea how many times I have watched children die over a false scientific idea, killed by children defending a false religious idea.

Pride keeps children from admitting they were wrong.

Even to themselves.

It takes a lot of courage to admit to others you have been wrong. It takes even more courage to admit to yourself that you have been wrong.

You are here to learn that you are only right when you possess the truth.

There is no shame in having been wrong when you discard it.

As soon as you accept truth, you become part of it, and you share in it as a universal possession. It becomes yours. Truth is universal.

Dress yourself in what is true.

Blessed are the sons and the daughters who read the word today in the face of all learning as it has arrived, and see in their bodies the stamp of my planning and organizing into its marvelous and perfect functioning and life.

What marvels you are, my children, and yet you hardly know it! Blessed is the child who sees the body around him and her, holding up their hands to their eyes, who reads in the scripture that I AM the one after whom their bodies have been fashioned in like manner as my offspring, and in this find rejoicing.

Blessed are they, for they have within them the power to become my Sons and Daughters indeed.

There are many who ridicule all who believe in any religion.
These ridicule even the scriptures of your Chosen.

Pay them no mind. They do what they do for diverse reasons, some you now know: even as they have found fault with many teachings, so many teachings are of men, and are false. They will some day discover that they have only found fault with that which is of man, and it is faulty.

Yet there are those who are bitter, who kick against the pricks.

Pay them no mind.

They have become shamed by their own conscience, and until the day of their repentance, they live in fear, though they appear unto all as brave. They have lifted themselves up in vanity, and have liked the taste of their power. They have learned the secret of the Vandals: it is easier to take glory in destroying a thing than in building a thing. They have heard the ancient deception which still whispers among the children: If the hands which made this were great, and took long time, then the hands which can destroy quickly are mightier than those which built.

They find great joy in their cleverness and their destructions.

Yet they mostly fight battles against the teachings of men mingled with scripture, and the institutions of men built upon soft foundations; their battles are seldom with me.

Those who fight truly against me, shall fail.

This I can see is true.

Father, ...gee, it feels a little strange to call you that. I really haven't known how, or what to call you during this whole time. I have sometimes prayed in my life, and there are titles and phrases I use, but this is, this is...... you're so real. I'm not used to it.

That's OK. Your prayers are just as real, always, to me. I hope they will all be real for you from now on. I love you.

Father, it is late, and though not nearly as late as we stayed up together several nights ago, I have no more questions on these things to ask tonight. My last questions can wait until tomorrow.

That's fine. However, as you have asked what you have asked tonight, there is something I would like to share with you. Because you have asked well, and listened well, and received what you have been given, you are prepared.

Yes?

I would like to give you the answer to an age old question.

What is that?

Can I make a rock so heavy that I cannot pick it up?

I've heard this question. It's the question which refutes Omnipotence, being an all powerful God. If you're Omnipotent, all powerful, you should be able to make a rock so heavy you can't pick it up. But if you can't pick it up, how can you be Omnipotent? It's the old question of the Greek Sophist philosophers. It's used a lot to challenge the existence of God. Your Existence, I mean.

So what is the answer to the question?

I can.

You can what?

I can make a rock so heavy that I can't pick it up.

Then how can you be Omnipotent?

My glory is Intelligence. Men think only of the power of physical force. There are many ways to move mass. You know so little. You think of moving mass where you can stand, and pick up mass. You have yet to begin the engineering of large scale motions of mass in space by manipulation of mass charge, gravitational attraction, accretion, mass density and force of Spirit, the power of Faith. There is more to moving mass in space than you have any way to comprehend yet at all. The initial positioning of triggered charging of uncharged matter must be carefully planned, or it should be left undone. Designing and engineering new mass accretion areas in large scale space makes your chess, even three-dimensional chess, even Vulcan chess seem infantile by comparison. You can only begin to comprehend the calculation and prediction of eventualities of such mass attraction and how to use it beneficially in large scale motions. The purpose is to locally end up with something balanced and functional, not show off to bullies. To be all powerful is to have all powers, of which Exalted Intelligence and Faith are the most powerful of all, not mere physical force. Yet I wish you to learn, so let us pursue this that you might begin to have understanding.

I will again affirm: Yes, I can make a rock which is too heavy for me to pick up.

But if you can't pick it up, you're not Omnipotent.

That is exactly the sophistry of the Sophists. I will give you a better question in response.

Yes?

What do I want this rock for?

What?

Why do I want this big heavy rock?

Just to see how heavy you can make a rock.

Why?

To see how heavy you can make a rock.

Why?

To see if you can make one too heavy to pick up.

682

Why?

To see if you're really Omnipotent.

Why?

I suddenly couldn't think of any more reasons.

To show people you can do it, that you're Omnipotent.

Why?

To show the Sophists they were wrong.

Why would I want to do something just to satisfy the challenge of a bully?

I was really out of reasons now. That would be dumb, to do something useless just to prove some stupid challenge.

I don't know.

For those reasons you've given, I don't know either. I repeat my question: Why would I want to make such a big, heavy rock?

I don't know.

What purpose would it serve in the universe?

I don't know.

If it would serve no purpose, why would I want to make it?

I don't know.

I am Omniscient, and I can't think of a good reason to make such a huge and heavy rock just now. Why would I make such a heavy rock?

I'm not omniscient, and I can't think of a good reason either.

If there's no good reason to make such a rock now, why would I do it?

I don't know.

If it serves no purpose in an expanding universe which is affected by gravitational attraction everywhere at all distances, which needs to remain balanced in equilibrium, why would I want to make a rock with such a huge mass that it would absolutely disrupt the delicate balance of the universe and cause wide spread if not total gravitational collapse of everything in the Cosmos all into the spot wherever I made and put this heavy rock?

I don't know.

If I caused such an immense accretion and made such a rock and it collapsed the universe, what would the Sophists say then?

I don't know. I guess they'd say you should have known that it would happen, and since you didn't think of the consequences before, you aren't Omniscient.

Very Good. But if I am Omniscient, and I knew that doing this - making a rock so heavy that I could not pick it up - would destroy the universe, and I did it anyway, would that show very much intelligence?

No.

What do you think? Should I do it?

No!

My glory is my Intelligence. The Sophists have deceived you all, for this is not a question of the paradox of Omnipotence, but the disguised challenge of Omniscience and the temptation of ego, designed to destroy the Cosmos.

Ask yourself: Who is the author of this temptation to God to prove himself and in so doing, destroy all of Creation over petty personal ego? Who is the author of this trick played upon the minds of men, to persuade them by this deception that there is no God?

To be God is more demanding than this question assumes.

To know what should not be done to upset the delicate balance of even small scale things in the universe is the Intelligence of God; to resist the foolish ignorance of sophists and those who in their disbelief would make you doubt yourself is the Intelligence and ultimate test of Omniscience, and Omnipotence.

To not do that which the bully challenges though he declares that he will not believe unless you do it is to obey the highest law.

This is power: to not do that which is senseless; to not do that which you can do yet must not do because you have perceived the consequences; to not do what you can do especially because it would be destructive and never produce anything afterwards you may look upon and say: *IT IS GOOD.* This is to have the power and the capability of becoming the Sons and Daughters of God.

When you have learned to be obedient in all things, and have the power of Faith, and the power of all ordinances distills upon your Intelligence, then you may become Co-Heirs of all things as you have been promised.

I see the truth of it.

Tell the Sophists that the answer to the question is that an Omniscient God understands the balance of gravity in an expanding universe and therefore would never be tricked into making a mass so great that it would, by its mass and gravitational attraction, cause the accretion and collapse of the universe.

Tell them that all masses in the universe are well within my abilities to influence, gravitationally and otherwise, and that Omnipotence is the power to do all that is required and useful, not to show off. Omnipotence is power shown by wisdom and restraint, not ego and brute force.

Tell them that those children who would give attention to such vain egotistical stunts are not able to receive the powers endowing them to do such things, and such will not be endowed with power.

Tell them that yes, I can make a rock so heavy that I cannot pick it up, but there are ways to move large scale mass they have yet to imagine, and that which I cannot pick up, I am Intelligence enough to set in motion with appropriate means.

Tell them that to be Omnipotent is to obey all of the laws of nature, and to use them in complete wisdom, not to defy them, and override them. This is the vanity of men. To be God is not to do as whim pleases, but to adhere to and do all which is right and good in accordance with all Eternal Laws of the universe.

And most importantly, tell them I would not make such a mass, for I love my children. I love all of them. I love you. I know what such a mass would do to the Cosmos, and so I must choose not to do it. Love is the ultimate controlling power of the universe. Love is all caring, all knowing, and all powerful.

Yet tell them I know what to do with a mass which is as small as a dot at the end of a written sentence, which is as heavy as all the matter in the cosmos.

Tell them they are looking at the answer.

Tell them: They live in one small part of the answer.

They will understand.

I finished reading this last download. I smiled.

It must be pretty difficult to have patience with all this sometimes, I typed.

Thank you for recognizing that.

685

Yes, I never get used to it. It is always tiresome. I get more weary of it than frustrated and angry these days. You probably think that knowing something will be a certain way would make it easier. I among all Beings know it is this way, yet you know how it feels. For this reason you are also here, to learn this.

You are my child, and you must know.

It is frustrating, no matter how much you have seen it and heard it, no matter how often it happens. It hurts.

You are tired, aren't you?

Yes, I'm really tired. I need to sleep.

Very well. Goodnight. I'll be with you.
However, there is one more thing.

Yes?

Tomorrow morning, as soon as you are up, come to talk again.

In the morning?

Yes. It is your last day. There is good purpose.

OK. Tomorrow morning.

I love you.

I love you too, I typed.

And I turned off the power.

Chapter 20

Day 39 in the Wilderness: Parting Words

I was surprised at how early I awoke. I felt refreshed, really fully rested.

Well, we had not stayed up so late.

Without delay I got up, got dressed, and went out to the spring for some water. I splashed my face, drank my fill, and went back to the tent for breakfast.

The food was so used up that putting together a meal at this point was sit-down comedy. I ate the last of the Halava, the last can of fruit, some pretzels that had been open for over a week but which had not gotten the least bit stale - dry air has some advantages - and a can of sardines. Actually, it was all pretty good.

With nothing more to do, I went to the lab tent and sat down in front of the computer.

I switched on the power, booted up, went through the programs until I got to the search engine, and typed in

WWW. URIM AND THUMMIM .GOD

The page dropped into place on the screen, cursor waiting.

Good Morning! I typed. This was a bit different.

Good morning. Did you have a good night's sleep?

Yes, thank you. How have your last few hours been?

Very good, thank you. A really wonderful thing happened.

What was that?

Oh, just something one person did for many, but it was very special. Too bad you won't read about it in the paper. It was very special. And there were a number of other wonderful things that children did for each other. It has been an unusually special few hours around your world.

What were they?

Special things. Good things. Very loving. Brave. Very compassionate.

Tell me.

Why don't you use your imagination, and think about what they might be?

I'm glad you're happy.

Thank you.

Well, you wanted me here this morning. I'm here.

Thank you for your promptness. So, what shall we talk about?

I pulled the very wrinkled piece of paper out of my pocket, and held it up before my eyes. After having scribbled out the things I could see I did not need to ask any more, there were not many questions left. Here was an interesting one.

As you have explained very well, you set the universe in motion to pretty much unfold systemically, and it mostly takes care of itself. I'm sure that's a gross oversimplification, but you have made it pretty clear to me that you Designed it that way on purpose, for good purpose, because it could be done that way and you saw that would be good, and now it is naturally following its initial direction and process.

What do you do.......... now?

Think of a large family, with children at home, children leaving home all the time, children away at school, children grown and off working at jobs; children grown and moved away now raising their own families, having difficulties, having opportunities to learn, sometimes learning, sometimes needing a whisper to understand what is going on around them; children returning home all the time, some are happy, with joys to share, some are tearful, some are in shock, needing comfort and compassion and nurturing.

Imagine areas of the universe where matter yet unorganized, in space yet unused is seen to be well situated for organization, organization into star groups and amid these, skenas, topos for habitation - planets for Life Worlds. This work too, goes on, and requires far-reaching algorithm perceptions in long-term planning, conversion of dark matter by Spark and Charge, and choosing among the Intelligences those who shall assist as Leaders; presentation and acceptance of the plans, Faithful obedience among the Spirit Intelligences which choose to follow and serve that they may earn their Eternal Portion; Faithful supervision in initiating and following the circular swirling Dance of the Great Gathering, Directing Faith into the creation of large scale motions set in swirling processes first large and then separating into many smaller circles, and these dividing and swirling into ever smaller circles set in motion and organized to create their gathering, unto the formation of all things needed for the establishing of worlds whereon the Children may come to learn what they will.

In relationship with your world, imagine a Father and Mother who love their children so much, they keep somewhat an arm's length of the children who are at school, raising their families, and in their jobs, because the children must learn how to use Free Agency and experience a wide range of circumstances and especially consequences of all things; and also so the children can enjoy feeling they do what they do all by themselves, which they strongly insist on doing more often than you can imagine. Children are very independent. They want to do things so often by themselves. They want to say 'I did this by myself.' You would be surprised how often they angrily push away all help.

Now imagine a Host of helpful administering attendants who, wanting to serve, are called to serve, who are then called to watch the children and help as much as possible to promote learning and right choices, form records and regularly communicate with higher levels of attendants who advise as they have been instructed to advise on how to best fulfill the needs of all the children, within each individual need's being helped, or of allowing things to run to their consequences so that all who might learn might learn; and who help as much as possible within the purposes of this process. I see much good, and also the evil you see, and also I see children strengthened in the good as they behold all things and their consequences.

How much do we get helped?

Much more than you imagine. Many times the children believe that they have prayed and no answer has been given because they do not receive what they wish, such as life, which in their perception they think is best. They do not understand that often through that which they see as tragedy, Spirits are spared worse things which would otherwise come to befall them later; or that many, having already proven themselves good, are freed to go on to fulfill work on the other side of the veil; and, that the death or tribulant experience of one becomes a turning point in the life of someone else, or of many whom therein they have profoundly served. Or, they complain that they must learn by their experience the lessons they must learn, as they do not die, but go on and live.

Often the answer to prayer is that the children must endure the consequences they have brought upon themselves, so they and others may learn. The children get themselves into all kinds of predicaments because they are stubborn, head strong, and so often think they know what is best. They do what they want to do, though they have been warned, no matter what the cost might be, for they perceive pleasure and gratification. As long as things go as they like them, they find happiness in these things. Yet as they begin to see their fantasy worlds fall, and fall hard, as consequences begin to follow as they naturally will, even though they have brought evil upon themselves by triumphantly walking into the face of foolishness, they kneel, and weep when the cost falls upon them, and beg to be released from the consequences they have so well known loomed ever in the shadows they were creating.

To learn truth for the Eternities is answer to prayer; to teach others by suffering one's own consequences is answer to prayer. It is also to serve in the answer to prayer. Many have asked in their prayers that their lives might be of some Service to Me, or to their fellow beings. Many need to be taught; even in this there is reward to those who endure. And know that each one who sees the foolish in suffering and winces, who learns and thereby avoids that pit, has been the recipient of answered prayer: mothers and fathers pray that their beloved children will learn Wisdom to flee such evils, and refuse these follies.

You pray for many things. Yet you pray without knowing how best your prayers will be answered, nor in what ends your own true needs find fulfilling.

Still, many are often spared the worst of what they have brought upon themselves, especially if it is the first time they have dared such folly. Yet if they are spared and soon forget the mercy they have received, the next time they are allowed to learn what they will not learn in other ways. Sadly, many children suffer the consequences of their follies over and over, each time asking for deliverance from the pit they have willingly entered, only to enter it again.

The cries of the Innocent who are victimized by children working in evil are the most difficult to hear, and you have no idea how often the Innocent are saved from such evils, by whisperings to go somewhere else, to leave now, to not go, to do something else in another direction, to wait until later. Often when they will not hear for they are preoccupied, or are children who do not listen but who are loved just the same, those who do listen to promptings and whisperings and inspirations are prompted, and by their momentarily blocking the way, turning left, turning right, pausing a moment longer, calling and talking, coming and visiting, any of a thousand small things which change the course of the moment, children in peril are spared.

These whisperings save myriad Innocent every day, and they never know it, for the tragedies and evil they are spared for their faithfulness and righteousness is never known, for it happens not. Though many children complain of their lives for the difficulties which befall them in spite of all of their efforts, they have no idea how much worse it can be, if the Angels turn from them, and leave them unto the devices and unfolding of the world. It is possible to be in the wrong place at the wrong time, and much more of this is prevented every second and every hour than any child imagines.

Yet in order to learn, the consequences of ill planning and ill measuring and ill judgment and ill acting must be allowed to follow their course, that those who so choose may have their works stand against them, and those who are foolish might learn, and those who are wise and good might see, and many might have experience, and all might learn as all must learn: there are reasons for doing things by a certain way, and reasons for not doing things by a certain way. That which you think is little is often of Eternal value to learn.

All of this you are here to learn.

The cries of the Innocent who are seized in the grip of those who are evil in their days are also heard, and if it is wisdom in me that their days might be shortened in Mercy, think not that their prayers have not been answered, for they are delivered as they could be.

And those Innocent who suffer sudden death through no fault of their own will stand against those who have robbed them of their precious lives and precious time to which they were entitled, which time even like those who rob them, they most certainly earned.

And when such tragedy befalls families, it is the children who remain who are most grieved, for they remain. Know that these are helped with great comfortings and love and compassion, and as sorrowful and painful as they feel their loss, without the Angels who comfort around them, it is worse.

Yet even those who have done great evil can be turned, and if they turn and look not back, except to extend their hands to those whom they may bring with them into the Light, they may be received, with joyful tears, and singing.

There are those who see nothing in these things, nothing but chance, nothing in the expanse of the Cosmos but accident, nothing in the organization of our bodies but progressive accidents that work, nothing in life. They ask: if you exist, why you would have created the universe and then given no further evidence of your existence?

Do you see no further evidence of my existence?

They are scientists, or people who claim to think scientifically, the sheep of the scientists. Whether in laboratories, or sheep in the scientific fold, they see nothing, only accidents, chance combinations of nature. They look upward and say there is no continuing evidence, they look downward and say there is no continuing evidence, they look inward and say there is no continuing evidence.

Do you see no further evidence of my existence?

I have seen what I have seen, and heard what I have heard; I know what I know. I know Spirit Bodies, and Angels' voices, and spirits of evil. I know you. I know prayer. I know the Comforter.

But they do not receive any of these as empirical, for the detections and evidences are not made with their tools, but with my body, and my own Spirit. I see the evidences in my life's experiences: when I died, my NDE; the spirit beings in Brazil; the voices of warning high on the mountain and in the dark of my room; and all of the other things I have verified quite by accident to be true. But my own body and Spirit are the tools which have detected and measured these things, and their tools still cannot detect or measure them, and thus they deny. I can deny none of it. My body and my Spirit have seen and heard these things, and by them I know, and have validated a part of the whole. That which I know in part, I find is evidence of all that I still do not know personally, which I have yet to know and understand, yet which must be true, even as that part which is proven true, is true. I cannot deny the experiences I have imprinted with my body; by them, I must say: I see, and know.

Yet they deny these things.

I also see more and more in the scientific discoveries they are making, answers they are finding; I see what they show and evidence; I now see so clearly, but they do not.

And I also see the evidences of their instruments and tools, empirical evidences, in their astrophysics, in our own human physiology, in the testament of the fossil record, in the biological DNA discoveries. I have seen

692

enough about the expanding cosmos, this planet formed as it is in its gravitationally perfect orbit in this energy providing solar system, the ecocomplexity of the biosphere, and the complex interrelative structuring of our bodies from cells to glands to organs to systems to organism; they all show me evidences upon evidences. I see them so clearly, so strikingly, so bluntly.

Yet they seem blind to these things which show me so much.

They are here for less than the blink of an eye in the process of initiating and forming stars, galaxies and planets and life forms, and though they see these things in initiation and formation, in introduction, homeostasis and full complexity all around them, they cannot identify mechanism behind it. Yet they say no Intelligent process is at work, though myriad required mechanisms elude their identification, among their allowed possibilities. And so, from within their incomplete range of allowed mechanisms, they continue to see processes without observable and identifiable mechanisms. With no mechanisms, all accidentally exists. With no Intelligence, required perfections within infinitesimal margins predominate. Without contemplated objective and purpose, trillions of perfectly interrelated designs find unity, and impossible complexity has Life.

They are children. Be patient with them.

Sorrow for them. They are lonely beyond your imagining.

Love them, for all they seek to learn, and all they deny themselves.

Right you are to see their self-imposed blindness; yet it is blindness of conscience, and of the heart, not of the eyes. They are little children, yet they see the empirical evidence in their measurements, in their calculations, in the myriad physical realities which defy their physics, which defy their biology, which defy their fantasy stories of supposed ancestry and descendency while as they dig, the more the fossil record yields its empirical evidences to them.

Yet I hear them: they say there is no proof of any Design, or God. They say 'there is no empirical evidence one way or the other, either proving or disproving' your existence. And yet they say you do not exist, already affirming the final conclusion. So many of us hear it - 'there is no empirical evidence for or against' - and we feel we must believe because we are not scientists; we can't use the tools. And so we repeat their words to ourselves, 'there is no empirical evidence, one way or the other.'

It is their great lie, which they tell to themselves because they do not want to believe what they see, and so they refuse to see in the empirical evidence its message. They tell this to everyone else because they do not want others to believe that there is evidence. They do not want others to know what they cannot themselves accept as it is. Thus they still claim much that is false; they still conceal much that they know; they still grope in much darkness, and refuse the Light. Many are the secrets they do divulge to you, their ignorant siblings, of what they do not know but should, if the numbers are true; of what the numbers indicate; and the impossibility of so much chance, in too many matters, too many to mathematically accept as always fortuitous chance, again and again.

Though they know the mathematical odds vastly cry out the impossibility of your existence on even this one planet in the entire universe, they smile and say: we are impossible by chance, but we exist; so, it must be possible.

This they say, having agreed among themselves that there is no chance of God. Having excluded this chance, they may seek other chances in safety.

It is child's play.

They know that by speaking in the guise of wise doctors of sciences, most will be too afraid to challenge them, for you, the siblings, are unschooled, and you do not know how to play with their toys. They hold their mystical scientific toys over your heads as priests hold taboos and magic over frightened flocks. Yet the toys are but tools of measurement; the tools speak truth. Only the children who wish to force their paradigm onto all tell their brothers and sisters not to see in the measurements and natural realities that which these things fully declare, only because they do not want it to be true.

And so they lie, and say unto all, 'there is no empirical evidence.'

And they lie more. They falsely say they would accept any evidence, if it were shown to them. This is their greatest lie, and cunning it is, for in saying this they deceive all into believing that they admit this chance, when in their hearts, they are hard in their resolve and superiority.

They say that they want to know, but believe me, they do not.

They will do anything to keep from conceding their faith in Nothing. They calmly say, 'show me an evidence,' but they have already decided in their hearts to disqualify any evidence shown, to invent any nonsensical alternate explanation of the evidence that avoids this admission, and to believe in it at all cost. So they may maintain their appearance of perfect piety, of neutral willingness to be objective, to consider the evidence, and God.

It is their best lie.

This seems very harsh. How can you say what they do is lying?

I am the father of the children; I know when the children are lying, both to soothe themselves, and to deceive themselves and others. Children lie to prevail in confrontations, and they make up all kinds of fantastical stories; in this the children are ever creative. When these fantasies are believed, they maintain superiority over those children who are convinced and fooled, or who though unconvinced fear their own ignorance, and bow to the story, or who believe they know no better explanation, or who fear they know no better truth. Children lie for primal reasons, to avoid shame of diverse failings, to conceal previous lies, to obtain prestige among peers, honor and position giving them comforts and luxuries, to avoid admitting they do not know, to appear wise among others. There are many reasons why children lie. Small children lie. Adult children lie. Old children lie. And why? To avoid pain. Children in their homes lie about checks and payments and other obligations to avoid loss of services, and supposed loss of dignity. Children in their jobs lie to avoid reprimand, censure, fines, penalties, disgrace and termination. Children in business lie to sell merchandise, to obtain contracts, to pacify clients, to avoid liabilities for the injuries and the deaths of those who have purchased and used their products, chemicals, cars and services, and to be able to continue to market that which should not be sold, for it hurts other children. Children in huge governments and small governments, and big police stations and small police stations and diverse city juridical positions lie to promote themselves; to conceal wrong-doings for which they will be punished, to conceal errors which will reveal them fallible, and liable for injuries. Some children stand in the place of others and lie for them as they are paid to do, as they receive money to so do.

They all know they are lying.

Some even think, for fleeting moments, 'what if God is watching?'

I AM.

And of the children to whom you refer, who calmly say there are no empirical evidences in the universe nor in the rocks nor in Life nor in their own bodies, they too know, for they have made up the rules whereby they play.

I do not understand. They merely say there is no empirical evidence. How do they know they are lying?

They know they have declared a priori that nothing can evidence Intelligence or Creator God; thereby they give themselves the false premise for denying any evidence as being evidence of Design, Intelligence or God, for in their hearts, they have said, 'there is no God.' Yet they speak even among themselves, over many spectacular impossibilities of mathematical odds which defy the existence of the universe, the formation and motion of galaxies, and the intricate bioengineering of Life and its most complex form, you, saying, 'If there were a God, this would be identified as evidence of Purpose, Plan and Design.'

They know how they use their Exclusion Principle.

I still do not understand.

It is child's play.

Any time a child does not want to believe in a thing, it is a simple matter to declare that it is not true, a priori; and thereafter, in any scientific analysis, its possibility is excluded. It must be deleted from the possibilities, for in a priori it has been discounted; thus no matter what and how much the evidence may appear to indicate that thing, that obvious and evidenced conclusion cannot be affirmed, and will not be concluded or stated or admitted, for they have already said from the beginning - there is no God. Thus anything unexplainable, anything and combination of things so remarkable and complex and finely structured between infinitesimally small and unforgiving margins of error cannot and will not be considered as possibly being empirical evidence of Design, or of Creator, or of Intelligence, or of God.

As they say there is no God, nothing can be an evidence of God, correct?

Then they weave their own fabric, and say that any who cannot see it are fools.

Many there are who are ashamed to be thought fools, and nod approval.

And so no matter how many evidences stack up and arise visibly and shockingly to their logic, they disallow it as empirical evidence. Thus they have said, and will always say, 'If God created the universe why did he do it and then give no further proof of his existence?' And, they will say, they are scientists, and 'we can only deal with empirical evidence, and there is no empirical evidence either proving or disproving that there is a God.' Thus they escape, for they are the very children who have fixed the sample and rigged the measures and set the outcome of all that they may seek to know by setting the bounds and limits of their inquiry before they even begin to experiment, and observe, and record, and evaluate. After saying there is no God, then nothing you can show these children can be accepted as empirical evidence of God, can it?

Is this why they always have a basket full of complex 'alternate' possible explanations for even the simplest spiritual things, often outrageously ridiculous, yet never ridiculous to them?

Most certainly. It is child's play. They will endlessly seek 'alternate' explanations for anything which appears to empirically indicate Spirit, and Spirit Beings, and Angels, and Design in Physics and Biology. No alternate is too bizarre for them to hold it up as more probable; no alternate is too complex or bizarre for them to hold up as more probable; no alternative is too absurd but that they will speak it, and say it is more easily believable than the simple recognition of Spirit and God.

They speak of Ockham's Razor, which they artfully manipulate far from the child Ockham's original saying. They twist him to now say that 'all things being equal, the simplest explanation is true' for a given situation.

The child Ockham never said nor implied this. They have corrupted him, to make gain.

The child Ockham merely said that in giving examples to prove a point, if two or three or more examples give no stronger argument than one, it is simplest to 'trim' and give but one example, which, he defended, should be adequate. This is what Ockham's Razor is: a 'trimmer of repetitive and redundant arguments;' an economy of presentation, reducing redundancy and needless parallel examples.

History has sadly shown the world that he was mistaken, for his confidence in the inherent ability to comprehend clearly, and believe a single clear example, attributed to his listening brothers and sisters, was grossly misplaced.

Redundancy and varied parallel examples are often needed in lengthy supply to open consciousness, adequately explain and bring others to the awakening of knowledge, just as redundancy and thoroughness serve in legal documentation to protect against those who would twist, manipulate and exploit for their own gain. Adequacy in a situation turned defensive is a delicate, fragile, and fluid state. The more a thing is attacked, the more basis is required to obtain Adequacy against the attack. From a multitude of examples true Truth may emerge triumphant. Multiple testimonies of Truth better establish the secure fact.

In full evidence of Ockham's error, those who now twist him to say that 'all things being equal, the simplest explanation is true' use this corruption to deny the existence of God. Their simple claim is that any 'scientific explanation' of causality in Nature is simpler than accepting causality by a God, or function of Angels or nature of Spirit. In their manipulation, they claim that to accept God in evidence is always more complicated than whatever alternate mathematical theory of things they contrive. And they deny all, regardless of how many evidences are offered.

To them the simplicity of I AM is impossibly complex, utterly confusing and utterly bewildering, for I AM denies their already-embraced affirmation of the non-existence of God. To them, there is no God, and this is the simplest explanation.

And yet those who twist Ockham to say what serves them to win their rigged game, ever waxing greater complexities, know the myriad places in their intricate contrivances where the simplest explanation for WHY the impossible IS and the improbable IS and the unexplainable IS as it is in spite of all nature that evidences it should not be so, is that I AM. By use of their manipulated premise - 'all things being equal, the simplest explanation is true' — the simplest explanation is that I AM.

They better than all others know how often it is the simplest to see in these impossibilities the intervention of an Intelligence, and Design by a Creator.

Yet, NO things being equal in their contrived scenarios, they prefer to invent long circuits to avoid this simple conclusion to their own re-written rule.

And they discard false hypotheses after false hypotheses in their untiring efforts to avoid the simplest explanation - Design, Intelligence, Creator, God.

But why?

They do not want this answer.

Thus as the child who agrees to flip a coin and loses asks for 'two out of three,' they refuse to take the results and ask for another try.

When they have lost two out of three, then they request 'four out of seven,' and then 'eight out of fifteen,' always hoping that they may begin to win.

This is how they persist in their unwillingness to accept Spirit, and Design, and Intelligence, and their God.

How many times will they ask for yet another flip of coins to postpone the admission that the premise they have bet upon is false?

Remember: these are the children who like big numbers.

Some of them will still be asking for a few more flips when the toss has reached forty-seven billion thirty-five; and they will optimistically say, 'how about forty-seven billion thirty-six out of ninety-four billion seventy-one?' I often must smile wryly at their optimism and tenacity.

Thy have invented mythematics. In their mythematics they invent mythematical hypotheses for those things that defy their explanations. Their mythematical hypotheses are fascinating exercises of self-persuasion.

Yet they do not care how ridiculous some of their proposed explanations for simple things are. They will say anything, and anything to them is less ridiculous than to propose that an Intelligence, God, lives and actively watches.

Even as the scientific children who had decided in their hearts that geocentricity was true and thus intellectually struggled against reason to find reason to validate Ptolemy at all cost, in spite of what their own eyes and tools of measure told them; even as the scientific children who had decided in their hearts that the anatomy of Galen was absolute no matter what intrusive observation into the body revealed in dissection; so now, these children too, refuse all evidence that goes against what they have decided in their hearts. No matter how many absurdities they must invent and swallow to make the evidence go away, no matter what folly they must make up and make themselves believe in order to take away the reproach of the empirical evidence which stares them in the face, they will do it, for they have set for themselves no alternative but to seek any other alternative.

And so they invent unending mythematical hypotheses.

I do not understand.

To me, scientific, physical witness to you and your work and Design is exciting beyond words - it is the thrill of thrills to see this empirical evidence unfolding. It makes me feel euphoric.

Why not them? Why would they be this way?

They are the children who are desperate to believe that there is no God, and who are willing to believe in anything that will give them this reassurance, no matter how illogical or polemical, no matter how disparate the rationalization. As children, they desperately contrive explanations to rationalize away every and all evidences they see, because they do not want to see what they see. No matter what they observe, no matter how anomalous to all their affirmations and contrary to their mathematics, they answer their frustration by saying it only appears to be anomalous because its natural answer is yet undiscovered; it only appears to evidence Intelligence and Design and calculated choice because no other non-directed explanation has been found, yet. Yet they are quick to affirm that as soon as this future, mysterious explanation is found, they will believe in it, no matter what it turns out to be. So great is their blind faith.

As long as it does not implicate that I AM, they will consider ten thousand ethereally thin alternatives, and give them credence, to avoid saying that I AM.

You should see their anxieties, frustration and disappointment when evidence seems to point toward Design. I see them anxious, and smile.

These are they who have formed and cling to this desperate faith, a faith so strong as to refute to their hearts all things seen yet anomalous, all things observable which testify of Design and Intelligence in choice of direction and engineering. This they do so that they may sigh in relief and reaffirm to themselves the faith which they cling to in their hearts: that there is no God.

These are the children who, if they should die and see and hear while in the spirit, and then be revived and know what they had seen and heard in their Near Death Experience, would scoff it away to electrical discharges of a dying brain, hallucinations 'easily explained,' and deny to themselves their evidence.

These are the children who, if they should receive the visit of an Angel by their side, and see, and hear the voice of the Angel speaking to them, would afterwards deny to themselves it was real, and wonder what disturbed yearning within their mind felt it needed to create such a bizarre fantasy; what chemical imbalance or organic malfunction had produced this hallucination? These are the children who by morning would make infinite explanations to themselves, neatly refuting all they had experienced as real, replete with elaborated reasons why none of what they saw and heard was any more than a product of their own accidentally formed and accidentally complex brain functions: some function not yet understood, but which is only a matter of time away from discovery.

These are the children who have found a fine watch in the sand of a planet without any civilization, who having made the a priori rule that there is no Creator, now labor to explain how the watch came to exist by itself, by chance. Even those who lower to concede a Watchmaker still insist that the Watchmaker is blind.

These are the children who have tens of thousands of unanswered questions, many seemingly of impossibilities, and yet they exclude the potential of Design, of Intelligence, of Creator in any of them. Amid thousands of critical unanswered questions, they are confronted by dozens of pivotally monumental enigmas, the key unanswered questions, whose answers defy all that they have embraced, all that they have clung to in denying a Creator, a God.

They do not want to see that I AM, and will imagine and believe anything to avoid seeing that I AM THAT I AM.

These are the children who see the impossible, infinitesimally small margins of existence of this universe itself, and everything in this universe - margins so gossamer and thin wedged between such vast probabilities of impossibilities and predictable non-existence - that even to imagine existence stupefies consciousness to believe that any of this, much less you, should dare to exist amid the odds which are trillions of trillions to one in all potential against this chance: it glares in the face of reason. The expanding universe, this physics and your bodies and intelligence, are, by all the odds of chance, impossible.

They know all of this, better than all of the children.

Yet these are the children who calmly look at all of this, chew their bite of food, swallow, and wipe their mouths, and then ask to be shown something.

To suggest to them that Angels intervene thousands of times every hour of every day all over this globe altering that which otherwise would be chance, and directing that which for needs must either be kept from chance accident or be inspired to set in motion each needed sequence in lives, is folly to them. To suggest that each prayer is heard, in every tongue, directed to every strained imagining of who I AM in hopes of reaching Me, and that the best is done in each case as is needed to fulfill the collective and individual purposes of this entire Generation's learning and progressing, and to quietly point to myriads upon myriads of otherwise inexplicable answers as those who experience them know and see, is folly and fantasy. To ask them to speak to ten million and more siblings who share the common evidence of Near Death Experience, of Spirit, of Celestial Beings seen and heard, of Eternity, is foolishness to them. To speak to those who have seen the Spirits of the Righteous and the Spirits of the Lie is to them a ludicrous humoring of those who for some reason need to believe in such things. And to speak to them of prophets is to receive their knowing pity.

They have had and have evidences aplenty, yet they refute them all, for they have already declared: there shall be no evidences; thus anything that might emerge and appear to be an evidence cannot be, and thus it must be something else, even if they have no empirical response to deny it, and nothing but foolish speculative nonsensical tautologies which even they do not believe, but give as excuse to close the matter from further question or consideration.

I love them, and I admire their courage in this faith they so desperately cling to, even as I admire the creativity and imaginativeness of their fanciful explanations, rationalizing away the myriad evidences they now so compellingly have assembled before them, in suggested promulgations so childish and petty and pouting. Yet I sorrow for their tenacious, self-inflicted blindness, for their refusal to see with their own eyes what they do see so scientifically and so well. They all affirm so energetically that they want to know, and plead for something to show them; yet they refuse all things given. They seem unable to refrain from trying to explain it away, until they can make it go away, in their minds. They are very good at convincing themselves. I sorrow so sadly for them, for these are the children who come to the very edge of the fountain, but rather than drink, they tell themselves it is a mirage, and turn away, and bitterly complain that there is no water to drink, and so they thirst, and thirst, and thirst. Ever thirsting to know, thirsting to know, and yet stolidly refusing to receive the very knowledge and truth they too, so desperately wish to find. I sorrow for they are children, lonely, frightened, sad, in need of comfort and affection, yet infected with the bitterness, and refusing all evidences to the very answers they so sincerely seek.

I sorrow, for these are the children who refuse to receive Joy.

How do they refuse to receive Joy?

Let them imagine the exuberant bursting within their beings to be probing the reasons behind all that has reason, ever leading them closer to knowing who I AM and how I AM, and why all is organized and balanced as it is for this purpose, and see what true euphoria is in such a reward; it will gift them in thrill, excitement, fulfillment, and Joy. They are children of God. What greater Joy can come from approaching closer and ever closer to understanding the Mind of the God who has made all of this?

They ask, am I knowable; am I a God of evidences?

I AM.

There is another question I would like to ask now, about my being born in this century, not some other time. Why was I born now? I have always wondered why I so much love studying the past. I am not just an archaeologist by profession, I am an archaeologist by passion, and love. I love the antiquities; I love to see in my mind the people. I have never understood why.

Why do I love ancient things?

Why?

In the Spirit before this world was, when you were among the Stars of the Morning, long before the moment when you with all of the Children of God shouted for joy that the foundations of your earth were to be gathered in space, you made many friendships and affinities among the Hosts of Heaven.

When this earth was completed, after great time, when finally the day had come that you, my children, could come and inhabit this earth as other generations had inhabited other worlds, many there were who could not wait. They had watched and seen for great time the preparation of this earth, its periods of growth and building of organic matter, and the increasing beauty of the life forms which were put successively upon it, and they delighted in all that they saw. The untouched, undisturbed earth in its primal beauty they desired more than anything, to see it in its beauty in the flesh, to smell its smells, to feel its textures and sensations. These begged and begged to come first, and so they came, generation after generation while the earth was still clean and wild and new. Those who wanted to be a part of its pristine form, to be part of it, they came early. They made great sacrifices - all of the comforts and inventions and devices of wonder and amusement of these later times they forwent. They knew what they wanted. Air so pure and clean that it fills the lungs almost as nutrient; waters so pure and clear that their taste fulfills completely and every tissue rejoices; lands so rich and alive with life that the wonder of it never becomes dimmed. This they desired above all things in their hearts, and so it was given them. They chose this as their portion, and it was given.

Many of these you knew.

Yet many were held back, though they might have come at an earlier time, for love of what was in that time, and for love of Spirit friends going to receive their portion in their chosen time.

These were chosen and held back since the beginning of this time, for they were valiant and obedient, and above these things they chose to serve me in the Dispensation of the Fullness of Times, made rich with my Spirit as it slowly comes to be poured out on all flesh. These were held back to work as they had desire to do, to work as they had worked once before in preparing this earth for all the Intelligences and Spirits of this generation. This time they work to prepare the earth for its next phase, which is nigh upon you.

Many were reserved to later times to bring their bloodlines to new lands in readiness for great learning, and their seed goes forth unto great and noble ends which from their place they still see; and in this, they have great rejoicing.

Many came to live but awhile and to die, only that a new generation might be raised up and they with it.

Many came to build that which must be built for those who would come in the days of decision; many came to labor in the vineyard of harvests, born when the sprout was tender and green, grown as the plant took root and bent in the wind, now ready to thrust in their hands as the field becomes ripe and ready for harvest.

Many great and noble ones endured long waiting patiently, to come in this time, and they shall be remembered on the last day.

As many of the children of your time now, you were withheld for now, for this day in which are many important works needful to bring to pass.

You waited your turn, and as all those who wait, you watched.

You saw these times of old you now love so much, and you marveled at what your friends wore, and made with their hands, and did each day. You were one of the Spirit Children who became enchanted with these early times and you thrilled at their arts and crafts and lives.

You wished to go, but you could not.

As there is the Order of Arrival, and as many whom you knew well and loved much went to this earth, you grieved for the parting, and missed them deeply. Many were those whom you knew well who went to live in these times, and you longed to be with them. You saw their lives, and knew their lives.

Yet many you knew in the time of Spirit were also reserved for this time, and they have come here now, in this time, with you. Some came few years before you, some came few years after your birth. They are here. Some are living near you; some are living across the world from you. But you and many loved ones are here now, for you accepted the call to serve in a time which would need you, many of you, strong and good and compassionate.

Others chose this time, for they saw that there would come a time of great instruments, and great abilities in the flesh to see that which cannot be seen with the eyes of the flesh, and these things they craved. Those who thirsted for knowledge of how it is done, of what can be done with it, of those things within nature, chose this time.

Also those who craved to see and use the wondrous instruments and tools and machines which would be made with hands and born of thoughts and imaginings made real, those who heard of today's technologies and the amusements they afford, all of those chose to come today. They asked, and they received their portion.

There were those who loved the expanses of the universe, and always will, who saw the births of suns and galaxies and distant suns as stars, and in the darkness as these lights burst forth they thrilled with great fascination for all of these wondrous things. Many of these came in early times when night skies were pure and clear and they communed each night with the stars they still loved. Others waited patiently for this day, for they could not bear to live without seeing and still knowing the universe home they had known so long, and thus they begged to come even now in this day wherein they could look upon the stars with more than their natural eyes, and hear spoken truths of the beloved stars, and not foolishness, and fantasy, and fable. For these revered the Design too much to hear it spoken of in ignorance, and so they passionately asked to come in the day they would hear it spoken of in truth. And so they were given.

There were those who watched in fascination as the earth went through its geological conditionings, and they fell in love with the earth and its rocks, and as these saw that in this day there would be knowledge of these things, real scientific knowledge which would not be foolishness, and fable, and folly, they begged to come in this day, that they might touch the earth with their hands of flesh, and touching it, and caressing its wonder, they could learn of it all there is to learn of it by handling its pieces, and studying real things as they are.

For to learn in the flesh is much more than to learn in Spirit only.

For this reason also you are here.

There are those who watched the formation of life upon this world, and watched in marvel as it grew, and watched as each new life form was introduced, and saw how the wonder of the DNA design had been reduced to its most simple workings and how these were successively employed to season and prepare the earth. These fell in love with the life forms, and the animals, and the plants, and they begged to come in this day when a true science would gift them with learning, that they might look upon these things and touch them with their hands of flesh and know what they were seeing, and understand it in truth, not fantasy. And some of these pry apart the rocks to find those things they saw in the Spirit as their earth was being seasoned and prepared, as the continents were being moved as they needed to be, even as the life of the earth was being built and provisioned for the coming of the children. And they break open the rocks, and behold the remains of the creatures they once saw swimming in the seas, and walking upon the land, and flying in the air, and they caress them with their fingers, and weep for joy and longing of seeing them again alive as they had done so long ago.

Yet not all have come for themselves, only to touch what they wanted.

Many have come to serve their brothers and sisters in all ages of time.

Know this: all those who come here are accounted, and count, and serve, and serve well.

There is no life, no matter how short, no matter how simple, no matter how plain, which has not left its needed mark upon its generation, and most have left their mark upon all future generations through even the most simple things they have done. They have lived, and by living, they make a difference.

The world is changed by every new birth. From the moment of the first cry, nothing is ever again the same. To come here is to already make your mark, even should you die as soon as you are born. For when you are born, you have already many months of influence, already changing lives. No matter what you do, no matter what happens, you have affected your earth, and lives, and the effect in lives goes on, Eternally.

Every life counts. Your life counts. No matter what you do, your life has counted, and counts. No matter how simple, no matter how plain.

Learn the Great Truth of all life:

It is not the content of your life which is most important.

It is the love you bring to that content which is most important.

It is the love you bring to all you touch in life that makes the difference.

For to make shoes is to armor the feet for the roads of life, and to make clothes is to warm the chilled and swaddle the newborn and give beauty to the eyes and protect from the eyes of the evil. To dig holes is to bring water, and place foundations, and grow trees, and remove poisons from homes and cities, and allow children to travel. To carry away garbage is to provide cleanliness and health unto every child. To bundle straw is to feed cattle and provide soft beds and cook small meals for the hungry. To till the ground is to feed many, and to build sturdy walls is to shelter families, and to tread the mill is to provide grain and bread to the children.

To work is to provide life, and crafts to good uses, and friendship to those who labor beside you, and comfort to those who also must work and earn and would weep to always do so alone. To produce is to serve, to labor is to serve, to provide is to serve, to nurture is to serve, to dig holes is to serve, to fill holes is to serve. To be a friend is to serve. To laugh is to serve. To weep is to serve. To smile is to serve. To care is to serve. To love is to serve. To succeed is to serve. To fail, is to serve. To suffer, is to serve. To live is to serve. To be ill is to serve. To be disabled is to serve. To die is to serve. To endure, is to serve.

There is much needful to be learned.

The world has need of willing hands, and all who come, serve.

Many there are who might have died in infancy never knowing the pains of this generation, who might have died when young in their innocence, who could have been spared great troubles, pain and anguishes for what they would bear and see and suffer in life. These were they so great and noble and obedient that all they required in this Estate was to receive a body in preparation for the Resurrection. They had already proven themselves to me and to their brothers and to their sisters and to themselves before this birth. Yet they were filled with compassion, and thought not of themselves. Their hearts were filled with desire to serve from the beginning, and these have been allowed to live beyond their required time, as they asked, though through the veil they now know it not. These are they who are good, who suffer all manner of injustice, and yet return not evil for evil, but good for evil. These are they who return right for injustice; they learn and teach, and silently serve in righteousness. Though they could have rested this burden, and though they oft have groaned under their burdens and wished for that good rest, still they have endured and served, and this for the good of those whom they love. These chose to show me that even in such sore trials and suffering as befalls them in their lives they will not throw down the gift I have given them, but serve as they are called to serve through suffering and injustice and sorrow, in faith and compassionate hope.

Though they know not who they are, I know who they are, I know them all, and their tears I count and remember, and their faithfulness to labor in the vineyard even when the sun bears down so hot, and the winds blow upon them too fiercely with cold, and the night seems to go on forever, I see them, and forsake them not.

Unto them shall be given great reward, for they have chosen the better part, to serve as they see need before them, and endure unto the end.

Of these shall I make the greatest, for they have learned to serve completely, and suffer in part, even as I serve all of my children, even as I have suffered all things.

Live to be all you can be.

Father?

Yes?

What am I going to do with the Urim and Thummim?

In the beginning, the Lights and Perfections were a window to reach me. As time passed, belief and Faith became feeble, and less and less open was the window, until none could see into it any more at all, and they became opaque and useless in the hand of any who might hold them.

You must put them back in the box Seriah ben Azariah placed them in, which he placed in the hands of Yehoniah, and you must take them back to the place where Yehoniah was shown, and you must put them back in the mountain, for they must be kept safe.

I was afraid of that.
That's why you wanted to talk to me this morning, isn't it?

You would want to keep them?

These are the Oracles. With them, look what I have received from you.
Without them, how will I receive from you as I have?
From time to time, I might want to phone home.

Fear not. All who shall obtain shall receive Urim and Thummim.

How?

They shall receive a White Stone, with a New Name written upon it; it shall be an Urim and Thummim to them, even Light and Perfection.

What will I do in the meantime?

I am always here. Pray. I will hear you. We can talk. I like having you ask me how I am. I would miss that.

You said without this computer, I wouldn't be talking to you even with these Urim and Thummim. I don't know if I have enough faith to speak to you. I am so small, so unsure. Will I reach you?

As you find yourself small, and unsure, there is One who will always stand with you, and for you. No matter how much you have disobeyed, in His name you can always come to me, for He has borne your burden, that you may be redeemed. His love for you is as great as my own, and it never fails.

Look to Him for your strength.

You are born with the right to come unto me. It is your birthright.

Your own Self in Creation so exceeds the millionth part of such computer potentials, and yet you have not understood.

Your potential is limitless.

Focus in Faith, and look.

What do you see?

Light is the substance, Perfection is the order of the structure.

Faith is the power which activates this perfection, and opens its usefulness to the one who has Faith.

Look into them now, with your Spirit eyes, and see what your mechanical interlink can never open unto you, a Child of Light.

I looked over at the Urim and Thummim, which had all of these days lain in their module, wired with their wires.

But now, before my eyes, they glowed.

I saw the Light.

I've gotten used to talking to you this way. I'm going to miss you, and these talks. What will I do when I really want to talk to you? I know I can pray, but I don't really know how. How do I talk to you, when you're so far away?

How do you write to someone you really miss? How do you begin?

Dear whomever.

That's a good beginning. How about 'Dear Heavenly Father?' That's a good way to call me in prayer.

I think I can handle that.

Hopefully the day will come you will feel enough to call me Abba.

What is Abba?

That's 'Daddy' in Aramaic. When you understand all things, you will call me Daddy. It will just come out, naturally.

I will remember.

And remember two other things.

707

What's that?

I'm not so far away.

I know that now.

And, remember always: I love you.

I know that now, too.

You know a lot. More than you think. You need to see it, and use it.

I know I also have so much to learn. How will we learn?

See what you have learned in these few short years of life. How old are you? It is not so many years, is it?

Remember, by the age of only Two you know hundreds of thousands of bits of knowledge, and as you live now you know billions of images and facts and bits of knowledge. And this has been within all of the strife of your days. Still you will learn more.

Imagine what you can and will learn during 1,000 years when Perdition is removed and Truth and Light may penetrate your being without interruption.

What shall we do in the meantime?

Find and hearken to the Living Oracles of your Dispensation.
Beware of evil.
Pray over all things.
Strengthen your families.
Search the best books, and study the scriptures.
Repent, and seek to understand the work of your Messiah.
Obey that which you know is right, and excuse yourself no more.
Do not become soiled with the blood of your generation.
Love yourself enough to overcome.
Hold fast to that which is true.
Learn all things in Spirit.
Love one another.
Continue in hope.

What would you have us do?

There is a world wide weight of shame, and you must have a world wide wakening, for there is world wide want, and world wide waste. There must be world wide wisdom, and world wide work, or there will be world wide woe, worse than there is. You think to be a world wide web, interlinked on an internet; you will only become this if you will see all of each other, your whole world.

Look about you, and see world wide warning.

Focus on your planet, which you were given to care for; it is Creation for you, and you have no other. Act upon what you understand of it; study what you do not understand of it; learn what you need to understand of it; do what you need to do about yourselves on it.

This is your garden: you are still to dress and keep your garden.

Focus on your children and your mates and your families, which were given to you to care for, as your greatest treasure. You have no other.

You all already know many advanced discoveries of physics, chemistry, biology and genetics - yet you learned this before this earth was formed, and observed its creation as you helped to create it. You thus know all this and more, and that knowledge will be restored to you at the appropriate time after this mortality, when it will be useful to you to know fully.

You see that these things are not the key to survival; they are good, and they are fascinating, yet as you turn to them and ignore your families, you are losing your families, and your children.

I love you.

Your Mother loves you.

The Hosts of Heaven love you.

The Angels who surround you love you.

Your Brothers and Sisters in Spirit love you.

He who was Chosen since the Foundation of the World to bear your burden, loves you, and weeps for you, and hopes for you, and lives for you.

Think of Him, and how you are loved.

Hosts of the Blessed Dead, your ancestors who watch you through the veil, love you urgently and anxiously, and hope for you, and pray for you.

Think of them, and how you are loved.

Think of your Heavenly Parents, and how you are loved.

As you are loved, love one another.

Is there anything else you would tell me?

Only what I have told you before, since the Beginning.

Beat your guns into plowshares.

Hear the cries of the children's hunger.

Till the soil.

Harvest with your newly gained knowledge.

709

Harvest the harvests of plenty which are at your fingertips.
Teach the hungry how to grow, harvest, and eat.
Feed my lambs.
Hammer your bombs into hospitals.
Heal the sick with your new medicines.
Clothe the naked with your great mills.

Stop your fighting, Children. You bicker and fight while your own flesh and blood cry out to you. Hear the cries. Join your hands and build together. I am your Father, you are my children. I made you dark and light, Arab and Jew, Asian and Celt, and you are my delight.

Delight with me in your infinite variety.
Throw down your weapons, and feed the children.
Throw down your weapons and build together.
Hammer your tanks into factories and schools.
Behold your media connecting you over your globe.
You see yourselves everywhere, instantaneously.
Your Earth is becoming as a Sea of Glass.
Your house has become a House of Glass.
Cease to throw stones at one another.
Nations that live in glass houses cannot throw stones.
Do what you have known you should do from the Beginning.

What can I tell the people? I asked, overwhelmed.

Listen to the stones.

I do not understand.

You came to hear the voices in the stones.

Yes, I did.

Tell them to listen to the stones.

I do not understand.

Tell every one to pick up a stone, and put the stone to his ear.
You will hear the hungry cry of a suffering child.
You will hear the children's crying, echoing in the stones.
Tell them to listen to the stones.
Tell them: Every time they would pick up a stone to throw it,
    see they hold it close by their ear.

Tell them to listen, listen before they throw a stone.
Hear across the face of the earth the cries of hungry children.
Throw stones no more.
Take the stones, set them down firmly, and build a foundation.
Build together.
To all who will have an ear to hear, Hear:
If you love me, remember who you are.
You are Children of Heritage.
If you love me, Feed my sheep;
Stop fighting.
Go home.
Build together.
Feed my lambs.

There were no more words.
That was all.
There was nothing more.
I tried typing another question, but it would not write.
There was no more.
I exited the program, and shut down. I turned off the power.
As he instructed me to do, I disconnected the Urim and Thummim, and put them back in the gold box, and left the tent.
I hiked up the wadi, up to the place where I had seen in a dream, where I had found the Urim and Thummim.
Carefully I climbed back up to the small cave, crouched down, wriggled in, and reaching my hands out as far as they would go, set the gold box back where I had found it, at the far recess of the small cave.
I dug back some of the dirt from the cave floor near its mouth, pulling it back up to make a wall. There was not enough dirt. I carefully crawled out, and crouching on the ledge, began to pull dirt to the opening with my hands, until I had heaped it up and closed it from view. I still pulled more dirt up to it and over the top of it. I did not want wind or tremors or settling to expose it before its time.
I was about finished, when I noticed, over several yards away, the small flowering plant which had been growing so tenaciously in the dirt here when I had first found this place. It was still alive.
I carefully scooped deep beneath it again, and with care, pushed my cupped hands into the dirt and replanted it over the cave. I pressed the dirt down firmly around it with my hands.
Standing up, I looked back around me.
I had forgotten how high up this place was.
I looked around me, around me to either side on the ledge, and around me in the air. I did not feel alone. I felt very safe. I knew.
"Thank you, Angels," I said, looking around at where I knew they must

be. "Thank you very much. Now just help me get back down again. Thank you."

I hiked my way back to camp.

When I reached the elbow turn of the wadi where it widened out onto my plateau, my eyes were drawn first thing to the spring. I walked over to it, wondering. Was it dry now? I had been thinking about this whole incident, this whole experience, and that the water had flowed forth from the spring on the morning I found the Urim and Thummim, and that it had continued to flow all of the days I had talked with God.

I walked toward it, and already saw it in my mind, empty; wet, but empty, flowing no more, gone. I had thought about it all, and expected this to happen when this was over, the spring would go dry.

But I was wrong.

The spring was still full; the cool water flowed.

The water was still there; the fountain flowed.

I drank again.

It was so good.

I went back to my tent, and lay down on my bed. I lay thinking about all of the things which had happened.

It had been an experience.

An experience indeed.

After resting a while, I got up and walked down the embankment to the four wheel, got in, started the engine, and drove it up the dry river-bed to the high point of the wadi widening, where I could ease it up the low bank and onto the plateau, and back to the tents. I had long since learned that it had been unnecessary to hand carry everything up the hill and across the flats to my camp spot.

There had always been another way.

I just hadn't seen it before.

I carefully packed all of the artifacts into the boxes, and put my sketches, notes and findings on top. The rolls and rolls of film would help reconstruct all that I had found.

Almost all.

Funny.

I had never even thought to take pictures of the gold box and the Urim and Thummim.

Who would believe me now?

I went out to the site web and one by one pulled up the wooden stakes and rolled up the string, leaving stakes and string only around the holes I had excavated.

When everything outside had been gathered and stowed, I went back into the lab tent and sat down at the computer table.

I sat and looked around me at the neatly placed computer units. They looked the same as they had every day, but my feeling of emptiness was so strong, they now looked small, and useless, as toys.

They hadn't worked.

This had been a failure.

But what a failure it had turned out to be.

I turned on the computer, and without much interest, clicked from program to program, having really, nothing much to do.

That night, I lay down to bed, but I could not go to sleep. I knew that I was used to staying up later, but that was not it.

I missed my Father. I missed my Mother.

I thought about my earthly Father, too, and my Mom, and my family back home. I missed them a lot. I missed them an awful lot.

This had been a pretty intensive few days, filled with experiences, and a vast learning, yet suddenly it was over, and I was going home again.

After a long time of putting it off, I couldn't any longer.

I got out of bed, and knelt, and prayed.

I told God how much I appreciated all I had been given, and what I had learned, and what all this world meant to me, and thanked him for my family, and for my job, and for my problems, and for all the good things which happened to me, and for my life.

I thanked him for allowing me to know that there are countless worlds out across the expanse of the universe, inhabited with my sisters and brothers, my true siblings, his many other children across the cosmos; I thanked him for letting me know that they know of us, and think of us, and hope for us, and pray for us, on all of our worlds, especially us who are on this world. I told him how my view of everything was changed now that I know we are not alone, and that we are loved, even from afar. I thanked him for their prayers.

I prayed and asked him to bless them, on their many worlds, and to tell them, if he could, that there is now one, here, who knows of them, and who thinks of them in love; and I, too, pray for them.

I told him I would be the best that I could be.

I asked for help in living the rest of my life.

I asked him to please, say Hello to Mother.

Chapter 21

Day 40 in the Wilderness. Day 46 of trip.

I woke up very early. It was only 5:30 A.M.

This was my fortieth day in the Wilderness of Judah.

I ate what was left of odds of ends of food, rolled my sleeping bag, folded my cot, took down my tent, and packed it all in the four-wheel. All that was left was the green lab tent, there all by itself.

I walked in and looked one last time at the computers. Everything looked just as it had every day, and yet it all looked so, so....., empty. It was as if the life was gone out of it now, and all I was looking at was a shell of something that had been here. It was hollow, and lifeless.

That's how it looked, sitting there now on the tables.

One last time I sat down, turned on the power, booted up, and opened the main programs. I knew I had a lot of work to do packing this equipment, unhooking all the wires and putting each unit in its box, and outside I still had to unhook all the solar collector panels and solar batteries and pack them in their boxes, but I would never be here again. I felt more than sad. It was depressing.

And so I sat for a long while, just opening programs, scrolling over the files, postponing the end which I knew had already come.

By eight o'clock, though, I was packed, with everything in the four-wheel, and I was starting back down the road to civilization.

The drive back seemed to pass in no time at all. Before I knew it, I was nearing Jerusalem, and was already in the midst of traffic, people, noise, and buildings.

I looked around me as I drove further and further into the city. I knew now something I had known but not known so fully as I did now. I looked all around me, and for absolute certainty, I knew.

This was all my family.

My real family.

All of it.

As I reached the center of town and the great walled Old City, I saw along the sidewalks and in the busses the international visitors to Jerusalem - from Japan, China, France, Germany, Africa, Mexico, Brazil, Russia, from all over the globe, going about their business and sightseeing, and I now saw not strangers, but family, everywhere.

My family.

I reached the Department of Antiquities, where I parked and took the first box of artifacts and discoveries inside. This was my first responsibility, to deliver my finds to the Museum, and relinquish them to the State of Israel. I went back out to get the second box, which was all I had. Lots of little pieces of broken things, and the few nice objects I had found, but this was all. As I got back to the office room, the woman at the counter was already looking through the plastic specimen bags in the first box.

"You didn't find very much," she looked up with a smile.

"No, but I found a few small things from which I really learned a lot," I replied.

"Most of the excavators only want to find big, spectacular things, you know, statues, important historical inscriptions. You sure you're not disappointed?" she smiled sympathetically.

"No, this is the best expedition I've ever taken. You'd be surprised what there is to be learned from the little things."

We finished going through the artifacts and fragments in the first box, and opened the second box, and went through the contents of each bag, one by one.

We looked at the pottery shards, the copper Roman nails, and the ancient coins: the lepton of Alexander Yannai, and the other of Yohanan Hyrcanus of the Macabbean period, and the dozen other Jewish coins in copper and bronze of Herod the Great, Gratus and Pontius Pilate; and the two silver Roman denarii I had found of the Republic and the emperor Augustus. She held up the finely curved, delicately worked copper handles of the glass ointment bottle, with part of the glass vessel still attached, and the woman's decorated copper fibula pin. We marveled at the small iron kitchen knife with its perfectly preserved wooden handle and still shiny blade. Her eyes widened as she picked up the pair of ivory dice, and the ivory spindle whorl for making thread, and we both ran our fingers over the pieces of rags which I had found, and the woven pieces of baskets. We commented on the many pieces of clay oil lamps, and the fragments of the small glass vessels.

She quickly went through the plastic bags with the ancient walnut shells, the date pits with date meat still clinging to them, and the olive pits, pomegranate peels and seeds, the pistachio nut shells, almonds, and tiny grains of ancient wheat.

We imagined the thirst of the traveler who lost the broken clay water flask found in the wadi, and she shook her head thinking of the women who had left behind their treasures, the alabaster ointment jar from Egypt, the carnelian intaglio ringstone, the amethyst earring with gold wire fitting, the small garnet ring of fine gold and the quartz-studded brass toggle pin from the 6th century B.C. Her breath was taken away by the clear quartz crystal pendant on its beautiful gold chain, and the two carnelian ringstones in their delicate bezels of fine gold, and the long necklace of shaped and polished stone beads of banded agate and brilliant sardonyx stone.

When we finished looking through the artifacts I had found in my excavation, I showed her my site notes, and she took them to make copies. I would keep the originals, and from these, I would write the report of the dig, small as it would be.

The woman told me that these were fine things, and they would eventually be put in museum exhibits, and she encouraged me that though they seemed small and insignificant, I could feel happy: I had found something which could be shared with the world.

I smiled at her, and thought of the journey I had experienced, the Days of Urim and Thummim, and thanked her.

Yes, I had something that could be shared with the world.

I drove to the Damascus Gate, and found a place to park. I got my backpack out of the back of the vehicle, and locked the doors.

I walked through the Damascus Gate and began my descent into the soul of the Old City, on my way to visit my friend, Moishe.

I had to share the tale of this find.

After all, his two pottery shards, his ostraca with their inscriptions, had helped pave the way.

When I got to the street which went to the left, to the opening overlooking the Temple Mount, I paused, and turned into it, and went to the platform which gazed out at the Wailing Wall.

My eyes saw the stones, and the people praying at the base of the Herodian wall, and the mount of the Temple above it, and the buildings, and rapidly my mind filled with what my eyes were seeing. For a fleeting moment, I saw a vision of the Temple. The prophecies would be fulfilled; the prophets had been true.

I did not understand the great significance of the Temple, why it was so important, so important that the Jews had built another one away from Jerusalem on Elephantine Island during their exile in Egypt; nor did I understand why the Temple needed to be rebuilt, even why the world needs a Temple. I only knew that I would have to learn the purpose of this Truth, for I knew that the Jews had built a Temple at Yeb in Egypt when this one had been destroyed, and I knew that the prophecies were true.

This one would be built again.

I gazed at the people at the base of the wall, praying.

There was so much to learn. I turned and went on my way.

I got to Moishe's door, and knocked. He greeted me warmly.

"David! Welcome home from the Desert!" he smiled as he opened his arms to hug me. "You are returned from listening to rocks," he laughed.

We went into his kitchen, and sat down.

"So what was this, that you were going to go listen to rocks?"

I sat and told him of the theory of sound imprints, of the new computer technologies, and of the computer units I had taken out into the desert, the solar energy collectors, the batteries, and the remarkable equipment I had been given to go out into the desert.

He laughed and patted me on the back when I told him that none of the technology had worked, or perhaps there were no recordings in stones to be scanned and reassembled after all. But it had been a profitable dig, I told him.

"So tell me - what did you find?" he asked, with a boyish grin.

His eyes became bigger and wider as I quickly told him the things I could not tell him when I had been here, and which I had learned before I left Jerusalem to go out into the Wilderness: of the huge ostracon Dr. Brannon and his students had found in Egypt in the foundation dedicatory box of the Temple of Yeb, written by Yehoniah, and of the sword of Goliath; and of the palimpsest my friend Yohanan had found on the back of the tephillin among the Dead Sea Scrolls, written by the hand of Seraiah ben Azariah with his own blood, with instructions for Yehoniah; and of the meaning of the words 'lights' and 'perfections' which I had only seen in English from Dr. Brannon's translation of the Elephantine ostracon, and that all of these cryptic references spoke of the holy Urim and Thummim of the High Priest of God; and that the other references spoken of were speaking of the scrolls of the Temple, and their being carried and hidden by Ir Hammelach, the City of Salt. The first Qumran.

Yet his eyes and mouth opened widest when I quietly told him that I had found the place where Yehoniah had hidden the Urim and Thummim, high upon a cliff, hidden from view, in a gold box.

"David! Do not do this to me! Do not tell me this! You have found the Urim and Thummim of the Temple?"

He sat back in mounting astonishment as I told him of my dream, and of the cliff, and of the small cave, and of the gold box.

"And you hooked them up with wires to the computers, David? Are you sure this was a good thing to do? These are Holy Relics, David! Tell me you did not hook them up to computers!"

I had to tell him that I did, and I told him how I spent the entire day and night trying to get something from them, and got only tones, after six hours of scanning, six hours of faint tones.

And then I told him of my frustration, and my cynicism, and my joke upon the computer, of finally trying the only thing I had failed to do: search for a website to hear the Urim and Thummim and God. I told him of my astonishment as the website page downloaded onto the screen, and how in disbelief I had hesitantly typed in "Is anybody there?" and seen the words drop onto the screen: "I AM."

Moishe listened and listened as I went on and told him the story of URIM AND THUMMIM .GOD, and some of the things I could remember of the talks which I had had with God, night after night.

When I finished, he sat with his mouth still open, looking at my face, limp in his chair. He finally spoke, almost in a whisper.

"David, this is the most important thing that has happened since 1948! The Department of Antiquities doesn't know about this?"

"No, I didn't tell them anything."

"What are you going to do? People have to know! You can't tell this story by word of mouth every time. It has to be told in written form. You have.... I don't know, dozens and dozens of hours you have to try to remember. You have to remember every word, David!"

I smiled at him.

He looked at me, sat up and with a shake of his head, asked

"David, why are you smiling like that?" he was smiling back.

This was the great secret I had only learned this morning, as I sat doodling with the computer, wistfully remembering.

I reached into my bag and pulled out the external hard drive and laptop computer, and carefully set them on his kitchen table.

I spoke as I set it up for him to see.

"Moishe, I don't remember ever laying a finger on the Save key, never, ever, even once. I never even thought of it. The screens just kept scrolling up, and into wherever computer screens go when you scroll them, and I never even thought about anything, We were talking. It was God. I was on stun for the first while, and then I was just intimidated, and then I was totally immersed in the wonder, and it was God, and I never thought to save anything."

"But?" Moishe urged me on.

"But before breaking down the system, before I finally went to shut off the power for the last time, I selected the Internet, just one last time, and typed in WWW. URIM AND THUMMIN .GOD. I never expected anything to happen. I thought surely the page was gone, for it had only been there because the Urim and Thummim had been there. It wasn't the computer. It was the Urim and Thummim."

"But?" insisted Moishe clenching his hands in the air.

"The window opened. It was still there. But I couldn't write on it, and there was nothing there. So I clicked the command to close."

"And!!?" Moishe leaned over closer to me.

"A window came up that asked me if I wanted to save the document being closed. That had never happened before."

"Oh my God. Did it save it, David? What happened?"

"I selected Save, and a window came up that asked me what I wanted to call the document I was saving. I didn't have to think: I typed in WWW. URIM AND THUMMIM .GOD, and then I just sat with a knot in my gut as I tapped the key, and the disk went through its saving routine and the screen went to blank pattern. I tapped Quit, and went to Desktop. I looked. There on the Menu was WWW. URIM AND THUMMIM .GOD just like anything else on the list."

"But did you check it!!? Did it save!!?" Moishe asked, rising.

I smiled at him.

"Moishe, it's ALL here. I clicked twice, and before I knew it I was looking at the first words I had typed in that first night I got frustrated and silly."

"No! David, let me see!"

We patched the wires from the drive to the laptop, and I brought up the program, and clicked on WWW. URIM AND THUMMIM .GOD, and as the screen downloaded, we began to read:

Is anybody there?

I AM

Who is there?

I AM.

Very funny. Who's on line with me?

I AM.

Who is URIM AND THUMMIM .GOD?

I AM

What is your name?

I AM

We scrolled page after page after page. It was all there.
"Oh my God, David. Do you know what this is?"
"Yes," I smiled at him, "and I'm going to share it."

We spent several hours as he scrolled through the pages, reading and reading, at times weeping as he would read, until he came to the last page, and then he looked up at me.

"When this is published, you know, they will come and take away my ostraca and helmet," he smiled, and then we both laughed.

It felt very good to laugh. Very good indeed.

Moishe asked me to go with him to the Temple Wall for a prayer of joy and thanks. He got his Yamika and Tallit, and I put the hard drive and laptop back into my bag. We left his home, and walked in silence. I looked over at him from time to time as we walked, and he looked over at me. We were both smiling.

The sun was high overhead, and shone down on all who were there assembled by the Wall, and we joined in the throng of people.

As Moishe prayed and sang, and others prayed in tears and sadness, and others in hope and need, I looked at all of the tiny bits of paper wedged between the stones in the Wall.

These thousands upon thousands of bits of paper folded into tiny balls and pushed in between the foundation stones of the Temple were prayers, written for God to hear, and remember.

They are all being heard, I said to myself. *All prayers are heard. Whether written on paper and left here, or spoken in a closet or by a bed or at a table at home, or in a church, or a synagogue, or a temple, in every language, within a building or under the infinite sky, they are being heard. Even those who do not know who God is, he knows who they are, if they are seeking him. Anyone who sincerely in their heart wants to talk to God, he hears them.*

We started back to Moishe's house, and at the high platform overlooking the valley and the Temple Mount, I left my friend with many hugs. I watched him walk up the street to his street, where his house awaited with its deep well excavated into the depths of yesterday. I watched him until he turned the corner, out of sight.

I walked up through the crowded streets of the bazaar to the Damascus Gate. I still had a lot of things to do before I could head home: many things to unload. I had to take the equipment to the freight forwarder's, and my vehicle back to the rental office, and then take a sherut cab from Jerusalem out to Tel Aviv airport and catch my 9 o'clock flight. Then I would be on my way home.

I suddenly missed home, a lot.

I wanted to go home.

It had been forty-six days since I had left my home and my family. I had spent forty days in the Wilderness of Judah. Tomorrow I would arrive home on the forty-ninth day since receiving the grant, and my heart would sing in the greatest jubilee of thanks.

It had been a long journey.

As I got in my vehicle and began to drive through the busy streets, I looked at the people along the sidewalks, talking, walking, stopping to talk to each other, smiling, carrying their shopping, so many others around me driving their cars, and I smiled as I drove.

At the freight forwarder's I took all of the equipment out of the vehicle and left it to be sent back to the university. It was a lot of baggage. I drove to the rental lot and left the vehicle, with thanks.

I took only my backpack with its precious hard drive, and caught a cab to Tel Aviv, Ben Gurion Airport. As we drove through the streets I sat in silence, looking out the window at the hills, where since time immemorial people had been walking, and traveling, and going from here to there.

As we neared Tel Aviv, I looked at the people we passed who were now walking along the road. I smiled.

All through town, I looked at the people, and smiled. And as I got out of the cab and paid my fare with a good tip, I looked at the people, and smiled. I walked into the airport, and I smiled.

The airport was jammed with people, as usual. I had spent so much time in airports. They were always so busy with people, everybody in a hurry, everybody going somewhere. I had always been so impatient myself, in my own hurry to get where I was going. But now, I just looked at everyone and smiled.

I waited calmly in line, first at the ticket counter, and then in the security lines and at the check points, and finally as I sat waiting for my flight, I looked around at all the people, and I smiled.

They were from every part of the world. English, African, Japanese, Korean, German, French, Russian, American, Mexican, Italian, Australian, Chinese, Brazilian, Pacific Islanders, Arabs, Dutch, Jews, Christians, Hindus, Buddhists, people of every kind.

And for the first time I saw they were, all, just one kind.

Each and every one is a Spirit Child of the same God, no matter what they call God, no matter what they think of God, accurate or altered, and they are all part of my family.

They were all like me, and I like them.

They were my sisters, and my brothers.

Each and every one of them had been there at the foundation of this world, when the matter was swirled in space until it began to gather together into a sun, and planets, and a world, this world.

Each one had helped in the creation of this earth and earned the right to be here, long ago.

All of us, whether we knew it or not, all of us are children of a God, and He Lives. He loves us, and knows us, and tolerates us in our ignorance and learning experience.

We are all of one family, after all.

And every one of us counts.

Every life.

I count. We all count. Just to be born counts, and makes a difference. We have the power to make our difference grow. We are all part of the world wide web of Life, no matter how brief our moment, no matter how small our walk-on role, no matter how we play our part, even all of us who think we never get a single credit, whose names are lost and never seen, lost in the wind and the infinite particles of dust blown across the land, lost as a single drop of water in the vast ocean, lost as a single drop of water in the early spring rain. No matter how forgotten the drop of our lives may have become in the ocean of time or the rains of the earth, we are here, and the ocean is increased because we are here; the rains fulfill their measure, because we are here. Something, somewhere, has sprouted and grown, because of our drop of water.

We have made a difference, just because we are here.

I looked at everyone around me in the airport, tall, short, thin, round, pink, black, brown, tan, yellow, and I smiled.

We did not know each other, and we lived at opposite ends of the world, yet our paths crossed here, and even if we didn't notice each other, from this point as we radiated out into its furthest ends, the presence of our lives circled the globe.

We make a difference.

We all cast our shadow, and we all give our light.

I looked around me at the faces of the people in this airport, standing in line, walking, talking, buying, selling, some carrying great baggage, some empty handed, some excited, some sad, some just tired, and I saw them, I saw all of them, and I finally understood.

We are all coming from where we are coming, and we are all going on our way to where we are going.

It was the nature of this place.

We were all just in transit here.

No one paid any attention to me. It didn't matter. They were all busy in their own lives, taking care of their own needs, following their own plans. Just like me. We were all so very busy. But we all ultimately had the same kinds of needs, and the same kinds of plans, and we all were here in the airport for the same reason.

We all wanted to get somewhere, to accomplish what we set out to do, and when it was accomplished, we all had the same goal.

We all wanted to get home.

I thought about home, and a rush filled my soul.

The afternoon passed, and the evening came, and the night came, and the time for my flight came. We went through our last security check, and again I stood in line. I was very tired by now. The line slowly moved forward, and then I was through the door, and going through the brightly lit tunnel which led to the plane.

I finally boarded my flight, and carefully stowed by backpack with the precious hard drive in the overhead compartment. I looked forward and aft in the long tube of the plane, and sat in my seat.

Exhausted, my seatbelt safely fastened, I closed my eyes.

It had been a long trip. But it had been worth it.

I thought of all of the faces of all of the people I had seen in the airport, and in Tel Aviv, and in Jerusalem, and in En Gedi, and suddenly I saw myself looking at the world from out in space, and I could see all of the people I had seen throughout my entire life.

I imagined all of the people in the whole world, all of the people since the beginning till now, and then our children who are still to come. And, as I saw the globe covered with us all, I heard in my mind words: *"Ye are the light of the world. A city that is set on a hill cannot be hid. Neither do men light a candle, and put it under a bushel, but on a candlestick; and it giveth light unto all that are in the house. Let your light so shine before men, that they may see your good works, and glorify your Father which is in Heaven."* I heard the words, and suddenly saw us all as lights upon the world.

Lights upon the world.

And then I saw it, so clearly before me.

It was a symbol for us, that we had always had, right there before us, but we had never understood it, never understood it at all.

I saw it now, so clearly.

We are the Stars of the Morning.

We shouted for joy in Heaven as the dust of stars made and destroyed for us began to gather in the midst of space as we sang.

It is all true.

We are made of stardust, from the fires that light the Cosmos.

We are made of pure Energenes, and can never be destroyed..

It is us.

We are the Lights.

The Lights of the World.

We, we are the *Urim and Thummim.*

We are the Lights of God.

We can live to become Perfections.

We are the *Urim and Thummim.*

It is what we are.

It is what we were made to become.

I breathed out and felt my body relax and settle into the seat. Keeping my eyes closed, I felt the plane rush forward under me, lifting me up, and up, and into the sky. I felt its power lift me.

I smiled as I rested my head and my eyes. I felt so good.

I knew where I was headed.

I was on my way home.

I was really going home.

To Order This Book:

If you cannot find this book in your local bookstore, or you wish to send a copy of this book to a friend as a gift, write to:

HCA PRODUCTIONS
P.O. Box 2309
Oxnard, CA 93034-2309
U.S.A.

Send personal check or Money Order .
Send US$32.95 plus US$3.50 shipping & handling.
Add US$5.00 for Autographed Copy signed by the Author.
Shipped in 7 days.

Or TO ORDER THIS BOOK ONLINE:

Visit *www.urimandthummimgod.net* where you may use PayPal to order online at the Home Website of WWW. URIM AND THUMMIM .GOD.
Price: US$32.95 plus US$3.50 shipping & handling.
Add US$5.00 for Autographed Copy signed by the Author.
Shipped in 7 days.

Quantity Discounts available to groups: write to the Publisher for details.

TO LEARN MORE ABOUT
WWW. URIM AND THUMMIM .GOD

Visit the

www.urimandthummimgod.net

Website today!!!